H. P. ROBERTSON

THOMAS W. NOONAN

Relativity
and
Cosmology

W. B. SAUNDERS COMPANY • PHILADELPHIA • LONDON • TORONTO

1968

W. B. Saunders Company: West Washington Square
Philadelphia, Pa. 19105

12 Dyott Street
London W. C. 1

1835 Yonge Street
Toronto 7, Ontario

Relativity and Cosmology

Foreword

Relativity and Cosmology is an impressive memorial and fitting tribute to Howard Percy Robertson. His last student, Thomas W. Noonan, has resurrected the spirit and philosophy of Robertson's approach to special and general relativity from the notes for the graduate course which Robertson taught at Caltech from 1949 to 1961.

Those of us at Caltech were keenly aware of the wide difference between Robertson's concept of relativity and that of Richard Chace Tolman, our first great cosmologist. They both loved the subject and they both, in their different ways, brought the rest of us to some appreciation of its beauty and its power. It is difficult to express the difference in words, but in any case, it is hardly necessary because Robertson's and Noonan's work now stands as a comparison volume alongside Tolman's *Relativity, Thermodynamics and Cosmology*. The differences must not be overestimated, for the unity and symmetry of Einstein's theory permits of a wide variety of interpretations and insights.

Robertson had exceptional mathematical powers coupled with a deep insight into physical processes. Early in his career he gave the solution of Einstein's cosmological equations for the case of a homogeneous and isotropic universe. This solution is incorporated in the "line element" which bears his name. In all of his papers, Robertson emphasized that this solution was independently discovered by A. J. Walker. It has served as the basis of many of the numerous papers which have subsequently been written on relativistic cosmology. In addition Robertson succeeded in obtaining a general solution for two-body problems in general relativity.

The discovery of the red shift–distance relation and of the expanding universe by Edwin Hubble opened a continuing field of theoretical investigations for Robertson. From the beginning he was closely associated with Hubble and Milton Humason as well as Tolman, and this association extended in later years to Allan Sandage and other younger staff members of the Mount Wilson and Mount Palomar Observatories, who continued the red shift measurements. Robertson undertook to express the consequences of the general theory of relativity in regard to the red shift–distance observations in the most precise and explicit form possible. The greatest difficulty in the interpretation of these observations lies in the fact that distance is measured indirectly through measurements on the apparent luminosity or magnitude of the brightest stars in galaxies or of the brightest galaxies in clusters of galaxies. First of all Robertson succeeded in establishing the correction for the effect of the red shift on apparent luminosity by proving quite generally that this latter quantity is proportional to the absolute luminosity divided by the square of the Doppler shift. He ultimately succeeded in establishing the second-order terms in the red shift–magnitude relations which take into account the acceleration or deceleration of the universal expansion as well as the evolutionary history of stellar or galactic systems. He pointed out that the various expanding cosmologies all agree, except in physical interpretation, on the mathematical nature of the first-order Hubble relation, but that differing cosmologies gave differing theoretical values for the acceleration parameter in the second-order term.

Thus Robertson pointed the way to the critical observational test of relativistic cosmologies and made clear the necessity for great care in correcting for evolutionary effects. These tests were begun in Robertson's lifetime using the 200-inch Hale telescope, but they were by no means completed. Their completion in the decades to come will mark the final culmination of his contribution to science. Robertson, himself, remained aloof in the controversies between the advocates of the various theoretical cosmologies. He preferred to have laid the basis within the framework of general relativity on which these cosmologies could be put to the observational test. His point of view was expressed beautifully in the last lines of his article in the *Astrophysical Journal* for May, 1936: "In fine, we are inclined to believe that our investigations may in some measure strengthen, on purely formal grounds, the claims of the general theory of relativity; in any event, we maintain that it cannot be rejected on such grounds, and are the more content to rest the case with the empirical."

Noonan has incorporated all this and much more into what is truly a joint effort of student and teacher. Physicists, astronomers and mathematicians will find lucid treatments of practically every problem in relativity and cosmology of interest to them. The presentation is concise and precise. The coverage is complete from foundations to applications. A unique and invaluable portion of the volume is an appendix containing an abstract of all the material treated in the text.

Within its limitations special relativity is faultless. Whether this be true of general relativity remains to be seen. Cosmology is mostly a dream of zealots who would oversimplify at the expense of deep understanding. Much remains to be done—experimentally, observationally and theoretically. *Relativity and Cosmology*—Robertson's legacy made manifest by Noonan—surveys the fruit of past endeavors and is an almanac for the harvests to come.

WILLIAM A. FOWLER

Pasadena

Preface

The idea for this book arose following the sad and untimely death of H. P. Robertson as a consequence of an automobile accident. Mrs. Angela Robertson called the attention of Lt. Col. Charles K. Reed, U.S.A.F., to the existence of a substantial body of notes of her late husband, suggesting that therein might be information of value to the scientific community. Not only has the Air Force through recent years played a major role in supporting research in relativity and cosmology, but Professor Robertson had given great and valuable service to the Air Force in its scientific and technological activities. We in the Air Force Office of Scientific Research thus had what we believed to be the happy and appropriate idea that the publication of a book based on Robertson's notes would not only serve as a treatise of value to students of this subject, but would also constitute a worthy gesture of respect and remembrance for him both as distinguished scientist and as great and good servant of his country.

Because the notes were for the most part only Robertson's *aides mémoires* for his lectures, far more than editing was required in order to provide necessary explanatory text and discussion. It therefore seemed essential to have the work undertaken by one who had had the benefit of Robertson's lectures. We believe we were particularly fortunate in having been able to interest Professor Thomas W. Noonan of the University of North Carolina in this undertaking, in part, at least, for the sentimental reason that he was Robertson's last doctoral student. We wish to thank Professor Noonan, and to express the wish that the merit of this book will be such as to encourage interested scholars to join us in our appreciation to him for providing this remembrance of Professor Robertson.

LLOYD A. WOOD

Director, Physical Sciences
Air Force Office of Scientific Research
Office of Aerospace Research
United States Air Force

ix

Introduction

This book is based on Professor Robertson's notes for the relativity course which he taught at Caltech in the alternate academic years 1949–1950, 1952–1953, 1954–1955, 1956–1957, 1958–1959, and 1960–1961. I had the privilege of taking his course in 1956–1957, being teaching assistant to him in 1959–1960, and receiving my doctorate under him in 1961. In addition, I have had access to several notebooks which contain various calculations: some scratchwork in studying the work of others, and some original work. A description of Robertson's published and unpublished work will be found in Section B.3.

I have attempted to reproduce, as far as possible, Robertson's approach to the subject. For example, Robertson's notes contain numerous calculations of cosmological distances. It is in this spirit that I present Table 18.2, which differs from Robertson's work only in the values of H and z. Robertson's inclination to compare cosmological theory with observation led me to include Sections 18.2 to 18.7. I also found it necessary to impose an order of arrangement on the cosmological material in Chapters 15 through 18, because Robertson's notes had no constant arrangement. He continued thinking through cosmological theory during the decade before his death in 1961, as evidenced by the publication of the density-age diagram in 1955.

The reader should note that certain sections and subjects are insertions which I have made in the interest of clarity or continuity: the solar wind in Section 4.9, the orbit calculation in Section 6.2 (Robertson would have put Sections 6.3 and 6.4 in Chapter 4 and then done orbit calculations as they were needed), the contradiction between special relativity and light deflection in Chapter 6, the need for non-Minkowski space-time to supply the context for gravitational theory in Section 6.8, the geodesic definition in Section 8.14, the derivation of the general-relativistic equation of motion from the principle of equivalence in Section 9.2, the irrotational congruence of geodesics in the Gödel model in Section A.5, the μ–λ diagram of Section A.7, and the inclusion of gravitational energy in the cosmological pressure in Section A.8.

The reader will find an abstract of the book in Appendix C. This is to enable a reader who is familiar with some parts of relativity to determine which parts of the book he wants to read.

THOMAS W. NOONAN

Acknowledgments

It would be impossible to mention all those whose discussion with me provided insight and encouragement in the preparation of this book. Financial support was provided by the Air Force, and Robertson's notes were made available by Angela Robertson. An insight into Robertson's presentation of his course was gained from both my own lecture notes and those of J. S. Zmuidzinas (of the Caltech Jet Propulsion Lab). Mention should be made of my wife Annabel for sharing the chore of proofreading the typewritten and printer's copies.

But the greatest contribution to my scientific outlook came from Robertson himself in the several years of my association with him. He stands out in my memory not only as a man whose insight into scientific questions was instantaneous and of perfect clarity; not only as a man who devoted much of his time to governmental responsibilities; but also as a man who, when relaxing in his home, used a water pistol to control his Siamese cats. It was difficult for me during the preparation of this book to avoid the feeling that this book is to be a memorial to an outstanding scientist whose life and work were tragically cut short.

THOMAS W. NOONAN

Symbols

The following symbols are used throughout this book. Exceptions may be found in individual sections, but they are distinguishable by the context.

a	semi-major axis of Keplerian ellipse
a	automorphism parameter
a^i	unit vector
A	energy constant in Einsteinian orbits
A_i	electromagnetic vector potential
B	magnetic induction vector*
c	speed of light in free space*
c^i_{jk}	group constants
d	differential*
D	electric displacement vector*
e	mathematical constant $= 2.71828\ldots$
e	electron charge
e	eccentricity of Keplerian ellipse
$e(ijk\ldots)$	permutation symbol
$e_{\mu\nu\rho\sigma}, e^{\mu\nu\rho\sigma}$	permutation symbol
E	event
E	coefficient of skew term in gravitational theories in Chapter 6
E	electric field intensity*
$\in$	energy; energy per unit mass*

f	function in metric in Chapter 7
$\mathbf{f}$	force density (force in Section 5.2)
F	function in equation of motion, Section 6.2
F	function in metric in Chapter 7
$\mathbf{F}$	force (force density in Section 5.2)
$F^{\mu\nu}$	electromagnetic field tensor for $\mathbf{E}$, $\mathbf{B}$*
g	determinant of metric tensor*
$\mathbf{g}$	gravitational field intensity*
g_{ij}	metric tensor*
G	Newtonian gravitational constant*
G_{ij}	Einstein tensor
h	determinant of h_{ij}
h	$= h_{00}$ in Section A.8
h	Planck's constant
h	coefficient of heat expansion
h	angular momentum per unit mass (lower case when constant)
h_{ij}	$= g_{ij} - \eta_{ij}$, deviation of metric from Minkowski
h_{ij}	spatial metric tensor
H	Hamiltonian
H	angular momentum per unit mass (upper case when variable)
H	Hubble constant
$\mathbf{H}$	magnetic field intensity
$H_{\mu\nu}$	electromagnetic field tensor for $\mathbf{D}$, $\mathbf{H}$
I	moment of inertia
J	function in equation of motion, Section 6.2
$\mathbf{J}$	current density*
k	spatial curvature index $= \kappa S^2$
K	Gaussian curvature
K	absorption coefficient
l	apparent brightness
$\mathbf{l}$	length vector
l^{μ}, l_{μ}	propagation "vector"
$l^{\mu\nu}$	angular momentum

L	Lagrangian
L	length of inverse order $\partial/\partial x^i$
L	absolute luminosity
L_i	angular momentum
m	mass
M	mass
M_i	momentum
$M^{\mu\nu}$	matter stress-energy tensor
n	index of refraction
n	number of dimensions
$\mathbf{n}$	unit vector in direction of light waves
N	function in orbit equation, Section 6.2
O	origin; observer; order of magnitude
p	semi-latus rectum of Keplerian ellipse
p	parameter along curve; preferred parameter on geodesic
p	pressure; cosmological pressure; proper pressure
p	heat-source density
p_0	proper pressure
p^μ, p_μ	momentum; conjugate momentum
P	period
P	point; event
$\mathbf{P}$	Poynting vector
q	charge
q	the cosmological ratio $\kappa\rho/3H^2$
r	radius; radial coordinate
R	radius of curvature
R	curvature scalar
R	earth radius
R	impact parameter for light ray or fast particle near gravitating body
R_{ij}	Ricci tensor
R_{ijkl}	Riemann tensor
s	proper time; metric interval

$s, s^\mu, s^{\mu\nu}$	(see photon description, Sections 5.2, 12.3)
S	arbitrary scalar
S	inertial frame
S	cosmological function equal to spatial radius of curvature
$S, \mathbf{S}$	area, surface area
$S^{\mu\nu}$	electromagnetic stress-energy tensor
$S^{\mu\nu}$	gravitational stress-energy tensor in scalar theory
t	time; cosmic time; parameter along curve; transformation parameter
T	temperature
T	kinetic energy
T_i	torque
$T^{\mu\nu}$	total stress-energy tensor
u	$= 1/r$ in orbit problems
u	cosmological parameter
u^μ	world velocity
U	energy density*
$\mathbf{v}$	velocity
V	volume*
V_π	proper volume
V_μ	vector volume
w	cosmological radial coordinate
W	work
W	function in Section 7.8
x	first Cartesian coordinate
x^μ	coordinates
X_α	$= \xi^i_\alpha \, \partial/\partial x^i$ in automorphisms
X_{ij}	Maxwell stress tensor
y	second Cartesian coordinate
y^μ	geodesic coordinates
z	third Cartesian coordinate
z	red shift

α	acceleration parameter in cosmology
α^i	acceleration vector
γ	$= \left(1 - \dfrac{v^2}{c^2}\right)^{-1/2}$ in Lorentz transformation
δ	variation; differential; automorphic differential
δ_{ij}	Kronecker delta*
Δ	difference
Δ	automorphic derivative
ε	electric permittivity
ε_0	electric permittivity in free space
$\varepsilon_r,\ \varepsilon(\mathbf{a})$	index in Section 8.8
$\varepsilon_{\mu\nu\rho\sigma},\ \varepsilon^{\mu\nu\rho\sigma}$	tensor form of permutation symbol
η_{ij}	Minkowski metric tensor; diagonalized metric tensor*
κ	$= 8\pi G$
κ	ether drag coefficient
κ	curvature of curve
κ	spatial curvature in Chapter 14
λ	wavelength
λ	metric coefficient exponent in Section 9.4
λ	cosmological ratio $\Lambda/3\mathrm{H}^2$
λ	intergalactic distance in Section A.8
λ	length in Section 3.3
$\lambda^\mu \lambda_\mu$	propagation vector
λ^μ_α	ennuple
Λ	cosmological constant
Λ^μ	conserved quantity
Λ^μ_ν	Lorentz transformation matrix
Λ^μ_ν	Coriolis vector in Section 11.2
μ	gravitational radius $= GM/c^2$
μ	cosmological ratio $k/H^2 S_0^2$
μ	magnetic permeability
μ_0	magnetic permeability in free space

ν	frequency
ν	metric coefficient exponent in Section 9.4
ξ^i	Killing vector; automorphism generator
π	mathematical constant $= 3.14159\ldots$*
Π	four-dimensional volume
ρ	geodesic radius; radial coordinate in geodesic polar coordinates
ρ	charge density
ρ	mass density; proper mass density
ρ_0	proper mass density
σ	perihelion advance (perihelion revolution $\div$ planet revolution)
σ	cosmological function $=$ either $\sin w$, w, or $\sinh w$ according as $k = +1, 0,$ or -1
$\sum$	summation
Σ	inertial frame at rest in ether
τ	proper time (τ is usually used in Minkowski space-time and s in general relativity)
τ	cosmological ratio $= Ht_0$
ϕ	electromagnetic scalar potential
ϕ	angle in geodesic polar coordinates
ϕ^μ, ϕ_μ	electromagnetic 4-vector potential
$\phi_{\mu\nu}$	potential in Chapter 6
Φ	Newtonian gravitational potential; scalar-theory gravitational potential*
$\boldsymbol{\Phi}$	heat-flow vector
ω, Ω	angular velocity*
∂	partial differentiation
∇^2	Laplacian operator*
$\square^2$	d'Alembertian operator*

		absolute value of scalar
		magnitude of vector
		determinant of matrix*
·	differentiation with respect to either time or independent variable
=	equality*
$\simeq$, $\approx$	approximate equality*
>	greater than*
<	less than*
$\geq$	greater than or equal to*
$\leq$	less than or equal to*
$\frown$	inverse matrix*
$\int$	integral*
d^3x	element of three-dimensional volume
[ ], { }	Christoffel symbols

A.U.	astronomical unit
cm	centimeter
const	constant
cos	cosine
cosh	hyperbolic cosine
cot	cotangent
coth	hyperbolic cotangent
csc	cosecant
csch	hyperbolic cosecant
gm	gram
kg	kilogram
km	kilometer
ln	natural logarithm (to base e)
log	logarithm to base 10
ly	light year
m	meter
Mpc	megaparsec
psc	parsec
sec	second
sec	secant
sech	hyperbolic secant

sin	sine
sinh	hyperbolic sine
tan	tangent
tanh	hyperbolic tangent
yr	year

* Asterisks in the above list indicate cases where I have attempted to use the given symbol *only* for the designated quantity throughout the book. The list is intended as an aid to the reader whenever he may encounter any uncertain notation in the text.

Electromagnetic quantities are defined by the so-called *mks* system, and the units for numerical quantities are generally those of the *mks* system.

The Greek and Latin indices for vectors are used in accordance with the following convention: Latin for arbitrary number of dimensions; Greek for four dimensions of space-time; Latin for three spatial dimensions of space-time. Space-time indices run over $\mu = 0, 1, 2, 3$ (with $\mu = 0$ for the temporal component); $i = 1, 2, 3$. No attempt will be made to distinguish the superscript 2 (e.g., $y = x^2$) from the exponent 2 (e.g., $|x|^2 = x^2$), since the distinction will be clear from context.

When a matrix A_{ij} is written out in components, the order is:

$$A_{ij} = \begin{bmatrix} A_{11} & A_{12} & A_{13} & \cdots \\ A_{21} & A_{22} & A_{23} & \\ A_{31} & A_{32} & A_{33} & \cdots \\ \cdots & & \cdots & \end{bmatrix}$$

In equations which involve numerical quantities and units, the *units* will be carried along *as if they were quantities*. For example, the Hubble relation $v = HD$ with $H = 100$ km sec^{-1} Mpc^{-1} becomes $v = 100D$ km sec^{-1} Mpc^{-1}. The substitution $D = 50$ Mpc then cancels the Mpc, leaving $v = 5000$ km sec^{-1}.

Contents

CHAPTER 9

GENERAL RELATIVITY **228**

CHAPTER 10

SELECTED TOPICS IN GENERAL RELATIVITY **263**

CHAPTER 11

INERTIAL FRAMES 282

CHAPTER 12

EQUATIONS OF MOTION 301

CHAPTER 13

AUTOMORPHISMS 310

CHAPTER 14

FOUNDATIONS OF COSMOLOGY 335

CHAPTER 15

OBSERVABLE QUANTITIES 349

CHAPTER 16

SPECIAL COSMOLOGICAL MODELS 362

CHAPTER 17

GENERAL-RELATIVISTIC COSMOLOGY 372

CHAPTER 18

COSMOLOGICAL OBSERVATIONS 384

List of Illustrations

The page number in parentheses follows the figure number.

Figure

Figure

CHAPTER I

EUCLIDEAN SPACE

1.1 INTRODUCTION

Since a background in Euclidean geometry is the necessary starting point for understanding non-Euclidean geometry, this chapter constitutes a review of kinematics in three-dimensional Euclidean space. In rectangular Cartesian coordinates x^i ($i = 1, 2, 3$), the distance dl between two points $P(x^i)$ and $Q(x^i + dx^i)$ is given by the Pythagorean theorem:

$$dl^2 = (dx^1)^2 + (dx^2)^2 + (dx^3)^2.$$

The convention that repeated indices are to be summed will be used throughout this book, unless specified to the contrary. Thus the above equation becomes

$$dl^2 = dx^i \, dx^i. \tag{1-1}$$

There is only one kind of vector. Upon transformation from one set of Cartesian coordinates x^i to another set $\bar{x}^r$, a vector V^i transforms according to either of the equations

$$\bar{V}^r = \frac{\partial \bar{x}^r}{\partial x^i} V^i$$

$$\bar{V}^r = \frac{\partial x^i}{\partial \bar{x}^r} V^i.$$

The above two equations are equivalent, because the two transformation matrices

$$\frac{\partial \bar{x}^r}{\partial x^i} \quad \text{and} \quad \frac{\partial x^i}{\partial \bar{x}^r}$$

are identical. However, if the space is non-Euclidean, or if the Cartesian coordinates are not rectangular, then the above transformation equations define two different transformation laws, and there accordingly exist *two* kinds of vectors.

1.2 OBLIQUE CARTESIAN COORDINATES

In two dimensions, oblique Cartesian coordinates are defined by two axes which intersect in an angle α. (See Figure 1.1.) The origin O is the point of intersection of the two axes. An arbitrary point P then has two different sets of coordinates (x^1, x^2) and (x_1, x_2), depending on whether P is projected parallel to the axes or perpendicular to the axes. The contravariant components x^i $(i = 1, 2)$ of the vector $\mathbf{x} = OP$ are the lengths of the respective parallel projections of $\mathbf{x}$. For example, x^1 is the length of the projection of OP onto the x^1-axis, with P projected parallel to the x^2-axis. On the other hand, the *covariant* components x_i are the lengths of the vector OP projected onto the corresponding axis by perpendicular projection. For example, P is projected perpendicular to the x^1-axis, onto the x^1-axis, to give the covariant length x_1. The two sets of coordinates are related by the equations

$$\left.\begin{aligned} x_1 &= x^1 + x^2 \cos \alpha \\ x_2 &= x^2 + x^1 \cos \alpha. \end{aligned}\right\} \tag{1-2}$$

We note that the length of the vector OP is given by

$$|\mathbf{x}|^2 = g_{ij}x^i x^j = g^{ij}x_i x_j$$

where the matrices g_{ij} and g^{ij} are defined

$$g_{ij} = \begin{pmatrix} 1 & \cos \alpha \\ \cos \alpha & 1 \end{pmatrix}$$

$$g^{ij} = \frac{1}{\sin^2 \alpha} \begin{pmatrix} 1 & -\cos \alpha \\ -\cos \alpha & 1 \end{pmatrix}.$$

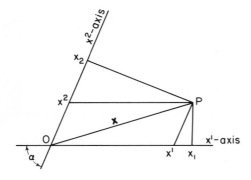

FIGURE 1.1 Oblique Cartesian coordinates.

Equations (1-2) can be written

$$x_i = g_{ij}x^j.$$

The inverse transformation is

$$x^i = g^{ij}x_j,$$

since g^{ij} is the inverse of g_{ij}, i.e.,

$$g^{ij}g_{jk} = \begin{pmatrix} 1 & 0 \\ 0 & 1 \end{pmatrix}.$$

In three dimensions, the directions of the three coordinate axes are defined by three non-collinear, non-coplanar unit vectors $\mathbf{e}_1$, $\mathbf{e}_2$, and $\mathbf{e}_3$. A point O is selected as the origin, and each coordinate axis x^i ($i = 1, 2, 3$) is constructed through O parallel to $\mathbf{e}_i$. The vector $\mathbf{x}$ from O to an arbitrary point P has contravariant components x^i defined by the vector equation

$$\mathbf{x} = x^i\mathbf{e}_i. \tag{1-3}$$

The x^i are uniquely defined, because $\mathbf{x}$ has a unique decomposition into the unit vectors $\mathbf{e}_i$. In fact, x^i is the length of the projection of $\mathbf{x}$ onto the x^i-axis with P projected *parallel* to the plane of the remaining two axes. In distinction to this, the covariant component x_i is defined as the length of the projection of $\mathbf{x}$ onto the x^i-axis with P projected perpendicular to the x^i-axis. In vector notation

$$x_i = \mathbf{x} \cdot \mathbf{e}_i. \tag{1-4}$$

With the further definitions

$$g_{ij} = \mathbf{e}_i \cdot \mathbf{e}_j$$

and

$$g^{ij} = \text{inverse of } g_{ij},$$

there follow the relations

$$|\mathbf{x}|^2 = g_{ij}x^ix^j \tag{1-5}$$

$$|\mathbf{x}|^2 = g^{ij}x_ix_j \tag{1-6}$$

$$x_i = g_{ij}x^j \tag{1-7}$$

$$x^i = g^{ij}x_j. \tag{1-8}$$

Equation (1-5) follows from the scalar multiplication of eq. (1-3) by itself. Equation (1-7) results from substituting eq. (1-3) into eq. (1-4). Equations (1-6) and (1-8) follow by inversion.

If a new set of base vectors $\bar{\mathbf{e}}_r$ ($r = 1, 2, 3$) is introduced, the new coordinates $\bar{x}^r$ of the point P are related to the old coordinates x^i by the transformation equation

$$\bar{x}^r = a_i^r x^i, \tag{1-9}$$

where the matrix a_i^r is defined

$$\mathbf{e}_i = \bar{\mathbf{e}}_r a_i^r. \tag{1-10}$$

This follows from substituting eq. (1-10) into eq. (1-3):

$$\mathbf{x} = x^i \bar{\mathbf{e}}_r a_i^r = (x^i a_i^r)\bar{\mathbf{e}}_r = \bar{x}^r \bar{\mathbf{e}}_r.$$

If b_r^i is the inverse of the matrix a_i^r, then eq. (1-10) becomes

$$\bar{\mathbf{e}}_r = b_r^i \mathbf{e}_i.$$

It is then easy to prove

$$g_{ij} = a_i^r a_j^s \bar{g}_{rs}$$

$$\bar{g}_{rs} = b_r^i b_s^j g_{ij}$$

where barred quantities are evaluated in the new coordinates. It is also easily found from eq. (1-7) that $\bar{x}_r$ is given by

$$\bar{x}_r = b_r^i x_i. \tag{1-11}$$

Equations (1-9) and (1-11) are the transformation laws for the contravariant and covariant components of the vector $\mathbf{x}$, respectively.

1.3 THE KRONECKER DELTA

The Kronecker delta, denoted equivalently $\delta^i_{\ j}$, δ_{ij}, or δ^{ij}, is the matrix whose components are $+1$ if $i = j$ and zero if $i \neq j$. That is, $\delta^i_{\ j}$ is an $n \times n$ matrix whose components are zero except along the diagonal where the values are $+1$. In three dimensions,

$$\delta^i_{\ j} = \begin{pmatrix} 1 & 0 & 0 \\ 0 & 1 & 0 \\ 0 & 0 & 1 \end{pmatrix}.$$

In matrix language, $\delta^i_{\ j}$ is merely the *unit matrix*.

1.4 THE PERMUTATION SYMBOL

In n-dimensional geometry, the permutation symbol, denoted $e(ijk \cdots)$, has n indices, each of which may assume any of the values $1, 2, 3, \ldots, n$. Among the various possible combinations, there are permutations of the n integers $1, 2, 3, \ldots, n$. The value of $e(ijk \cdots)$ is defined to be $+1$ if the permutation is even, -1 if the permutation is odd, and zero for all other combinations. The evenness or oddness of a permutation is the same as the evenness or oddness of the permutation index. The latter is the sum over all k from 1 to n of N_k, where N_k is the number of integers of the permutation to the right of the kth position which are smaller than the integer in the kth position.

When any index is repeated, the permutation symbol is zero. When two indices are interchanged, the permutation symbol changes sign. Any cyclic rearrangement of the indices leaves the value unchanged. In three dimensions, the perturbation symbol is

$$e(123) = e(231) = e(312) = +1$$
$$e(321) = e(213) = e(132) = -1$$
$$\text{all other } e(ijk) = 0.$$

Two identities which prove useful in calculations are:

$$e(ijk)e(irs) = \delta_{jr}\delta_{ks} - \delta_{js}\delta_{kr} \tag{1-12}$$
$$\begin{aligned} e(ijkl)e(irst) = &\ \delta_{jr}\delta_{ks}\delta_{lt} + \delta_{js}\delta_{kt}\delta_{lr} + \delta_{jt}\delta_{kr}\delta_{ls} \\ &- \delta_{jr}\delta_{kt}\delta_{ls} - \delta_{ks}\delta_{jt}\delta_{lr} - \delta_{lt}\delta_{js}\delta_{kr}. \end{aligned}$$

Vector operations in three dimensions may be written in terms of components by the use of the permutation symbol. The vector cross product

$$\mathbf{C} = \mathbf{A} \times \mathbf{B}$$

becomes

$$C_i = e(ijk)A_j B_k$$

and the curl

$$\mathbf{D} = \text{curl } \mathbf{A}$$

becomes

$$D_i = e(ijk)\nabla_j A_k$$

where

$$\nabla_j = \frac{\partial}{\partial x^j}.$$

An antisymmetric tensor T_{ij} may be written

$$T_{ij} = e(ijk)A^k$$

where A^k is defined with the use of eq. (1-12):

$$A^k = \tfrac{1}{2}T_{ij}e(ijk).$$

The determinant of a matrix g_{ij} is written

$$|g_{ij}| = e(klm)g_{1k}g_{2l}g_{3m}$$

or, as may be easily verified,

$$|g_{ij}| = \tfrac{1}{6}e(klm)e(rst)g_{kr}g_{ls}g_{mt}.$$

1.5 TRANSFORMATIONS OF EUCLIDEAN SPACE

We return to the use of rectangular Cartesian coordinates in which eq. (1-1) holds, and ask for the most general transformation $\bar{x}^r = f^r(x^i)$ which leaves eq. (1-1) unchanged. The condition imposed on the transformation is

$$d\bar{x}^r\, d\bar{x}^r = dx^i\, dx^i \tag{1-13}$$

or

$$\frac{\partial \bar{x}^r}{\partial x^i}\frac{\partial \bar{x}^r}{\partial x^j}\, dx^i\, dx^j = dx^k\, dx^k \tag{1-14}$$

since

$$d\bar{x}^r = \frac{\partial \bar{x}^r}{\partial x^i}\, dx^i.$$

The necessary and sufficient condition for eq. (1-14) to hold is

$$\frac{\partial \bar{x}^r}{\partial x^i}\frac{\partial \bar{x}^r}{\partial x^j} = \delta_{ij}. \tag{1-15}$$

Equation (1-15) in turn requires that the transformation be linear, as may be verified in the following way. We first differentiate eq. (1-15) with respect to x^k, then permute the indices ijk to obtain two additional equations, and finally add and subtract the resulting three equations in such a way as to obtain

$$\frac{\partial \bar{x}^r}{\partial x^k}\frac{\partial^2 \bar{x}^r}{\partial x^i\, \partial x^j} = 0$$

or, since

$$\left|\frac{\partial \bar{x}^r}{\partial x^k}\right| \neq 0,$$

$$\frac{\partial^2 \bar{x}^r}{\partial x^i\, \partial x^j} = 0. \tag{1-16}$$

The solution of eq. (1-16) is immediately seen to be

$$\bar{x}^r = a_i^r x^i + b^r \tag{1-17}$$

where the a_i^r and b^r are constants. Substitution of eq. (1-17) into eq. (1-15) yields the condition

$$a_i^r a_j^r = \delta_{ij}. \tag{1-18}$$

We conclude that *the most general transformation of Euclidean space into itself in rectangular Cartesian coordinates is given by eq. (1-17) where the b^r are constants and the a_i^r are constants subject to the condition (1-18).*

The matrix a_i^r is thus its own inverse. We proceed to interpret the constants a_i^r and b^r as follows.

The identity transformation $\bar{x}^r = x^r$ is given by the case $a_i^r = \delta_i^r$, $b^r = 0$. The term b^r represents a translation, since, with $a_i^r = \delta_i^r$, eq. (1-17) becomes

$$\bar{x}^r = x^r + b^r.$$

It remains to interpret the term $a_i^r x^i$ which, as will be seen in the following analysis, represents a rotation.

Consider the family of transformations described by a parameter t,

$$\bar{x}^r = a_i^r(t)x^i + b^r(t), \tag{1-19}$$

and which includes the identity transformation. There is no loss of generality in choosing the value of t for the identity transformation to be zero. Then we have the values

$$a_i^r(0) = \delta_i^r, \qquad b^r(0) = 0.$$

For a small value of the parameter t, denoted by δt, the transformation elements are

$$a_i^r = \delta_i^r + \omega_{ri}\, \delta t \tag{1-20}$$

$$b^r = \beta^r\, \delta t$$

where

$$\omega_{ri} = \left(\frac{da_i^r}{dt}\right)_{t=0}$$

$$\beta^r = \left(\frac{db^r}{dt}\right)_{t=0}.$$

Quantities of order higher than the first power of δt are neglected in eq. (1-20). (Up to this point, the number of dimensions need not be restricted to three; however, three dimensions will be assumed in what follows.)

The condition (1-18) on the transformation matrix a_i^r requires that the ω_{ri} in eq. (1-20) be antisymmetric. Hence ω_{ri} may be written in the form

$$\omega_{ri} = e(rik)\omega^k$$

where

$$\omega^k = \tfrac{1}{2}e(ijk)\omega_{ij}.$$

Thus eq. (1-19) becomes

$$\bar{x}^r = x^r + e(rik)x^i\omega^k\, \delta t + \beta^r\, \delta t. \tag{1-21}$$

Equation (1-21) is known as the *infinitesimal transformation*.

If the x^3-axis is chosen in the direction of the vector ω^k, the transformation becomes

$$\bar{x} = x + y\,\delta\theta + \beta^1\,\delta t$$
$$\bar{y} = y - x\,\delta\theta + \beta^2\,\delta t$$
$$\bar{z} = z + \beta^3\,\delta t$$

where x^1, x^2, x^3 are denoted respectively x, y, z (as will frequently be done in this book) and $\delta\theta = \omega\,\delta t$. The quantity $\delta\theta$ is immediately recognized as the angle of rotation around the z-axis. Thus, in general, $\omega^k\,\delta t$ represents a rotation through an angle $\omega\,\delta t$ about an axis ω^k.

We may extend the concept of rotation to any number of dimensions by the definition: the transformation represented by the a^i_k in eqs. (1-17) and (1-18) is a *rotation*. Thus the possible transformations of Euclidean space into itself in any number of dimensions (except one) consist only of translations and rotations. The number of independent translations is equal to the number of b^r, namely n, and the number of independent rotations is equal to the number of independent a^r_i which, from eq. (1-18), is $\frac{1}{2}n(n-1)$. Thus three-dimensional Euclidean space admits three translations and three rotations. Four-dimensional Euclidean space admits four translations and six rotations.

1.6 INFINITESIMAL MOTION

We turn our attention now to the motions of a solid body in a fixed rectangular Cartesian coordinate system in three-dimensional Euclidean space. A solid body is defined as an arrangement of points in which the distance between each pair of points is a constant. From this definition, it is clear that although the case under study is a *moving* set of points in a *fixed* coordinate system, it differs from the preceding case, which involved a *fixed* set of points in a *changing* coordinate system, only in the distinction of whether the set of points or the coordinate system is considered stationary.

The eq. (1-21) for the infinitesimal transformation therefore applies to this case:

$$\bar{x}^r = x^r + e(rik)\omega^i x^k\,\delta t + \beta^r\,\delta t \tag{1-22}$$

where x^i is the initial position of a point P and $\bar{x}^r$ is its final position. The change in the sign of ω^k, seen in the interchange of ω^i and x^k from eq. (1-21), is simply the consequence of interpreting $\omega^k\,\delta t$ as the rotation of P in the coordinate system rather than the apparent rotation of the coordinate system relative to P.

We therefore conclude that the motion of the points in a solid body is given by eq. (1-22). Note that six independent motions are possible (corresponding to the components of β^r and ω^k). In general, any motion

$$\bar{x}^r = f^r(x^i, t)$$

of one parameter t must have the infinitesimal form

$$\bar{x}^r = x^r + \xi^r(x^i)\,\delta t \qquad (1\text{-}23)$$

where

$$\xi^r(x^i) = \left[\frac{\partial f^r(x^i, t)}{\partial t}\right]_{t=0}$$

The vector ξ^r in eq. (1-22) has the form

$$\xi^r = e(rik)\omega^i x^k + \beta^r \qquad (1\text{-}24)$$

because of the requirement of solid-body motion, i.e., eq. (1-15). It may be verified either by differentiating eq. (1-24) or by substituting eq. (1-23) into eq. (1-15) that the condition imposed on ξ^r is

$$\frac{\partial \xi^i}{\partial x^j} + \frac{\partial \xi^j}{\partial x^i} = 0$$

which is known as *Killing's equation*.

1.7 INSTANTANEOUS AXIS OF ROTATION

Any solid body in motion possesses an instantaneous axis of rotation defined as that axis L on which there is no motion perpendicular to ω^k. The motion of any point x^i in the body is represented by the derivative of eq. (1-22):

$$\frac{dx^r}{dt} = e(rik)\omega^i x^k + \beta^r. \qquad (1\text{-}25)$$

(If the parameter t is *time*, to be introduced later, then dx^r/dt is velocity.) The direction of L is parallel to ω^k; the problem is to locate L. If β^r is perpendicular to ω^k, i.e., there is no translation parallel to L, then L may be defined as the locus of points at which eq. (1-25) vanishes. However, in general, β^r may not be perpendicular to ω^k. There is then no place where eq. (1-25) vanishes, because it has a non-zero component parallel to ω^k:

$$\omega^k \frac{dx^k}{dt} = \omega^r \beta^r.$$

Therefore we must define L as the locus of points where eq. (1-25) is parallel to ω^r:

$$e(rik)\omega^i x^k + \beta^r = \lambda\omega^r. \qquad (1\text{-}26)$$

Multiplication of eq. (1-26) by ω^r and by $e(rjl)\omega^j$ give respectively the equations

$$\lambda = \frac{\omega^k \beta^k}{\omega^l \omega^l} \tag{1-27}$$

and

$$\omega^k \omega^k x^l - \omega^l \omega^k x^k = e(lmn)\omega^m \beta^n. \tag{1-28}$$

The left-hand side of eq. (1-28) is equal to ω^2 times the component of $\mathbf{x}$ perpendicular to $\boldsymbol{\omega}$. Thus eq. (1-28) defines a line L parallel to $\boldsymbol{\omega}$ which passes a distance

$$\sqrt{\frac{\beta^2}{\omega^2} - \lambda^2}$$

from the origin.

The line L can be easily identified as the instantaneous axis of rotation by the use of special coordinates. The z-axis is chosen parallel to $\boldsymbol{\omega}$ so that eq. (1-25) becomes

$$\frac{dx}{dt} = -\omega y + \beta^1$$

$$\frac{dy}{dt} = \omega x + \beta^2$$

$$\frac{dz}{dt} = \beta^3.$$

Equations (1-27) and (1-28) become

$$\lambda = \frac{\beta^3}{\omega}$$

$$\omega^2 x = -\omega \beta^2 \quad \text{or} \quad x = -\beta^2/\omega$$

$$\omega^2 y = \omega \beta^1 \quad \text{or} \quad y = \beta^1/\omega.$$

On transforming to new coordinates

$$x' = x + \frac{\beta^2}{\omega}$$

$$y' = y - \frac{\beta^1}{\omega}$$

$$z' = z,$$

the motion is given by

$$\frac{dx'}{dt} = -\omega y'$$

$$\frac{dy'}{dt} = \omega x'$$

$$\frac{dz'}{dt} = \beta^3.$$

The motion around the line L $(x' = 0, y' = 0)$ is screw-like or helical. As the body advances through a distance $\delta z = \beta^3 \delta t$ along L, it rotates through an angle $\omega \, \delta t$ about L.

I.8 INVARIANTS OF MOTION

We know that the distances and angles between points in a solid body remain constant under any solid-body motion. But are these the *only* invariants? It is desired to find *all* functions $f(x_\alpha^i)$ of N points P_α ($\alpha = 1, 2, \ldots, N$) which are invariant under a general infinitesimal solid-body motion. The condition

$$f(x_\alpha^i + \delta x_\alpha^i) = f(x_\alpha^i)$$

where, from eq. (1-23), $\delta x_\alpha^i = \xi^i(x_\alpha^j) \, \delta t$ may be rewritten

$$\frac{\partial f}{\partial x_\alpha^r} \, \xi^r(x_\alpha^i) \, \delta t = 0. \tag{1-29}$$

Equation (1-24), which represents the condition that space be Euclidean, is substituted into eq. (1-29) to give

$$\left(e(rik) \frac{\partial f}{\partial x_\alpha^r} x_\alpha^k \omega^i + \sum_\alpha \frac{\partial f}{\partial x_\alpha^r} \beta^r \right) \delta t = 0. \tag{1-30}$$

The necessary and sufficient conditions for eq. (1-30) to hold for all δt, β^r, and ω^i are

$$e(rik) \frac{\partial f}{\partial x_\alpha^r} x_\alpha^k = 0 \tag{1-31}$$

and

$$\sum_\alpha \frac{\partial f}{\partial x_\alpha^r} = 0. \tag{1-32}$$

Equation (1-32) implies that f is a function only of differences, for example $\xi_\beta^i = x_\beta^i - x_N^i$ ($\beta = 1, 2, \ldots, N - 1$); since when f is considered to be a function only of ξ_β^i ($\beta = 1, 2, \ldots, N - 1$) and x_N^i, eq. (1-32) becomes

$$\frac{\partial f}{\partial x_N^i} = 0.$$

We may without loss of generality choose $x_N^i = 0$. Equation (1-29) then becomes

$$\sum_{\beta=1}^{N-1} e(rik) \frac{\partial f}{\partial x_\beta^r} x_\beta^k = 0.$$

The case $N = 1$ has no solution.

The case $N = 2$ has the requirement

$$e(rik)x_1^k \frac{\partial f}{\partial x_1^r} = 0$$

which has the solution

$$\frac{\partial f}{\partial x_1^r} = Ax_1^r.$$

The latter in turn gives

$$df = Ax_1^r \, dx_1^r = \tfrac{1}{2}A \, d(|\mathbf{x}_1|^2).$$

Thus, the only invariants of two points are functions of the distance between them.

The case $N = 3$ has the condition

$$e(rik)\left(x_1^k \frac{\partial f}{\partial x_1^r} + x_2^k \frac{\partial f}{\partial x_2^r}\right) \tag{1-33}$$

which upon multiplication by x_2^i and x_1^i respectively gives

$$e(rik)x_2^i x_1^k \frac{\partial f}{\partial x_1^r} = 0$$

$$e(rik)x_1^i x_2^k \frac{\partial f}{\partial x_2^r} = 0.$$

Hence both $\dfrac{\partial f}{\partial x_1^r}$ and $\dfrac{\partial f}{\partial x_2^r}$ must be linear combinations of x_1^r and x_2^r:

$$\frac{\partial f}{\partial x_1^r} = Ax_1^r + Bx_2^r$$

$$\frac{\partial f}{\partial x_2^r} = Cx_1^r + Dx_2^r.$$

Equation (1-33) requires $B = C$. Hence

$$df = \tfrac{1}{2}A \, d(|\mathbf{x}_1|^2) + B \, d(\mathbf{x}_1 \cdot \mathbf{x}_2) + \tfrac{1}{2}D \, d(|\mathbf{x}_2|^2).$$

That is, the only invariants of three points are angles and lengths of the sides of the triangle which they form.

1.9 TIME

It is postulated that an observer can determine whether events occur simultaneously, and that he can order non-simultaneous events according to time. An *event* E is a point x^i $(i = 1, 2, 3)$ at a time t. It will be postulated that *distances* can be measured in any three-dimensional space consisting of all events at a given time $t = $ const.

Space-time is regarded as striated into three-dimensional spaces $t = $ const. Two events $E_1(t_1, x_1^i)$ and $E_2(t_2, x_2^i)$ are separated by a time interval $\Delta t = t_2 - t_1$. If $\Delta t = 0$, then E_2 and E_1 are separated by a distance $l = |\mathbf{x}_2 - \mathbf{x}_1|$. But if $\Delta t \neq 0$, there exists as yet no concept of distance between the events E_1 and E_2.

We follow Lange's[B] method of defining both an inertial frame and a measurement of time.

DEFINITION 1. An *inertial frame* is any coordinate system in which three free particles projected non-collinearly from a given point will have straight-line motion.

THEOREM 1. Every free particle will move in a straight line in any inertial frame.

DEFINITION 2. A freely moving particle in an inertial frame traverses equal distances in equal *times*.

THEOREM 2. Any freely moving particle in any inertial frame traverses equal distances in equal times.

The above definitions and theorems allow the construction of space-time in which free particles go in straight lines and cover equal distances in equal times. The concept of simultaneity allows space-time to be striated into different three-dimensional spaces S_k $(k = 1, 2, \ldots)$, each with a different (but as yet unknown) time t_k. Three freely moving particles A, B, and C are then used to align the spaces. Particle A is chosen as the origin in all the S_k. Particle B is used to fix the axis of polar coordinates in each space, and particle C is used to determine the meridian plane $\phi = 0$ in each space. Figure 1.2a represents the resulting arrangement with one spatial dimension omitted. The vertical dimension in the diagram represents time.

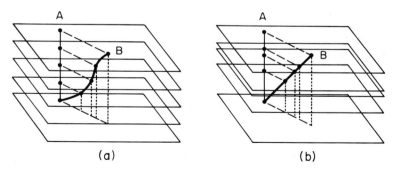

(a)   (b)

FIGURE 1.2   (a) Alignment of three-dimensional spaces (with one spatial dimension omitted) and (b) introduction of measurement of time.

The measurement of time is introduced by rearranging the spacing of the planes in Figure 1.2a so that particle B covers equal distances in equal times. The result is represented in Figure 1.2b. It follows from Theorem 2 that particle C also covers equal distances in equal times.

A practical difficulty arises in that no particles are really free. Even in a perfect vacuum and in the complete absence of all electromagnetic effects, there still remains the force of gravity between the particles. Further, there is no way of detecting the position of a *free* particle, since any method of locating it produces a force on it. However, Lange's method may be carried through if we understand that we are to take the *limit* of the particles' behavior as all forces, including gravity, approach zero.

1.10 KINEMATICS

Consider the motion of a single point P in Euclidean space. Two sets of rectangular Cartesian coordinates x^i and $\bar{x}^r$ will be used, and the time t will be taken as the parameter. Then the position of P is, respectively, a set of functions $x^i(t)$ in one coordinate system and another set of functions $\bar{x}^r(t)$ in the other coordinate system. The two sets of coordinates are related by eq. (1-19):

$$\bar{x}^r(t) = a_i^r(t)x^i(t) + b^r(t). \tag{1-34}$$

It is assumed that at $t = 0$ the coordinate systems coincide, so that we have $a_i^r(0) = \delta_i^r$ and $b^r(0) = 0$. The condition on a_i^r represented by eq. (1-18) may be differentiated to give

$$\dot{a}_i^r(t)a_j^r(t) + a_i^r(t)\dot{a}_j^r(t) = 0 \tag{1-35}$$

where the dot denotes differentiation with respect to t. Equation (1-35) requires that $\dot{a}_i^r(t)a_j^r(t)$ be antisymmetric with respect to i, j. Therefore the angular velocity $\omega^k(t)$ may be defined:

$$\dot{a}_i^r(t)a_j^r(t) = e(ijk)\omega^k(t). \tag{1-36}$$

Differentiation of eq. (1-36) gives

$$\ddot{a}_i^r(t)a_j^r(t) + \dot{a}_i^r(t)\dot{a}_j^r(t) = e(ijk)\dot{\omega}^k(t). \tag{1-37}$$

Evaluation at $t = 0$ gives, from eq. (1-36),

$$\dot{a}_i^r(0) = e(irk)\omega^k(0) \tag{1-38}$$

and hence, from eq. (1-37),

$$\ddot{a}_i^r(0) = e(irk)\dot{\omega}^k(0) - \delta_{ir}|\omega(0)|^2 + \omega^i(0)\omega^r(0). \tag{1-39}$$

Double-differentiation of eq. (1-34) and evaluation at $t = 0$ by means of eqs. (1-38) and (1-39) produces the formula

$$\frac{d^2 \bar{x}^r}{dt^2} = \frac{d^2 x^r}{dt^2} + 2e(irk)\omega^k(0)\frac{dx^i}{dt} + e(irk)\dot{\omega}^k(0)x^i$$

$$- x^r |\omega(0)|^2 + \omega^r(0)\omega^i(0)x^i + \ddot{b}^r(0). \quad (1\text{-}40)$$

Equation (1-40) will be interpreted shortly.

1.11 FORCE

Newton's three laws of motion may be stated:

1. A body not acted upon by any force maintains uniform motion.
2. The time-rate of change of a body's vector momentum is proportional to the vector force **F** acting on the body.
3. For every force **F** acting on a body there exists a force $-\mathbf{F}$ exerted by the body.

The first law was used in Section 1.9 to define inertial frames and the measurement of time. The second and third laws allow the definitions of *mass* and *force*. Suppose that two masses initially at rest are sprung away from each other by a massless spring. Then the masses are inversely proportional to the velocities.

Force is defined as the product of mass and acceleration. The acceleration must be taken with reference to an inertial frame in order that a free particle (for which the force is zero) have uniform motion (zero acceleration). If the point P of Section 1.10 represents a particle of mass m and the coordinate system $\bar{x}^r$ is an inertial frame, then the force F^r on the particle is

$$F^r = m\frac{d^2 \bar{x}^r}{dt^2}.$$

Equation (1-40) then becomes

$$m\frac{d^2 x^i}{dt^2} = F^i - m\ddot{b}^i - me(ijk)\dot{\omega}^j x^k + m(\omega^2 x^i - \omega^i \omega^k x^k)$$

$$- 2me(ijk)\omega^j \frac{dx^k}{dt}. \quad (1\text{-}41)$$

The terms $-m\ddot{b}^i - me(ijk)\dot{\omega}^j x^k$, known as the d'Alembert force, are due to the *acceleration* of translation and rotation of the x^i system. The term $m(\omega^2 x^i - \omega^i \omega^k x^k)$ or $m(\boldsymbol{\omega} \times \mathbf{x}) \times \boldsymbol{\omega}$ is the centrifugal force directed along the component of **x** which is perpendicular to $\boldsymbol{\omega}$. The term

$$-2me(ijk)\omega^j \, dx^k/dt \quad \text{or} \quad -2m\boldsymbol{\omega} \times d\mathbf{x}/dt$$

is the Coriolis force. The centrifugal and Coriolis forces are due to the *rotation* of the x^i system.

The Coriolis effect is of special significance for two reasons: (1) it is the only effect of first order in $\boldsymbol{\omega}$, and (2) it is the only effect which depends on the *velocity* of the particle. Thus the Coriolis effect can be used by an observer on the slowly rotating earth to detect the earth's rotation—the centrifugal effect is of order ω^2 and is easily masked because it depends on position rather than velocity. And the Coriolis effect is not easily imitated; only one other force in nature—magnetism—is known to have the same dependence on velocity.

1.12 NEWTONIAN GRAVITY

It is found experimentally that a force **F** is exerted on a point mass m at a distance **r** from another point mass M in accordance with the law

$$\mathbf{F} = -\frac{GmM}{r^3}\,\mathbf{r}.$$

The universal constant G is found to have the value

$$G = 6.67 \times 10^{-11}\mathrm{m^3\,kg^{-1}\,sec^{-2}}.$$

The field intensity $\mathbf{g(x)}$, defined as the force per unit mass, is therefore

$$\mathbf{g} = -\frac{GM}{r^3}\,\mathbf{r} \tag{1-42}$$

in the neighborhood of a point mass M. The gravitational potential $\Phi(\mathbf{x})$ is the work per unit mass required to bring material from infinity to the position **x**, provided the new material does not appreciably alter the gravitational field. Thus the potential at a distance r from a point mass M is given by

$$\Phi = \int_\infty^r \frac{GM}{r^2}\,dr = -\frac{GM}{r}.$$

It is also found experimentally that when more than one body is present, the field intensity $\mathbf{g(x)}$ is equal to the sum of the field intensities due to each body separately. It then follows that the field intensity due to a continuous distribution of matter having density $\rho(\mathbf{x})$ is given by

$$\mathbf{g(x)} = -G\int \frac{\rho(\mathbf{x}')}{|\mathbf{x} - \mathbf{x}'|^3}\,(\mathbf{x} - \mathbf{x}')\,d^3\mathbf{x}' \tag{1-43}$$

where $d^3\mathbf{x}'$ denotes the volume element $dx'\,dy'\,dz'$. The principle of superposition also applies to the potential, so that we have the equations

$$\mathbf{g} = -\mathrm{grad}\,\Phi \tag{1-44}$$

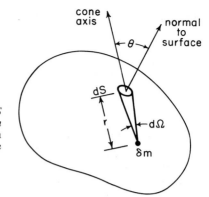

cone
axis

normal
to
surface

θ

dS

r

$d\Omega$

δm

FIGURE 1.3 The element of area dS subtends a solid angle $d\Omega$ at the mass δm located at a distance r. The angle between the axis of the infinitesimal cone and the normal to the surface is θ.

and

$$\Phi = -G \int \frac{\rho(\mathbf{x'})}{|\mathbf{x} - \mathbf{x'}|} d^3\mathbf{x'}. \tag{1-45}$$

Gauss' law states that the gravitational flux which leaves any closed surface is equal to $-4\pi G$ times the mass enclosed by the surface. The mathematical statement of Gauss' law is

$$\int_S \mathbf{g} \cdot d\mathbf{S} = -4\pi G \int_V \rho \, dV. \tag{1-46}$$

The left-hand side of eq. (1-46) is integrated over the area of the surface S, and the right-hand side is integrated over the volume V interior to the surface. Gauss' law is proved by adding the contributions $\delta \mathbf{g}$ due to elementary masses δm inside the surface. (See Figure 1.3.)

$$\int_S \delta\mathbf{g} \cdot d\mathbf{S} = \int_S \left(-\frac{G \, \delta m}{r^2} \right) \cos\theta \left(\frac{r^2 \, d\Omega}{\cos\theta} \right) = -G \, \delta m \int d\Omega.$$

The above expression is zero for a mass outside the surface and is equal to $-4\pi G \, \delta m$ for a mass inside the surface. Integration over all mass δm inside the surface then gives eq. (1-46).

The differential form of eq. (1-46)

$$\text{div } \mathbf{g} = -4\pi G\rho$$

or

$$\frac{\partial g_i}{\partial x^i} = -4\pi G\rho \tag{1-47}$$

may be obtained from eq. (1-46) by the use of Gauss' theorem

$$\int \mathbf{g} \cdot d\mathbf{S} = \int \frac{\partial g_k}{\partial x^k} dV.$$

Equation (1-44) implies both

$$\text{curl } \mathbf{g} = 0 \tag{1-48}$$

and, in view of eq. (1-47),

$$\nabla^2 \Phi = 4\pi G \rho \tag{1-49}$$

where

$$\nabla^2 = \frac{\partial^2}{\partial x^i \, \partial x^i}.$$

Equation (1-49) has as its solution eq. (1-45).

The basic problem in gravitation is to determine the field intensity $\mathbf{g}(\mathbf{x})$ for a given mass distribution $\rho(\mathbf{x})$. The most straightforward method is to evaluate the integral of eq. (1-43). An alternate method which has two variations is to regard either the pair of equations (1-47) and (1-48) or the pair (1-44) and (1-49) as defining the intensity $\mathbf{g}(\mathbf{x})$.

1.13 PLANETARY ORBITS

The motion of a particle of negligible mass in the neighborhood of a stationary mass M at a point O is defined by eq. (1-42) which, with Newton's second law, becomes

$$\frac{d^2\mathbf{r}}{dt^2} = -\frac{GM}{r^3}\mathbf{r} \tag{1-50}$$

where $\mathbf{r}$ is the position vector from O to the test particle. In spherical polar coordinates centered at O, eq. (1-50) becomes the equations of motion

$$\ddot{r} - r\dot{\theta}^2 - r\dot{\phi}^2 \sin^2 \theta = -GMr^{-2}$$

$$\frac{1}{r}\frac{d}{dt}(r^2\dot{\theta}) - r\dot{\phi}^2 \sin\theta \cos\theta = 0$$

$$\frac{1}{r \sin\theta}\frac{d}{dt}(r^2 \sin^2\theta \dot{\phi}) = 0$$

where the dot denotes d/dt. Under the initial condition $\theta = \frac{\pi}{2}$ and $\dot{\theta} = 0$, the angle θ remains constant. Thus we may choose the $\theta = \frac{\pi}{2}$ plane as the orbital plane. The equations of motion are then reduced to

$$\ddot{r} - r\dot{\phi}^2 = -GMr^{-2}$$

$$\frac{d}{dt}(r^2\dot{\phi}) = 0. \tag{1-51}$$

Hence the quantity

$$h = r^2\dot{\phi}$$

is a constant of the motion, and we may therefore write

$$\frac{d}{dt} = \frac{h}{r^2} \frac{d}{d\phi}.$$

With the above substitutions for $\dot{\phi}$ and d/dt, and the further substitution $r = 1/u$, eq. (1-51) becomes

$$\frac{d^2u}{d\phi^2} + u = \frac{1}{p} \tag{1-52}$$

where

$$p = \frac{h^2}{GM}.$$

The most general solution of eq. (1-52) is

$$u = \frac{1}{p}[1 + e \cos(\phi - \alpha)] \tag{1-53}$$

where e and α are the constants of integration. We now proceed to examine the solutions represented by eq. (1-53).

The constant e may be chosen non-negative without loss of generality, since the cosine term changes sign upon increasing α by π. And a suitable rotation of coordinates allows α to be chosen as zero. Thus eq. (1-53) takes the simple form

$$u = \frac{1}{r} = \frac{1}{p}(1 + e \cos \phi) \qquad e \geq 0. \tag{1-54}$$

The particle's closest approach to O occurs when $\phi = 0$. This point, located a distance $p/(1 + e)$ from O, is called *perihelion* if M is the sun, *periastron* if M is a star, or *perigee* if M is the earth. For the sake of simplicity, *perihelion* will be consistently used throughout this book in all orbit problems without distinguishing whether M is the sun, a star, or the earth.

The curves represented by eq. (1-54) are conic sections, i.e., ellipses, parabolas, and hyperbolas; this property is verified by straightforward calculation which need not be given here. In all cases the line $\phi = 0$, $\phi = \pi$ is the axis of symmetry, and the origin O is a focus. The parameter p is the distance from O to the curve, measured along a radius perpendicular to the axis, i.e., along $\phi = \pm \frac{\pi}{2}$. Accordingly, p has the name *semi-latus rectum*. If e is in the range $0 \leq e < 1$, then the figure is an ellipse of eccentricity e and semi-major axis

$$a = \frac{p}{1 - e^2}. \tag{1-55}$$

If e is equal to unity, the figure is a parabola. If e is greater than unity, the figure is a hyperbola with asymptotes parallel to

$$\phi = \pm \left(\pi - \cos^{-1} \frac{1}{e} \right).$$

The period for a planet in an elliptical orbit is

$$P = 2\pi \sqrt{\frac{a^3}{GM}}.$$

CHAPTER 2

CLASSICAL ELECTRO-MAGNETISM

2.1 INTRODUCTION

The fundamental problem of electromagnetism is to find the force on a charged particle for a given charge density $\rho(t, \mathbf{x})$ and a given current density $\mathbf{J}(t, \mathbf{x})$. The solution of this problem is usually facilitated by the use of field intensities $\mathbf{E}$, $\mathbf{B}$, $\mathbf{D}$, and $\mathbf{H}$. The force on a particle with charge q and velocity $\mathbf{v}$ is given by

$$\mathbf{F} = q(\mathbf{E} + \mathbf{v} \times \mathbf{B}). \qquad (2\text{-}1)$$

The field intensities are given by Maxwell's equations

$$\text{curl } \mathbf{H} = \mathbf{J} + \frac{\partial \mathbf{D}}{\partial t} \qquad \text{a}$$
$$\text{div } \mathbf{D} = \rho \qquad \text{b}$$
$$(2\text{-}2)$$

$$\text{curl } \mathbf{E} = -\frac{\partial \mathbf{B}}{\partial t} \qquad \text{a}$$
$$\text{div } \mathbf{B} = 0 \qquad \text{b}$$
$$(2\text{-}3)$$

and are related to each other in isotropic, homogeneous substances by the constitutive relations

$$\mathbf{D} = \epsilon \mathbf{E} \qquad \text{a}$$
$$\mathbf{B} = \mu \mathbf{H} \qquad \text{b}$$
$$(2\text{-}4)$$

where the constants ϵ and μ are, respectively, the permittivity and the permeability of the material. The permittivity and permeability of free space are denoted ϵ_0 and μ_0, respectively. The set of basic electromagnetic equations is completed by writing the equation of conservation of charge:

$$\frac{\partial \rho}{\partial t} + \text{div } \mathbf{J} = 0. \tag{2-5}$$

2.2 POTENTIALS

Since $\mathbf{B}$ has zero divergence, a potential $\mathbf{A}$ may be defined by the relation

$$\mathbf{B} = \text{curl } \mathbf{A}. \tag{2-6}$$

And since, by the substitution of eq. (2-6) into eq. (2-3a), $\mathbf{E} + \partial \mathbf{A}/\partial t$ has zero curl, another potential ϕ may be defined by the equation

$$\mathbf{E} = -\frac{\partial \mathbf{A}}{\partial t} - \text{grad } \phi. \tag{2-7}$$

The scalar potential ϕ and the vector potential $\mathbf{A}$ are arbitrary in the sense that for any scalar field χ, the quantities $\mathbf{A} + \text{grad } \chi$ and $\phi - \partial \chi/\partial t$ give the same field intensities $\mathbf{E}$ and $\mathbf{B}$ as do $\mathbf{A}$ and ϕ. Substitution of eqs. (2-6) and (2-7) into eqs. (2-2) gives the field equations for $\mathbf{A}$ and ϕ:

$$\nabla^2 A_i - \epsilon\mu \frac{\partial^2 A_i}{\partial t^2} = -\mu J_i + \frac{\partial}{\partial x^i}\left(\frac{\partial A_k}{\partial x^k} + \epsilon\mu \frac{\partial \phi}{\partial t}\right) \tag{2-8}$$

$$\nabla^2 \phi - \epsilon\mu \frac{\partial^2 \phi}{\partial t^2} = -\frac{\rho}{\epsilon} - \frac{\partial}{\partial t}\left(\frac{\partial A_k}{\partial x^k} + \epsilon\mu \frac{\partial \phi}{\partial t}\right). \tag{2-9}$$

The arbitrary scalar χ is now chosen in such a way that the relation

$$\frac{\partial A_k}{\partial x^k} + \epsilon\mu \frac{\partial \phi}{\partial t} = 0 \tag{2-10}$$

holds. Such a choice can be made because if $\mathbf{A}'$ and ϕ' do not satisfy eq. (2-10), then $\mathbf{A} = \mathbf{A}' + \text{grad } \chi$ and $\phi = \phi' - \partial \chi/\partial t$ do satisfy eq. (2-10) provided χ is the solution of

$$\nabla^2 \chi - \epsilon\mu \frac{\partial^2 \chi}{\partial t^2} = -\left(\text{div } \mathbf{A}' + \epsilon\mu \frac{\partial \phi'}{\partial t}\right).$$

Equations (2-8) and (2-9) consequently become

$$\nabla^2 \mathbf{A} - \epsilon\mu \frac{\partial^2 \mathbf{A}}{\partial t^2} = -\mu \mathbf{J} \qquad \text{a}$$

$$\nabla^2 \phi - \epsilon\mu \frac{\partial^2 \phi}{\partial t^2} = -\frac{\rho}{\epsilon} \qquad \text{b} \tag{2-11}$$

which have the well-known solutions

$$\left.\begin{array}{ll} \phi(t, \mathbf{x}) = \dfrac{1}{4\pi\epsilon} \displaystyle\int \dfrac{\rho\left(t - \dfrac{|\mathbf{x} - \mathbf{x}'|}{c}, \mathbf{x}'\right)}{|\mathbf{x} - \mathbf{x}'|}\, d^3x' & \text{a} \\[4ex] \mathbf{A}(t, \mathbf{x}) = \dfrac{\mu}{4\pi} \displaystyle\int \dfrac{\mathbf{J}\left(t - \dfrac{|\mathbf{x} - \mathbf{x}'|}{c}, \mathbf{x}'\right)}{|\mathbf{x} - \mathbf{x}'|}\, d^3x' & \text{b} \end{array}\right\} \quad (2\text{-}12)$$

where

$$c = \frac{1}{\sqrt{\epsilon\mu}}.$$

The situation is analogous to the gravitational case in Section 1.12. The field intensities $\mathbf{E}$ and $\mathbf{B}$ are obtained by eqs. (2-6) and (2-7) through the mediation of potentials ϕ and $\mathbf{A}$ which are given by eq. (2-12). In the gravitational case, the field intensity $\mathbf{g}$ is obtained through the mediation of a potential Φ given by eq. (1-45).

2.3 ENERGY AND MOMENTUM

The rate at which work is done on a fluid which has charge density $\rho(t, \mathbf{x})$ and velocity $\mathbf{v}(t, \mathbf{x})$ is found from eq. (2-1) to be

$$-\frac{dW}{dt} = \int \mathbf{v} \cdot (\mathbf{E} + \mathbf{v} \times \mathbf{B})\rho\, dV = \int \rho\mathbf{v} \cdot \mathbf{E}\, dV \qquad (2\text{-}13)$$

where dV is the volume element. The substitution

$$\mathbf{J} = \rho\mathbf{v} \qquad (2\text{-}14)$$

and the use of eqs. (2-2a) and (2-3a) put eq. (2-13) into the form

$$-\frac{dW}{dt} = -\int\left(\mathbf{E} \cdot \frac{\partial \mathbf{D}}{\partial t} + \mathbf{H} \cdot \frac{\partial \mathbf{B}}{\partial t}\right) dV - \int (\mathbf{E} \times \mathbf{H}) \cdot d\mathbf{S}$$

where the first integral extends over the volume of interest and the second integral is a surface integral over the boundary of the region. Substitution of eqs. (2-4) yields

$$\frac{dW}{dt} = \frac{d}{dt}\int (\tfrac{1}{2}\epsilon E^2 + \tfrac{1}{2}\mu H^2)\, dV + \int \mathbf{P} \cdot d\mathbf{S}$$

where

$$\mathbf{P} = \mathbf{E} \times \mathbf{H}.$$

The energy $-W$ which is transferred to the fluid may be interpreted as coming from the electromagnetic field $\mathbf{E}$ and $\mathbf{H}$. The energy density of the field is then $\frac{1}{2}\epsilon E^2 + \frac{1}{2}\mu H^2$, and the energy flow (energy per unit time per unit area) is Poynting's vector $\mathbf{P}$.

The total force on the same charge distribution is given by

$$-\frac{dM_i}{dt} = \int \rho(E_i + e(ijk)v^j B_k)\,dV.$$

Substitution of eqs. (2-2) and (2-14) and the use of eqs. (2-3) and (2-4) gives

$$-\frac{dM_i}{dt} = -\frac{d}{dt}\int \mu\epsilon P_i\,dV + \int X_{ij}\,dS_j$$

where, as before, the first integral is a volume integral and the second integral is a surface integral. The *stress tensor* X_{ij} is defined

$$X_{ij} = \epsilon E_i E_j + \mu H_i H_j - \tfrac{1}{2}\delta_{ij}(\epsilon E^2 + \mu H^2).$$

The momentum $-M_i$ which is transferred to the fluid may be interpreted as coming from the electromagnetic field. The momentum density of the field is $\epsilon\mu\mathbf{P}$ and the flow of momentum through the boundary of the region is given by X_{ij}. A momentum $X_{ij}\,dS_j\,dt$ is transferred through an area dS_i in a time dt.

The torque T_i exerted on the charged fluid is given by

$$T_i = \int e(ijk)x^j \rho(E_k + e(klm)v^l B_m)\,dV.$$

The same treatment as was used for total force yields

$$T_i = -\frac{d}{dt}\int e(ijk)x^j \epsilon\mu P_k\,dV + \int e(ijk)x^j X_{kl}\,dS_l,$$

provided x^i is regarded as stationary, i.e., not moving with the fluid. Thus the torque transferred to the charges is the same as if the field has momentum density $\epsilon\mu\mathbf{P}$ and the transfer of momentum across the surface dS_i is $X_{ij}\,dS_j\,dt$.

To summarize our results, the electromagnetic field appears to possess energy density $\frac{1}{2}(\epsilon E^2 + \mu H^2)$, energy flow $\mathbf{P}$, momentum density $c^{-2}\mathbf{P}$, and momentum flow X_{ij}. These results will be used in subsequent sections.

2.4 RADIATION PRESSURE AND INERTIA

It is proved in this section that electromagnetic radiation of energy E in a vacuum possesses mass $c^{-2}\mathsf{E}$ and momentum $c^{-1}\mathsf{E}$. The symbol c will henceforth denote $(\epsilon_0\mu_0)^{-\frac{1}{2}}$ or 2.9979×10^8 m sec^{-1}, i.e., the velocity of light in empty space. Consider a plane-polarized, plane-front, sinusoidal light wave striking a plane, absorbing surface at normal incidence. The

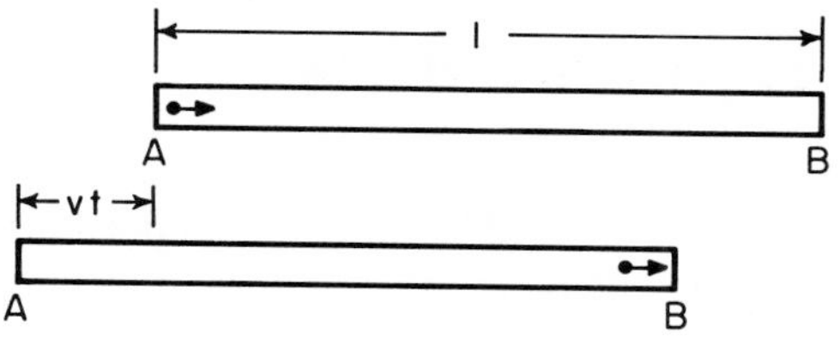

FIGURE 2.1 Inertia of electromagnetic radiation.

field intensities of the wave are given by

$$E = \frac{a}{\sqrt{\epsilon_0}} \sin \omega \left(t - \frac{x}{c} \right)$$

$$H = \frac{a}{\sqrt{\mu_0}} \sin \omega \left(t - \frac{x}{c} \right)$$

and are at right angles to each other. The x-axis has been chosen in the direction of the Poynting vector **P** and hence normal to the surface. The average values of the energy density and the Poynting vector are, respectively, $\frac{1}{2}a^2$ and $\frac{1}{2}ca^2$. The only non-vanishing component of the stress tensor is X_{11} which has an average value of $\frac{1}{2}a^2$. Thus in a time t, the wave delivers a momentum $\frac{1}{2}a^2At$ and an energy $\frac{1}{2}a^2Act$ to an area A of the surface. Therefore the momentum transfer is c^{-1} times the energy.

In order to derive the inertia of a pulse of radiation, consider a long, hollow cylinder AB of length l initially at rest. (See Figure 2.1.) A pulse of radiation with energy E suddenly leaves the end A heading toward the end B. The pulse imparts a momentum $c^{-1}\mathsf{E}$ to the cylinder, and the cylinder moves to the left with velocity

$$v = \frac{\mathsf{E}}{Mc} \tag{2-15}$$

where M is the mass of the cylinder. After a time t, the pulse, traveling with velocity c, reaches B. The cylinder then comes to rest again, after having moved a distance vt to the left. Since no external forces have been applied to the cylinder, the center of mass has presumably not moved. Hence the radiation must have a mass m given by

$$Mvt = m(l - vt).$$

The condition $l - vt = ct$ allows the elimination of l and t to give

$$m = M \frac{v}{c}$$

and hence, by eq. (2-15),

$$m = \frac{\mathsf{E}}{c^2}.$$

2.5 MOVING MEDIA

The case of a moving medium requires special consideration, because eqs. (2-2) and (2-3) cannot be applied directly. Equations (2-2) and (2-3) are the differential forms of the integral equations

$$\left.\begin{aligned}
\int_{C.C.} \mathbf{H} \cdot d\mathbf{l} &= \int_S \mathbf{J} \cdot d\mathbf{S} + \frac{d}{dt} \int_S \mathbf{D} \cdot d\mathbf{S} \qquad &a \\
\int_{C.C.} \mathbf{E} \cdot d\mathbf{l} &= -\frac{d}{dt} \int_S \mathbf{B} \cdot d\mathbf{S} \qquad &b
\end{aligned}\right\} \qquad (2\text{-}16)$$

$$\left.\begin{aligned}
\int_{C.S.} \mathbf{D} \cdot d\mathbf{S} &= \int_V \rho \, dV \qquad &a \\
\int_{C.S.} \mathbf{B} \cdot d\mathbf{S} &= 0 \qquad &b
\end{aligned}\right\} \qquad (2\text{-}17)$$

where C.C. denotes a closed curve, S is any surface bounded by the closed curve, C.S. denotes a closed surface, and V is the volume interior to the closed surface. It is the set of integral equations (2-16) and (2-17) rather than the set of differential equations (2-2) and (2-3) which comes closest to expressing the experimental results.

In the study of electromagnetism in moving media, the decision must be made whether the curves and surfaces in eqs. (2-16) and (2-17) are to be stationary or are to be moving with the medium. This question does not affect eqs. (2-17), since no time-rates are involved. However, the forms assumed by eqs. (2-16) depend on the alternative which is used. We will follow Hertz (see Whittaker[B]) in choosing the second of the two alternatives. The curves and surfaces in eqs. (2-16) are regarded as fixed in the material.

An expression for the right-hand side of eq. (2-16b) in terms of instantaneous curves and the instantaneous values of $\mathbf{B}$, $\partial \mathbf{B}/\partial t$, and $\partial \mathbf{B}/\partial x^i$ is obtained by regarding the integral as the sum over surface elements, each of which moves with the medium. The right-hand side of eq. (2-16b) is the sum of terms of the form

$$\frac{d}{dt} \mathbf{B} \cdot \delta \mathbf{S}.$$

The indicated differentiation is easily carried out:

$$\frac{d}{dt} B_i \, \delta S_i = \frac{dB_i}{dt} \delta S_i + B_i \frac{d \, \delta S_i}{dt} = \left(\frac{\partial B_i}{\partial t} + v^k \frac{\partial B_i}{\partial x^k} \right) \delta S_i + B_i \frac{d \, \delta S_i}{dt}.$$

But the quantity $d\, \delta S_i/dt$ requires some calculation in order to express it in terms of v^i and δS_i. The symbol v^i denotes the velocity of the medium at the element δS_i. The element of area δS_i is chosen to have the shape of a parallelogram formed by two vectors a_i and b_i in the surface. Thus δS_i is equal to $e(ijk)a_jb_k$. As a_i and b_i move with the fluid, they change at rates given by

$$\frac{da_i}{dt} = a_k\frac{\partial v^i}{\partial x^k}, \qquad \frac{db_i}{dt} = b_k\frac{\partial v^i}{\partial x^k}.$$

Therefore, we have

$$\frac{d\,\delta S_i}{dt} = e(ijk)\frac{\partial v^j}{\partial x^l}(a_lb_k - a_kb_l) = e(ijk)\frac{\partial v^j}{\partial x^l}\,e(lkm)\,\delta S_m$$

$$= \frac{\partial v^k}{\partial x^k}\,\delta S_i - \frac{\partial v^k}{\partial x^i}\,\delta S_k,$$

and hence

$$\frac{d}{dt}B_i\,\delta S_i = \left[\frac{\partial B_i}{\partial t} + v^k\frac{\partial B_i}{\partial x^k} + B_i\frac{\partial v^k}{\partial x^k} - B_k\frac{\partial v^i}{\partial x^k}\right]\delta S_i$$

which is easily changed by the use of vector identities to the form

$$\frac{d}{dt}\mathbf{B}\cdot\delta\mathbf{S} = \left[\frac{\partial\mathbf{B}}{\partial t} + \text{curl}\,(\mathbf{B}\times\mathbf{v}) + \mathbf{v}\,\text{div}\,\mathbf{B}\right]\cdot\delta\mathbf{S}.$$

Integration over the surface gives

$$\frac{d}{dt}\int\mathbf{B}\cdot d\mathbf{S} = \int\left[\frac{\partial\mathbf{B}}{\partial t} + \text{curl}\,(\mathbf{B}\times\mathbf{v}) + \mathbf{v}\,\text{div}\,\mathbf{B}\right]\cdot d\mathbf{S}. \qquad (2\text{-}18a)$$

Thus far the vector $\mathbf{B}$ can be any field quantity, and when it is replaced by $\mathbf{D}$ the result is

$$\frac{d}{dt}\int\mathbf{D}\cdot d\mathbf{S} = \int\left[\frac{\partial\mathbf{D}}{\partial t} + \text{curl}\,(\mathbf{D}\times\mathbf{v}) + \mathbf{v}\,\text{div}\,\mathbf{D}\right]\cdot d\mathbf{S}. \qquad (2\text{-}18b)$$

The substitution of eqs. (2-18) into eqs. (2-16) and the use of eqs. (2-17) yield the differential forms

$$\text{curl}\,\mathbf{H} = \mathbf{J} + \frac{\partial\mathbf{D}}{\partial t} + \rho\mathbf{v} - \text{curl}\,(\mathbf{v}\times\mathbf{D}) \qquad a$$

$$\text{curl}\,\mathbf{E} = -\frac{\partial\mathbf{B}}{\partial t} + \text{curl}\,(\mathbf{v}\times\mathbf{B}). \qquad b$$

$$(2\text{-}19)$$

Equations (2-2b), (2-3b), and (2-19) describe electromagnetism in a moving medium with velocity $\mathbf{v}(\mathbf{x})$. The current density $\mathbf{J}$ is measured *in* the medium *with respect* to the medium, i.e., the current per unit area crossing a surface moving with the medium.

The special case of a uniformly moving medium has field equations

$$e(ijk)\frac{\partial H_k}{\partial x^j} = J_i + \frac{\partial D_i}{\partial t} + v^k \frac{\partial D_i}{\partial x^k} \tag{2-20}$$

$$e(ijk)\frac{\partial E_k}{\partial x^j} = -\frac{\partial B_i}{\partial t} - v^k \frac{\partial B_i}{\partial x^k} \tag{2-21}$$

which are obtained from eqs. (2-19) by holding **v** constant. It is to be noted that the electric displacement **D** and the magnetic induction **B** enter eqs. (2-20) and (2-21) as a total time derivative, e.g.,

$$\frac{dB_i}{dt} = \frac{\partial B_i}{\partial t} + v^k \frac{\partial B_i}{\partial x^k}.$$

But this is the rate at which B_i changes at a point moving with the medium, and is hence independent of the inertial frame. Therefore, eqs. (2-20) and (2-21) are invariant under a *Galilean transformation*, i.e., the transformation from one inertial frame $S(t, x^i)$ to another inertial frame $S'(t', x'^i)$. If the spatial axes of the two frames are parallel, the transformation is given by

$$\left. \begin{array}{l} t' = t \\ x'^i = x^i - u^i t \end{array} \right\} \tag{2-22}$$

where u^i is the velocity of the S' frame relative to the S frame. We may see the invariance of eqs. (2-20) and (2-21) more clearly in the following way. It is assumed that the field quantities are the same in either frame:

$$\mathbf{B}(t, \mathbf{x}) = \mathbf{B}'(t', \mathbf{x}') = \mathbf{B}'(t, \mathbf{x} - \mathbf{u}t).$$

The total time-rate of change of **B** is

$$\frac{dB_i}{dt} = \frac{\partial B_i}{\partial t} + v^k \frac{\partial B_i}{\partial x^k} = \frac{\partial B_i'}{\partial t} - u^k \frac{\partial B_i'}{\partial x'^k} + v^k \frac{\partial B_i'}{\partial x'^k}. \tag{2-23}$$

And since the velocity follows the transformation rule $\mathbf{v}' = \mathbf{v} - \mathbf{u}$, eq. (2-23) is equal to

$$\frac{\partial B_i'}{\partial t'} + v'^k \frac{\partial B_i'}{\partial x'^k}.$$

Thus eq. (2-21) is invariant under the Galilean transformation (2-22). Similarly the same transformation leaves eq. (2-20) invariant.

Up to this point, the theory appears to be satisfactory. We have a theory which applies to moving objects as well as to stationary objects. The equations of the theory transform in a prescribed way from one coordinate system to another. But there is one thing wrong with the theory—it does not agree with experiment.

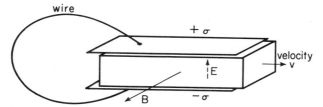

FIGURE 2.2 Dielectric moving in magnetic field and bounded by shorted conductors.

Consider a slab of dielectric material with permittivity ϵ, permeability μ, and thickness l moving between two conducting plates with a uniform velocity v. A magnetic field B is applied parallel to the plates and perpendicular to the velocity. The two plates are connected by a wire. (See Figure 2.2.) The surface charge density $\pm\sigma$ which appears on the plates may be calculated by the use of eqs. (2-4), (2-16), and (2-17a) as follows. Application of eq. (2-16b) to the closed circuit formed by the wire, the plates, and a line through the dielectric (see Figure 2.3) gives

$$El = -\mu Hlv$$

or simply

$$E = -v\mu H,$$

where H is the magnetic field intensity inside the dielectric. Since there is no current in either the plates or the dielectric, eq. (2-16a) requires that the magnetic intensity inside the dielectric be the same as that outside. By eq. (2-17a), the surface charge density on the conducting plates is

$$\sigma = \pm\epsilon E = \pm v\epsilon\mu H \tag{2-24}$$

where H is the externally applied magnetic field intensity.

The theory predicts eq. (2-24), but experiment shows that the charge is more nearly given by

$$\sigma = \pm v(\epsilon\mu - \epsilon_0\mu_0)H.$$

The experiment was performed by H. A. Wilson,[B] first in 1904 for $\mu = \mu_0$ and again with M. W. Wilson in 1914 for $\mu > \mu_0$. He used a rapidly rotating cylinder of dielectric between two concentric cylindrical plates and measured the charge which passed through the wire when the magnetic field was reversed.

FIGURE 2.3 Calculation of eq. (2-24).

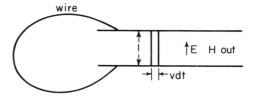

A new theory was needed to explain Wilson's result. But before proceeding to the special theory of relativity, it is appropriate to examine a series of experiments which gave results in agreement with an erroneous theory of the propagation of light.

2.6 THE ETHER

In empty space, eqs. (2-11) become

$$\nabla^2 \mathbf{A} - \frac{1}{c^2} \frac{\partial^2 \mathbf{A}}{\partial t^2} = 0$$

$$\nabla^2 \phi - \frac{1}{c^2} \frac{\partial^2 \phi}{\partial t^2} = 0 \qquad (2\text{-}25)$$

where, as was stated in Section 2.4, c denotes $(\epsilon_0 \mu_0)^{-\frac{1}{2}}$.

$$c = \frac{1}{\sqrt{\epsilon_0 \mu_0}}. \qquad (2\text{-}26)$$

These equations represent waves traveling with velocity c. The agreement between the value of c obtained from eq. (2-26) and the value of the speed of light first led to the recognition that light is an electromagnetic wave. But light cannot travel with the same velocity c in all inertial frames. Clearly, if light moves with speed c in the direction of a unit vector $\mathbf{n}$ relative to one observer α, then for a second observer β moving with velocity $\mathbf{v}$ relative to α, the light ray has a velocity $c\mathbf{n} - \mathbf{v}$ according to the Galilean transformation.

It was hypothesized that a medium known as the *ether* fills all space. In empty space, the velocity of light is c relative to the ether. Inside a transparent medium with index of refraction n, the velocity of light is c/n relative to the ether within the material.

A coherent, monochromatic light ray with frequency $\nu = \omega/2\pi$ and velocity c relative to the ether has electric and magnetic field intensities proportional to $\cos \psi$ where

$$\psi = \omega \left(t - \frac{\mathbf{n} \cdot \mathbf{x}}{c} \right) \qquad (2\text{-}27)$$

and $\mathbf{n}$ is the unit vector in the direction of propagation of the light wave. In a reference frame moving with a velocity $\mathbf{v}$ relative to the ether, the light wave has a different direction, a different frequency $\nu' = \omega'/2\pi$, and a different velocity c' which are found as follows. The x-axis is chosen in the direction of $\mathbf{v}$, and the z-axis is chosen perpendicular to both $\mathbf{v}$ and $\mathbf{n}$, so that $\mathbf{n}$ is equal to $(-\cos \theta, -\sin \theta, 0)$, where θ is the angle between $-\mathbf{n}$ and $\mathbf{v}$. (See Figure 2.4.)

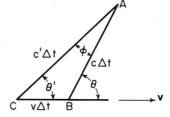

FIGURE 2.4 Direction and velocity of light in frame moving relative to ether.

In the ray description, the ray moves from point A to point B in the ether system but from point A to point C in the moving system in a time interval Δt. The geometry requires

$$c'^2 = c^2 + 2cv\cos\theta + v^2, \tag{2-28}$$

$$\tan\theta' = \frac{\sin\theta}{\cos\theta + \dfrac{v}{c}} \tag{2-29}$$

and

$$\frac{\sin\phi}{\sin\theta'} = \frac{v}{c}. \tag{2-30}$$

The same results are obtained by differentiating eqs. (2-22):

$$n_i'c' = \frac{dx'^i}{dt'} = \frac{dx^i}{dt} - v^i = n_i c - v^i$$

(the **u** is replaced by **v** in the present context).

Equation (2-30) finds observational verification in the phenomenon of *aberration* of starlight, discovered by Bradley in 1725 (see Whittaker[B]). A star viewed in a direction which makes an angle θ' with the earth's direction of motion appears displaced from its true position by an angle ϕ in the direction of the earth's motion; ϕ is given by

$$\phi \simeq \frac{v}{c}\sin\theta'$$

which is the small-angle approximation to eq. (2-30). The total displacement of the image of any star during the course of the year is thus $2v/c$, which is found by observation to be $41''$. One-half of this value, $20''.5$ or 1.2×10^{-4} radian, is known as the *constant of aberration*. The value of v/c so obtained is in agreement with the speed with which the earth must travel to cover the circumference of its orbit in one year.

In the wave description of light, the wave fronts, each represented by $\psi = $ constant, have the same unit normal **n** and the same wavelength in the moving system, but their frequency is different. Upon application of the Galilean transformation

$$t = t'$$

$$x = x' + vt$$

$$y = y'$$

$$z = z',$$

eq. (2-27) becomes

$$\psi = \omega'\left(t - \frac{\mathbf{n} \cdot \mathbf{x'}}{c''}\right)$$

where

$$\omega' = \omega\left(1 + \frac{v}{c}\cos\theta\right) \tag{2-31}$$

and

$$c'' = c + v\cos\theta.$$

The velocity c'' is the phase velocity of the waves. It is the component of the ray velocity which is normal to the wave fronts. Since the angle between the ray direction and $\mathbf{n}$ in the moving system is $\phi = \theta - \theta'$, an alternate derivation of the above equation is the evaluation of $c'\cos\phi$ by the use of the trigonometric formula for $\cos(\theta - \theta')$ and the relations $c'\cos\theta' = c\cos\theta + v$ and $c'\sin\theta' = c\sin\theta$ from Figure 2.4.

The change in frequency given by eq. (2-31), known as the *Doppler effect*, was first expounded in 1842 (see Whittaker[B]). The Doppler effect provided a further argument in favor of the ether theory, on the basis of which eq. (2-31) was derived.

There remained the question of how the ether was affected by a moving body. Did the ether remain stationary, or did it move with the body? The answer came as the result of several experiments performed during the two decades from 1851 to 1871.

In the ether theory, it was supposed that light inside a medium with index of refraction

$$n = \sqrt{\frac{\epsilon\mu}{\epsilon_0\mu_0}}$$

travels with a velocity c/n *relative to the ether inside the body*. Thus the speed c' of a light beam having the direction of the unit vector $\mathbf{n}$ (in the ether system) as measured relative to the medium is found by an obvious modification of eq. (2-28) to be

$$c'^2 = \frac{c^2}{n^2} + 2\frac{cv}{n}\cos\theta + v^2$$

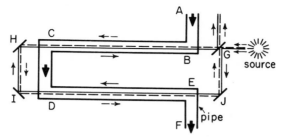

FIGURE 2.5 Fizeau's experiment.

where **v** is the velocity of the ether relative to the medium and θ is the angle between **v** and **n**. The two cases $\theta = 0, \pi$ are of special interest:

$$c' = \frac{c}{n} + v \qquad (\theta = 0)$$

$$c' = \frac{c}{n} - v \qquad (\theta = \pi).$$

2.7 ETHER DRAG

In 1851, Fizeau[B] performed the experiment indicated in Figure 2.5. Water flowed through a pipe $ABCDEF$ with velocity v. A light beam was split at G by a half-silvered mirror into two beams which went around the circuit $GHIJG$ in opposite directions. The two beams were then reunited to give interference fringes. It was assumed that the ether within the water has a velocity κv, where the coefficient κ was to be determined by experiment. The travel time for light which completes the circuit $GHIJG$ is then

$$t_1 = \frac{GB + CH + HI + ID + EJ + JG}{c} + \frac{BC + DE}{\dfrac{c}{n} + \kappa v},$$

and the travel time for the reverse circuit is

$$t_2 = \frac{GJ + JE + DI + IH + HC + BG}{c} + \frac{ED + CB}{\dfrac{c}{n} - \kappa v}.$$

The difference in travel times

$$\Delta t = \frac{4\kappa n^2 lv}{c^2 - \kappa^2 n^2 v^2} \simeq \frac{4\kappa n^2 lv}{c^2},$$

where $l = BC = DE$, produces a fringe shift

$$\Delta N \simeq \frac{4\kappa n^2 lv}{\lambda c}$$

where λ is the wavelength of the light. A fringe shift *was* observed, and it could be represented by the expression

$$\Delta N = 4(n^2 - 1)\frac{lv}{\lambda c},$$

leading to the relation

$$\kappa = 1 - \frac{1}{n^2}. \tag{2-32}$$

Hoek[B] in 1868 performed the experiment indicated in Figure 2.6. A dielectric BC with index of refraction n is carried at a velocity v by the earth in its orbit. The dielectric rod is oriented so that it is moving longitudinally, say to the right in Figure 2.6. As in Fizeau's experiment, a light beam is split and made to traverse the circuit $ADEFA$ in opposite directions before being made to interfere. The travel time for the circuit $ADEFA$ is

$$t_1 = \frac{AB + CD}{c + v} + \frac{EF}{c - v} + \frac{ED + FA}{\sqrt{c^2 - v^2}} + \frac{BC}{\dfrac{c}{n} + (1 - \kappa)v}.$$

The travel time for the reverse circuit $AFEDA$ is

$$t_2 = \frac{AF + ED}{\sqrt{c^2 - v^2}} + \frac{FE}{c + v} + \frac{DC + BA}{c - v} + \frac{CB}{\dfrac{c}{n} - (1 - \kappa)v}.$$

The difference is

$$\Delta t = t_2 - t_1 = \frac{2vl}{c^2}\left[\frac{n^2(1 - \kappa)}{1 - n^2(1 - \kappa)^2\dfrac{v^2}{c^2}} - \frac{1}{1 - \dfrac{v^2}{c^2}}\right] \simeq \frac{2vl}{c^2}[n^2(1 - \kappa) - 1]$$

where $l = BC$. Hoek used $l = 100 \text{ mm}$ and $n = 4/3$ which, for the earth's velocity, should give a fringe shift

$$\Delta N = \frac{c\,\Delta t}{\lambda} = \frac{2 \times 10^{-2} \text{ mm}}{\lambda}[n^2(1 - \kappa) - 1].$$

However, the result was negative to the accuracy

$$\Delta N < \frac{2.2 \times 10^{-4} \text{ mm}}{\lambda}.$$

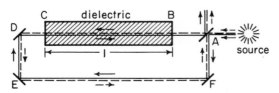

FIGURE 2.6 Hoek's experiment.

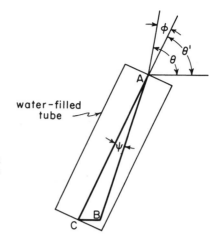

FIGURE 2.7 Aberration of starlight in water-filled telescope. The distance AB is ct/n, and the distance CB is $(1 - \kappa)vt$.

Hence it was concluded that κ is given by eq. (2-32).

Airy[B] in 1871 made observations of the aberration of starlight using a telescope filled with water. The telescope tube was filled with water from the objective down to a plane glass sheet located 90 cm from the objective. The principle is illustrated by Figure 2.7. The tube has a uniform velocity v to the right. The tube axis is pointed in a direction which makes an angle θ' with the direction of motion. The light from the star is incident at an angle ϕ to the axis. (The angles θ, θ', and ϕ are as in Figure 2.4.) The incident light is refracted to an angle ψ to the axis. By Snell's law,* ϕ, ψ, and n have the relation

$$n = \frac{\sin \phi}{\sin \psi}.$$

In the time t required for the light to travel through the tube with velocity c/n relative to the ether in the water, the tube has moved forward a distance $(1 - \kappa)vt$ relative to the ether in the water, where $(1 - \kappa)v$ is the velocity of the water relative to the ether. With the sine law applied to the two angles $CAB = \psi$ and $ACB = \theta'$, there immediately results the relation

$$\frac{c}{n} \sin \psi = (1 - \kappa)v \sin \theta'.$$

Hence, by Snell's law, aberration is given by

$$\frac{\sin \phi}{\sin \theta'} = (1 - \kappa)n^2 \frac{v}{c}$$

---

* Arago in 1810 (see Whittaker[B]) concluded from observational considerations that light acts as if the source is in the place that it appears to occupy due to aberration. Hence Snell's law is applied in the telescope's reference frame.

which is the generalization of eq. (2-30) to include the presence of a material with index of refraction n. Airy found the constant of aberration to be the same as for air, to an accuracy of 10 per cent. Therefore, the coefficient κ must be given by eq. (2-32).

The observations indicated that a material with index of refraction n moving with velocity v through the ether dragged the ether with it, so that the ether inside the material has a velocity κv relative to the outside ether, with κ given by eq. (2-32).

Attempts to account for eq. (2-32) by theoretical methods met with a measure of success. The ether was postulated to have a density proportional to n^2. This postulate was plausible from comparison with other wave theories. For example, the velocity of sound waves in an elastic medium is $(E/\rho)^{\frac{1}{2}}$, where E is the elastic constant and ρ is the density of the medium.

In Fresnel's theory (see Whittaker[B]), the ether in excess of the free-space density, i.e., with relative density $n^2 - 1$, was assumed to be carried by the medium with the same velocity as the medium. The remainder of the ether was stationary. Therefore, the average velocity of the ether was

$$\kappa v = \frac{(n^2 - 1)v + 0}{n^2} = \left(1 - \frac{1}{n^2}\right)v.$$

In Stokes' theory (see Whittaker[B]), the ether was regarded as a compressible but conserved fluid. If it flowed into a medium with a velocity v, then by conservation of ether its velocity $(1 - \kappa)v$ inside the medium must be given by

$$n^2(1 - \kappa)v = v.$$

Therefore

$$\kappa = 1 - \frac{1}{n^2}.$$

2.8 HAMMAR'S EXPERIMENT

The twentieth century saw the performance of two further experiments which were consistent with the ether theory. Hammar's[B] experiment will be described in this section and Sagnac's[B] experiment will be presented in the next section.

When Miller in 1933 objected to the Michelson-Morley experiment (to be described later) with the contention that the ether was dragged by the heavy construction of the apparatus, G. W. Hammar[B] in 1935 performed an experiment to disprove Miller's claim. A heavy lead pipe with closed ends was fitted with a mirror at each end and a hole in the pipe opposite each mirror so that light could traverse the circuit $ABCDA$

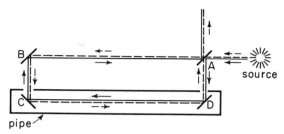

FIGURE 2.8 Hammar's experiment.

(Fig. 2.8). A half-silvered mirror at A provided a beam going in the reverse direction, and the two beams produced an interference pattern. It is assumed that when the apparatus is carried by the earth through the ether with a velocity v to the right, the lead pipe entrains the ether within it, so that the ether within the pipe moves to the right with a velocity Δv. The time for light to traverse the circuit $ABCDA$ is

$$t_1 = \frac{AB}{c+v} + \frac{BC+DA}{\sqrt{c^2-v^2}} + \frac{CD}{c-v+\Delta v}$$

whereas the time for the reverse circuit is

$$t_2 = \frac{AB}{c-v} + \frac{BC+DA}{\sqrt{c^2-v^2}} + \frac{CD}{c+v-\Delta v}.$$

Hence, the time difference

$$\Delta t = t_2 - t_1 = \frac{2l\,\Delta v}{c^2} \frac{1 + \dfrac{v^2}{c^2} - \dfrac{v\,\Delta v}{c^2}}{\left(1-\dfrac{v^2}{c^2}\right)\left[1-\left(\dfrac{v-\Delta v}{c}\right)^2\right]} \simeq \frac{2l\,\Delta v}{c^2}$$

for a length $l = CD$ should have produced a fringe shift of

$$\Delta N = \frac{2l\,\Delta v}{\lambda c}.$$

Hammar, with $l = 89.4$ cm, detected not so much as $\frac{1}{10}$ of a fringe shift. Hence it must be concluded that Δv is given by the inequality

$$\frac{2l\,\Delta v}{\lambda c} < \frac{1}{10} \quad \text{or} \quad \Delta v < \frac{\lambda c}{20l}.$$

For $\lambda = 4.4 \times 10^{-5}$ cm this gives a value

$$\Delta v < 0.074 \text{ km sec}^{-1}.$$

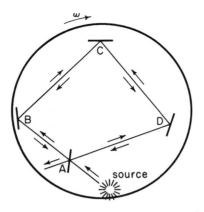

FIGURE 2.9 Sagnac's experiment.

The earth's orbital velocity is 30 km sec⁻¹. Thus, practically speaking, there was no entrainment of the ether by the pipe.

2.9 SAGNAC'S EXPERIMENT

Sagnac[B] in 1915 performed an experiment to detect the apparent change in the velocity of light in a rotating system. The apparatus was mounted on a rotating platform. (See Figure 2.9.) Light passed a half-silvered mirror at A to be split into two beams. The two beams went around the circuit $ABCDA$ in opposite directions and then were rejoined to produce interference fringes. A simplified version of the circuit is sufficient to derive the theoretical fringe shift (Fig. 2.10). The four mirrors are placed at 90 degree intervals on the circumference of a circle of radius r. The beam from the source reaches the half-silvered mirror at position A_1. The unreflected part of the beam continues in a straight line (relative to an observer at rest) to mirror B which is at position B_1. The beam is reflected and goes in successive straight lines to C, D_2, and A_2. When the beam reaches the half-silvered mirror, the mirror has moved through an angle

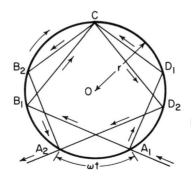

FIGURE 2.10 Theory for Sagnac's experiment.

ωt to position A_2. The beam which is reflected at A_1 takes the shorter path $A_1D_1CB_2A_2$. Thus there is a time difference equal to c^{-1} times the difference in path length between the circuit $A_1B_1CD_2A_2$ and the circuit $A_1D_1CB_2A_2$. To a first approximation, the travel time t is the same around either circuit, so that the angle COD_2 may be taken as $\frac{\pi}{2} + \frac{1}{4}\omega t$, and the angle COD_1 is $\frac{\pi}{2} - \frac{1}{4}\omega t$. The other angles around the circle may be treated similarly. Thus the clockwise path has length $8r\sin\left(\frac{\pi}{4} + \frac{1}{8}\omega t\right)$, and the counterclockwise path has length $8r\sin\left(\frac{\pi}{4} - \frac{1}{8}\omega t\right)$. The difference in path length is therefore

$$\Delta l \simeq \sqrt{2}r\omega t.$$

With the substitutions

$$t = \frac{4\sqrt{2}r}{c}$$

and

$$A = 2r^2,$$

the difference in path length takes the form

$$\Delta l \simeq \frac{4A\omega}{c}$$

where A is the area of the circuit. This path difference leads to a time difference

$$\Delta t = \frac{4A\omega}{c^2}$$

and a fringe shift

$$\Delta N = \frac{4A\omega}{c\lambda}$$

which are valid for a circuit of any shape with area A.

Sagnac used an area of 863 cm² and an angular velocity of about 14 rad sec⁻¹. The source of light was a mercury lamp with wavelength $\lambda = 0.436$ micron. Hence, the predicted fringe shift was $\Delta N = 0.037$. The observed fringe shift agreed with the predicted fringe shift to within the accuracy of the measurements.

Pogány[B] repeated Sagnac's experiment with an area of 1178 cm² and a rotational velocity of 157 rad sec⁻¹. With a wavelength $\lambda = 0.546$ micron, the predicted fringe shift was $2\,\Delta N = 0.906$; the observed fringe shift was 0.92 ± 0.02. A more recent experiment was done by Cranshaw[B] et al. with similar results.

Michelson[B] in 1925 used a circuit of area 0.2 km² to detect the earth's rotation. The formula becomes

$$\Delta N = \frac{4A\omega}{c\lambda} \sin \phi$$

where ϕ is the latitude. Michelson was at latitude $41°\!.8$ and looked for a predicted fringe shift of $\Delta N = 0.236 \pm 0.002$. The observed fringe shift was 0.230 ± 0.005.

2.10 THE MICHELSON-MORLEY EXPERIMENT

The ether theory of light propagation seemed to be well established when the Michelson-Morley experiment (hereafter abbreviated MM) was performed, first by Michelson[B] alone in 1881 and then with Morley in 1887. The experiment gave a null result which was inexplicable by the ether theory.

A beam of light was split by a half-silvered mirror at A (see Figure 2.11) into two beams, one of which went straight on to a mirror at C and the other of which went at right angles to a mirror at B. The two beams were thus reflected back to A where they were recombined so that the interference fringes could be observed. According to the ether theory, there should be a difference in the travel times for the two beams which depends on the angle between AB and the motion through the ether. Assume that the apparatus has a velocity v through the ether to the right (in the direction AB). The light beam which traverses the arm AB has a travel time

$$t_1 = \frac{AB}{c - v} + \frac{AB}{c + v} = \frac{2(AB)}{c\left(1 - \dfrac{v^2}{c^2}\right)}.$$

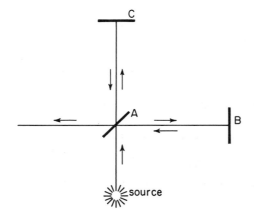

FIGURE 2.11   The Michelson-Morley experiment.

The beam which traverses the arm AC has a travel time

$$t_2 = 2\frac{AC}{\sqrt{c^2 - v^2}}.$$

The difference in travel time is

$$\Delta t = t_1 - t_2 = \frac{2}{c}\left[\frac{AB}{1 - \dfrac{v^2}{c^2}} - \frac{AC}{\sqrt{1 - \dfrac{v^2}{c^2}}}\right].$$

The apparatus is now rotated through 90 degrees so that the arm AC is parallel to the motion through the ether. The new difference in travel time is

$$\Delta t' = \frac{2}{c}\left[\frac{AB}{\sqrt{1 - \dfrac{v^2}{c^2}}} - \frac{AC}{1 - \dfrac{v^2}{c^2}}\right].$$

Thus the change in fringe shift $c\,\Delta t/\lambda$ should be, to lowest order in the velocity,

$$\frac{2}{\lambda}\left(\frac{1}{\sqrt{1 - \dfrac{v^2}{c^2}}} - \frac{1}{1 - \dfrac{v^2}{c^2}}\right)(AB + AC) \simeq -\frac{2lv^2}{\lambda c^2}$$

where $l \simeq AB \simeq AC$. (The arms were made of equal length, but this was not critical.)

By means of multiple reflections, the arms had a length equivalent to 11 meters in the 1887 experiment. The wavelength of the light was $\lambda = 0.59$ micron. With the earth carrying the apparatus through the ether with a velocity $v = 10^{-4}c$, the expected fringe shift upon rotation through 90 degrees was 0.4. The observed fringe shift, if it existed, had to be less than 0.02, and was probably less than 0.01.

The negative result[*] of the MM experiment was inexplicable by the ether theory. There should have been no drag effect, because the light beams traversed empty air. A radically new explanation was needed—and it was found in the Fitzgerald contraction.

2.11 THE FITZGERALD CONTRACTION

In 1893 it was proposed that the explanation of the MM result lay in a contraction of the arms parallel to the motion. If it is assumed that the

---

[*] A more recent experiment to detect the earth's motion with the use of maser beams has also given a null result. See Cedarholm[B].

ratio of the length of an arm when it is parallel to the motion to the length of the *same arm* when it is perpendicular to the motion is $\sqrt{1 - v^2/c^2}$, then the predicted fringe shift is zero.

Such a contraction is reasonable on the basis of electromagnetic theory. The electromagnetic field around each charge within a material is given by the field equation (2-25):

$$\frac{\partial^2 \phi}{\partial x^2} + \frac{\partial^2 \phi}{\partial y^2} + \frac{\partial^2 \phi}{\partial z^2} - \frac{1}{c^2} \frac{\partial^2 \phi}{\partial t^2} = 0. \tag{2-33a}$$

The potential ϕ must satisfy the equation

$$\frac{\partial \phi}{\partial t} + v \frac{\partial \phi}{\partial x} = 0 \tag{2-33b}$$

if the material moves in the x-direction with uniform velocity v. Elimination of $\partial \phi / \partial t$ from eqs. (2-33) leads to the equation

$$\left(1 - \frac{v^2}{c^2}\right) \frac{\partial^2 \phi}{\partial x^2} + \frac{\partial^2 \phi}{\partial y^2} + \frac{\partial^2 \phi}{\partial z^2} = 0$$

for which the solution is obviously the same as any solution of the equation

$$\frac{\partial^2 \phi}{\partial x^2} + \frac{\partial^2 \phi}{\partial y^2} + \frac{\partial^2 \phi}{\partial z^2} = 0,$$

provided the x-coordinate is contracted by a factor $\sqrt{1 - v^2/c^2}$.

The suspicion had been aroused that *length* was affected by motion. But the real advance came when *time* was also included. The special theory of relativity, in which both length and time are affected by motion, proved itself to be in remarkable agreement with all experiments. Let us therefore proceed to a description of the fundamental kinematic transformation of special relativity.

CHAPTER 3

THE LORENTZ TRANSFORMA-TION

3.1 BASIC POSTULATES

The *Lorentz transformation* is the linear transformation of coordinates between two inertial frames which results from two postulates.

The first postulate is that there exists a *set* of preferred reference systems which are in uniform translational motion relative to each other. They are *preferred* reference systems in the sense that each system is an inertial frame and that no one system has preference over another. The assumption may be stated in an alternate form as the *principle of relativity:* no physical experiment can distinguish one inertial frame from another.

The second postulate concerns any two of the preferred reference systems S and $\bar{S}$. Let P and $\bar{P}$ be observers who are stationary in S and $\bar{S}$, respectively, and let $\mathbf{v}$ be the velocity of $\bar{P}$ relative to P. The second postulate states that the Fitzgerald contraction exists. All distance measurements by $\bar{P}$ in $\bar{S}$ are judged by P to be contracted in the ratio $\sqrt{1 - v^2/c^2}$ parallel to $\mathbf{v}$. (Distances perpendicular to $\mathbf{v}$ are not affected.)

The temporal and spatial (rectangular Cartesian) coordinates in S and $\bar{S}$ will be denoted t, x, y, z and $\bar{t}$, $\bar{x}$, $\bar{y}$, $\bar{z}$, respectively. The spatial origins are chosen so as to coincide at $t = \bar{t} = 0$, and the spatial axes in S and $\bar{S}$ are chosen parallel to one another, with the x- and $\bar{x}$-axes in the direction of $\mathbf{v}$.

Consider a rod at rest in $\bar{S}$ with one of its ends at the origin $\bar{x}^i = (0, 0, 0)$ and the other end at a point $\bar{x}^i = (\bar{x}, \bar{y}, \bar{z})$. The ends of the rod as seen by P are at $x^i = (vt, 0, 0)$ and $x^i = (x, y, z)$, respectively. The second postulate requires the transformation

$$
\left.
\begin{aligned}
x - vt &= \bar{x}\sqrt{1 - \frac{v^2}{c^2}} \\
y &= \bar{y} \\
z &= \bar{z}.
\end{aligned}
\right\}
\tag{3-1}
$$

Equations (3-1) apply to any event observed by P and $\bar{P}$. The first postulate requires that the same equations apply to observations by $\bar{P}$ of distance measurements by P. Since P has velocity $-\mathbf{v}$ relative to $\bar{P}$, the corresponding equations are

$$
\left.
\begin{aligned}
\bar{x} + v\bar{t} &= x\sqrt{1 - \frac{v^2}{c^2}} \\
\bar{y} &= y \\
\bar{z} &= z.
\end{aligned}
\right\}
\tag{3-2}
$$

Equations (3-1) and (3-2) may be solved for t and $\bar{t}$ to give the *Lorentz transformation*:

$$
\left.
\begin{aligned}
\bar{t} &= \gamma\left(t - \frac{v}{c^2}x\right) && \text{a} \\
\bar{x} &= \gamma(x - vt) && \text{b} \\
\bar{y} &= y && \text{c} \\
\bar{z} &= z && \text{d}
\end{aligned}
\right\}
\tag{3-3}
$$

and the inverse transformation

$$
\left.
\begin{aligned}
t &= \gamma\left(\bar{t} + \frac{v}{c^2}\bar{x}\right) && \text{a} \\
x &= \gamma(\bar{x} + v\bar{t}) && \text{b} \\
y &= \bar{y} && \text{c} \\
z &= \bar{z}, && \text{d}
\end{aligned}
\right\}
\tag{3-4}
$$

where

$$
\gamma = \frac{1}{\sqrt{1 - \dfrac{v^2}{c^2}}}.
$$

Time is no longer the same for all observers. The time $\bar{t}$ for an event E depends not only on the time t in the other system, but also on the location x of the event, as seen by inspection of eq. (3-3a). The consequences of this temporal transformation will be investigated more fully later in this chapter.

Equations (3-3) apply only if the coordinate axes are parallel, and if the relative motion is parallel to the x- and $\bar{x}$-axes. On the other hand, the vector form of the Lorentz transformation does not depend on the orientation of the axes. Equations (3-3) may be expressed in the vector form

$$\bar{t} = \gamma\left(t - \frac{\mathbf{v} \cdot \mathbf{r}}{c^2}\right) \tag{3-5}$$

$$\bar{\mathbf{r}} = \mathbf{r} + \mathbf{v}\Theta, \tag{3-6}$$

where the scalar Θ is determined as follows. Scalar multiplication of eq. (3-6) by $\mathbf{v}$ gives

$$v^2\Theta = \bar{\mathbf{r}} \cdot \mathbf{v} - \mathbf{r} \cdot \mathbf{v}$$

which, with application of eq. (3-3b), yields

$$v^2\Theta = \gamma(\mathbf{r} \cdot \mathbf{v} - v^2 t) - \mathbf{r} \cdot \mathbf{v}.$$

It follows that Θ is given by

$$\Theta = \frac{\gamma - 1}{v^2} \mathbf{r} \cdot \mathbf{v} - \gamma t. \tag{3-7}$$

Substitution of eq. (3-7) into eq. (3-6) gives the vector form of the Lorentz transformation:

$$\bar{t} = \gamma\left(t - \frac{\mathbf{v} \cdot \mathbf{r}}{c^2}\right) \tag{3-5}$$

$$\bar{\mathbf{r}} = \mathbf{r} + \mathbf{v}\left[\frac{\gamma - 1}{v^2} \mathbf{r} \cdot \mathbf{v} - \gamma t\right]. \tag{3-8}$$

The inverse transformation is obtained by reversing the sign of $\mathbf{v}$:

$$t = \gamma\left(\bar{t} + \frac{\mathbf{v} \cdot \bar{\mathbf{r}}}{c^2}\right) \tag{3-9}$$

$$\mathbf{r} = \bar{\mathbf{r}} + \mathbf{v}\left[\frac{\gamma - 1}{v^2} \bar{\mathbf{r}} \cdot \mathbf{v} + \gamma\bar{t}\right]. \tag{3-10}$$

The Lorentz transformation can also be derived by using the principle of relativity, i.e., the first of the two postulates, and the principle that the velocity of light is the same in any inertial frame. The latter principle would account for the failure of the optical experiments in the previous chapter to detect the ether wind. We therefore ask the question: Under what transformations does the speed of light remain a constant?

3.2 TRANSFORMATIONS IN WHICH THE SPEED OF LIGHT IS CONSTANT

The time dt required for a light wave with velocity c to move through a Cartesian-coordinate interval dx, dy, dz is given by

$$dt^2 = \frac{1}{c^2}(dx^2 + dy^2 + dz^2). \tag{3-11}$$

We make the hypothesis that the velocity c is the same for all observers. With the definitions

$$x^1 = ct$$
$$x^2 = ix$$
$$x^3 = iy$$
$$x^4 = iz,$$

eq. (3-11) becomes

$$0 = dx^i\, dx^i.$$

(In what follows, the number n of dimensions will not be restricted to four.)

Consider the transformation from one set of coordinates x^i to another set of coordinates $\bar{x}^r$. Since the transformation is to be represented by a set of differentiable functions $\bar{x}^r(x^i)$, we may write

$$d\bar{x}^r = \frac{\partial \bar{x}^r}{\partial x^i}\, dx^i. \tag{3-12}$$

Thus, the $d\bar{x}^r$ are *linear* in the dx^i. Therefore $d\bar{x}^r\, d\bar{x}^r$ is quadratic in dx^i.

The purpose of our investigation is to find all possible transformations such that $dx^i\, dx^i = 0$ implies $d\bar{x}^r\, d\bar{x}^r = 0$. Therefore $d\bar{x}^r\, d\bar{x}^r$ must be a multiple of $dx^i\, dx^i$:

$$d\bar{x}^r\, d\bar{x}^r = \frac{1}{\rho^2}\, dx^i\, dx^i. \tag{3-13}$$

Equation (3-13) is the necessary and sufficient condition that $dx^i\, dx^i = 0$ imply $d\bar{x}^r\, d\bar{x}^r = 0$. In turn, the necessary and sufficient condition for eq. (3-13) is, by substitution of eq. (3-12),

$$\frac{\partial \bar{x}^r}{\partial x^i}\frac{\partial \bar{x}^r}{\partial x^j} = \frac{\delta_{ij}}{\rho^2}. \tag{3-14}$$

Multiplication of eq. (3-14) by the inverse transformation matrix $\partial x^i/\partial \bar{x}^s$ yields

$$\frac{\partial \bar{x}^s}{\partial x^j} = \frac{1}{\rho^2}\frac{\partial x^j}{\partial \bar{x}^s}. \tag{3-15}$$

Differentiation of eq. (3-14) with respect to x^k, cyclic permutation of the indices ijk, subtraction and addition among the resulting three equations, multiplication by $\partial x^j/\partial \bar{x}^s$, and the use of eq. (3-15) yield

$$\frac{\partial^2 \bar{x}^s}{\partial x^i \, \partial x^j} = -\frac{1}{\rho}\left[\frac{\partial \rho}{\partial x^i}\frac{\partial \bar{x}^s}{\partial x^j} + \frac{\partial \rho}{\partial x^j}\frac{\partial \bar{x}^s}{\partial x^i} - \delta_{ij}\frac{\partial \rho}{\partial x^l}\frac{\bar{x}^s}{\partial x^l}\right]. \quad (3\text{-}16)$$

Differentiation of eq. (3-16) with respect to x^k, and application of the condition of integrability

$$\frac{\partial}{\partial x^k}\frac{\partial^2 \bar{x}^s}{\partial x^i \, \partial x^j} = \frac{\partial}{\partial x^j}\frac{\partial^2 \bar{x}^s}{\partial x^i \, \partial x^k}$$

then yields

$$\delta_{ij}\frac{\partial^2 \rho}{\partial x^k \, \partial x^l} + \delta_{kl}\frac{\partial^2 \rho}{\partial x^i \, \partial x^j} - \delta_{jk}\frac{\partial^2 \rho}{\partial x^i \, \partial x^l} - \delta_{il}\frac{\partial^2 \rho}{\partial x^j \, \partial x^k}$$

$$= \frac{1}{\rho}\frac{\partial \rho}{\partial x^m}\frac{\partial \rho}{\partial x^m}(\delta_{ij}\delta_{kl} - \delta_{il}\delta_{jk}). \quad (3\text{-}17)$$

Contraction (i.e., summation) of indices kl in eq. (3-17) results in the relation

$$(n-2)\frac{\partial^2 \rho}{\partial x^i \, \partial x^j} + \delta_{ij}\left[\frac{\partial^2 \rho}{\partial x^k \, \partial x^k} - \frac{n-1}{\rho}\frac{\partial \rho}{\partial x^k}\frac{\partial \rho}{\partial x^k}\right] = 0 \quad (3\text{-}18)$$

which may be further contracted to give, with $n \neq 1$,

$$\frac{\partial^2 \rho}{\partial x^i \, \partial x^i} = \frac{n}{2\rho}\frac{\partial \rho}{\partial x^k}\frac{\partial \rho}{\partial x^k}. \quad (3\text{-}19)$$

Substitution of eq. (3-19) into eq. (3-18) yields

$$(n-2)\left[\frac{\partial^2 \rho}{\partial x^i \, \partial x^j} - \frac{\delta_{ij}}{2\rho}\frac{\partial \rho}{\partial x^k}\frac{\partial \rho}{\partial x^k}\right] = 0. \quad (3\text{-}20)$$

Equations (3-19) and (3-20) are necessary conditions for eq. (3-14) to hold. Let us next examine the consequences of eqs. (3-19) and (3-20).

Two Dimensions. For $n = 2$, eq. (3-20) becomes an identity, and eq. (3-19) becomes

$$\frac{\partial^2 \ln \rho}{\partial x^k \, \partial x^k} = 0.$$

Thus $\ln \rho$ is a two-dimensional harmonic function having the form

$$\ln \rho = f(\xi) + g(\eta) \quad (3\text{-}21)$$

where

$$\xi = x^1 + ix^2$$
$$\eta = x^1 - ix^2.$$

With eq. (3-21) and the definitions

$$F(\xi) = \int e^{-2f(\xi)} \, d\xi$$

$$G(\eta) = \int e^{-2g(\eta)} \, d\eta$$

$$\bar{\xi} = \bar{x}^1 + i\bar{x}^2$$

$$\bar{\eta} = \bar{x}^1 - i\bar{x}^2$$

eq. (3-13) becomes

$$d\bar{\xi} \, d\bar{\eta} = dF(\xi) \, dG(\eta). \tag{3-22}$$

The substitutions $x^1 = ct$ and $x^2 = ix$ and $F'(\xi) = dF/d\xi$, $G'(\eta) = dG/d\eta$ put eq. (3-22) into the form

$$c^2 \, d\bar{t}^2 - d\bar{x}^2 = F'(\xi)G'(\eta)(c^2 \, dt^2 - dx^2)$$

which shows clearly that the speed of light is constant under the transformation. Note that we may choose $\bar{\xi} = F(\xi)$, $\bar{\eta} = G(\eta)$, in which case the transformation is given by

$$c\bar{t} - \bar{x} = F(ct - x)$$
$$c\bar{t} + \bar{x} = G(ct + x)$$

where F and G are arbitrary functions.

More Than Two Dimensions. For $n > 2$, eq. (3-20) reduces to the form

$$\frac{\partial^2 \rho}{\partial x^i \, \partial x^j} = \frac{\delta_{ij}}{2\rho} \frac{\partial \rho}{\partial x^k} \frac{\partial \rho}{\partial x^k}. \tag{3-23}$$

The vanishing of the diagonal components of eq. (3-23) requires that ρ be the sum of n functions of each of the n coordinates:

$$\rho = \sum_{i=1}^{n} f_i(x^i).$$

The common value of the diagonal components of eq. (3-23) produces the condition

$$\frac{d^2 f_i}{dx^{i^2}} = 2A, \qquad \text{no sum on } i, \tag{3-24}$$

where A (a constant, since it cannot be a function of any one of the x^i) is given by

$$A = \frac{1}{4\rho} \frac{\partial \rho}{\partial x^k} \frac{\partial \rho}{\partial x^k}. \tag{3-25}$$

Integration of eq. (3-24) immediately yields the result

$$f_i(x^i) = Ax^{i^2} + a^i x^i + b^i. \qquad \text{(No sum on } i)$$

The function ρ is therefore given by

$$\rho = Ax^jx^j + a^kx^k + b, \tag{3-26}$$

and eq. (3-25) requires

$$4Ab = a^ka^k, \tag{3-27}$$

where A, b, and the a^k are constants.

The case $\rho = 1$ (i.e., $A = 0$, $a^k = 0$, $b = 1$) is the same as the case which was studied in Section 1.5. The only possible transformations are *translations* and *rotations*.

The case $A = 0$, $a^k = 0$, $b \neq 1$ merely adds the transformation known as *dilatations*:

$$\bar{x}^i = \frac{x^i}{b}.$$

For the case of non-constant ρ, the two cases $A \neq 0$ and $A = 0$ arise. If $A \neq 0$, then by a suitable translation and dilatation, the a^i can be chosen equal to zero, and A can be chosen as unity. Then by eq. (3-27), b is zero, and eq. (3-26) becomes $\rho = r^2 = x^ix^i$. Thus eq. (3-13) becomes

$$d\bar{x}^r\, d\bar{x}^r = \frac{dx^i\, dx^i}{r^4}$$

which has as its solution the *inversion*

$$\bar{x}^i = \frac{x^i}{r^2}.$$

For the case in which ρ is not constant but $A = 0$, eq. (3-26) can, by a suitable translation, be put into the form $\rho = a^kx^k$. Equation (3-27) now requires $a^ka^k = 0$. At least one of the a^i, say a^1, must be non-zero in order that ρ be non-zero. By dilatation we can choose $a^1 = 1$. By rotation among the remaining coordinates, we can choose one other a^i to be non-zero, say a^2. Thus we obtain $a^1 = 1$, $a^2 = i$, $a^3 = 0$, $a^4 = 0, \ldots,$ $a^n = 0$. The function ρ assumes the form $\rho = x^1 + ix^2$, and the transformation is given by

$$\bar{x}^1 = \frac{r^2 - 1}{2\rho}$$

$$\bar{x}^2 = \frac{r^2 + 1}{2i\rho}$$

$$\bar{x}^h = \frac{x^h}{\rho} \qquad h = 3, 4, \ldots, n$$

where

$$r^2 = x^ix^i,$$

as may be verified by differentiation. Substitution of $n = 4$, $x^1 = ct$, $x^2 = ix$, $x^3 = iy$, $x^4 = iz$ gives what is known as *Kelvin's transformation:*

$$c\bar{t} = \frac{c^2 t^2 - x^2 - y^2 - z^2 - 1}{2(ct - x)}$$

$$\bar{x} = \frac{-c^2 t^2 + x^2 + y^2 + z^2 - 1}{2(ct - x)}$$

$$\bar{y} = \frac{y}{ct - x}$$

$$\bar{z} = \frac{z}{ct - x}.$$

In summary, we find that the only transformations for which $dx^i \, dx^i = 0$ implies $d\bar{x}^r \, d\bar{x}^r = 0$ are translations, rotations, dilatations, inversions, and the generalization of Kelvin's transformation. Upon returning to the problem with which we started, we find that the only transformations in four-dimensional space-time which leave the velocity of light constant are

    (1) translations,   (2) rotations,   (3) dilatations,

    (4) inversions, and (5) Kelvin's transformation.

3.3 GEOMETRICAL INTERPRETATION OF THE LORENTZ TRANSFORMATION

Not all the transformations obtained in the previous section are satisfactory for describing two inertial frames in uniform relative motion. The requirement that the velocity $d\bar{x}^a / d\bar{x}^0$ ($a = 1, 2, 3$) not vanish for constant x^a ($a = 1, 2, 3$) discards translations and dilatations. The condition that the velocity $d\bar{x}^a / d\bar{x}^0$ for constant x^a be independent of x^a eliminates inversions and Kelvin's transformation. We will now show that the Lorentz transformation is a four-dimensional rotation.

Consider a rotation about the x^1- and x^2-axes:

$$\left.\begin{aligned}
\bar{x}^1 &= x^1 \cos\theta + x^2 \sin\theta \\
\bar{x}^2 &= x^2 \cos\theta - x^1 \sin\theta \\
\bar{x}^3 &= x^3 \\
\bar{x}^4 &= x^4
\end{aligned}\right\} \tag{3-28}$$

We now choose

$$\left.\begin{aligned}
\bar{x}^1 &= c\bar{t} & x^1 &= ct \\
\bar{x}^2 &= i\bar{x} & x^2 &= ix \\
\bar{x}^3 &= i\bar{y} & x^3 &= iy \\
\bar{x}^4 &= i\bar{z} & x^4 &= iz,
\end{aligned}\right\} \tag{3-29}$$

and define $\theta = i\phi$. Equations (3-28) become

$$\left.\begin{aligned}
\bar{t} &= (t - c^{-1}x \tanh \phi) \cosh \phi \\
\bar{x} &= (x - ct \tanh \phi) \cosh \phi \\
\bar{y} &= y \\
\bar{z} &= z.
\end{aligned}\right\} \tag{3-30}$$

The requirement that the coordinates be real imposes the condition that ϕ be real. The substitution

$$\tanh \phi = \frac{v}{c}$$

throws eqs. (3-30) into the form of the Lorentz transformation of eq. (3-3). Equations (3-3) or (3-30) will be used equivalently for the Lorentz transformation along the x-axis.

The substitution of $\rho = 1$ and eqs. (3-29) into eq. (3-13) gives

$$c^2\, d\bar{t}^2 - d\bar{x}^2 - d\bar{y}^2 - d\bar{z}^2 = c^2\, dt^2 - dx^2 - dy^2 - dz^2.$$

Therefore the quantity

$$ds^2 = dt^2 - c^{-2}(dx^2 + dy^2 + dz^2) \tag{3-31}$$

is an invariant under the allowed transformations. In Section 1.5 it was found that there are ten independent transformations—four translations and six rotations. We interpret these as one temporal translation, three spatial translations, three spatial rotations, and three Lorentz transformations—one along each spatial coordinate axis. Under the above ten transformations eq. (3-31) is invariant.

The quantity ds^2 may be positive or negative according as the temporal interval dt between two events is larger or smaller than c^{-1} times the spatial interval $\sqrt{dx^2 + dy^2 + dz^2}$. In case ds^2 is negative it should be replaced by $-c^{-2}\, dl^2$ in order to have a quantity dl which is real:

$$dl^2 = -c^{-2}\, dt^2 + dx^2 + dy^2 + dz^2. \tag{3-32}$$

3.4 STRUCTURE OF SPACE-TIME

An observer P in an inertial frame S with Cartesian coordinates x, y, z and time t can construct a space-time diagram by the procedure of Section 1.9. (Different observers will now in general have different spaces $t = $ const.) The result is represented in Figure 3.1, in which the y and z dimensions are omitted. A particle having a coordinate $x(t)$ may be plotted as a curve in the diagram. In three spatial dimensions, one has the curve given by the three parametric equations $x = x(t)$, $y = y(t)$,

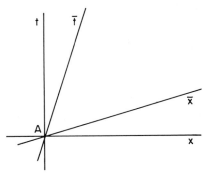

FIGURE 3.1 Two inertial frames in relative motion.

$z = z(t)$. Such a curve is known as the *world-line* of the particle. The world-line of any free particle is then a straight line in space-time, since x, y, and z are linear functions of t.

The origin O of the second inertial frame S of Section 3.1 moves along the x-axis with a uniform velocity v. Hence, its world-line is the line $\bar{t}$ in Figure 3.1 having slope v^{-1}. The passage of $\bar{t}$ through the intersection A of the x- and t-axes is due to the condition that the event $t = 0$, $x^i = 0$ be the same event as $\bar{t} = 0$, $\bar{x}^i = 0$.

The space $\bar{t} = $ const intersects the surface $y = z = \bar{y} = \bar{z} = 0$ in the $\bar{x}$-axis shown in Figure 3.1 with slope vc^{-2}. Thus different observers have different $t = $ const spaces in distinction with the kinematics of the Galilean transformation where all observers have the same $t = $ const spaces. From eq. (3-5), the time difference between an event at $t = 0$, $\mathbf{r} = \mathbf{r}$ in S and the event A as measured by $\bar{P}$ is $\bar{t} = -\gamma c^{-2}\mathbf{v} \cdot \mathbf{r}$. Thus two events which are simultaneous with spatial separation $\mathbf{r}$ for one observer are not simultaneous for another observer who has a velocity $\mathbf{v}$ relative to the first, unless $\mathbf{v} \cdot \mathbf{r} = 0$.

The four-dimensional character of space-time will be utilized in our notation. The coordinate x^μ ($\mu = 0, 1, 2, 3$) shall stand for any of the four coordinates

$$x^0 = t$$
$$x^1 = x$$
$$x^2 = y$$
$$x^3 = z.$$

The practice of writing three-dimensional vectors in triplet form (x^1, x^2, x^3) is extended to the four-dimensional case by writing (x^0, x^1, x^2, x^3). Often it will be convenient to write the latter in the form $(x^0, \mathbf{x})$ or $(t, \mathbf{x})$, where $\mathbf{x}$ is the three-dimensional spatial vector. For example, an event at $t = 7$, $x = 3$, $y = 5$, $z = 2$ is denoted $(7, 3, 5, 2)$. Greek indices will be used for four-dimensional coordinates; i.e., Greek indices take the values 0, 1, 2, 3. Roman indices will be used for three-dimensional spatial coordinates; i.e., Roman indices take the values 1, 2, 3. This notation will be used in all cases where space-time is studied. (For n-dimensional spaces, Roman indices will in general be used.) Thus an event x^μ may also be denoted t, x^i.

Equation (3-31) may now be written

$$ds^2 = dt^2 - \frac{dx^i\, dx^i}{c^2}$$

or

$$ds^2 = \eta_{\mu\nu}\, dx^\mu\, dx^\nu \tag{3-33}$$

where the matrix $\eta_{\mu\nu}$ is defined

$$\eta_{\mu\nu} = \begin{bmatrix} 1 & 0 & 0 & 0 \\ 0 & -c^{-2} & 0 & 0 \\ 0 & 0 & -c^{-2} & 0 \\ 0 & 0 & 0 & -c^{-2} \end{bmatrix}.$$

Thus for two adjacent events there is an invariant ds^2 which is equal to the difference between the square of the time difference of the events and c^{-2} times the square of their Euclidean spatial separation. For example, in spherical polar coordinates r, θ, ϕ, the invariant is given by

$$ds^2 = dt^2 - c^{-2}[dr^2 + r^2(d\theta^2 + \sin^2\theta\, d\phi^2)].$$

The invariant ds^2 is known as the *Minkowski metric*, and the theory which asserts the invariance of ds^2 with respect to the transformations among inertial systems is known as the *special theory of relativity* or simply *special relativity*. One important property of eq. (3-33) is that it vanishes along any light ray.

3.5 CONSEQUENCES OF THE LORENTZ TRANSFORMATION

In the notation of Sections 3.1 and 3.4, we consider two events B and C located at $\bar{x}^\mu = (0, \bar{L}, 0, 0)$ and $\bar{x}^\mu = (\bar{T}, 0, 0, 0)$, respectively (Figure 3.2). It is readily verified that, under the ten transformations described in Section 3.3 (and in particular under the Lorentz transformation of our present circumstances), not only is ds^2 an invariant but so also is $\Delta s^2 = \eta_{\mu\nu}\, \Delta x^\mu\, \Delta x^\nu$ where Δx^μ is not infinitesimal. Thus the interval AB has the invariant $\Delta l^2 = -c^2\, \Delta s^2 = L^2$, and the interval AC has the invariant $\Delta s^2 = \bar{T}^2$. We conclude that Δl is the distance between two events measured in the inertial frame in which the events are simultaneous, and Δs is the time between two events measured in an inertial frame in which the two events have the same spatial position.

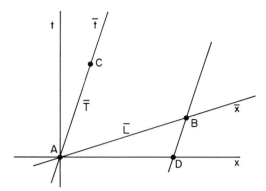

FIGURE 3.2 Time dilation and Fitzgerald contraction.

   It immediately follows from the foregoing argument that for a particle moving on an arbitrary world-line $\mathbf{x}(t)$, the rate at which the particle's time s passes with respect to the coordinate time t is given instantaneously (through the use of an inertial frame in which the particle is momentarily at rest) by

$$\left(\frac{ds}{dt}\right)^2 = 1 - \frac{v^2}{c^2} \tag{3-34}$$

where the particle's velocity is given by

$$v = \sqrt{\left(\frac{dx}{dt}\right)^2 + \left(\frac{dy}{dt}\right)^2 + \left(\frac{dz}{dt}\right)^2}.$$

Thus a moving particle has its time slowed down by the ratio $\sqrt{1 - v^2/c^2}$. This effect will be called the *time dilation*.

   The parallel lines AC and DB in Figure 3.2 can represent the world-lines of the ends of a rod of length $\bar{L}$ which is stationary in $\bar{S}$. The observer P in S sees the events AD at $t = 0$ rather than the events AB. Therefore his measurement of the length L of the rod is given by the distance AD. From eq. (3-3b) with the substitutions $t = 0$, $\bar{x} = \bar{L}$, and $x = L$, we have

$$L = \frac{\bar{L}}{\gamma}$$

where

$$\gamma = \frac{1}{\sqrt{1 - \dfrac{v^2}{c^2}}}.$$

   Thus an object moving with uniform velocity v has its linear dimensions shortened by the ratio $\sqrt{1 - v^2/c^2}$ in the direction of motion; dimensions perpendicular to the direction of motion are unaffected. This effect is of course the Fitzgerald contraction which was introduced to explain the

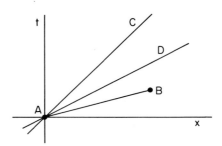

FIGURE 3.3 Causality.

MM experiment. Another name often used for this effect is the *Lorentz contraction*.

The principle of *causality* demands that no signal travel faster than light. By *causality* is meant the existence of a cause-effect relationship between two events. When two events are related to each other, the earlier one is said to *cause* the later one. But such a causal relationship is impossible if signals can travel faster than light. Suppose that a signal traveled from event A to event B with a speed w faster than that of light (Figure 3.3). Now A can, without loss of generality, be chosen as the origin for space and time coordinates. Since A is before B in time, A is said to cause B. The slope of the line AB is the inverse of the speed w of the signal. Light, traveling with velocity $c < w$, follows the line AC. But now consider the events A and B as observed in a system $\bar{S}$ in uniform motion with velocity v in the position x-direction. The events simultaneous with A for an observer $\bar{P}$ in $\bar{S}$ fall on a line AD having slope v^{-1}. The velocity v is chosen to lie between c^2/w and c. Then B lies in the past from A; thus A cannot be said to cause B from the standpoint of $\bar{P}$. Therefore, the existence of causality requires that no signal travel faster than the speed of light in free space.

The spherical pulse of light, whether actual or imagined, which emanates from an event A both forward and backward in time has special significance. This pulse forms a cone in four-dimensional space-time; the cone is known as the *light-cone* for the event A. In the x-t diagram which has been used in Figures 3.1, 3.2, and 3.3 (often called the *Minkowski diagram*), the cone appears as two lines having slopes c^{-1} and $-c^{-1}$. (See Figure 3.4.) The cone divides space-time into three regions: the past for A, the elsewhere for A, and the future for A. Events in the past of A can cause A but cannot be caused by A. Events in the future of A can be caused by A but cannot cause A. Events in the elsewhere of A cannot influence nor be influenced by A.

A word of caution about the Minkowski diagram is in order. The coordinates $\bar{x}$ and $\bar{t}$ for an event E in Figure 3.2 are obtained by extending lines CE and BE parallel respectively to the $\bar{x}$ and $\bar{t}$ axes (Fig. 3.5). The lengths AC and AB are then the coordinates $\bar{t}$ and $\bar{x}$. However, these

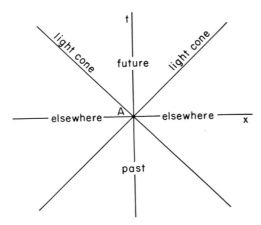

FIGURE 3.4 Light cone.

lengths are to be measured in the system $\bar{S}$, not the system S. Pythagorean relations do not hold because it is the quantity $c^2 t^2 - x^2$ rather than $c^2 t^2 + x^2$ which is invariant under the x-axis-Lorentz transformation.

The locus of events at $\bar{x}^\mu = (\bar{t}, 0, 0, 0)$ for all possible values of v is the hyperbola

$$c^2 t^2 - x^2 = c^2 \bar{t}^2;$$

and the locus of events at $\bar{x}^\mu = (0, \bar{x}, 0, 0)$ for all possible values of v is the hyperbola

$$x^2 - c^2 t^2 = \bar{x}^2.$$

For a light ray, eq. (3-33) vanishes; light does not age as it travels.

In summary, the Lorentz transformation is characterized by the following features.

1. The speed c of light in free space is the same in any inertial frame.
2. The quantity $c^2\,\Delta t^2 - \Delta x^i\,\Delta x^i$ is invariant.
3. A moving object appears to be shorter in the direction of motion.
4. A moving clock appears to run slower.
5. No signal can travel faster than c.

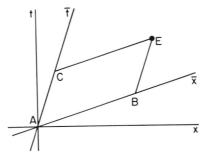

FIGURE 3.5 Coordinates in the Minkowski diagram.

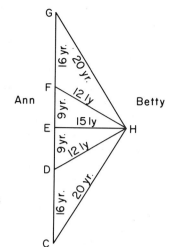

FIGURE 3.6 Minkowski diagram for twin paradox.

The violent difference between the Lorentz transformation and the Galilean transformation has inspired people to invent more so-called paradoxes than we have either the space or the desire to explain. In each case there is some aspect of the Lorentz transformation which is forgotten, usually the dependence of time on spatial position. However, two notable cases will be studied.

3.6 THE TWIN PARADOX

Consider the twins Ann and Betty. Ann remains on the earth, while Betty makes a round trip to a distant star. We consider the earth's motion to be uniform (i.e., unaccelerated). It is assumed that Betty makes the trip in both directions at a uniform velocity v, and that she possesses a mechanism which is capable of changing her speed by amounts of order v in times which are small compared with her travel time.

The alleged paradox is this: Ann sees Betty's time slowed down by the factor $\sqrt{1 - v^2/c^2}$, so that as Betty travels the distance l to the star and back, Betty has aged $2lv^{-1}\sqrt{1 - v^2/c^2}$ while Ann has aged $2lv^{-1}$. On the other hand, from Betty's point of view, Ann's time is slowed down, so that while Betty ages $2lv^{-1}\sqrt{1 - v^2/c^2}$, Ann ages only $2lv^{-1}(1 - v^2/c^2)$.

Which is correct? Does Ann age by $2lv^{-1}$ or by $2lv^{-1}(1 - v^2/c^2)$ during Betty's trip? Actually, both conclusions are correct. Consider Figure 3.6.

Inertial coordinates are chosen in which Ann is at rest. Then Ann's world-line is represented by the straight line $CDEFG$. Betty's world-line leaves Ann at C and goes in a straight line with slope v^{-1} to Betty's encounter with the star at H. Betty's world-line then returns by a straight line with slope $-v^{-1}$ to Ann at G. As a specific illustration, suppose that the star is located at a distance of 15 light-years from the earth, and that Betty travels with a velocity $\frac{3}{5}c$. The time dilation factor is then $\frac{4}{5}$. In Figure 3.6, EH is 15 ly, and the two times CE and EG are each 15 ly $\div \frac{3}{5}c$ or 25 years. According to Ann, the time it takes for Betty to reach the star is 25 years, and the time for the return trip is also 25 years—a total of 50 years. Due to the time dilation, Ann sees Betty's time slowed down by a factor $\frac{4}{5}$, so that it takes Betty only 20 years to reach the star and another 20 years to return—a total of 40 years. Thus, upon Betty's return, Ann is 10 years older than Betty.

From Betty's point of view, both the earth and the star are moving with velocity $\frac{3}{5}c$. Hence their distance of 15 ly is contracted to a distance of 12 ly. Betty covers that distance in 12 ly $\div \frac{3}{5}c$ or 20 years. The return trip then takes another 20 years, so that Betty ages a total of 40 years. Betty sees Ann's time slowed down by the factor $\frac{4}{5}$, so that when Betty reaches the star, Ann has aged only 16 years. But this is Ann's age by Betty's standard. It must be remembered that, due to Betty's motion, Betty's space $t = $ const is represented by DH, not EH. The 16 years is the time CD, not CE. In the brief time interval in which Betty changes her velocity at the star, Betty's space $t = $ const switches from DH to FH. The earth-time suddenly zooms through 18 years. This 18 years is twice the value of t obtained from eq. (3-4a) by substituting $\bar{t} = 0$, $v = \frac{3}{5}c$, and $\bar{x} = 12$ ly. Finally, on the return trip, Ann ages 16 years. When the twins are reunited, Ann has aged 50 years and Betty has aged 40 years. The aging as observed by either twin is the same; it may be verified by calculation that allowance for finite acceleration times for Betty does not appreciably alter the conclusion.

3.7 ROTATING RING

A ring of radius r rotates with constant angular velocity ω. Each point on the ring therefore moves with velocity $v = \omega r$ in a circle. It is often claimed that the circumference of the ring should be $2\pi r \sqrt{1 - v^2/c^2}$; but this is incorrect.

Consider a point O on the ring. Its world-line is the spiral $ABCD$ in Figure 3.7. The locus of the world-lines of all the points on the ring is a cylinder in space-time. The unrolled cylinder is shown in Figure 3.8. The world-line ABC has slope v^{-1}. Then AEC, which represents the space $t = $ const according to the step-by-step synchronization of the points on the ring, has slope vc^{-2}. Thus the situation is exactly like the moving rod of Section 3.5, except that the $t = $ const line intersects the world-line O at an infinite number of events A, C, etc.

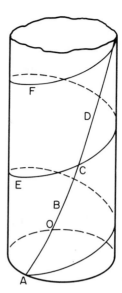

FIGURE 3.7 The space-time diagram of a rotating ring. The spatial dimension perpendicular to the ring is omitted.

It was found that the length AA is equal to $\sqrt{1 - v^2/c^2}$ times the length AEC. But AA is equal to $2\pi r$. Therefore the observers on the ring find the circumference AEC to be $2\pi r(1 - v^2/c^2)^{-\frac{1}{2}}$. The length AAG is found to be $2\pi r(1 - v^2/c^2)^{-1}$ by substituting $\bar{t} = 0$ and $\bar{x} = 2\pi r(1 - v^2/c^2)^{-\frac{1}{2}}$ into eq. (3-4b).

Note that complete synchronization around the ring is impossible. There has to be a break of $2\pi r v/c^2\sqrt{1 - v^2/c^2}$ somewhere around the ring.

For a ring of physical material initially at rest, the molecules see themselves stretched apart by a factor $(1 - v^2/c^2)^{-\frac{1}{2}}$. For N equally spaced molecules around the ring, the initial inter-molecular separation is $2\pi r/N$,

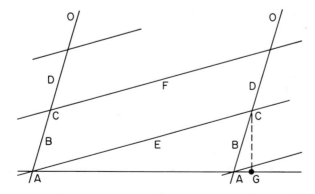

FIGURE 3.8 Rotating ring. Same as Figure 3.7 but unrolled.

but the separation at angular velocity ω is $2\pi r/N\sqrt{1 - \omega^2 r^2 c^{-2}}$, i.e., $AEC \div N$. This example illustrates the impossibility of the existence of *solid bodies* in special relativity.

To Robertson, who had to explain the rotating disk to students each time he taught the course, the explanation seemed simple, as is shown by the following quotation from his private notes of October 29, 1952.

THAT DARNED* ROTATING DISK

O is supposed to say that since matter is shortened by [the] Fitzgerald contraction the periphery of the disk will be $2\pi r\sqrt{1 - v^2/c^2}$ where $v = r\omega$. This is nonsense; true situation shown on diagrams, the second* one of which is obtained from the first* by developing the cylinder $x^2 + y^2 = r^2$ on a plane— and to heck* with it! (There has been more bulk written about this than any other "paradox"—all seeming to stem from the premise that the integrated moving observer must consider the periphery of the disk as $2\pi r$—about the only number *not* applicable to the moving observer!)

3.8 COSMIC-RAY μ-MESONS

The penetration of cosmic-ray μ-mesons provides one observational verification of the time dilation of moving objects. The μ-meson has an exponential lifetime of 2.2×10^{-6} sec (see Bell[B] and Hincks). During this time, a cosmic-ray μ-meson, having a velocity nearly that of light, should travel a distance of 0.66 km. However, cosmic-ray μ-mesons reach the ground in such numbers that it must be concluded that their lifetimes are many times longer than measured in the laboratory.

Observations (see Rossi[B] et al.) of the flux of μ-mesons at different angular altitudes and at different linear altitudes shows that the (exponential) mean distance of penetration through the atmosphere due to decay rather than collisions is 9.5 km. Since the mesons have nearly the velocity of light, their exponential lifetime is 32×10^{-6} sec—a factor of 15 times the exponential lifetime of μ-mesons at rest!

According to eq. (4-52) which will be derived later, the time dilation ratio $\sqrt{1 - v^2/c^2}$ should be equal to the ratio $mc^2/\mathcal{E}$ where m is the μ-meson's rest mass and $\mathcal{E}$ is its energy. Unfortunately, the cosmic-ray μ-mesons have a wide energy spectrum, making it difficult to apply a quantitative check to the time dilation. Their momenta range principally

---

* Censored or revised.

from 1000 to 5000 Mev/c (see Jánossy[B]). But there is at least consistency. A time dilation of 15 corresponds to a momentum of 1600 Mev/c which lies well within the momentum spectrum.

3.9 VECTORS AND TENSORS

In any n-dimensional space in which exist at least two continuous systems of coordinates x^i and $\bar{x}^r$ and differentiable transformation equations $\bar{x}^r = \bar{x}^r(x^i)$ and $x^i = x^i(\bar{x}^r)$, vectors and tensors are defined as follows. A *covariant vector* V_i (all indices run over 1, 2, . . . , n) is a set of n quantities which transforms by the rule

$$\bar{V}_r = \frac{\partial x^i}{\partial \bar{x}^r} V_i. \tag{3-35}$$

A *contravariant vector* V^i is a set of n quantities which transforms by the rule

$$\bar{V}^r = \frac{\partial \bar{x}^r}{\partial x^i} V^i. \tag{3-36}$$

A second-rank, covariant *tensor* T_{ij} is a set of n^2 quantities which transforms by the rule

$$\bar{T}_{rs} = \frac{\partial x^i}{\partial \bar{x}^r} \frac{\partial x^j}{\partial \bar{x}^s} T_{ij}. \tag{3-37a}$$

And in general, covariant indices, denoted by lower indices, are transformed by the matrix $\partial x^i/\partial \bar{x}^r$ while contravariant indices, denoted by upper indices, are transformed by the matrix $\partial \bar{x}^r/\partial x^i$. For example, we have for the other two types of second-rank tensors

$$\bar{T}^{rs} = \frac{\partial \bar{x}^r}{\partial x^i} \frac{\partial \bar{x}^s}{\partial x^j} T^{ij} \tag{3-37b}$$

$$\bar{T}^r_s = \frac{\partial \bar{x}^r}{\partial x^i} \frac{\partial x^j}{\partial \bar{x}^s} T^i{}_j. \tag{3-37c}$$

Note that the Kronecker delta δ^i_j with upper and lower indices is a tensor, but the Kronecker deltas with both upper or both lower indices are not tensors in general. Note also that the coordinate differential dx^i is a contravariant vector because it transforms according to the rule

$$d\bar{x}^r = \frac{\partial \bar{x}^r}{\partial x^i} dx^i.$$

A *scalar* is a quantity which is unchanged by the transformation.

The scalar product $V_k W^k$ of two vectors V_k and W^k is a scalar; so also is the contraction T^k_k of a second-rank tensor with mixed indices. The gradient of a scalar S is a covariant vector:

$$V_i = \frac{\partial S}{\partial x^i}.$$

The double gradient

$$T_{ij} = \frac{\partial^2 S}{\partial x^i \, \partial x^j}$$

is a second-rank covariant tensor provided the transformation matrix $\partial \bar{x}^r / \partial x^i$ has constant components. Also, T_{ij} is *symmetric* because it is unchanged by the interchange of its indices.

In the space-time of special relativity, the choices of coordinates will in general be restricted to inertial frames which contain rectangular Cartesian coordinates. (The only exception will be the use of polar coordinates in certain orbit problems.) First, we note that the transformation matrices $\partial x^\mu / \partial \bar{x}^\alpha$ and $\partial \bar{x}^\alpha / \partial x^\mu$ have *constant* components. Second, we recall from Section 3.3 that the quantity ds^2 given by eq. (3-31) or eq. (3-33) is a scalar; it is given by the relation

$$ds^2 = \eta_{\mu\nu} \, dx^\mu \, dx^\nu = \eta_{\mu\nu} \frac{\partial x^\mu}{\partial \bar{x}^\alpha} \frac{\partial x^\nu}{\partial \bar{x}^\beta} \, d\bar{x}^\alpha \, d\bar{x}^\beta = \eta_{\alpha\beta} \, d\bar{x}^\alpha \, d\bar{x}^\beta$$

which necessarily implies the condition

$$\eta_{\alpha\beta} = \eta_{\mu\nu} \frac{\partial x^\mu}{\partial \bar{x}^\alpha} \frac{\partial x^\nu}{\partial \bar{x}^\beta}. \tag{3-38}$$

It is immediately seen from eqs. (3-37a) and (3-38) that $\eta_{\mu\nu}$ is a second-rank covariant tensor.

The tensor $\eta_{\mu\nu}$ is known as the *metric tensor* because it defines measurements of distance and time. Under the permissible transformations (inertial Cartesian frames), $\eta_{\mu\nu}$ retains the same components. If other coordinates are used, e.g., polar coordinates, then $\eta_{\mu\nu}$ transforms as a tensor but does not retain the same components.

Some further properties of the metric tensor will be of later use. Equation (3-38) may be multiplied by $\partial \bar{x}^\alpha / \partial x^\mu$ to give

$$\eta_{\mu\nu} \frac{\partial x^\nu}{\partial \bar{x}^\beta} = \eta_{\alpha\beta} \frac{\partial \bar{x}^\alpha}{\partial x^\mu}. \tag{3-39}$$

Equation (3-39) may now be multiplied twice by the matrix $\eta^{\mu\nu}$ which is the inverse of $\eta_{\mu\nu}$ to give

$$\eta^{\sigma\gamma} \frac{\partial x^\rho}{\partial \bar{x}^\gamma} = \eta^{\nu\rho} \frac{\partial \bar{x}^\sigma}{\partial x^\nu}. \tag{3-40}$$

When eq. (3-40) is multiplied by $\partial \bar{x}^\lambda / \partial x^\rho$, the result is

$$\eta^{\sigma\lambda} = \eta^{\nu\rho} \frac{\partial \bar{x}^\sigma}{\partial x^\nu} \frac{\partial \bar{x}^\lambda}{\partial x^\rho}. \tag{3-41}$$

Thus the inverse $\eta^{\mu\nu}$ of the metric tensor is also a tensor whose components retain the same values under the permitted transformations.

$$\eta^{\mu\nu} = \begin{bmatrix} 1 & 0 & 0 & 0 \\ 0 & -c^2 & 0 & 0 \\ 0 & 0 & -c^2 & 0 \\ 0 & 0 & 0 & -c^2 \end{bmatrix}.$$

Equations (3-35) to (3-41) allow us to set up the following rules. If V^μ is a contravariant vector, then $V_\mu = \eta_{\mu\nu}V^\nu$ is a covariant vector. If $T^{\mu\nu}$ is a contravariant second-rank tensor, then $T_{\mu\nu} = \eta_{\mu\rho}\eta_{\nu\sigma}T^{\rho\sigma}$ is a covariant second-rank tensor. If V_μ is a covariant vector, then $V^\mu = \eta^{\mu\nu}V_\nu$ is a contravariant vector. The operation of *lowering* an index (i.e., converting from the contravariant form to the covariant form) is performed by multiplication by $\eta_{\mu\nu}$; the operation of *raising* an index (i.e., converting from the covariant form to the contravariant form) is performed by multiplication by $\eta^{\mu\nu}$. Two contravariant vectors V^μ and W^μ have the *scalar product* $\eta_{\mu\nu}V^\mu W^\nu$. Two vectors are *perpendicular* or *orthogonal* if their scalar product is zero. If a vector is orthogonal to itself, the vector is said to be a *null vector*.

Any transformation matrix is constant because it is the matrix product of the matrices for the ten elementary transformations, each of which is constant. It follows that the transformation matrix commutes with the gradient operator $\partial/\partial x^i$. It may also be noted that if eqs. (3-3) hold, then for *any* contravariant vector V^μ the same transformation holds:

$$\bar{V}^0 = \gamma(V^0 - vc^{-2}V^1)$$
$$\bar{V}^1 = \gamma(V^1 - vV^0)$$
$$\bar{V}^2 = V^2$$
$$\bar{V}^3 = V^3.$$

The operator

$$\square^2 = \eta^{\mu\nu}\frac{\partial^2}{\partial x^\mu \partial x^\nu},$$

known as the *d'Alembertian*, is a scalar operator. For example, the d'Alembertian of a vector is a vector. The d'Alembertian was encountered in electromagnetism in the form

$$\square^2 = \frac{\partial^2}{\partial t^2} - \frac{1}{c^2}\nabla^2.$$

The determinant of the transformation matrix $\partial x^\mu/\partial \bar{x}^\alpha$ is

$$\left|\frac{\partial x^\tau}{\partial \bar{x}^\epsilon}\right| = e(\mu\nu\rho\sigma)\frac{\partial x^\mu}{\partial \bar{x}^0}\frac{\partial x^\nu}{\partial \bar{x}^1}\frac{\partial x^\rho}{\partial \bar{x}^2}\frac{\partial x^\sigma}{\partial \bar{x}^3}.$$

Then by arrangement of indices, we have

$$e(\alpha\beta\gamma\delta)\left|\frac{\partial x^\tau}{\partial \bar{x}^\epsilon}\right| = e(\mu\nu\rho\sigma)\frac{\partial x^\mu}{\partial \bar{x}^\alpha}\frac{\partial x^\nu}{\partial \bar{x}^\beta}\frac{\partial x^\rho}{\partial \bar{x}^\gamma}\frac{\partial x^\sigma}{\partial \bar{x}^\delta}. \tag{3-42}$$

But from eq. (3-38), the determinant of the transformation matrix is ± 1. And since no transformation built up continuously from the identity transformation can have a negative determinant, the determinant of the transformation matrix is unity. Equation (3-42) therefore shows that $e(\mu\nu\rho\sigma)$ is a covariant tensor, in which case we write it $e_{\mu\nu\rho\sigma}$. The permutation symbol can similarly be proved to be a contravariant tensor, in which case we write it $e^{\mu\nu\rho\sigma}$.

As a by-product of the above analysis, we have the result that, since the determinant of the transformation matrix is unity, the determinant of *any* second-rank tensor is a scalar, i.e., it is invariant under transformations.

3.10 VELOCITY

The world-line for any particle is given by parametric equations $x^\mu = x^\mu(p)$, where p is a monotonic parameter along the world-line. The particle has an instantaneous velocity

$$v^k = \frac{dx^k}{dx^0} \qquad k = 1, 2, 3 \tag{3-43}$$

at an event E on its world-line, where dx^μ is given by

$$dx^\mu = \left[\frac{dx^\mu(p)}{dp}\right]_{p=p_E} dp.$$

Consider the inertial frame $\bar{S}$ which has a velocity v^k and the accompanying Lorentz transformation from the coordinates $\bar{x}^\mu$ to the original coordinates x^μ. The system $\bar{S}$, in which the particle is momentarily at rest, is known as the *proper system* of the particle at the event E. The proper system is determined by this definition to within an arbitrary spatial rotation or translation.

From Section 3.5 it is clear that the particle's time $\bar{t}$ or s proceeds at a different rate than the coordinate time t. The ratio in rates is given by

$$\frac{ds}{dt} = \sqrt{1 - \frac{v^2}{c^2}} \tag{3-34}$$

where $v^2 = v^k v^k$. The time s is termed the *proper time* of the particle. In many cases it is convenient to choose the parameter p to be the proper time s. This cannot be done, of course, for a photon, because $ds = 0$. Comparison of eqs. (3-33) and (3-34) shows that eq. (3-34) results from eq. (3-33) with the substitution of eq. (3-43) and that ds may be regarded as the proper time.

The *world-velocity* u^μ of the particle at the event E is given by the alternate forms

$$u^\mu = \frac{dx^\mu}{ds} = v^\mu \frac{dt}{ds} = v^\mu u^0$$

where $v^0 = 1$. It is immediately seen from eq. (3-33) that u^μ must always satisfy the condition

$$1 = \eta_{\mu\nu} u^\mu u^\nu. \tag{3-44}$$

From eq. (3-34),

$$u^0 = \frac{1}{\sqrt{1 - \dfrac{v^2}{c^2}}}.$$

(No effort will be made to distinguish between the y-component and the square of the magnitude such as $v^2 = dy/dt$ and $v^2 = (dx/dt)^2 + (dy/dt)^2 + (dz/dt)^2$, since the distinction will usually be evident from context.) It was noted in Section 3.9 that the displacement dx^μ is a contravariant vector. Consequently, the world-velocity u^μ, being the quotient of dx^μ by a scalar ds, is also a contravariant vector.

Consider a particle having a world-velocity $(u^0, u, 0, 0)$ in one inertial frame S and a world-velocity $(\bar{u}^0, \bar{u}, 0, 0)$ in another inertial frame $\bar{S}$ which has a velocity $(v, 0, 0)$ relative to S. Since u_μ is a contravariant vector, it transforms according to eqs. (3-30).

$$\left. \begin{aligned} \bar{u}^0 &= (u^0 - c^{-1} u \tanh \phi) \cosh \phi \\ \bar{u} &= (u - c u^0 \tanh \phi) \cosh \phi \end{aligned} \right\} \tag{3-45}$$

where

$$\phi = \tanh^{-1} \frac{v}{c}.$$

The substitutions

$$u^0 = \cosh \theta \qquad \bar{u}^0 = \cosh \bar{\theta}$$
$$u = c \sinh \theta \qquad \bar{u} = c \sinh \bar{\theta},$$

which are clearly consistent with eq. (3-44), put eqs. (3-45) into the form

$$\cosh \bar{\theta} = \cosh \theta \cosh \phi - \sinh \theta \sinh \phi$$
$$\sinh \bar{\theta} = \sinh \theta \cosh \phi - \cosh \theta \sinh \phi$$

which are obviously merely the hyperbolic identities for the relation $\bar{\theta} = \theta - \phi$. Thus the velocities add as their hyperbolic arc-tangents, since the quotients $u/u^0 = c \tanh \theta$ and $\bar{u}/\bar{u}^0 = c \tanh \bar{\theta}$ are the velocities in the respective inertial frames. We have then the relations

$$\tanh \bar{\theta} = \frac{\tanh \theta - \tanh \phi}{1 - \tanh \theta \tanh \phi}$$

and

$$\tanh \theta = \frac{\tanh \bar{\theta} + \tanh \phi}{1 + \tanh \bar{\theta} \tanh \phi}.$$

For example, a particle with speed $c \tanh \bar{\theta} = \frac{3}{4}c$ in an inertial frame $\bar{S}$ which is moving with speed $c \tanh \phi = \frac{3}{4}c$ relative to S has speed $c \tanh \theta = c[(\frac{3}{4} + \frac{3}{4}) \div (1 + \frac{3}{4} \cdot \frac{3}{4})] = \frac{24}{25}c$ relative to S. The addition of velocities which are less than the velocity of light always gives a sum which is less than the velocity of light.

3.11 THOMAS PRECESSION

The vector form of the Lorentz transformation, eqs. (3-5), (3-8), (3-9), and (3-10) may be written in index notation:

$$x^\mu = \Lambda^\mu_\alpha \bar{x}^\alpha, \qquad \bar{x}^\alpha = \check{\Lambda}^\alpha_\mu x^\mu$$

where

$$\begin{matrix} \Lambda^0_0 = u^0 & \Lambda^0_k = -u_k \\ \Lambda^k_0 = u^k & \Lambda^k_l = \delta^k_l - (1 + u^0)^{-1} u^k u_l \end{matrix} \right\} \tag{3-46}$$

and

$$\begin{matrix} \check{\Lambda}^0_0 = u^0 & \check{\Lambda}^0_k = u_k \\ \check{\Lambda}^k_0 = -u^k & \check{\Lambda}^k_l = \delta^k_l - (1 + u^0)^{-1} u^k u_l \end{matrix} \right\} \tag{3-47}$$

with

$$u^0 = \frac{1}{\sqrt{1 - \dfrac{v^2}{c^2}}}$$

$$u^k = u^0 v^k$$

$$u_k = -\frac{u^k}{c^2}.$$

The coordinates x^μ are measured in one inertial frame S, and the coordinates $\bar{x}^\alpha$ are measured in another inertial frame $\bar{S}$ which has a velocity v^k relative to S.

Suppose now that the u^μ and hence the transformation matrix Λ^μ_α are functions of a parameter τ. Then the equation $x^\mu = \Lambda^\mu_\alpha(\tau)\bar{x}^\alpha$ defines a family of Lorentz transformations in which there is *no rotation* between the S frame and the $\bar{S}$ frame, since eqs. (3-46) and (3-47) are merely the vector forms of eqs. (3-3) and (3-4) which involve parallel axes. The surprising result is that, in general, two members of the family are rotated with respect to each other.

Consider two frames $\bar{S}$ and $\bar{\bar{S}}$ corresponding to the values τ and $\tau + d\tau$ of the parameter, and having coordinates $\bar{x}^\alpha$ and $\bar{\bar{x}}^\alpha$. The transformation equations are then

$$x^\mu = \Lambda^\mu_\alpha(\tau)\bar{x}^\alpha$$

$$x^\mu = \Lambda^\mu_\alpha(\tau + d\tau)\bar{\bar{x}}^\alpha.$$

Equating the two equations and multiplying by the inverse matrix $\check{\Lambda}^\beta_\mu(\tau)$ gives the result

$$\bar{x}^\beta = \bar{\bar{x}}^\beta + \check{\Lambda}^\beta_\mu \, \delta\Lambda^\mu_\alpha \bar{\bar{x}}^\alpha \tag{3-48}$$

where

$$\delta\Lambda^\mu_\alpha = \frac{\partial \Lambda^\mu_\alpha}{\partial u^\gamma} \frac{du^\gamma}{d\tau} \, \delta\tau.$$

It is desired to find a frame $\hat{S}$ (with coordinates $\hat{x}^\mu$) which has the same velocity relative to $\bar{S}$ as does $\bar{\bar{S}}$ but which does not have any rotation relative to $\bar{S}$. The spatial difference between $\hat{S}$ and $\bar{\bar{S}}$ will then be a rotation. In order to find $\hat{S}$, it is necessary to know the velocity w^μ of $\bar{\bar{S}}$ relative to $\bar{S}$. The origin of $\bar{\bar{S}}$ is given by $\bar{\bar{x}}^\beta = \delta^\beta_0 \bar{\bar{x}}^0$. Substitution of the latter into eq. (3-48) yields

$$\bar{x}^\beta = \bar{\bar{x}}^0[\delta^\beta_0 + \check{\Lambda}^\beta_\mu \, \delta\Lambda^\mu_0]$$

which clearly represents a world-velocity

$$w^\mu = \delta^\mu_0 + \check{\Lambda}^\mu_\nu \, \delta\Lambda^\nu_0.$$

Direct evaluation of w^μ with the use of eqs. (3-46) and (3-47) gives

$$\left. \begin{array}{l} w^0 = 1 \\[2mm] w^i = \delta u^i - \dfrac{u^i \, \delta u^0}{1 + u^0} \end{array} \right\} \tag{3-49}$$

where

$$\delta u^\mu = \frac{du^\mu}{d\tau} \, \delta\tau.$$

With w^μ inserted in place of u^μ in eqs. (3-46) and (3-47), the result is the Lorentz transformation from $\bar{S}$ to $\hat{S}$ without rotation. The corresponding transformation matrices will be denoted $\overline{\Lambda}^\mu_\alpha$ and $\breve{\overline{\Lambda}}^\alpha_\mu$:

$$\bar{x}^\mu = \overline{\Lambda}^\mu_\alpha \hat{x}^\alpha. \tag{3-50}$$

The dependence on w^μ is given by

$$\overline{\Lambda}^0_0 = w^0 \qquad \overline{\Lambda}^0_k = -w_k$$

$$\overline{\Lambda}^k_0 = w^k \qquad \overline{\Lambda}^k_l = \delta^k_l - (1 + u^0)^{-1} w^k w_l.$$

Direct substitution of eq. (3-49) gives

$$\overline{\Lambda}^0_0 = \breve{\Lambda}^0_0 = 1$$

$$\overline{\Lambda}^k_0 = -\breve{\Lambda}^k_0 = \delta u^k - (1 + u^0)^{-1} u^k \, \delta u^0$$

$$\overline{\Lambda}^0_k = -\breve{\Lambda}^0_k = -\delta u_k + (1 + u^0)^{-1} u_k \, \delta u^0$$

$$\overline{\Lambda}^k_l = \breve{\Lambda}^k_l = \delta^k_l + O^2(\delta\tau)$$

The two frames $\overline{\overline{S}}$ and $\hat{S}$ can now be compared. The transformation is given by equating eqs. (3-48) and (3-50) and multiplying by $\breve{\Lambda}^\alpha_\beta$:

$$\hat{x}^\alpha = \breve{\Lambda}^\alpha_\beta (\delta^\beta_\gamma + \breve{\Lambda}^\beta_\epsilon \, \delta\Lambda^\epsilon_\gamma) \bar{\bar{x}}^\gamma$$

where

$$\delta\Lambda^\epsilon_\gamma = \frac{\partial\Lambda^\epsilon_\gamma}{\partial u^\nu} \, \delta u^\nu.$$

Direct evaluation gives

$$\hat{x}^0 = \bar{\bar{x}}^0$$

$$\hat{x}^i = \bar{\bar{x}}^i + \bar{\bar{x}}^j R^i_j$$

where

$$R^i_j = \frac{1}{1 + u^0} (u^i \, \delta u_j - u_j \, \delta u^i).$$

The time axes coincide, but the spatial axes differ by the rotation R^i_j.

Following the method of Section 1.5, the transformation matrix R^i_j, since it is antisymmetric, can be written

$$R^i_j = -e(ijk)\omega^k \, \delta\tau$$

with ω^k given by

$$\omega^k = -e(kij) \frac{u_i}{1 + u^0} \frac{du^j}{d\tau}. \tag{3-51}$$

The transformation is then given by

$$\hat{x}^i = \bar{\bar{x}}^i - e(ijk)\bar{\bar{x}}^j \omega^k \, \delta\tau,$$

in which form the rotational character is more apparent. (See eq. 1-22.)

The result of this effect is that an accelerated body rotates without any applied torques. To see this, let us regard the family of inertial frames $\bar{S}(\tau)$ to be the proper systems of a particle, and let τ be the proper time of the particle. Under the assumption that the particle passes from $\bar{S}$ to $\hat{S}$ without rotating, there is a rotation relative to S (the "stationary" observer), since $\overline{\overline{S}}$ was obtained without rotation from S. Therefore a body which does not rotate relative to itself rotates with angular velocity ω^k given by eq. (3-51) relative to an observer in an inertial frame. The quantity $du^i/d\tau$ is the body's proper acceleration a^i, i.e., dv^i/dt evaluated in the proper system. With $u_i = -c^{-2}u^i$, eq. (3-51) is now

$$\boldsymbol{\omega} = +\frac{\mathbf{u} \times \mathbf{a}}{c^2(1 + u^0)}$$

which, in the slow-velocity approximation, becomes

$$\boldsymbol{\omega} = +\frac{\mathbf{v} \times \mathbf{a}}{2c^2}. \tag{3-52}$$

Any body in torque-free, accelerated motion undergoes rotation at the rate given by eq. (3-52). This effect is known as the *Thomas precession*. An observer moving with the body would observe no centrifugal or Coriolis effects. Yet an external, unaccelerated observer would say that the body is rotating with angular velocity $\boldsymbol{\omega}$. For a satellite in orbit around the earth, skimming the earth's surface, ω is $2''8$ per year. For the earth revolving around the sun, ω is $0''64$ per century.

3.12 COMPOSITION OF THE LORENTZ TRANSFORMATION

It may not have been clear exactly what assumptions were used in the derivation of the Lorentz transformation which was given at the beginning of this chapter. Therefore, the Lorentz transformation will now be constructed with the use of as few assumptions as possible. The first step is to postulate the existence of two reference frames Σ and S.

POSTULATE 1. There exists a preferred reference frame Σ with origin Ω and stationary observer Π for which the following conditions hold: (a) time is measured by clocks, all of which are synchronized, (b) space is Euclidean, with distances measured by means of rods; and (c) light in free space has rectilinear propagation at a velocity c which is independent of the direction of propagation and the position or motion of the source.

POSTULATE 2. There exists another reference frame S with origin O and stationary observer P for which the following conditions hold: P is supplied with rods and clocks having the same physical constitution as those used by Π. The spatial geometry is found by measurements with the rods to be Euclidean. It is further postulated that the velocity of O relative to Σ is less than c. Note that *no* synchronization of the clocks in S is assumed.

The following notation will be used.

$\xi^0 = \tau$ temporal coordinate in Σ

$\xi^i = (\xi^1, \xi^2, \xi^3) = (\xi, \eta, \zeta)$ spatial Cartesian coordinates in Σ

$x^0 = t$ temporal coordinate in S

$x^a = (x^1, x^2, x^3) = (x, y, z)$ spatial Cartesian coordinates in S.

$d\sigma^2 = d\tau^2 - c^{-2}(d\xi^2 + d\eta^2 + d\zeta^2) = \eta_{\mu\nu}\, d\xi^\mu\, d\xi^\nu$ definition of σ

$$(3\text{-}53)$$

$v^i = \dfrac{d\xi^i}{d\tau}$ definition of velocity of world-line of O in Σ.   (3-54)

$v = \sqrt{v^k v^k}$

$\xi^\mu = (\xi^0, \xi^i)$

$x^\alpha = (x^0, x^i)$.

It is noted that Π can use $d\sigma$ for making measurements. At a fixed point, $\sqrt{d\sigma^2}$ measures time. At a fixed time $\tau = \text{const}$, $c\sqrt{-d\sigma^2}$ measures distance. And all light beams through an event E are characterized as generators of the cone $d\sigma = 0$ with E as the vertex.

The problem is to find the transformation T between the two sets of coordinates:

$$\xi^\mu = \xi^\mu(x^\alpha), \qquad x^\alpha = x^\alpha(\xi^\mu).$$

First we make the postulate:

POSTULATE 3. The transformation T involves v^i as the only essential parameter, and must reduce to the identity transformation for $v^i = 0$.

Next we confine our attention to events E in a space-time neighborhood about a given event E_0, and assume that the neighborhood is so small that the linear form of T is valid. E_0 is chosen as the common origin $x^\alpha = 0$ and $\xi^\mu = 0$.

ASSUMPTION. T has the linear form

$$\xi^\mu = a^\mu_\alpha x^\alpha, \qquad x^\alpha = \breve{a}^\alpha_\mu \xi^\mu, \qquad a^\mu_\alpha \breve{a}^\alpha_\nu = \delta^\mu_\nu. \tag{3-55}$$

The problem is to determine the 16 coefficients a^μ_α of eq. (3-55). The final result of the analysis which follows is that, by the use of definitions, constructions, and one further postulate, the number of undetermined parameters is reduced from 16 to 4, including v. Three experiments are then utilized to reduce the undetermined parameters to one, namely v.

The substitution of eq. (3-55) into eq. (3-54), remembering that the world-line of O in S is given by $x^\alpha = x^0 \delta^\alpha_0$, gives the result

$$v^i = \frac{a^i_0}{a^0_0}$$

or

$$a_0^i = v^i a_0^0. \tag{3-56}$$

The synchronization of clocks in S is defined as follows. A light beam leaves O at $t = 0$ as recorded by the master clock which is maintained there. The beam is reflected from a point $x^a = p^a$ at an event E and reaches O again at $t = t_0$. The stationary clock at $x^a = p^a$ is set to read $t = \frac{1}{2}t_0$ at the event E of reflection. This definition imposes conditions on the coefficients a_α^μ. These conditions are obtained from the property $d\sigma = 0$ for the light cone. The substitution of eq. (3-55) into eq. (3-53) gives

$$d\sigma^2 = g_{\alpha\beta} \, dx^\alpha \, dx^\beta$$

where

$$g_{\alpha\beta} = \eta_{\mu\nu} a_\alpha^\mu a_\beta^\nu. \tag{3-57}$$

The beam from O to E lies on the cone $0 = g_{\alpha\beta}x^\alpha x^\beta$ with $x^\alpha = (t, x^a)$, and the beam from E to O lies on the cone $0 = g_{\alpha\beta}x^\alpha x^\beta$ with $x^\alpha = (t_0 - t, x^a)$. The necessary and sufficient condition that $E(\frac{1}{2}t_0, p^a)$ lies on both cones is that the cross term $g_{0a}tp^a$ vanish. Since p^a is arbitrary, the condition which results is

$$g_{0a} = 0. \tag{3-58}$$

Equations (3-56) to (3-58) give

$$a_a^0 = \frac{v^k a_a^k}{c^2}. \tag{3-59}$$

The spatial coordinate axes in S and Σ are chosen as follows. The ξ-axis in Σ is chosen along the world-line of O. Then $v^2 = 0$ and $v^3 = 0$, which, by eq. (3-56), give

$$a_0^2 = 0, \qquad a_0^3 = 0 \tag{3-60}$$

and

$$a_0^1 = v a_0^0. \tag{3-61}$$

Also, from eq. (3-59) we have

$$a_a^0 = \frac{v a_a^1}{c^2}. \tag{3-62}$$

The x-axis in S is chosen along the world-line of Ω, which is given by $\xi^\mu = \delta_0^\mu = a_0^\mu t + a_1^\mu x$. By eqs. (3-60), therefore,

$$a_1^2 = 0, \qquad a_1^3 = 0. \tag{3-63}$$

The y-z plane in S is described parametrically in Σ by the equation

$$\xi^\mu = a_2^\mu y + a_3^\mu z. \tag{3-64}$$

The y-axis in S is chosen in such a direction that along it $\tau = 0$, i.e., $a_2^0 y + a_3^0 z = 0$ for $z = 0$ and arbitrary y. Therefore, with eq. (3-62),

$$a_2^0 = 0 \quad \text{and} \quad a_2^1 = 0. \tag{3-65}$$

The η-axis in Σ is chosen along the same direction. For zero z and arbitrary y, eq. (3-64) is to give $\xi^\mu = \xi^2 \delta_2^\mu$. Since we have $\xi^i = a_2^i y$, and a_2^1 already vanishes, the only new condition is

$$a_2^3 = 0. \tag{3-66}$$

Thus by an appropriate choice of axes, eqs. (3-60) to (3-63) and (3-65) and (3-66) are obtained. These results may be expressed in matrix form:

$$a_\alpha^\mu = \begin{bmatrix} a_0^0 & va_1^1 c^{-2} & 0 & va_3^1 c^{-2} \\ va_0^0 & a_1^1 & 0 & a_3^1 \\ 0 & 0 & a_2^2 & a_3^2 \\ 0 & 0 & 0 & a_3^3 \end{bmatrix}.$$

There remain six undetermined parameters besides v.

POSTULATE 4A. The only significant vector for the kinematical structure of space-time in the frame S is the world-line of Ω.

POSTULATE 4B. The one-way velocity of light in S is independent of its azimuth about the x-axis.

Either Postulate 4A or Postulate 4B leads to the results

$$a_3^1 = 0, \qquad a_3^2 = 0, \qquad a_3^3 = a_2^2$$

which are obtained as follows. The intersection of the two three-dimensional surfaces $t = 0$ and $\tau = 0$ is the two-dimensional plane R given in S by

$$0 = a_1^0 x + a_2^0 y + a_3^0 z.$$

But by eq. (3-62), this is the same as the equation

$$0 = a_1^1 x + a_2^1 y + a_3^1 z. \tag{3-67}$$

Thus the plane R is also the plane $t = 0$, $\xi = 0$, and also the plane $\tau = 0$, $\xi = 0$. We now have two planes in S: R given by eq. (3-67) and the plane $x = 0$. Their intersection is the line

$$0 = a_2^1 y + a_3^1 z$$

or, by eq. (3-65), $0 = a_3^1 z$. If $a_3^1 \neq 0$, then there exists a direction in S different from the x-axis, contrary to Postulate 4A. Therefore, $a_3^1 = 0$ and hence, by eq. (3-62), $a_3^0 = 0$. Equation (3-67) now becomes $0 = a_1^1 x$. Therefore, the plane R is also given by $t = 0$, $x = 0$. Thus R is both the y-z plane and the η-ζ plane. The transformation

$$\eta(y, z) = a_2^2 y + a_3^2 z$$
$$\zeta(y, z) = a_3^3 z$$

must be invariant under the replacements of y with z, z with $-y$, η with ζ, and ζ with $-\eta$. Therefore, $a_2^2 = a_3^3$ and $a_3^2 = 0$.

The same result is obtained from Postulate 4B. The condition

$$0 = d\sigma^2 = g_{\alpha\beta}\,dx^\alpha\,dx^\beta \tag{3-68}$$

must be satisfied for any light beam, where now

$$g_{00} = \left(1 - \frac{v^2}{c^2}\right)(a_0^0)^2$$

$$g_{0a} = 0$$

$$g_{11} = -c^{-2}\left(1 - \frac{v^2}{c^2}\right)(a_1^1)^2$$

$$g_{22} = -c^{-2}(a_2^2)^2$$

$$g_{33} = -c^{-2}\left[\left(1 - \frac{v^2}{c^2}\right)(a_3^1)^2 + (a_3^2)^2 + (a_3^3)^2\right]$$

$$g_{12} = 0$$

$$g_{13} = -c^{-2}\left(1 - \frac{v^2}{c^2}\right)a_1^1 a_3^1$$

$$g_{23} = -c^{-2}a_2^2 a_3^2.$$

In order that light have a velocity which is independent of azimuth about the x-axis in S, it is necessary that dy and dz enter eq. (3-68) only in the combination $dy^2 + dz^2$. Therefore we obtain $g_{13} = 0$, $g_{23} = 0$, and $g_{22} = g_{33}$, which give the results $a_3^1 = 0$, $a_3^2 = 0$, and $a_2^2 = a_3^3$.

To summarize the results thus far, the transformation matrix a_α^μ has been reduced to the form

$$a_\alpha^\mu = \begin{bmatrix} a_0^0 & va_1^1c^{-2} & 0 & 0 \\ va_0^0 & a_1^1 & 0 & 0 \\ 0 & 0 & a_2^2 & 0 \\ 0 & 0 & 0 & a_2^2 \end{bmatrix}$$

which involves the three parameters a_0^0, a_1^1, and a_2^2 and the velocity v. The metric

$$d\sigma^2 = g_{\alpha\beta}\,dx^\alpha\,dx^\beta$$

is given by

$$\left.\begin{array}{l} g_{00} = (1 - v^2/c^2)(a_0^0)^2 \\ g_{11} = -c^{-2}(1 - v^2/c^2)(a_1^1)^2 \\ g_{22} = g_{33} = -c^{-2}(a_2^2)^2 \\ g_{\alpha\beta} = 0, \qquad \alpha \neq \beta. \end{array}\right\} \tag{3-69}$$

The first experiment for consideration is the Michelson-Morley experiment (Section 2.10). The null result of the experiment is here interpreted to mean that *the total time required for light in free space to traverse a distance l and return is independent of its direction*. The definition of the synchronization of clocks in S ensures that the forward and backward velocities of light in any direction are equal. Therefore it is sufficient to require that the one-way travel time for a light beam be independent of direction in S. The time t for light to traverse a distance l which makes an angle θ with the x-axis is given by eqs. (3-68) and (3-69):

$$t = \frac{l}{cg_0} \sqrt{g_1^2 \cos^2 \theta + g_2^2 \sin^2 \theta}$$

where

$$g_0 = \sqrt{g_{00}}$$
$$g_1 = c\sqrt{-g_{11}}$$
$$g_2 = c\sqrt{-g_{22}}.$$

In order that t be independent of θ it is necessary to have

$$g_1 = g_2. \tag{3-70}$$

The condition which eq. (3-70) imposes on the a_α^μ is

$$a_1^1 = \frac{a_2^2}{\sqrt{1 - \dfrac{v^2}{c^2}}}.$$

The Fitzgerald contraction is a consequence of the transformation in its present form. Consider two rods at rest in S, one of length l along the x-axis and one of length l along the y-axis. The ends of the rods are joined at O. The three world-lines of the ends of the rods are given in Σ by

$$\begin{pmatrix} \xi - v\tau = 0 \\ \eta = 0 \\ \zeta = 0 \end{pmatrix} \begin{pmatrix} \breve{a}_1^1(\xi - vt) = l \\ \eta = 0 \\ \zeta = 0 \end{pmatrix} \begin{pmatrix} \xi - v\tau = 0 \\ \breve{a}_2^2\eta = l \\ \zeta = 0 \end{pmatrix},$$

where $\breve{a}_\mu^\alpha$ is the inverse of a_α^μ. At $\tau = 0$ these three world-lines fall at the three points $\xi^i = (0, 0, 0)$, $\left(\dfrac{l}{\breve{a}_1^1}, 0, 0\right)$, and $\left(0, \dfrac{l}{\breve{a}_2^2}, 0\right)$. Since

$$\breve{a}_1^1 = \frac{1}{a_2^2\sqrt{1 - \dfrac{v^2}{c^2}}},$$

the lengths of the rods on the x- and y-axes as measured by Π are in the ratio

$$\frac{\xi}{\eta} = \sqrt{1 - \frac{v^2}{c^2}}.$$

The time for light to travel a distance l is now

$$t = \frac{l}{c} \frac{a_1^1}{a_0^0}.$$ (3-71)

3.13 THE KENNEDY-THORNDIKE EXPERIMENT

The next question to ask is whether the velocity of light in the system S depends on the velocity v of S relative to Σ. Kennedy[B] and Thorndike performed an experiment which gives the answer. They assumed the existence of the preferred frame Σ, but they also assumed the existence of the Fitzgerald contraction as stated in Section 2.11. This is more specific than the assumptions of Section 3.12, since it implies $\breve{a}_2^2 = 1$ and hence $a_2^2 = 1$.

The theory for the Kennedy-Thorndike experiment is as follows. A hollow rod of length L fixed in S has coordinate components $L_x = L \cos \theta$ and $L_y = L \sin \theta$, where θ is the angle between the rod and the x-axis. According to the Fitzgerald contraction, the rod in Σ has components $L_\xi = L \cos \theta \sqrt{1 - v^2/c^2}$ and $L_\eta = L \sin \theta$. Thus in Σ the total distance covered by a light ray traveling down the rod from one end to the other is

$$c\tau = \sqrt{(L \sin \theta)^2 + \left(L \cos \theta \sqrt{1 - \frac{v^2}{c^2}} \pm v\tau\right)^2}$$

where τ is the time for the traversal. Hence

$$\tau = \frac{cL \pm vL \cos \theta}{c^2 \sqrt{1 - \frac{v^2}{c^2}}}.$$ (3-72)

Note that τ is the time in Σ, but L is the length in S.

In the experiment, a beam of light in S was split at one point A and reunited at another point B, with the separated beams traversing different routes (Fig. 3.9). The difference in travel time for the two routes as

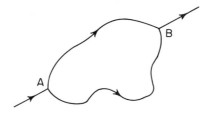

FIGURE 3.9 The Kennedy-Thorndike experiment.

measured in Σ is found by direct integration of eq. (3-72) to be

$$\Delta\tau = \frac{\Delta l}{c\sqrt{1 - \frac{v^2}{c^2}}}$$

where Δl is the difference in length between the two paths measured in S. The number of waves represented by this time interval is

$$n = \frac{\nu_\Sigma \Delta l}{c\sqrt{1 - \frac{v^2}{c^2}}}$$

where ν_Σ is the frequency of the light in the frame Σ. With allowance for the possibility that the frequency ν_S in S may depend both on ν_Σ and on v^2, we have for small v,

$$\nu_\Sigma = \nu_s\left[1 + \alpha\frac{v^2}{c^2} + O^4\left(\frac{v}{c}\right)\right]$$

where α is a coefficient yet to be determined. Thus we have the result

$$n = \frac{\nu_S \Delta l}{c}\left[1 + (\alpha + \tfrac{1}{2})\frac{v^2}{c^2} + O^4\left(\frac{v^2}{c^2}\right)\right].$$

The observations consisted of attempts to measure a variable fringe shift in the reunited beam due to variations in v as the apparatus was carried by the earth around the earth's axis, around the sun, and through the galaxy. The variable part of n is given approximately by

$$\delta n = \frac{\nu_s \Delta l}{c}(2\alpha + 1)\frac{v}{c}\delta\left(\frac{v}{c}\right)$$

where $\delta\left(\frac{v}{c}\right)$ is the variation in the velocity of the apparatus due to the earth's rotation and revolution. Using the known values for the latter, the observed variation in fringe shift gave the result

$$(2\alpha + 1)v = 10 \pm 10 \text{ km/sec}.$$

Since velocities of the order of hundreds of km/sec are to be expected (the sun revolves around the galaxy at 200 km/sec), this result is taken to indicate $\alpha = -\tfrac{1}{2}$, and therefore, to the accuracy of the experiment,

$$\nu_\Sigma = \nu_S\sqrt{1 - \frac{v^2}{c^2}}.$$

In our construction of the Lorentz transformation, we must place a different interpretation on the experimental result, because we have not made the assumption of the Fitzgerald contraction. We have, in fact, assumed no relation between lengths in S and lengths in Σ. The null result of the Kennedy-Thorndike experiment is taken to mean that *the total time required for light to traverse a closed path in S is independent of the velocity v of S relative to* Σ. This in turn implies that the velocity of light in S, already known from eq. (3-71) to be the constant $c a_0^0 / a_1^1$ which can at most depend on v, must be independent of v. But, according to Postulate 3, $a_0^0 / a_1^1 = 1$ when $v = 0$. Hence $a_0^0 = a_1^1$.

The transformation in its present form implies that the velocity of Σ relative to S is $(-v, 0, 0)$, because the world-line of Ω is given by $0 = \xi = a_0^1 t + a_1^1 x = a_0^0 (vt + x)$.

In summary, the transformation is given by

$$a_\alpha^\mu = g^2(v) \begin{bmatrix} \gamma & v\gamma c^{-2} & 0 & 0 \\ v\gamma & \gamma & 0 & 0 \\ 0 & 0 & 1 & 0 \\ 0 & 0 & 0 & 1 \end{bmatrix}$$

where

$$\gamma = \frac{1}{\sqrt{1 - \dfrac{v^2}{c^2}}},$$

and the metric is given by

$$ds^2 = \frac{d\sigma^2}{g^2(v)} = dt^2 - \frac{1}{c^2}(dx^2 + dy^2 + dz^2)$$

where $g(v) = a_2^2$.

3.14 THE IVES-STILWELL EXPERIMENT

In contrast with the Michelson-Morley and Kennedy-Thorndike experiments, the experiment performed by Ives[B] and Stilwell was designed to look for a *positive* result—the time dilation. The purpose of the experiment was to measure the wavelength of the line $\lambda_0 = 4861$ Å from hydrogen ions moving in a beam with a velocity of order $5 \times 10^{-3}c$. By the use of mirrors, the radiation in both the forward and backward directions of the beam could be recorded simultaneously to give two spectral lines of wavelengths λ_1 and λ_2 ($\lambda_2 > \lambda_1$). The Doppler effect produces the separation $\lambda_2 - \lambda_1$, but any shift $\Delta\lambda = \frac{1}{2}(\lambda_1 + \lambda_2) - \lambda_0$ in the center of the lines must be due to the time dilation. The measured values of $\Delta\lambda$, which ranged up to 11×10^{-12} meter with an accuracy 0.3×10^{-12} meter, were found to agree with the special theory of relativity.

In order to obtain a theoretical expression for $\Delta\lambda$, we postulate, in addition to the reference frames Σ and S of Section 3.12, a third reference frame S'. The frame S corresponds to the laboratory and the frame S' corresponds to the atom. The x-axis in S has already been chosen to be in the direction of motion of Σ relative to S, but the y- and z-axes are to some degree arbitrary. We therefore choose the y- and z-axes in S in such a way that the velocity u of S' relative to S lies in the x-y plane. If ϕ is the angle between u and the x-axis, the world-line of the atom in S is given by

$$t = pt'$$
$$x = put' \cos \phi$$
$$y = put' \sin \phi$$
$$z = 0$$

where t' is the atom's time and p is yet to be determined. Three transformations are necessary to go from S to S': first, a Lorentz transformation from S to Σ; second, a rotation in Σ; and third, a Lorentz transformation from Σ to S'. The spatial rotation is necessary if the direction of the atom relative to Σ is different from the direction of the laboratory relative to Σ. The use of the Lorentz transformation of the previous section shows that p is given by

$$p = \frac{g(v')}{g(v)} \frac{1}{\sqrt{1 - \dfrac{u^2}{c^2}}}$$

where v and v' are, respectively, the velocities of S and S' relative to Σ. A light signal which leaves the atom at time t' then reaches the origin of S at a time

$$t = pt' + p\frac{u}{c}|t'|.$$

The wavelength in S is therefore given by

$$\lambda = p\lambda_0\left(1 \pm \frac{u}{c}\right)$$

where λ_0 is the wavelength relative to the atom, and the $\pm$ sign refers to light which goes backward or forward from the atom.

Thus we obtain the expressions

$$\lambda_2 = p\lambda_0\left(1 + \frac{u}{c}\right)$$

$$\lambda_1 = p\lambda_0\left(1 - \frac{u}{c}\right)$$

which give a theoretical result

$$\Delta\lambda = \lambda_0(p - 1).$$

In the experiment, $\Delta\lambda/\lambda_0$ was found to be equal to $\frac{1}{2}u^2/c^2$ to an accuracy of several per cent; the u/c was determined from the Doppler effect. This result in turn implies that the ratio $g(v')/g(v)$ is unity up to terms of order

u^2/c^2. If the function $g(v)$ is expanded in powers of $(v/c)^2$:

$$g(v) = 1 + \beta \left(\frac{v}{c}\right)^2 + \cdots ,$$

the ratio $g(v')/g(v)$ is given by

$$\frac{g(v')}{g(v)} = 1 + \beta \frac{v'^2 - v^2}{c^2} + O^4.$$

The velocity v' is given in terms of v, u, and ϕ by the relation

$$1 - \frac{v'^2}{c^2} = \frac{\left(1 - \dfrac{u^2}{c^2}\right)\left(1 - \dfrac{v^2}{c^2}\right)}{\left(1 + \dfrac{uv}{c^2} \cos \phi\right)^2} .$$

Since no correlation is to be expected between $u \cos \phi$ and v, the difference $v'^2 - v^2$ must be of order u^2. Therefore $\beta = 0$, and we may conclude that $g(v)$ is itself equal to unity up to terms of order v^2/c^2. Although it is possible that higher-order terms enter the function $g(v)$, we follow Ives and Stilwell in interpreting their results to mean that *the frequency of a moving atomic source is altered by the factor $\sqrt{1 - u^2/c^2}$, where u is the velocity of the source with respect to the observer.* Then $g(v)$ is taken rigorously as unity, and the Lorentz transformation of Section 3.1 is deduced.

This completes the derivation of the Lorentz transformation based on three experimental results and a minimum of postulates. The essential features of the postulates may be summarized as follows.

1. There exists a reference frame in which light has constant, isotropic velocity.

2. There exists a second reference frame in which measurements are made with rods and clocks of the same physical constitution as those used in the first reference frame.

3. The transformation is linear, depends only on the velocity v, and reduces to the identity transformation for $v = 0$.

4. There is no preferred direction in space.

3.15 OPTICAL PHENOMENA

A plane electromagnetic wave with frequency ν has electric and magnetic fields given by

$$\mathbf{E} = \mathbf{E}_0 \cos 2\pi\nu \left(t - \frac{1}{c} \mathbf{n} \cdot \mathbf{x}\right)$$

$$\mathbf{B} = \mathbf{B}_0 \cos 2\pi\nu \left(t - \frac{1}{c} \mathbf{n} \cdot \mathbf{x}\right).$$

The transformation rules for **E** and **B** will be studied in Chapter 4, but we will use here the result that the transformations are *linear* in **E** and **B**. Hence in all coordinate systems there is the same phase factor

$$\cos 2\pi\nu l_\mu x^\mu \tag{3-73}$$

where

$$l^\mu = (1, cn^i)$$

$$l_\mu = (1, -c^{-1}n^i)$$

and n^i is a unit spatial vector ($n^k n^k = 1$) in the direction of propagation. The requirement that (3-73) be a scalar and the fact that x^μ is a contra-variant vector imply that νl_μ is a covariant vector λ_μ:

$$\lambda_\mu = \nu l_\mu.$$

The contravariant form is given by

$$\lambda^\mu = \nu l^\mu. \tag{3-74}$$

The expression l^μ is not a vector, and the frequency ν is not a scalar, because l^0 is required to be unity in any coordinate system. However, we see immediately how to transform the frequency from one system to another—*the frequency transforms as the temporal component of a vector* λ^μ. The spatial part of λ^μ is νcn^i, where n^i is the unit vector in the direction of propagation of the wave. Thus νn^i *transforms as the spatial part of a vector*. Consequently the single principle that λ^μ is a vector allows us to derive the Doppler effect, the aberration of starlight, and the time dilation.

Consider a light ray represented by the vector $\lambda^\mu = \nu(1, cn^i)$ and $\bar{\lambda}^\mu = \bar{\nu}(1, c\bar{n}^i)$, respectively, in the reference frames S and $\bar{S}$ of Section 3.1. The z- and $\bar{z}$-axes are chosen perpendicular to the direction of the ray. We then have the spatial unit vectors

$$n^i = (c \cos \theta, c \sin \theta, 0)$$

$$\bar{n}^i = (c \cos \bar{\theta}, c \sin \bar{\theta}, 0)$$

where θ and $\bar{\theta}$ are, respectively, the angles between **n** and the x-axis in S and between **ñ** and the $\bar{x}$-axis in $\bar{S}$. The transformation of eqs. (3-3) applied to λ^μ gives

$$\bar{\lambda}^\mu = \bar{\nu}(1, c \cos \bar{\theta}, c \sin \bar{\theta}, 0) = \nu\left[\gamma\left(1 - \frac{v}{c} \cos \theta\right), \gamma(c \cos \theta - v),\right.$$
$$\left. c \sin \theta, 0\right].$$

Hence $\bar{\nu}$ and $\bar{\theta}$ are related to ν, θ, and v by the equations

$$\bar{\nu} = \nu\gamma\left(1 - \frac{v}{c}\cos\theta\right) = \frac{1 - \frac{v}{c}\cos\theta}{\sqrt{1 - \frac{v^2}{c^2}}} \tag{3-75}$$

$$\tan\bar{\theta} = \frac{\sin\theta}{\gamma\left(\cos\theta - \frac{v}{c}\right)} = \frac{\sin\theta\sqrt{1 - \frac{v^2}{c^2}}}{\cos\theta - \frac{v}{c}}. \tag{3-76}$$

Equations (3-75) and (3-76), which are relativistically correct, may be compared with eqs. (2-31) and (2-29) which were based on the ether theory. The Doppler effect is represented by eq. (3-75), and the aberration of starlight is represented by eq. (3-76). We may note that eq. (3-75) contains the time dilation, because when $\theta = \frac{\pi}{2}$ we have $\nu = \bar{\nu}/\gamma$. However, the correction to the ether theory is of second order in v/c and hence is extremely small for normal velocities. The Doppler effect in the Ives-Stilwell experiment corresponds to eq. (3-75) with $\bar{\nu} = c/\lambda_0$, $\nu = c/\lambda$, and $\theta = 0$ or π.

Note that in *all* reference frames in special relativity, the ray direction of a light ray is *perpendicular* to the wave fronts of the ray. This was not true in the older theory based on the Galilean transformation.

Consider the case of a light beam of frequency ν which is reflected by a moving mirror. The mirror is perpendicular to the x-axis and is moving in the positive x-direction with a uniform velocity v. The ray has a direction which is perpendicular to the z-axis and makes an angle θ with the x-axis (Fig. 3.10). The problem is to find the frequency and direction of the reflected ray.

The incident ray has the propagation vector

$$\lambda^\mu_{\text{inc}} = \nu(1, c\cos\theta, c\sin\theta, 0).$$

Upon transforming to the mirror's system $\bar{x}^\mu$, the propagation vector becomes

$$\bar{\lambda}^\mu_{\text{inc}} = \nu\left[\gamma\left(1 - \frac{v}{c}\cos\theta\right), \gamma(c\cos\theta - v), c\sin\theta, 0\right].$$

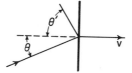

FIGURE 3.10 Reflection of light from moving mirror.

Original frame   Mirror's frame

Upon reflection, only the x-component is reversed:

$$\bar{\lambda}^{\mu}_{\text{refl}} = v\left[\gamma\left(1 - \frac{v}{c}\cos\theta\right), \gamma(v - c\cos\theta), c\sin\theta, 0\right].$$

The Lorentz transformation back to the original frame finally gives

$$\lambda^{\mu}_{\text{refl}} = v\left[\gamma^2\left(1 - 2\frac{v}{c}\cos\theta + \frac{v^2}{c^2}\right), -\gamma^2 c\left(\cos\theta - 2\frac{v}{c} + \frac{v^2}{c^2}\cos\theta\right),\right.$$
$$\left. c\sin\theta, 0\right].$$

Thus the reflected ray has a direction angle θ' to the x-axis given by

$$\tan\theta' = \frac{\sin\theta\left(1 - \frac{v^2}{c^2}\right)}{\cos\theta\left(1 + \frac{v^2}{c^2}\right) - 2\frac{v}{c}}, \quad \text{or} \quad \tan\frac{\theta'}{2} = \frac{1 - \frac{v}{c}}{1 + \frac{v}{c}}\tan\frac{\theta}{2}$$

and the reflected frequency v' is given by

$$v' = v\frac{1 - 2\frac{v}{c}\cos\theta + \frac{v^2}{c^2}}{1 - \frac{v^2}{c^2}}.$$

A ray which strikes the mirror normally ($\theta = 0$) is reflected normally ($\theta' = 0$) with frequency

$$v' = v\frac{1 - \frac{v}{c}}{1 + \frac{v}{c}}.$$

A ray which is incident parallel to the mirror $\left(\theta = \frac{\pi}{2}\right)$ strikes the mirror if $v < 0$ and is reflected at an angle

$$\theta' = \tan^{-1}\left[-\frac{2c}{v}\left(1 - \frac{v^2}{c^2}\right)\right]$$

with frequency

$$v' = \frac{1 + \frac{v^2}{c^2}}{1 - \frac{v^2}{c^2}}.$$

If a ray strikes the $+x$ side of the mirror, a reflection for $\theta = \frac{\pi}{2}$, $v > 0$ is possible.

We are now in a position to interpret the results of the ether-drift experiments of Section 2.7 in terms of the special theory of relativity. Hoek's experiment should obviously yield a null result because there is no motion of the rod relative to the laboratory. In Airy's observation the water in the telescope tube did not move relative to the observer and the telescope. Therefore, in the reference frame of the observer, the direction of the incoming light could not have been changed except by refraction arising from non-parallel surfaces. And that was excluded by the construction of the experiment.

The explanation of Fizeau's experiment requires more care. The light within the water has a velocity c/n relative to the water. If the water is moving with velocity v relative to the observer, then the rules for addition of velocities in Section 3.10 show that the velocities of the rays parallel and opposite to the direction of the water are

$$\frac{v \pm \dfrac{c}{n}}{1 \pm \dfrac{vc}{nc^2}}$$

or

$$\pm \frac{c}{n} \frac{1 \pm \dfrac{nv}{c}}{1 \pm \dfrac{v}{nc}}.$$

For $v \ll c$ these velocities are

$$\pm \frac{c}{n} + v\left(1 - \frac{1}{n^2}\right) + cO^2\left(\frac{v}{c}\right)$$

which, upon neglecting the second order term, is exactly what was obtained in the ether theory, provided an ether drag coefficient of $1 - n^{-2}$ is used. This shows why it was impossible to distinguish the ether theory from the special theory of relativity by means of experiments which measured only effects of first order in $\frac{v}{c}$. It was the execution of a second-order experiment—the Michelson-Morley experiment—which first showed a flaw in the ether theory.

CHAPTER 4

ELECTRO-MAGNETISM IN SPECIAL RELATIVITY

4.1 CURRENT DENSITY

The spatial 3-vector current density J^i and the charge density ρ combine to form the 4-vector current density $J^\mu = (\rho, J^1, J^2, J^3)$. The vector nature of J^μ is proved with the use of three postulates: (1) if $J^\mu = 0$ holds in one system, then it holds in all systems; (2) if $\partial J^\mu / \partial x^\mu = 0$ holds in one system, then it holds in all systems; and (3) the principle of relativity holds. The second postulate is an expression of the law of conservation of charge eq. (2-5).

The vector nature of J^μ is proved as follows. Consider two coordinate systems x^α and $\bar{x}^\mu$ and the corresponding current densities J^α and $\bar{J}^\mu$, respectively. As was noted earlier, the transformation matrices

$$a^\mu_\alpha = \frac{\partial \bar{x}^\mu}{\partial x^\alpha}, \qquad \breve{a}^\alpha_\mu = \frac{\partial x^\alpha}{\partial \bar{x}^\mu}$$

have constant components. The current density $\bar{J}^\mu$ must be a function of J^α and $\breve{a}^\beta_\nu$:

$$\bar{J}^\mu = f^\mu(J^\alpha; \breve{a}^\beta_\nu).$$

Differentiation with respect to $\bar{x}^\mu$ and summation over the index μ yields

$$\frac{\partial \bar{J}^\mu}{\partial \bar{x}^\mu} = \frac{\partial f^\mu}{\partial J^\alpha} \breve{a}^\beta_\mu \frac{\partial J^\alpha}{\partial x^\beta}.$$

Postulate 2 requires the relation

$$\frac{\partial f^\mu}{\partial J^\alpha} \breve{a}^\beta_\mu = F\delta^\beta_\alpha,$$

where $F(J^\mu; \breve{a}^\beta_\nu)$ is a multiplier. Multiplication by a^ν_β gives

$$\frac{\partial f^\nu}{\partial J^\alpha} = Fa^\nu_\alpha. \qquad (4\text{-}1)$$

The function F is found to be constant in the following way. Equation (4-1) is differentiated with respect to J^β and the integrability condition

$$\frac{\partial^2 f^\nu}{\partial J^\beta\,\partial J^\alpha} = \frac{\partial^2 f^\nu}{\partial J^\alpha\,\partial J^\beta}$$

is applied to give

$$a^\nu_\alpha \frac{\partial F}{\partial J^\beta} = a^\nu_\beta \frac{\partial F}{\partial J^\alpha}.$$

Multiplication by $\breve{a}^\alpha_\nu$ gives the result

$$(n - 1)\frac{\partial F}{\partial J^\beta} = 0.$$

Since $n > 1$, it is concluded that F can at most depend only on the a^μ_α. Equation (4-1) can therefore be integrated to give

$$f^\mu = Fa^\mu_\alpha J^\alpha + G^\mu(a^\nu_\beta).$$

Postulate 1 requires $G^\mu = 0$. Thus we obtain the result

$$\bar{J}^\mu = Fa^\mu_\alpha J^\alpha. \qquad (4\text{-}2)$$

There immediately follows the relation

$$\eta_{\mu\nu}\bar{J}^\mu\bar{J}^\nu = F^2\eta_{\alpha\beta}J^\alpha J^\beta.$$

Postulate 3 requires $F^2 = 1$. But $F = 1$ for the identity transformation; therefore F is always unity. Thus eq. (4-2) becomes

$$\bar{J}^\mu = a^\mu_\alpha J^\alpha$$

which, by eq. (3-36), defines a contravariant vector. The current density J^μ is a contravariant four-dimensional vector.

Consider the special case that the currents are due solely to charges which move locally in unison with world-velocity u^μ. At an event $E(x^\mu)$ there exists a Lorentz transformation with velocity

$$v^i = \frac{u^i(E)}{u^0(E)}$$

which relates the coordinates x^μ to the proper frame $\bar{x}^\alpha$ of the fluid at E. Due to the Fitzgerald contraction, the fluid which occupies an element of volume dV in the system x^μ occupies a volume

$$dV_\pi = \gamma \, dV$$

in the proper system $\bar{x}^\alpha$, where

$$\gamma = \frac{1}{\sqrt{1 - \dfrac{v^2}{c^2}}} = u^0(E).$$

From the Lorentz transformation and the requirement that the spatial components of the current density vanish in the proper system, we obtain the relation

$$J^0 = \gamma \bar{J}^0,$$

or

$$\rho = \bar{\rho} u^0.$$

Multiplication by dV shows that the total charge

$$dq = \rho \, dV = \bar{\rho} \, dV_\pi$$

contained in the volume dV is a scalar, independent of the coordinate system. The current density J^μ is given by

$$J^\mu = J^0 u^\mu = J^0 v^\mu \tag{4-3}$$

where $v^0 = 1$.

Not all currents are of the type considered above. An electric power line, for example, has no charge density but carries a current. However, in any case, the charge density is J^0 and the spatial current density is J^i. For example, in a case where $\eta_{\mu\nu} J^\mu J^\nu < 0$, it is always possible to find a reference frame in which $J^0 = 0$.

4.2 THE FIELD EQUATIONS

The classical theory of electromagnetism as applied to empty space may be carried over with perfect validity to all inertial frames in special relativity, because of the principle of relativity. It is impossible to determine a preferred reference frame by any experiment, and this includes electromagnetic experiments. Thus eqs. (2-2), (2-3), (2-6), (2-7), (2-10), and (2-11) remain as before, provided $\mu = \mu_0$ and $\epsilon = \epsilon_0$.

The 4-vector electromagnetic potential ϕ^μ is defined

$$\left. \begin{aligned} \phi^\mu &= \left(\frac{\phi}{c^2}, A_x, A_y, A_z \right) \\[2mm] \phi_\mu &= \left(\frac{\phi}{c^2}, -\frac{A_x}{c^2}, -\frac{A_y}{c^2}, -\frac{A_z}{c^2} \right). \end{aligned} \right\} \tag{4-4}$$

It immediately follows from eqs. (2-11) that ϕ^μ and J^μ have the relation

$$\Box^2\phi^\mu = \frac{1}{\epsilon_0}J^\mu. \tag{4-5}$$

Equation (2-10) becomes

$$\frac{\partial\phi^\mu}{\partial x^\mu} = 0. \tag{4-6}$$

The vector nature of ϕ^μ is proved with the use of eq. (4-5) in the following way. In another coordinate system $\bar{x}^\mu$, the invariance of $\Box^2$ gives eq. (4-5) the form

$$\Box^2\bar{\phi}^\nu = \frac{1}{\epsilon_0}\bar{J}^\nu. \tag{4-7}$$

Equation (4-5) is multiplied by

$$a^\nu_\mu = \frac{\partial\bar{x}^\nu}{\partial x^\mu} \tag{4-8}$$

and subtracted from eq. (4-7) to give, using the vector nature of J^μ,

$$\Box^2(\bar{\phi}^\nu - a^\nu_\mu\phi^\mu) = 0.$$

The above equation has the solution $\bar{\phi}^\nu - a^\nu_\mu\phi^\mu = 0$; hence, ϕ^μ is a vector. The field tensor $F_{\mu\nu}$ defined

$$F_{\mu\nu} = \frac{\partial\phi_\mu}{\partial x^\nu} - \frac{\partial\phi_\nu}{\partial x^\mu}$$

is a tensor, since it is formed from the gradient of a vector. Substitution of eq. (4-4) shows that the components of $F_{\mu\nu}$ are merely the field intensities

$$\left.\begin{array}{l}F_{0i} = -c^{-2}E_i \\ F_{ij} = c^{-2}e(ijk)B_k.\end{array}\right\} \tag{4-9}$$

The components of the field tensor are therefore given by the expressions

$$F_{\mu\nu} = \frac{1}{c^2}\begin{bmatrix} 0 & -E_x & -E_y & -E_z \\ E_x & 0 & B_z & -B_y \\ E_y & -B_z & 0 & B_x \\ E_z & B_y & -B_x & 0 \end{bmatrix} = \frac{\mu_0}{c^2}\begin{bmatrix} 0 & -c^2D_x & -c^2D_y & -c^2D_z \\ c^2D_x & 0 & H_z & -H_y \\ c^2D_y & -H_z & 0 & H_x \\ c^2D_z & H_y & -H_x & 0 \end{bmatrix}$$

$$F^{\mu\nu} = \begin{bmatrix} 0 & E_x & E_y & E_z \\ -E_x & 0 & c^2B_z & -c^2B_y \\ -E_y & -c^2B_z & 0 & c^2B_x \\ -E_z & c^2B_y & -c^2B_x & 0 \end{bmatrix} = \mu_0c^2\begin{bmatrix} 0 & D_x & D_y & D_z \\ -D_x & 0 & H_z & -H_y \\ -D_y & -H_z & 0 & H_x \\ -D_z & H_y & -H_x & 0 \end{bmatrix}.$$

Thus E_i and B_i are actually components of a four-dimensional tensor, and they transform accordingly from one coordinate system to another. Under the Lorentz transformation

$$t = \gamma(\bar{t} + vc^{-2}\bar{x})$$
$$x = \gamma(\bar{x} + v\bar{t})$$
$$y = \bar{y}$$
$$z = \bar{z}$$

the field intensities transform according to the relations

$$
\left.
\begin{aligned}
\bar{E}_x &= E_x & \bar{B}_x &= B_x \\
\bar{E}_y &= \gamma(E_y - vB_z) & \bar{B}_y &= \gamma(B_y + vc^{-2}E_z) \\
\bar{E}_z &= \gamma(E_z + vB_y) & \bar{B}_z &= \gamma(B_z - vc^{-2}E_y) \\
\bar{D}_x &= D_x & \bar{H}_x &= H_x \\
\bar{D}_y &= \gamma(D_y - vc^{-2}H_z) & \bar{H}_y &= \gamma(H_y + vD_z) \\
\bar{D}_z &= \gamma(D_z + vc^{-2}H_y) & \bar{H}_z &= \gamma(H_z - vD_y).
\end{aligned}
\right\}
\tag{4-10}
$$

Equation (4-6) allows eq. (4-5) to be written in the form

$$\eta^{\alpha\beta} \frac{\partial F_{\mu\alpha}}{\partial x^\beta} = \frac{1}{\epsilon_0} J_\mu. \tag{4-11}$$

The vector potential ϕ^μ is a convenience, not a necessity, in deriving eq. (4-11); the latter can be obtained directly from Maxwell's equations. However, only two equations (2-2) are expressed by eq. (4-11). The remaining two equations (2-3) may be written in the form

$$\frac{\partial F_{\beta\gamma}}{\partial x^\alpha} + \frac{\partial F_{\gamma\alpha}}{\partial x^\beta} + \frac{\partial F_{\alpha\beta}}{\partial x^\gamma} = 0,$$

or, with the use of the permutation symbol,

$$e^{\alpha\beta\gamma\delta} \frac{\partial F_{\beta\gamma}}{\partial x^\alpha} = 0. \tag{4-12}$$

Note that the *dual* of $F_{\mu\nu}$, defined

$$F^{\star\mu\nu} = \tfrac{1}{2}c^3 e^{\mu\nu\alpha\beta} F_{\alpha\beta},$$

gives eq. (4-12) the simpler form

$$\frac{\partial F^{\star\mu\nu}}{\partial x^\nu} = 0$$

and has the components

$$
F^{\star\mu\nu} = c
\begin{bmatrix}
0 & B_x & B_y & B_z \\
-B_x & 0 & -E_z & E_y \\
-B_y & E_z & 0 & -E_x \\
-B_z & -E_y & E_x & 0
\end{bmatrix}.
$$

The field tensor $F_{\mu\nu}$ has two invariants:

$$|F_{\alpha\beta}| = c^{-8}(E_k B_k)^2$$

and

$$F^{\alpha\beta}F_{\alpha\beta} = 2c^{-2}(c^2 B^2 - E^2).$$

Thus the two three-dimensional scalars $\mathbf{E} \cdot \mathbf{B}$ and $c^2 B^2 - E^2$ are also four-dimensional scalars. Other possible invariants, for example $e_{\alpha\beta\gamma\delta}F^{\alpha\beta}F^{\gamma\delta}$ and $F^{\alpha\beta}F_{\beta\gamma}F^{\gamma\delta}F_{\delta\alpha}$, are only combinations of the above two invariants.

4.3 THE STRESS-ENERGY TENSOR

According to eq. (2-1), the force density f^i on a system of charges with charge density ρ and current density J^i is given by

$$f^i = \rho E_i + e(ijk)J^j B_k. \tag{4-13}$$

With the use of eq. (4-9), eq. (4-13) may be written in the form

$$f^i = J^\alpha F_{\alpha.}{}^i. \tag{4-14a}$$

We define the temporal component f^0 by the relation

$$f^0 = J^\alpha F_{\alpha.}{}^0, \tag{4-14b}$$

so as to make f^μ a four-dimensional vector. Equations (4-14) are then combined into one form

$$f^\mu = J^\alpha F_{\alpha.}{}^\mu. \tag{4-15}$$

With the aid of the field equations (4-11) and (4-12), the right-hand side of eq. (4-15) may be expressed as the divergence of a tensor $S^{\mu\nu}$:

$$f^\mu = -\frac{\partial S^{\mu\nu}}{\partial x^\nu} \tag{4-16}$$

where $S^{\mu\nu}$ is defined

$$S^{\mu\nu} = \epsilon_0\left(F^{\mu\alpha}F_{\alpha.}{}^\nu + \tfrac{1}{4}\eta^{\mu\nu}F^{\alpha\beta}F_{\alpha\beta}\right). \tag{4-17}$$

The tensor $S^{\mu\nu}$, known as the electromagnetic *stress-energy tensor*, has as its components the energy density, the energy flow density, the momentum density, and the stress tensor of the classical theory of Section 2.3. Direct evaluation of eq. (4-17) gives

$$S^{00} = \tfrac{1}{2}\epsilon_0 c^{-2}(E^2 + c^2 B^2)$$
$$S^{0i} = S^{i0} = c^{-2}P_i$$
$$S^{ij} = -X_{ij}$$

(see Section 2.3). Thus $c^2 S^{00}$ is the field energy density, $c^2 S^{0i}$ is the field energy flow density (Poynting's vector), S^{i0} is the field momentum density, and $-S^{ij}$ is the stress tensor.

The contraction $S^\alpha_{.\alpha}$ vanishes. Other properties of $S^{\mu\nu}$ are found by diagonalizing it. The usual procedure for diagonalizing a tensor will be followed. We transform to coordinates which have the eigenvectors ξ^μ as axes. The eigenvectors are given by the eigenvector equation

$$S^\mu_{.\nu}\xi^\nu = \Lambda\xi^\mu. \tag{4-18}$$

Since $S^{\mu\nu}$ will in general vary from one event to another, the analysis will be valid only at a given event.

The electric and magnetic vectors **E** and **B** at the given event are used to construct a local coordinate system x^i. The x-axis is chosen in the direction **E** × **B**. The y-axis is chosen in the direction **E**. The electric and magnetic vectors are then given by

$$\mathbf{E} = (0, E, 0)$$
$$\mathbf{B} = (0, B\cos\theta, B\sin\theta),$$

where θ is the angle between **E** and **B**. Poynting's vector becomes

$$\mathbf{P} = \epsilon_0 c^2 EB \sin\theta(1, 0, 0).$$

The field tensor has the form

$$F_{\mu\nu} = \frac{1}{c^2}\begin{bmatrix} 0 & 0 & -E & 0 \\ 0 & 0 & B\sin\theta & -B\cos\theta \\ E & -B\sin\theta & 0 & 0 \\ 0 & B\cos\theta & 0 & 0 \end{bmatrix},$$

and evaluation of the stress energy tensor gives

$$S^\mu_{.\nu} = \frac{1}{c^2}\begin{bmatrix} U & -Pc^{-2} & 0 & 0 \\ P & -U & 0 & 0 \\ 0 & 0 & A & C \\ 0 & 0 & C & -A \end{bmatrix} \tag{4-19}$$

where

$$U = \tfrac{1}{2}\epsilon_0(E^2 + c^2B^2)$$
$$P = \epsilon_0 c^2 EB\sin\theta$$
$$A = \tfrac{1}{2}\epsilon_0(E^2 + c^2B^2\cos 2\theta)$$
$$C = \tfrac{1}{2}\epsilon_0 c^2 B^2\sin 2\theta.$$

The identity

$$A^2 + C^2 = U^2 - c^{-2}P^2 = I^2$$

serves to define the quantity I which will be used in what follows.

The eigenvalue equation

$$|S^\mu_{.\nu} - \Lambda\delta^\mu_\nu| = 0$$

becomes

$$(c^4\Lambda^2 - I^2)^2 = 0.$$

Thus the eigenvalues of $S^\mu_{\cdot\nu}$ are

$$\Lambda = \pm c^{-2}I.$$

There is a degeneracy of the roots—two of the roots have the value $+c^{-2}I$ and two have the value $-c^{-2}I$. The invariant I can be expressed in terms of the two basic invariants

$$I_1 = \tfrac{1}{2}(c^2 B^2 - E^2)$$

$$I_2 = cEB \cos\theta$$

with the result

$$I^2 = \epsilon_0^2(I_1^2 + I_2^2).$$

It may be recalled from Section 4.2 that I_1 and I_2 are the only two invariants of the field tensor.

The coordinates $\bar{x}^\mu$ in which $S^\mu_{\cdot\nu}$ is diagonalized will be called *canonical coordinates*. The values of the various quantities in the canonical system will be denoted by bars.

A surprising amount of information can be learned about the values $\bar{E}$ and $\bar{B}$ of the field intensities in the canonical coordinate system without using the transformation itself. First, we note that if $\bar{S}^\mu_{\cdot\nu}$ is to be diagonal, then the angle $\bar{\theta}$ between $\bar{E}$ and $\bar{B}$ must be either 0 or π. Hence

$$I_2 = \pm c\bar{E}\bar{B}.$$

But then, with

$$I_1 = \tfrac{1}{2}(c^2 \bar{B}^2 - \bar{E}^2),$$

it follows that $\bar{E}$ and $\bar{B}$ are given by the relations

$$\left.\begin{aligned} \bar{E}^2 &= \epsilon_0^{-1} I - I_1 \\ c^2\bar{B}^2 &= \epsilon_0^{-1} I + I_1. \end{aligned}\right\} \tag{4-20}$$

We also note that the energy density $\bar{U} = \bar{S}^0_{\cdot 0} c^2$ is merely I. Thus,

$$\bar{U} = I = \tfrac{1}{2}\epsilon_0(\bar{E}^2 + c^2\bar{B}^2).$$

The transformation to canonical coordinates $\bar{x}^\mu$ involves the eigenvectors ξ^μ. The four equations represented by eq. (4-18) have solutions

$$\frac{\xi^1}{c\xi^0} = \tanh\phi, \qquad \frac{c\xi^0}{\xi^1} = \tanh\phi, \qquad \frac{\xi^2}{\xi^3} = -\tan\psi, \qquad \frac{\xi^3}{\xi^2} = \tan\psi,$$

where

$$\tan 2\psi = \frac{C}{A}$$

$$\tanh 2\phi = \frac{P}{cU}.$$

Hence the eigenvectors may be chosen

$$\xi_0^\mu = (\cosh \phi, c \sinh \phi, 0, 0)$$
$$\xi_1^\mu = (c^{-1} \sinh \phi, \cosh \phi, 0, 0)$$
$$\xi_2^\mu = (0, 0, \cos \psi, \sin \psi)$$
$$\xi_3^\mu = (0, 0, -\sin \psi, \cos \psi)$$

which have eigenvalues $+c^{-2}I$, $-c^{-2}I$, $+c^{-2}I$, and $-c^{-2}I$, respectively. Then ξ_0^μ is a unit time-like vector, and the ξ_a^μ ($a = 1, 2, 3$) are unit space-like vectors; i.e., $\eta_{\mu\nu}\xi_0^\mu\xi_0^\nu = 1$ and $\eta_{\mu\nu}\xi_a^\mu\xi_a^\nu = -c^{-2}$ (no sum on a in the latter expression). Note that we thus have

$$\eta_{\alpha\beta} = \xi_\alpha^\mu\xi_\beta^\nu\eta_{\mu\nu}.$$

Therefore the ξ_α^μ form the components of a transformation matrix in special relativity. By using the transformation

$$x^\mu = \xi_\alpha^\mu \bar{x}^\alpha \tag{4-21}$$

or

$$\bar{x}^\alpha = \check{\xi}_\mu^\alpha x^\mu,$$

where

$$\check{\xi}_\mu^\alpha = \eta_{\mu\nu}\xi_\beta^\nu\eta^{\beta\alpha}$$

as found from eq. (3-39), we indeed obtain a coordinate system in which the vectors $\bar{x}^\alpha = \delta_\sigma^\alpha$ ($\sigma = 0, 1, 2, 3$) are eigenvectors. In fact, the vector $\bar{x}^\alpha = \delta_\sigma^\alpha$ becomes the vector $x^\mu = \xi_\sigma^\mu$.

The transformation to canonical coordinates consists of a Lorentz transformation with velocity $v = c \tanh \phi$ along the x-axis and a spatial rotation through angle ψ about the x-axis. The coordinates obtained after the Lorentz transformation and before the rotation will be denoted x'^μ. An alternate method for deriving the velocity v is to require $p'_x = 0$ using eqs. (4-10). A third method is to obtain, by means of eqs. (4-10), the transformation rules for U and P:

$$U' = \gamma^2\left[U\left(1 + \frac{v^2}{c^2}\right) - 2\frac{v}{c^2}P \right]$$

$$P' = \gamma^2\left[P\left(1 + \frac{v^2}{c^2}\right) - 2vU \right]$$

where

$$\gamma = \frac{1}{\sqrt{1 - \dfrac{v^2}{c^2}}}.$$

The requirement that P' vanish then gives the condition $v = c \tanh \phi$ where ϕ is given by

$$\tanh 2\phi = \frac{P}{cU}.$$

In the canonical coordinates, the vectors $\bar{\mathbf{E}}$ and $\bar{\mathbf{B}}$ are parallel and are given by

$$\bar{\mathbf{E}} = (0, \bar{E}, 0)$$

$$\bar{\mathbf{B}} = (0, \pm\bar{B}, 0).$$

The $\pm$ sign refers to the sign of $\cos\theta$, since I_2 is an invariant. The field tensor is

$$\bar{F}_{\mu\nu} = \frac{1}{c^2}\begin{bmatrix} 0 & 0 & -\bar{E} & 0 \\ 0 & 0 & 0 & \mp\bar{B} \\ \bar{E} & 0 & 0 & 0 \\ 0 & \pm\bar{B} & 0 & 0 \end{bmatrix},$$

and the stress-energy tensor is

$$\bar{S}^{\mu}_{\cdot\nu} = \frac{I}{c^2}\begin{bmatrix} 1 & 0 & 0 & 0 \\ 0 & -1 & 0 & 0 \\ 0 & 0 & 1 & 0 \\ 0 & 0 & 0 & -1 \end{bmatrix}. \tag{4-22}$$

The relations

$$\frac{v}{c} = \tanh\phi = \frac{cEB\sin\theta}{\frac{1}{2}(E^2 + c^2B^2) + \epsilon_0^{-1}I} = \frac{\frac{1}{2}(E^2 + c^2B^2) - \epsilon_0^{-1}I}{cEB\sin\theta}, \tag{4-23}$$

$$\sin 2\psi = \frac{C}{I}, \qquad \cos 2\psi = \frac{A}{I} \tag{4-24}$$

will be used in what follows.

A special case of interest is that in which $\mathbf{E}$ and $\mathbf{B}$ are perpendicular. The invariant I_2 vanishes, and we are left with

$$I = \epsilon_0 |I_1|. \tag{4-25}$$

There are three possibilities: cB is larger than E, equal to E, or less than E. If cB is larger than E, then I_1 is positive. Equations (4-20), (4-23), and (4-24) give

$$\bar{E}^2 = 0$$

$$c^2\bar{B}^2 = 2I_1$$

$$v = \frac{E}{B}$$

$$\psi = \frac{\pi}{2}.$$

If cB is less than E, then I_1 is negative. Equations (4-20), (4-23), and (4-24) give

$$\bar{E}^2 = -2I_1$$
$$c^2\bar{B}^2 = 0$$
$$v = \frac{c^2B}{E}$$
$$\psi = 0.$$

In both cases, v is the velocity of the frame in which $\bar{E}$ or $\bar{B}$ vanishes. The case $cB = E$ has no solution; the canonical frame must move with the speed of light—which is impossible!

The limiting case where cB and E are equal and perpendicular can also be approached by first using their equality. If $cB = E$, then I_1 vanishes, and we have

$$I = \epsilon_0 |I_2|. \tag{4-26}$$

Equations (4-23) and (4-24) give

$$\frac{v}{c} = \frac{1 - |\cos\theta|}{\sin\theta} = \frac{\sin\theta}{1 + |\cos\theta|}$$

$$\psi = \begin{cases} \frac{1}{2}\theta, & \cos\theta > 0 \\ \frac{1}{2}(\theta - \pi), & \cos\theta < 0. \end{cases}$$

In the limiting case $\theta = \dfrac{\pi}{2}$, the velocity approaches c.

The determinant of $S^\mu_{.\nu}$ is equal to $c^{-8}I^4$. This result is obtained directly in canonical coordinates, but also holds in any coordinates because of the invariance of the determinant of a tensor. (See Section 3.9.)

The eigenvectors of the field tensor $F_{\mu\nu}$ are also eigenvectors of the stress-energy tensor $S^{\mu\nu}$. For if the eigenvector equation

$$F^\mu_{.\nu}\eta^\nu = \lambda\eta^\mu \tag{4-27}$$

holds, then direct evaluation of $S^\mu_{.\nu}\eta^\nu$ from eq. (4-17) gives

$$S^\mu_{.\nu}\eta^\nu = \epsilon_0(\lambda^2 + c^{-2}I_1)\eta^\mu. \tag{4-28}$$

Hence the equation

$$\Lambda = \epsilon_0(\lambda^2 + c^{-2}I_1) \tag{4-29}$$

relates the eigenvalues Λ of $S^\mu_{.\nu}$ to the eigenvalues λ of $F^\mu_{.\nu}$. In canonical coordinates, the eigenvalue equation

$$|\bar{F}^\mu_{.\nu} - \lambda\delta^\mu_\nu| = 0$$

becomes

$$(\lambda^2 + \bar{B}^2)(\lambda^2 - c^{-2}\bar{E}^2) = 0$$

which has solutions $\lambda = \pm c^{-1}\bar{E}$ and $\lambda = \pm i\bar{B}$, in consistency with eq. (4-29). The roots $\lambda = \pm c^{-1}\bar{E}$ correspond to $\Lambda = +c^{-2}I$, and the roots $\lambda = \pm i\bar{B}$ correspond to $\Lambda = -c^{-2}I$.

The eigenvector equation becomes*

$$\bar{\eta}^2 = \mp c\bar{\eta}^0, \qquad \lambda = \pm c^{-1}\bar{E}$$
$$\bar{\eta}^3 = \pm \pm i\bar{\eta}^1, \qquad \lambda = \pm i\bar{B}.$$

Thus the eigenvectors of $F^{\mu}_{.\nu}$ may be chosen to be

$$
\begin{aligned}
\bar{\eta}^{\mu}_0 &= (1, 0, -c, 0) & \lambda &= c^{-1}\bar{E} \\
\bar{\eta}^{\mu}_2 &= (1, 0, c, 0) & \lambda &= -c^{-1}\bar{E}
\end{aligned}
\Bigg\} \Lambda = +c^{-2}I
$$

$$
\begin{aligned}
\bar{\eta}^{\mu}_1 &= (0, 1, 0, \pm i) & \lambda &= i \\
\bar{\eta}^{\mu}_3 &= (0, 1, 0, \mp i) & \lambda &= -i\bar{B}
\end{aligned}
\Bigg\} \Lambda = -c^{-2}I.
$$

And in canonical coordinates the eigenvectors of $S^{\mu}_{.\nu}$ are

$$
\begin{aligned}
\bar{\xi}^{\mu}_0 &= (1, 0, 0, 0) & \Lambda &= c^{-2}I \\
\bar{\xi}^{\mu}_1 &= (0, 1, 0, 0) & \Lambda &= -c^{-2}I \\
\bar{\xi}^{\mu}_2 &= (0, 0, 1, 0) & \Lambda &= c^{-2}I \\
\bar{\xi}^{\mu}_3 &= (0, 0, 0, 1) & \Lambda &= -c^{-2}I.
\end{aligned}
$$

Therefore the two sets of eigenvectors are related by the equations

$$
\begin{aligned}
\bar{\eta}^{\mu}_0 &= \bar{\xi}^{\mu}_0 - c\bar{\xi}^{\mu}_2 \\
\bar{\eta}^{\mu}_2 &= \bar{\xi}^{\mu}_0 + c\bar{\xi}^{\mu}_2 \\
\bar{\eta}^{\mu}_1 &= \bar{\xi}^{\mu}_1 \pm i\bar{\xi}^{\mu}_3 \\
\bar{\eta}^{\mu}_3 &= \bar{\xi}^{\mu}_1 \mp i\bar{\xi}^{\mu}_3.
\end{aligned}
$$

Since the above equations are vector relations, the bars may be removed. Thus, in the original coordinates, we have

$$
\begin{aligned}
\eta^{\mu}_0 &= (\cosh\phi, c\sinh\phi, -c\cos\psi, -c\sin\psi) \\
\eta^{\mu}_2 &= (\cosh\phi, c\sinh\phi, c\cos\psi, c\sin\psi) \\
\eta^{\mu}_1 &= (c^{-1}\sinh\phi, \cosh\phi, \mp i\sin\psi, \pm i\cos\psi) \\
\eta^{\mu}_3 &= (c^{-1}\sinh\phi, \cosh\phi, \pm i\sin\psi, \mp i\cos\psi).
\end{aligned}
$$

It may seem at first sight to be a paradox that the ξ^{μ}_{α} are not the same as the η^{μ}_{α}, yet it was proved that the eigenvectors of $F^{\mu}_{.\nu}$ are also eigenvectors of $S^{\mu}_{.\nu}$. The explanation lies in the degeneracy of the roots Λ. We could have chosen the ξ^{μ}_{α} so as to agree with the η^{μ}_{α} if we had wished. However, the η^{μ}_{α} have an undesirable property which was avoided in our choice of the ξ^{μ}_{α}. The antisymmetry of $F^{\mu\nu}$ requires that any eigenvector of $F^{\mu}_{.\nu}$ be a null vector. The ξ^{μ}_{α} were chosen so as to be non-null and real.

---

* The extra $\pm$ sign here and in what follows is the sign of $\cos\theta$.

4.4 RADIATION

The special case $E = cB$ and $\theta = \dfrac{\pi}{2}$, which we will call *radiation*, could not be treated in the previous section for the simple reason that both I_1 and I_2 and hence I vanish. Therefore $S^\mu_{.\nu}$ cannot be diagonalized. The velocity for the canonical frame was found to be the speed of light. Hence there is no canonical frame for radiation.

With $cB = E$ and $\theta = \dfrac{\pi}{2}$ in eq. (4-19) we have

$$S^\mu_{.\nu} = \frac{U}{c^2}\begin{bmatrix} 1 & -c^{-1} & 0 & 0 \\ c & -1 & 0 & 0 \\ 0 & 0 & 0 & 0 \\ 0 & 0 & 0 & 0 \end{bmatrix}$$

where

$$U = \epsilon_0 E^2.$$

For a plane-polarized, plane-front, sinusoidal light beam, the electric and magnetic intensities throughout the region of space-time containing the beam are given by

$$E = cB = \epsilon_0^{-\frac{1}{2}} a \cos 2\pi\nu\left(t - \frac{x}{c}\right).$$

Hence the stress-energy tensor for such a beam is

$$S^{\mu\nu} = \frac{a^2}{c^2}\cos^2 2\pi\nu\left(t - \frac{x}{c}\right)\begin{bmatrix} 1 & c & 0 & 0 \\ c & c^2 & 0 & 0 \\ 0 & 0 & 0 & 0 \\ 0 & 0 & 0 & 0 \end{bmatrix}.$$

The average value of $S^{\mu\nu}$ is then

$$S^{\mu\nu} = \frac{U}{c^2}\begin{bmatrix} 1 & c & 0 & 0 \\ c & c^2 & 0 & 0 \\ 0 & 0 & 0 & 0 \\ 0 & 0 & 0 & 0 \end{bmatrix} \tag{4-30}$$

where U is now the average energy density $\frac{1}{2}a^2$.

For an arbitrary direction of propagation represented by the unit spatial vector n^i (i.e., $n^k n^k = 1$), the average stress-energy tensor for a plane-polarized, plane-wave radiation field is found by direct evaluation of eq. (4-17) to be

$$S^{\mu\nu} = c^{-2} U l^\mu l^\nu \tag{4-31}$$

where

$$l^\mu = (1, cn^i).$$

Equation (4-31) reduces to eq. (4-30) if the direction of propagation is along the x-axis.

Equation (4-31) looks deceptively simple. Under coordinate transformations, one can easily make the mistake of regarding U as a scalar and l^μ as a vector. However, it was noted in Section 3.15 that l^μ is not a vector, because l^0 must be unity in any coordinate system. Nevertheless, it was found that the components of l^μ are proportional to the components of a 4-vector. This same property may be noted in the transformation of $S^{0\mu}$. Upon transformation to another coordinate system $\bar{x}^\alpha$ (not to be confused with the notation of the previous section), we have, from the tensor nature of $S^{\mu\nu}$,

$$\bar{U}\bar{l}^\alpha = \bar{S}^{0\alpha} = \frac{\partial \bar{x}^0}{\partial x^\mu} \frac{\partial \bar{x}^\alpha}{\partial x^\nu} S^{\mu\nu} = U \left(\frac{\partial \bar{x}^0}{\partial x^\mu} l^\mu \right) \frac{\partial \bar{x}^\alpha}{\partial x^\nu} l^\nu. \tag{4-32a}$$

Thus l^μ is proportional to a 4-vector. Therefore $\bar{l}^\alpha$ in the new coordinates is proportional to the set of quantities obtained by transforming l^μ *as if it were a 4-vector*. We then have

$$\bar{l}^\alpha = \frac{1}{w} \frac{\partial \bar{x}^\alpha}{\partial x^\mu} l^\mu \tag{4-32b}$$

where $\dfrac{1}{w}$ is the factor of proportionality. The requirement that $\bar{l}^0$ be unity fixes the value of w:

$$w = \frac{\partial \bar{x}^0}{\partial x^\mu} l^\mu. \tag{4-33}$$

From the calculation

$$\frac{\partial \bar{x}^0}{\partial x^\mu} = \eta_{\mu\nu} \eta^{\nu\rho} \frac{\partial \bar{x}^0}{\partial x^\rho} = \eta_{\mu\nu} \eta^{\alpha\beta} \frac{\partial x^\nu}{\partial \bar{x}^\alpha} \frac{\partial x^\rho}{\partial \bar{x}^\beta} \frac{\partial \bar{x}^0}{\partial x^\rho} = \eta_{\mu\nu} \frac{\partial x^\nu}{\partial \bar{x}^0}$$

and the observation that $\partial x^\nu(\bar{x}^\alpha)/\partial \bar{x}^0$ is the world-velocity u^ν of the $\bar{x}^\alpha$-system relative to the x^μ-system, it is noted that eq. (4-33) has the much simpler form

$$w = u_\mu l^\mu.$$

Finally, we note from eqs. (4-32a) and (4-33) that $\bar{U}$ is given by

$$\bar{U} = Uw^2. \tag{4-34}$$

It is easily verified that eqs. (4-31), (4-32b), and (4-34) lead to the transformed stress-energy tensor

$$\bar{S}^{\alpha\beta} = c^{-2} \bar{U} \bar{l}^\alpha \bar{l}^\beta$$

which has the same form as eq. (4-31).

The transformation of U and l^μ may be described in the following way. Consider one reference frame $\bar{x}^\alpha$ to be the standard of reference, and let u^μ be the world velocity of its origin relative to any other reference frame x^μ. Then $U(u_\alpha l^\alpha)^2$ is a scalar and

$$\frac{l^\mu}{u_\alpha l^\alpha}$$

is a vector under transformations among all possible systems x^μ.

The stress-energy tensor for isotropic radiation is obtained by averaging eq. (4-31) over all spatial directions n^i. The result is

$$S^{\mu\nu} = \tfrac{1}{3}c^{-2}U(4\delta_0^\mu\delta_0^\nu - \eta^{\mu\nu}), \tag{4-35}$$

i.e.,

$$S^{\mu\nu} = \frac{U}{c^2}\begin{bmatrix} 1 & 0 & 0 & 0 \\ 0 & \tfrac{1}{3}c^2 & 0 & 0 \\ 0 & 0 & \tfrac{1}{3}c^2 & 0 \\ 0 & 0 & 0 & \tfrac{1}{3}c^2 \end{bmatrix}.$$

The spatial components represent a pressure $\tfrac{1}{3}U$, and the S^{00} component is c^{-2} times the average energy density U. It is important to realize that this radiation is isotropic only in one reference frame x^μ. For an observer who is stationary in another reference frame $\bar{x}^\alpha$ which is moving relative to the x^μ frame, the stress-energy tensor is

$$\bar{S}^{\alpha\beta} = \frac{\partial\bar{x}^\alpha}{\partial x^\mu}\frac{\partial\bar{x}^\beta}{\partial x^\nu}\frac{U}{3c^2}(4\delta_0^\mu\delta_0^\nu - \eta^{\mu\nu}) = \frac{U}{3c^2}(4\bar{u}^\alpha\bar{u}^\beta - \eta^{\alpha\beta}) \tag{4-36}$$

where $\bar{u}^\alpha$ is the world-velocity of the x^μ-system relative to the $\bar{x}^\alpha$-system. Note that U is the energy density in the frame in which the radiation is isotropic. In the $\bar{x}^\alpha$-system, the energy density is $\bar{U} = U[\tfrac{4}{3}(u^0)^2 - \tfrac{1}{3}]$. Equation (3-36) reduces to eq. (3-35) for the special case $\bar{u}^\alpha = \delta_0^\alpha$, as expected.

4.5 MOTION OF A CHARGED PARTICLE

The force $\mathscr{F}^\mu$ on a charged fluid within a spatial region R should be the volume integral

$$\mathscr{F}^\mu = \int_R f^\mu \, dV, \tag{4-37}$$

where f^μ is the force density given by eq. (4-15). However, $\mathscr{F}^\mu$ is not a 4-vector. To see this, we first assume that R is so small that the world-velocity u^μ of the fluid within R is constant. Then we define the 4-vector

$$F^\mu = \int f^\mu \, dV_\pi \tag{4-38}$$

where the integral extends over proper volume, i.e., over volume in the reference frame in which the fluid is stationary. The proper volume dV_π is a scalar, because it is independent of the original coordinates. The vector character of f^μ and the scalar character of dV_π then require that F^μ be a vector. It is recalled from Section 4.1 that dV_π is given by

$$\frac{dV_\pi}{dV} = u^0.$$

Therefore, from eqs. (4-37) and (4-38), we have

$$F^\mu = u^0 \mathcal{F}^\mu.$$

Since u^0 is not a scalar (it is the temporal component of a vector), $\mathcal{F}^\mu$ cannot be a vector. We will therefore adopt F^μ as *force* in special relativity.

For a charged fluid which has no internal currents, eq. (4-38), in view of eqs. (4-3) and (4-15), becomes

$$F^\mu = qu^\alpha F_{\alpha .}^{\ \mu}, \tag{4-39}$$

where q is the total charge inside the region R. If we now regard a charged particle as a charge distribution having infinitesimal volume, eq. (4-39) is applicable to a charged particle. (The procedure of going to the limit of a point particle will be considered later in more detail.) Note that, due to the antisymmetry of the field tensor, F^μ is perpendicular to u^μ.

To describe the effect of the force F^μ on the *motion* of a particle, we postulate the equation of motion

$$F^\mu = \frac{d}{d\tau}(mu^\mu) \tag{4-40}$$

where m is the proper mass (or rest mass) of the particle, u^μ is its world-velocity, and τ is its proper time given by

$$d\tau^2 = \eta_{\mu\nu}\,dx^\mu\,dx^\nu. \tag{4-41}$$

According to eqs. (4-39) and (4-40), the motion of a charged particle is given by

$$\frac{d}{d\tau}(mu^\mu) = qu^\alpha F_{\alpha .}^{\ \mu}. \tag{4-42}$$

Division of eq. (4-41) by $d\tau^2$ gives eq. (3-44) which is reproduced here for convenience:

$$1 = \eta_{\mu\nu}u^\mu u^\nu. \tag{4-43}$$

Equation (4-43) may be differentiated with respect to τ to give

$$u_\mu \frac{du^\mu}{d\tau} = 0. \tag{4-44}$$

The formulation of eq. (4-40) is motivated by the desire that it resemble the Newtonian equation of motion and by the requirement that it reduce to the Newtonian equation of motion for small velocities.

The proper mass m may in general be a function of τ. Therefore when the right-hand side of eq. (4-40) is expanded, there appear two terms:

$$F^\mu = m \frac{du^\mu}{d\tau} + u^\mu \frac{dm}{d\tau}. \qquad (4\text{-}45)$$

The first term in eq. (4-45) is perpendicular to u^μ because, by eq. (4-44), its scalar product with u^μ is zero. The second term is obviously parallel to u^μ. Thus F^μ consists of a component $m \, du^\mu/d\tau$ perpendicular to u^μ and a component $u^\mu \, dm/d\tau$ parallel to u^μ. Multiplication of eq. (4-45) by u_μ gives

$$\frac{dm}{d\tau} = u_\mu F^\mu. \qquad (4\text{-}46)$$

Substitution of eq. (4-46) back into eq. (4-45) gives

$$m \frac{du^\mu}{d\tau} = F^\mu - u^\mu u_\nu F^\nu. \qquad (4\text{-}47)$$

Equation (4-46) shows that the particle may in general have a variable proper mass. The proper mass can be held constant by postulating a different force law:

$$\frac{d}{d\tau}(mu^\mu) = F^\mu - u^\mu u_\nu F^\nu; \qquad (4\text{-}48)$$

for then $dm/d\tau$ is automatically zero. But for the case of electromagnetic forces, eqs. (4-40) and (4-48) are equivalent because of the antisymmetry of the electromagnetic field tensor.

Equation (4-47) is a special case of the *projection* operation, i.e., finding the component of one vector A^μ which is perpendicular to another vector B^μ. By subtracting the component of A^μ parallel to B^μ

$$B^\mu \frac{B_\nu A^\nu}{B_\rho B^\rho}$$

from A^μ we obtain the component of A^μ perpendicular to B^μ:

$$\left(\delta^\mu_\nu - \frac{B^\mu B_\nu}{B_\rho B^\rho} \right) A^\nu.$$

The above expression is clearly perpendicular to B^μ, because its scalar product with B^μ is zero; the expression reduces to the right-hand side of eq. (4-47) for the case $A^\mu = F^\mu$, $B^\mu = u^\mu$. For any case in which B^μ is a time-like vector, the projected A^μ has zero temporal component in the reference frame in which $B^i = 0$. Thus A^μ is projected onto the space which is perpendicular to B^μ. The projection operation can be extended to any tensor $T^{\mu\nu}$. The projected tensor

$$T_\perp^{\mu\nu} = \left(\delta^\mu_\alpha - \frac{B^\mu B_\alpha}{B_\rho B^\rho}\right)\left(\delta^\nu_\beta - \frac{B^\nu B_\beta}{B_\sigma B^\sigma}\right)T^{\alpha\beta}$$

has vanishing temporal components (i.e., $T_\perp^{00} = 0$, $T_\perp^{0i} = 0$, $T_\perp^{i0} = 0$) in the reference frame in which B^μ has *only* a temporal component. The operator

$$\delta^\mu_\alpha - \frac{B^\mu B_\alpha}{B_\rho B^\rho}$$

is called the *projection operator* because it projects a vector or a tensor into a spatial cross section which is perpendicular to a time-like vector B^μ.

For the case of a particle, the force $\mathcal{F}^\mu$ defined by eq. (4-37) is, from the definition of u^0, given by

$$\mathcal{F}^\mu = \frac{d}{dt}(mu^\mu) = \frac{d}{dt}\left(u^0 m \frac{dx^\mu}{dt}\right)$$

where the coordinate time is $t = x^0$. The equation of motion (4-47) becomes

$$\frac{d}{dt}\left(\frac{m}{\sqrt{1 - \frac{v^2}{c^2}}}\frac{dx^i}{dt}\right) = \sqrt{1 - \frac{v^2}{c^2}}(F^i - u^i u_\rho F^\rho). \qquad (4\text{-}49)$$

Experiment shows that eq. (4-49) correctly describes the motions of charged particles, and that the 4-vector momentum mu^μ is the quantity whose sum is conserved. Hence one is tempted to interpret momentum as the product of the "mass" $m / \sqrt{1 - \frac{v^2}{c^2}}$ with the velocity dx^i/dt. Such an interpretation encounters difficulty for accelerated motion, because when the left-hand side of eq. (4-49) is expanded, there are two terms: one term is the product of the "longitudinal mass" $m\left(1 - \frac{v^2}{c^2}\right)^{-\frac{3}{2}}$ with the component of the acceleration d^2x^i/dt^2 parallel to the velocity; the other term is the product of the "transverse mass" $m\left(1 - \frac{v^2}{c^2}\right)^{-\frac{1}{2}}$ with the component of the acceleration perpendicular to the velocity (in the spatial sense). A simpler interpretation, and the one used in this book, is that momentum is the product of proper mass with world-velocity, and that force, for constant proper mass, is the product of proper mass with world-acceleration $du^\mu/d\tau$.

The 4-vector momentum p^μ of a particle of proper mass m is given by $p^\mu = mu^\mu$ where u^μ is the world-velocity of the particle. From eq. (4-43) we have

$$p_\mu p^\mu = m^2. \tag{4-50}$$

Thus the "magnitude" of the 4-momentum is the mass of the particle.

The temporal components p^0 and F^0 of the momentum and force have an interesting interpretation. In three-dimensional notation, eq. (4-46) becomes

$$f^0 c^2 = F^k \frac{dx^k}{dt} + \frac{d}{dt}(mc^2).$$

For constant proper mass, the interpretation of the quantity

$$\frac{1}{u^0} F^k \frac{dx^k}{dt} = \mathcal{F}^k \frac{dx^k}{dt}$$

as the rate at which energy E is added to the particle requires that F^0 be given by

$$F^0 c^2 = \frac{d\mathsf{E}}{d\tau}, \tag{4-51}$$

and hence, by integration of eq. (4-40), that p^0 be given by

$$\mathsf{E} = mc^2 u^0 = p^0 c^2 \tag{4-52}$$

where

$$u^0 = \frac{1}{\sqrt{1 - \dfrac{v^2}{c^2}}}.$$

The constant of integration in eq. (4-52) is chosen as the *rest energy* mc^2. Then E is the *total energy* of the particle—rest energy plus kinetic energy. From eqs. (4-52) and (4-51) we interpret $p^0 c^2$ as the total energy of the particle and $F^0 c^2$ as the rate of change of the particle's energy per unit proper time. Equation (4-52) may be written

$$(p^0 c^2)^2 - p^2 c^2 = (mc^2)^2$$

where $p^2 = p^k p^k$. The rest energy mc^2 is not merely a theoretical concept; it can be converted into energy by reactions which involve the annihilation of particles.

4.6 LAGRANGIAN FORMULATION

The convenience of the Lagrangian formulation in obtaining the trajectories of a test particle around a force center merits a brief review of the Lagrangian and its application to electromagnetism. If one can find a function $L(x^i, \dot{x}^j, t)$ which depends upon the particle's coordinates x^i, the velocity $\dot{x}^i = dx^i/dt$, and the time t in such a way that the force equation may be written in the form of *Lagrange's equation*

$$\frac{d}{dt}\frac{\partial L}{\partial \dot{x}^i} - \frac{\partial L}{\partial x^i} = 0, \qquad (4\text{-}53)$$

then the function L is known as the *Lagrangian*. Equation (4-53) is the result of requiring that the integral

$$\int_{E_1}^{E_2} L\,dt$$

over all possible trajectories from an event $E_1(t_1, x_1^i)$ to an event $E_2(t_2, x_2^i)$ be an extremum; this is known as *Hamilton's principle* and may be abbreviated in the form

$$\delta \int L\,dt = 0. \qquad (4\text{-}54)$$

In going over to a four-dimensional Lagrangian formulation for the trajectory of a particle under the action of electromagnetic forces, it is desirable that the particle's proper time τ be used as the independent variable rather than the coordinate time t. Two considerations then suggest that the kinetic energy T, which appears in the usual form of the Lagrangian $T - V$, should be chosen to be $-mc^2\left(1 - \dfrac{v^2}{c^2}\right)^{\frac{1}{2}}$, where v is the velocity of the particle. First, this expression reduces for small velocities to $-mc^2 + \frac{1}{2}mv^2$, i.e., the kinetic energy plus a constant. Second, the equation of motion for a free particle is found to result from Hamilton's principle in the form

$$\delta \int \left(-mc^2\sqrt{1 - \frac{v^2}{c^2}}\right) dt = 0.$$

In an electrostatic situation, the potential energy would be $V = q\phi$. Thus eq. (4-54) takes the form

$$\delta \int \left(-mc^2\sqrt{1 - \frac{v^2}{c^2}} - qc^2\phi_0\right) dt = 0$$

or

$$\delta \int (-mc^2\sqrt{\eta_{\mu\nu}\dot{x}^\mu\dot{x}^\nu} - qc^2\phi_0\dot{x}^0)\, d\tau = 0 \qquad (4\text{-}55)$$

where the dot now indicates differentiation with respect to the particle's proper time τ: $\dot{x}^\mu = dx^\mu/d\tau$. The obvious generalization suggested by eq. (4-55) is to use a Lagrangian given by

$$L(x^\mu, \dot{x}^\nu) = -mc^2\sqrt{\eta_{\mu\nu}\dot{x}^\mu\dot{x}^\nu} - qc^2\phi_\alpha\dot{x}^\alpha. \qquad (4\text{-}56)$$

It may be easily verified that Lagrange's equation

$$\frac{d}{d\tau}\frac{\partial L}{\partial \dot{x}^\mu} - \frac{\partial L}{\partial x^\mu} = 0 \tag{4-57}$$

for the Lagrangian of eq. (4-56) is indeed a form of the equation of motion (4-42).

Note that the *value* of the expression inside the radical in eq. (4-56) is unity. Therefore eq. (4-56) is not a unique expression for the Lagrangian. Another possible form is given by

$$L = -\tfrac{1}{2}mc^2\eta_{\mu\nu}\dot{x}^\mu\dot{x}^\nu - qc^2\phi_\alpha\dot{x}^\alpha, \tag{4-58}$$

as may be verified by direct substitution into eq. (4-57). Indeed, the Lagrangian can be of the type

$$L = -mc^2 f(\sqrt{\eta_{\mu\nu}\dot{x}^\mu\dot{x}^\nu}) - qc^2\phi_\alpha\dot{x}^\alpha \tag{4-59}$$

where f is *any* function such that its derivative is equal to unity when its argument is equal to unity.

Although the Lagrangian of eq. (4-59) is the answer to our search, it is of interest to digress into the subject of the Hamiltonian formulation. The *momentum* which is *conjugate* to the coordinate x^μ is defined

$$p_\mu = \frac{\partial L}{\partial \dot{x}^\mu}. \tag{4-60}$$

(This p_μ should not be confused with the momentum mu_μ of the previous section.) Equation (4-60) can be solved for the velocity $\dot{x}^\mu$ as a function of p_μ and x^μ:

$$\dot{x}^\mu = \dot{x}^\mu(x^\nu, p_\sigma).$$

The *Hamiltonian H*, which is a function of the coordinates x^μ and the conjugate momenta p_μ, is defined

$$H = p_\mu \dot{x}^\mu(x^\nu, p_\sigma) - L[x^\lambda, \dot{x}^\theta(x^\eta, p_\pi)].$$

It is a straightforward calculation to verify that eqs. (4-57) and (4-60) take the forms

$$\frac{\partial H}{\partial x^\mu} = -\frac{dp_\mu}{d\tau}$$

$$\frac{\partial H}{\partial p_\mu} = \frac{dx^\mu}{d\tau}.$$

The conjugate momenta and the Hamiltonian for the Lagrangian of eq. (4-58) are

$$p_\mu = -mc^2\dot{x}_\mu - qc^2\phi_\mu \tag{4-61}$$

and

$$H = -\frac{1}{2mc^2}\eta^{\mu\nu}(p_\mu + qc^2\phi_\mu)(p_\nu + qc^2\phi_\nu).$$

If we desire to have a *three*-dimensional Hamiltonian which is special-relativistically correct, we may take our clue from the fact that in the classical conservative-force case, the Hamiltonian is the total energy $T + V$. We know from Section 4.5 that the total energy of a particle is the temporal component of its momentum, and we see from eq. (4-61) that the temporal component of the conjugate momentum is given by

$$-p_0 = \frac{mc^2}{\sqrt{1 - \dfrac{v^2}{c^2}}} + q\phi.$$

The Hamiltonian is therefore assumed to be

$$H = \frac{mc^2}{\sqrt{1 - \dfrac{v^2}{c^2}}} + q\phi \tag{4-62}$$

and the spatial conjugate momenta are assumed to be those given by eq. (4-61):

$$p_i = \frac{mv^i}{\sqrt{1 - \dfrac{v^2}{c^2}}} + qA_i$$

where

$$v^i = \frac{dx^i}{dt}.$$

Then

$$\frac{mc}{\sqrt{1 - \dfrac{v^2}{c^2}}} = \sqrt{m^2c^2 + (p_i - qA_i)(p_i - qA_i)},$$

and eq. (4-62) becomes

$$H = c\sqrt{m^2c^2 + (p_i - qA_i)(p_i - qA_i)} + q\phi. \tag{4-63}$$

Sufficient computation reveals that with t as the independent variable, eq. (4-63) as the Hamiltonian does indeed give the correct equations of motion.

We return to the Lagrangian method in order to note its invariance under coordinate transformations. Consider the effect of changing from the original rectangular Cartesian coordinates x^μ in which eq. (4-42) is valid to an arbitrary coordinate system ξ^α. It is assumed only that neither the transformation nor the Lagrangian depends explicitly on the independent variable τ. There is no restriction on the number of dimensions. The Lagrangian can be considered to be a function of the ξ^α and their derivatives $\dot{\xi}^\alpha = d\xi^\alpha/d\tau$. The ξ^α and $\dot{\xi}^\alpha$ are in turn functions of x^μ and $\dot{x}^\mu$:

$$\xi^\alpha = \xi^\alpha(x^\mu)$$
$$\dot{\xi}^\alpha = a_\mu^\alpha(x^\nu)\dot{x}^\mu \qquad (4\text{-}64)$$

where

$$a_\mu^\alpha(x^\nu) = \frac{\partial \xi^\alpha}{\partial x^\mu}.$$

Thus the Lagrangian has the functional form

$$L[\xi^\alpha(x^\mu),\ \dot{\xi}^\beta(x^\nu,\ \dot{x}^\rho)].$$

Substitution into eq. (4-57) and the use of eq. (4-64) then gives

$$a_\mu^\alpha\left(\frac{d}{d\tau}\frac{\partial L}{\partial \dot{\xi}^\alpha} - \frac{\partial L}{\partial \xi^\alpha}\right) + \frac{\partial L}{\partial \dot{\xi}^\alpha}\dot{x}^\nu\left(\frac{\partial a_\mu^\alpha}{\partial x^\nu} - \frac{\partial a_\nu^\alpha}{\partial x^\mu}\right) = 0.$$

The symmetry of $\partial^2 \xi^\alpha/\partial x^\nu\, \partial x^\mu$ wipes out the last term, and the remaining expression can be multiplied by the inverse of a_μ^α to give

$$\frac{d}{d\tau}\frac{\partial L}{\partial \dot{\xi}^\alpha} - \frac{\partial L}{\partial \xi^\alpha} = 0. \qquad (4\text{-}65)$$

Equation (4-65) is identical with eq. (4-57), but eq. (4-65) is not limited to rectangular Cartesian coordinates. Any coordinates, including spherical polar coordinates, can be used. Of course the Lagrangian of eq. (4-59) must be transformed over to the coordinates ξ^α. But this can be easily performed, because $\eta_{\mu\nu}\dot{x}^\mu\dot{x}^\nu$ is replaced by $\eta_{\mu\nu}\dfrac{\partial x^\mu}{\partial \xi^\alpha}\dfrac{\partial x^\nu}{\partial \xi^\beta}\dot{\xi}^\alpha\dot{\xi}^\beta$, and $\phi_\alpha\dot{x}^\alpha$ is replaced by $\phi_\mu\dfrac{\partial x^\mu}{\partial \xi^\alpha}\dot{\xi}^\alpha$, where ϕ_μ denotes the vector potential in rectangular Cartesian coordinates. In particular, for switching to spherical polar coordinates, we replace $\eta_{\mu\nu}\dot{x}^\mu\dot{x}^\nu$ with $\dot{t}^2 - c^{-2}[\dot{r}^2 + r^2(\dot{\theta}^2 + \sin^2\theta\dot{\phi}^2)]$.

4.7 MOTION OF A CHARGED PARTICLE IN UNIFORM ELECTRIC AND MAGNETIC FIELDS

We will study the motion of a charged particle in a space-time which contains a constant, uniform electric field **E** and a constant, uniform magnetic field **B**. The equation of motion (4-42) may be written

$$\ddot{x}^\mu = \frac{q}{m}F_{.\alpha}^{\mu}\dot{x}^\alpha \qquad (4\text{-}66)$$

where the upper dots indicate differentiation with respect to the proper time τ of the particle. Integration of eq. (4-66) gives

$$\dot{x}^\mu = \frac{q}{m}F_{.\alpha}^{\mu}x^\alpha + u^\mu \qquad (4\text{-}67)$$

for the initial conditions $x^\mu(0) = 0$, $\dot{x}^\mu(0) = u^\mu$. The substitution of eq. (4-67) into eq. (4-66) then gives

$$\ddot{x}^\mu - \frac{q^2}{m^2} F^\mu_{.\alpha} F^\alpha_{.\beta} x^\beta = \frac{q}{m} F^\mu_{\alpha.} u^\alpha,$$

or, with the use of eq. (4-17),

$$\ddot{x}^\mu - \frac{q^2}{m^2} \left(\frac{S^\mu_{.\nu}}{\epsilon_0} - \frac{I_1}{c^2} \delta^\mu_\nu \right) x^\nu = \frac{q}{m} F^\mu_{\alpha.} u^\alpha \qquad (4\text{-}68)$$

where $I_1 = \dfrac{c^2}{4} F^{\alpha\beta} F_{\alpha\beta}$.

We now choose canonical coordinates $\bar{x}^\alpha$ in which $S^\mu_{.\nu}$ is given by eq. (4-22). Equation (4-68) becomes

$$\ddot{\bar{t}} - \alpha^2 \bar{t} = \frac{\alpha}{c} \bar{u}^2$$

$$\ddot{\bar{x}} + \omega^2 \bar{x} = \mp \omega \bar{u}^3$$

$$\ddot{\bar{y}} - \alpha^2 \bar{y} = \alpha c \bar{u}^0$$

$$\ddot{\bar{z}} + \omega^2 \bar{z} = \pm \omega \bar{u}^1$$

where

$$\alpha = \frac{q\bar{E}}{mc}, \qquad \omega = \frac{q\bar{B}}{m}.$$

The double signs refer to whether $\bar{\mathbf{B}}$ is parallel to $\bar{\mathbf{E}}$ (upper sign) or opposite to $\bar{\mathbf{E}}$ (lower sign). The coordinates are the same as in Section 4.3. The above differential equations have the solutions

$$\left.\begin{aligned}
\bar{t} &= \frac{1}{\alpha c} \bar{u}^2 (\cosh \alpha\tau - 1) + \frac{1}{\alpha} \bar{u}^0 \sinh \alpha\tau \\[2mm]
\bar{y} &= \frac{c}{\alpha} \bar{u}^0 (\cosh \alpha\tau - 1) + \frac{1}{\alpha} \bar{u}^2 \sinh \alpha\tau \\[2mm]
\bar{x} &= \mp \frac{1}{\omega} \bar{u}^3 (1 - \cos \omega\tau) + \frac{1}{\omega} \bar{u}^1 \sin \omega\tau \\[2mm]
\bar{z} &= \pm \frac{1}{\omega} \bar{u}^1 (1 - \cos \omega\tau) + \frac{1}{\omega} \bar{u}^3 \sin \omega\tau
\end{aligned}\right\} \qquad (4\text{-}69)$$

for the initial conditions $\bar{x}^\mu(0) = 0$, $\dot{\bar{x}}^\mu(0) = \bar{u}^\mu$.

The transformation back to the original arbitrary coordinates is accomplished by the use of eq. (4-21). The $\bar{u}^\mu$, which are obtained from the u^μ by the inverse transformation

$$\tilde{\xi}^\alpha_{\cdot\mu} = \begin{bmatrix} \cosh\phi & -c^{-1}\sinh\phi & 0 & 0 \\ -c\sinh\phi & \cosh\phi & 0 & 0 \\ 0 & 0 & \cos\psi & \sin\psi \\ 0 & 0 & -\sin\psi & \cos\psi \end{bmatrix},$$

are given by

$$\left. \begin{aligned} \bar{u}^0 &= u^0\cosh\phi - c^{-1}u^1\sinh\phi \\ \bar{u}^1 &= -u^0c\sinh\phi + u^1\cosh\phi \\ \bar{u}^2 &= u^2\cos\psi + u^3\sin\psi \\ \bar{u}^3 &= -u^2\sin\psi + u^3\cos\psi. \end{aligned} \right\} \tag{4-70}$$

The coordinates x^μ are given by

$$\left. \begin{aligned} t &= \bar{t}\cosh\phi + c^{-1}\bar{x}\sinh\phi \\ x &= \bar{t}c\sinh\phi + \bar{x}\cosh\phi \\ y &= \bar{y}\cos\psi - \bar{z}\sin\psi \\ z &= \bar{y}\sin\psi + \bar{z}\cos\psi. \end{aligned} \right\} \tag{4-71}$$

Equations (4-69), (4-70), and (4-71) represent the equations of motion of a charged particle in uniform electric and magnetic fields.

The departure of the above results from the classical theory is most easily seen in the case of *perpendicular* electric and magnetic fields. The two cases $E > cB$ and $E < cB$ must be studied separately.

For $I_2 = 0$ and $E > cB$, we found in Section 4.3 that $\bar{B}$ and $\bar{E}$ are given by

$$\bar{B} = 0$$

$$\bar{E} = \sqrt{E^2 - c^2B^2}$$

$$\psi = 0.$$

Therefore ω vanishes, and α is given by

$$\alpha = \frac{q}{mc}\sqrt{E^2 - c^2B^2}.$$

The eigenvalue of $S^\mu_{\cdot\nu}$ is $I = \frac{1}{2}\epsilon_0(E^2 - c^2B^2)$. The velocity of the canonical frame is

$$v = \frac{c^2B}{E} = c\tanh\phi.$$

Hence eqs. (4-71) become

$$t = \frac{E\bar{t} + B\bar{x}}{\sqrt{E^2 - c^2 B^2}}$$

$$x = \frac{c^2 B\bar{t} + E\bar{x}}{\sqrt{E^2 - c^2 B^2}}$$

$$y = \bar{y}$$

$$z = \bar{z}.$$

Equations (4-69) become

$$\left.\begin{aligned}
\bar{t} &= \frac{1}{\alpha c} u^2 (\cosh \alpha\tau - 1) + \frac{1}{\alpha} \bar{u}^0 \sinh \alpha\tau \\
\bar{y} &= \frac{c}{\alpha} \bar{u}^0 (\cosh \alpha\tau - 1) + \frac{1}{\alpha} u^2 \sinh \alpha\tau \\
\bar{x} &= \bar{u}^1 \tau \\
\bar{z} &= u^3 \tau,
\end{aligned}\right\} \qquad (4\text{-}72)$$

and eqs. (4-70) become

$$\bar{u}^0 = \frac{Eu^0 - Bu^1}{\sqrt{E^2 - c^2 B^2}}$$

$$\bar{u}^1 = \frac{Eu^1 - c^2 Bu^0}{\sqrt{E^2 - c^2 B^2}} .$$

The particle accelerates continually. Its velocity approaches c, and its direction approaches that of the line $t:x:y:z = E:c^2 B:c\sqrt{E^2 - c^2 B^2}:0$.

For $I_2 = 0$ and $E < cB$, we have

$$\bar{E} = 0$$

$$c\bar{B} = \sqrt{c^2 B^2 - E^2}$$

$$\psi = \frac{\pi}{2}$$

$$\alpha = 0$$

$$\omega = \frac{q}{mc} \sqrt{c^2 B^2 - E^2}$$

$$v = \frac{E}{B} = c \tanh \phi.$$

Equations (4-69) become

$$\bar{t} = \bar{u}^0 \tau$$

$$\bar{y} = \bar{u}^2 \tau$$

$$\bar{x} = -\frac{1}{\omega} \bar{u}^3 (1 - \cos \omega\tau) + \frac{1}{\omega} \bar{u}^1 \sin \omega\tau$$

$$\bar{z} = +\frac{1}{\omega} \bar{u}^1 (1 - \cos \omega\tau) + \frac{1}{\omega} \bar{u}^3 \sin \omega\tau.$$

(The upper signs have been chosen because $I_2 = 0$.) Equations (4-71) become

$$t = \frac{cB\bar{t} + c^{-1}E\bar{x}}{\sqrt{c^2 B^2 - E^2}}$$

$$x = \frac{cE\bar{t} + cB\bar{x}}{\sqrt{c^2 B^2 - E^2}}$$

$$y = -\bar{z}$$

$$z = \bar{y}.$$

Equations (4-70) become

$$\bar{u}^0 = \frac{cBu^0 - c^{-1}Eu^1}{\sqrt{c^2 B^2 - E^2}}$$

$$\bar{u}^1 = \frac{cBu^1 - cEu^0}{\sqrt{c^2 B^2 - E^2}}$$

$$\bar{u}^2 = u^3$$

$$\bar{u}^3 = -u^2.$$

The particle gyrates with angular frequency ω and pursues an overall motion in the direction $t:x:y:z = (u^0 \cosh \phi - c^{-1}u^1 \sinh \phi) \cosh \phi : (cu^0 \cosh \phi - u^1 \sinh \phi) \sinh \phi : 0 : u^3$.

The exceptional case $\mathbf{E} \perp \mathbf{B}$ and $E = cB$, which possesses no canonical form, is obtained from either of the two cases which have $\mathbf{E} \perp \mathbf{B}$ by taking the limit as $E - cB \to 0$. The result is

$$t = \frac{q^2 E^2}{6m^2 c^2} \left(u^0 - \frac{u^1}{c} \right) \tau^3 + \frac{qEu^2}{2mc^2} \tau^2 + u^0 \tau$$

$$x = \frac{q^2 E^2}{6m^2 c} \left(u^0 - \frac{u^1}{c} \right) \tau^3 + \frac{qEu^2}{2mc} \tau^2 + u^1 \tau$$

$$y = \frac{qE}{2m} \left(u^0 - \frac{u^1}{c} \right) \tau^2 + u^2 \tau$$

$$z = u^3 \tau$$

for the initial conditions $x^\mu(0) = 0$ and $\dfrac{dx^\mu}{d\tau}(0) = u^\mu$. For the special case $u^\mu = \delta_0^\mu$, the trajectory is given by

$$x = \sqrt{\frac{2qE}{9mc^2}}\, y^{\frac{3}{2}}. \tag{4-73}$$

The motion of a charged particle starting from rest in uniform, perpendicular electric and magnetic fields may be described in the following way. For notation, let $\mathbf{E}$ be the electric field, $\mathbf{B}$ be the magnetic field, and $\mathbf{P} = \epsilon_0 c^2 \mathbf{E} \times \mathbf{B}$ be Poynting's vector. If E is greater than cB, the particle's velocity increases monotonically and approaches c in the $\mathbf{E}$-$\mathbf{P}$ plane; the particle's velocity in the $\mathbf{P}$ direction approaches $c^2 B/E$. If E is less than cB, then the particle gyrates with angular frequency $\omega = qm^{-1}\sqrt{B^2 - E^2 c^{-2}}$ in an elliptical orbit whose center travels in the $\mathbf{P}$ direction with velocity E/B; the ellipse has its plane perpendicular to $\mathbf{B}$ and has semi-axes $c^2 EB/\omega(c^2 B^2 - E^2)$ and $cE/\omega\sqrt{c^2 B^2 - E^2}$ in the $\mathbf{P}$ and $\mathbf{E}$ directions, respectively. If E is equal to cB, the particle follows the trajectory of eq. (4-73); the particle's speed increases monotonically and approaches c in the $\mathbf{P}$ direction.

In the classical theory, a charged particle starting from rest in uniform, perpendicular electric and magnetic fields gyrates with angular velocity $\omega = qB/m$ in a circle whose radius is $E/\omega B$ and whose center travels in the $\mathbf{P}$ direction with velocity E/B. The classical theory contains no case in which the particle's momentum takes off for infinity, as in the special-relativistic theory for $E \geq cB$. However, the classical theory is not applicable to cases in which E/cB is not negligible. The maximum velocity of the particle in the classical cycloid is $2E/B$, and if this velocity is not small compared to c, then the classical theory is invalid. There is one note of agreement: in both the classical theory and the relativistic theory, the velocity in the $\mathbf{B}$ direction is constant.

4.8 CONSTANT PROPER ACCELERATION

The motion of a charged particle in a constant, uniform electric field $\mathbf{E}$ is an example of motion in which the proper acceleration is constant. Since the coordinates are already canonical (there is no magnetic field), eqs. (4-72) are the equations of motion. For simplicity the initial velocity is taken to be zero. The motion of the particle is given by

$$t = \frac{\sinh \alpha\tau}{\alpha}$$
$$x = 0$$
$$y = ca^{-1}(\cosh \alpha\tau - 1)$$
$$z = 0$$

where τ is the proper time of the particle and α is the constant

$$\alpha = \frac{qE}{mc}.$$

The y-axis is in the direction of the electric field.

The vector acceleration $d^2x^\mu/d\tau^2$ is found by differentiation to be

$$\frac{d^2x^\mu}{d\tau^2} = \alpha(\sinh \alpha\tau, 0, \cosh \alpha\tau, 0).$$

By means of the Lorentz transformation

$$t' = \gamma(t - vc^{-2}y) \qquad x' = x$$

$$y' = \gamma(y - vt) \qquad z' = z$$

$$\gamma = \frac{dt}{d\tau} = \cosh \alpha\tau$$

$$v = \frac{dy}{dt} = c \tanh \alpha\tau$$

to the proper system x'^μ of the particle, the proper acceleration is obtained:

$$\frac{d^2x'^\mu}{d\tau^2} = \alpha c(0, 0, 1, 0).$$

Thus the motion is a case of *constant proper acceleration*. The proper acceleration is αc.

A *rigid rod* under constant acceleration provides some curious results. We ask for the motion of a rod in which each molecule undergoes constant proper acceleration and in which the molecules maintain constant proper separations. Consider two points of the rod separated by a proper distance l. At some arbitrary, simultaneous proper time, the two points are at the events O and A in Figure 4.1. The acceleration, the velocity, and the y-axis are to the right. The coordinate difference between O and A

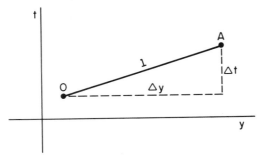

FIGURE 4.1 Accelerated rod.

in the proper system

$$\Delta \bar{x}^\alpha = (0, 0, l, 0)$$

is transformed by the Lorentz transformation into the coordinate difference in the stationary coordinates:

$$\Delta x^\mu = \gamma l(vc^{-2}, 0, 1, 0).$$

Thus we have $\Delta y = \gamma l$ and $\Delta t = \gamma l v c^{-2}$, where $\gamma = \left(1 - \dfrac{v^2}{c^2}\right)^{-\frac{1}{2}}$. The point O is assumed to have constant proper acceleration a:

$$y = c^2 a^{-1}(\cosh ac^{-1}\tau - 1)$$
$$t = ca^{-1} \sinh ac^{-1}\tau$$
$$v = c \tanh ac^{-1}\tau.$$

Therefore A has coordinates

$$y' = c^2 a^{-1}(\cosh ac^{-1}\tau - 1) + \gamma l$$
$$t' = ca^{-1} \sinh ac^{-1}\tau + \gamma l c^{-1} \tanh ac^{-1}\tau,$$

or since $\gamma = \cosh ac^{-1}\tau$,

$$y' = c^2 b^{-1} \cosh ac^{-1}\tau - c^2 a^{-1}$$
$$t' = cb^{-1} \sinh ac^{-1}\tau$$

where

$$\frac{1}{b} = \frac{1}{a} + \frac{l}{c^2}.$$

Differentiation of x' and t' shows that the ratio of proper time at A, $d\tau' = \sqrt{dt'^2 - c^{-2} dy'^2}$, to the proper time $d\tau$ at O is

$$\frac{d\tau'}{d\tau} = \frac{a}{b},$$

and that the proper acceleration of A is b.

Thus a rigid rod under constant proper acceleration has a proper acceleration a which varies from one point to another in the rod. Furthermore, the rate of passage of proper time τ varies from one point in the rod to another. The functional dependences of a and τ on the proper distance y along the rod are obtained by taking the limit $l \to dy$. The differential equation for $a(x)$ is

$$\frac{da}{a^2} = -\frac{dy}{c^2}$$

which has the solution

$$\frac{1}{a} = \frac{y}{c^2} + \text{const.}$$

The proper time is given by $a\, d\tau = \text{const.}$

4.9 RADIATION PRESSURE ON PARTICLES IN SPACE

Consider a spherical particle with proper mass m and world-velocity u^μ which scatters (whether by reflection or by absorption and re-radiation) electromagnetic radiation isotropically in all directions relative to its proper system. The incident radiation is assumed to be a plane wave represented by the stress-energy tensor $S^{\mu\nu} = c^{-2}Ul^\mu l^\nu$ of Section 4.4.

The proper system $\bar{x}^\alpha$ of the particle at a given event is used for writing down the equation of motion. The force on the particle is then due only to the incident radiation, because the re-emitted radiation is isotropic. The force is therefore $c^{-1}A\bar{P}^i$ or $c^{-1}A\bar{U}\bar{l}^i$, where A is the effective cross-sectional area of the particle, and $\bar{U}$ and $\bar{l}^i$ are the energy density and propagation "vector" for the incident radiation in the proper system. It is noted from the relations

$$\frac{d^2x^i}{d\tau^2} = u^0 \frac{d}{d\bar{t}} u^0 \frac{dx^i}{d\bar{t}} = u^{0^2} \frac{d^2x^i}{d\bar{t}^2} + u^0 \frac{du^0}{d\bar{t}} \frac{dx^i}{d\bar{t}}$$

and

$$\frac{du^0}{d\tau} = \frac{d}{d\tau} \frac{1}{\sqrt{1 - \dfrac{v^2}{c^2}}} = \frac{u^{0^3}}{c^2} v^k \frac{dv^k}{d\tau}$$

where τ is the proper time of the *accelerated* particle, $\bar{t}$ is the time of the proper *inertial* frame, and $v^k = u^k/u^0$, that in proper coordinates, where $\bar{u}^\mu = \delta_0^\mu$ and $\bar{v}^k = 0$, we have

$$\frac{d^2\bar{x}^i}{d\tau^2} = \frac{d^2\bar{x}^i}{d\bar{t}^2}$$

and

$$\frac{d\bar{u}^0}{d\tau} = 0.$$

Furthermore, the proper mass is constant because the particle re-emits all the energy which it absorbs. Therefore the equations of motion may be written

$$\frac{d}{d\tau}(m\bar{u}^i) = \frac{A\bar{U}}{c}\bar{l}^i \qquad\qquad \text{a} \left.\vphantom{\begin{array}{c}1\\1\\1\\1\end{array}}\right\}$$

$$\frac{d}{d\tau}(m\bar{u}^0) = 0. \qquad\qquad\quad \text{b} \quad \text{(4-74)}$$

Equations (4-74) can be combined into the four-dimensional form

$$\frac{d}{d\tau}(m\bar{u}^\mu) = \frac{A\bar{U}}{c}(\bar{l}^\mu - \bar{u}^\mu)$$

or, since $\bar{u}_\beta \bar{l}^\beta = 1$,

$$\frac{d}{d\tau}(m\bar{u}^\mu) = \frac{A}{c} \, \bar{U}(\bar{u}_\beta \bar{l}^\beta)^2 \left(\frac{\bar{l}^\mu}{\bar{u}_\gamma \bar{l}^\gamma} - \bar{u}^\mu\right). \tag{4-75}$$

Equation (4-75) is merely the equation

$$\frac{d}{d\tau}(mu^\mu) = \frac{A}{c} \, U(u_\beta l^\beta)^2 \left(\frac{l^\mu}{u_\gamma l^\gamma} - u^\mu\right) \tag{4-76}$$

evaluated in proper coordinates. But eq. (4-76) is, according to the results of Section 4.4, a *vector* equation. Now it is a general principle, and one which will be used throughout this book, that a tensor equation of any rank which is valid in one coordinate system is valid in all coordinate systems. The proof is merely to multiply the equation in the special coordinates by the appropriate transformation matrices. Therefore eq. (4-76) is valid in any inertial coordinate system. The effective area A is regarded as a scalar, since it is to be evaluated only in the proper system. Equation (4-76) may be re-written in the simplified form

$$\frac{du^\mu}{d\tau} = Rw(l^\mu - wu^\mu) \tag{4-77}$$

where

$$R = \frac{AU}{mc}$$

and

$$w = u_\alpha l^\alpha.$$

The force exerted on a particle by radiation in accordance with eq. (4-77) is known as the *Poynting-Robertson effect*.

The only conditions which we have placed on the structure of the particle are that it possess spherical symmetry and that it isotropically re-radiate all the energy that it absorbs. Although there are no further requirements on the nature of the particle, there are two specific models which are commonly used. One model is a perfect blackbody sphere with infinite thermal conductivity and zero specific heat. The other model is a sphere having a perfectly reflecting surface. It may not be obvious at first, but a straightforward calculation which can be carried out by the reader shows that the reflecting model produces isotropic reflection and has the same effective area as the blackbody model.

Two special cases are of practical interest. First, there is the case of motion in a field of uniform, uni-directional radiation. This provides an estimate of the rate at which stellar radiation flushes particles out of the galaxy. Second, there is the case of motion in radiation which is emitted isotropically from a stationary point. This will describe the behavior of particles which experience the sun's radiation.

For the case of a uniform, uni-directional radiation field, both R and l^μ are constant. Equation (4-77) may be multiplied by the null "vector" l^μ to give

$$\frac{dw}{d\tau} = -Rw^3. \tag{4-78}$$

The solution of eq. (4-78) is $w = (2R\tau + B)^{-\frac{1}{2}}$ where B is the constant of integration. Equation (4-77) therefore becomes

$$\frac{du^\mu}{d\tau} + \frac{R}{2R\tau + B} u^\mu = \frac{Rl^\mu}{\sqrt{2R\tau + B}}$$

which has the integral

$$u^\mu = \tfrac{1}{2}\sqrt{2R\tau + B}\, l^\mu + \frac{k^\mu}{2\sqrt{2R\tau + B}}. \tag{4-79}$$

It is easily verified from eq. (4-79) that the constants of integration k^μ satisfy the conditions

$$k_\mu k^\mu = 0,$$

$$k_\mu l^\mu = 2.$$

Equation (4-79) may be integrated to give

$$x^\mu = \frac{1}{6R} (2R\tau + B)^{\frac{3}{2}} l^\mu + \frac{1}{2R} (2R\tau + B)^{\frac{1}{2}} k^\mu + a^\mu,$$

where the a^μ are constants of integration. The velocity is

$$v^i = \frac{dx^i}{dx^0} = \frac{(2R\tau + B)l^i + k^i}{(2R\tau + B)l^0 + k^0}.$$

In order to understand the above results, k^μ is put into the form $k^\mu = k^0(1, cm^i)$ where, since k^μ is a null "vector," m^i is a unit spatial vector: $m^k m^k = 1$. As the particle's proper time τ approaches infinity, the particle's velocity approaches the speed of light in the direction of the radiation. When we follow the solution backward in time, we come to a singular event at $\tau = -B/2R$, $x^\mu = a^\mu$ at which the particle had a velocity equal to the speed of light in the direction of the spatial vector m^i. The motion of a particle which experiences radiation pressure is thus very different from the case of constant proper acceleration in the previous section. Here the force depends on the particle's velocity. The particle experiences a more intense flux when it heads *into* the radiation than when it moves *with* the radiation.

For the special case in which the particle starts from rest at the origin in a radiation field parallel to the x-axis, the motion is given by

$$t = \frac{1}{6R}(2R\tau + 1)^{\frac{3}{2}} + \frac{1}{2R}(2R\tau + 1)^{\frac{1}{2}} - \frac{2}{3R}$$

$$x = \frac{c}{6R}(2R\tau + 1)^{\frac{3}{2}} - \frac{c}{2R}(2R\tau + 1)^{\frac{1}{2}} + \frac{c}{3R}$$

$$y = 0$$

$$z = 0,$$

and the particle's velocity is

$$v = \frac{Rc\tau}{R\tau + 1} = \frac{c}{1 + \dfrac{1}{R\tau}}.$$

The constant $1/R$, which has the dimension of time, is a measure of the time required for the particle to attain a speed close to that of light. In a proper time $1/R$, the speed becomes $\frac{1}{2}c$. For a particle of density ρ and effective radius a, R is given by

$$\frac{1}{R} = \frac{4}{3}\frac{\rho ac}{U}.$$

For the radiation density in the galaxy, which is of order $Uc^{-2} = 10^{-33}$ gm cm^{-3}, this becomes

$$\frac{1}{R} = \frac{a\rho}{7} \times 10^{16} \text{ yr cm}^2 \text{ gm}^{-1}.$$

Hence in an interval of 10^6 years, the particle attains a speed of

$$\frac{v}{c} = \frac{1}{1 + \frac{1}{7}a\rho \cdot 10^{10} \text{ gm}^{-1} \text{ cm}^2} \simeq \frac{7}{a\rho} \cdot 10^{-10} \frac{\text{gm}}{\text{cm}^2}.$$

For a particle with density 1 gm cm^{-3} and radius 10^{-3} cm, the velocity is $10^{-6}c$. The time required for such a particle, starting from rest, to move a distance of 100 parsecs is 3×10^7 years, a time which is short by astronomical standards.

We turn now to the effect of the solar radiation on particles in the solar system. It will be sufficiently accurate to retain only terms of order v/c in eq. (4-77):

$$\frac{dv^i}{dt} = R[cn^i - (n^k v^k)n^i - v^i].$$

In the sun's vicinity, the density of radiation varies as the inverse square of the distance r from the sun. Therefore we may write

$$R = \frac{\alpha}{r^2} = \frac{AU}{mc}$$

where α is a constant having the dimensions of angular momentum per unit mass; α is given by

$$\alpha = \frac{3L}{16\pi a \rho c^2} = 2.5 \times 10^{11} \frac{1}{a\rho} \text{ gm sec}^{-1},$$

where L is the rate of emission of solar energy, for a particle of density ρ and radius a.

The trajectory of the particle is determined by two forces—gravity and radiation pressure. Newtonian gravity is sufficiently accurate for the problem. Therefore the total force per unit mass acting on the particle has radial component

$$\frac{d^2r}{dt^2} - r\left(\frac{d\phi}{dt}\right)^2 = -\frac{GM}{r^2} + \frac{\alpha c}{r^2}\left(1 - \frac{2}{c}\frac{dr}{dt}\right) \qquad \text{a}$$

and tangential component

$$\frac{1}{r}\frac{d}{dt}\left(r^2\frac{d\phi}{dt}\right) = -\frac{\alpha}{r}\frac{d\phi}{dt} \qquad \text{b}$$

(4-80)

where ϕ is the angle in the orbit plane and M is the mass of the sun. The quantity

$$H(\phi) = r^2\frac{d\phi}{dt} \qquad (4\text{-}81)$$

is, according to eq. (4-80b), given by

$$H(\phi) = h - \alpha\phi \qquad (4\text{-}82)$$

where h is the constant of integration. We may interpret h as the initial angular momentum per unit mass and H as the subsequent angular momentum per unit mass. The substitutions $r = 1/u$ and $d/dt = Hu^2\,d/d\phi$ into eq. (4-80a) result in the differential equation

$$\frac{d^2u}{d\phi^2} + \frac{\alpha}{H}\frac{du}{d\phi} + u = \frac{k}{H^2} \qquad (4\text{-}83)$$

where

$$k = GM - \alpha c.$$

If α is small compared to H, then the perturbation method can be applied to eq. (4-83). The second term on the left-hand side is omitted in finding the unperturbed orbit. The latter is represented by eq. (1-54):

$$u = \frac{1}{p}(1 + e \cos \phi).$$

However, to distinguish the unperturbed orbit from the perturbed orbit, the former will be denoted by u':

$$u' = \frac{1}{p}(1 + e \cos \phi) \tag{4-84}$$

where p is given by

$$p = \frac{h^2}{k}. \tag{4-85}$$

The function $u'(\phi)$ of eq. (4-84) satisfies the differential equation

$$\frac{d^2u'}{d\phi^2} + u' = \frac{k}{h^2}. \tag{4-86}$$

The difference between eqs. (4-83) and (4-86) is then

$$\frac{d^2u_1}{d\phi^2} + u_1 = \frac{2\alpha}{hp}\phi + \frac{\alpha e}{hp}\sin\phi \tag{4-87}$$

where $u_1 = u - u'$. Equation (4-87), which is the equation for the perturbation u_1, has the solution

$$u_1 = \frac{2\alpha}{hp}\phi - \frac{\alpha e}{2hp}\phi\cos\phi.$$

Thus the orbit is given by

$$u = \frac{1}{p}(1 + e \cos \phi) + \frac{2\alpha}{hp}\phi - \frac{\alpha e}{2hp}\phi\cos\phi$$

or

$$u = \frac{1 + \left(1 - \frac{5}{2}\frac{\alpha}{h}\phi\right)e\cos\phi}{p\left(1 - \frac{2\alpha}{h}\phi\right)} \tag{4-88}$$

(only terms of first order in α have been retained). Comparison of eqs. (4-88) and (4-84) shows that the perturbed eccentricity is

$$e\left(1 - \frac{5}{2}\frac{\alpha}{h}\phi\right)$$

and the perturbed semi-latus rectum is

$$p\left(1 - \frac{2\alpha}{h}\phi\right).$$

Thus, to first order in α, we have the rates

$$\frac{1}{e}\frac{\Delta e}{\Delta\phi} = -\frac{5}{2}\frac{\alpha}{h} \qquad\qquad \text{a}$$

$$\frac{1}{p}\frac{\Delta p}{\Delta\phi} = -\frac{2\alpha}{h} \qquad\qquad \text{b} \Bigg\} \quad (4\text{-}89)$$

$$\frac{1}{a}\frac{\Delta a}{\Delta\phi} = -\frac{2+3e^2}{1-e^2}\frac{\alpha}{h}. \qquad \text{c}$$

The last relation comes from eq. (1-55).

Equations (4-89) show that the orbit of the particle shrinks under the influence of the solar radiation, and that as the orbit shrinks, it becomes more and more circular. As the particle's orbit shrinks, so does the instantaneous unperturbed orbit. Thus eq. (4-85) must be replaced by

$$kp = H^2. \qquad (4\text{-}90)$$

Equation (4-89b) can be obtained by differentiation of eq. (4-90) and the use of eq. (4-82):

$$\frac{d\ln p}{d\phi} = 2\frac{d\ln H}{d\phi} = -\frac{2\alpha}{H}. \qquad (4\text{-}91)$$

The time t required for the particle to spiral from an initial radius r_0 to a final radius r (assuming zero eccentricity) is obtained from eqs. (4-81) and (4-91). The chain rule for differentiation gives

$$r\frac{dr}{dt} = -2\alpha$$

which has the integral

$$r_0^2 - r^2 = 4\alpha t. \qquad (4\text{-}92)$$

But since only the first order terms were carried along, we can only conclude that the ratio r/r_0 differs from unity by a term which, to lowest order in α, is $2\alpha t/r_0^2$:

$$1 - \frac{r}{r_0} = \frac{2\alpha t}{r_0^2}.$$

A more accurate result is obtained by using a correction to eq. (4-90). Substitution of $u = kH^{-2}$ into eq. (4-83) and the use of eq. (4-82) shows that the neglected terms are of order $(\alpha/H)^2 u$. If the more accurate solution

$$u = \frac{k}{H^2}\left(1 - \frac{8\alpha^2}{H^2}\right) \qquad (4\text{-}93)$$

is substituted into eq. (4-83), the neglected terms are of order $(\alpha/H)^4 u$. The use of eq. (4-93) to eliminate H from eq. (4-81) with the latter in the form

$$\frac{d\ln H}{dt} = -\frac{\alpha}{r^2} \qquad (4\text{-}94)$$

gives

$$4\alpha t = r_0^2 - r^2 + 16\alpha^2 k^{-1}(r_0 - r).$$

Thus as long as the quantity $(\alpha/H)^2$ or α^2/kr is small compared with unity, eq. (4-92) gives a rather accurate expression for the time t in which the orbit shrinks from radius r_0 to radius r. In particular, the time for an orbit of initial radius r_0 to contract to the origin is

$$t = \frac{r_0^2}{4\alpha}.$$

It is interesting to note that the perturbation method applies to cases in which the ratio k/GM is as small as 10^{-5}. We assumed that α/H is small, but not that k/GM is small. From eq. (4-90) we find

$$\left(\frac{\alpha}{H}\right)^2 \frac{p}{\mu} = \frac{\left(1 - \dfrac{k}{GM}\right)^2}{\dfrac{k}{GM}}. \tag{4-95}$$

The quantity

$$\mu = \frac{GM}{c^2}$$

is the *gravitational radius* of the mass M. For the sun, μ has the value 1.48 km. Thus, for a particle one astronomical unit from the sun, the ratio p/μ is 10^8. If the perturbation method is relied upon for $(\alpha/h)^2$ as large as 10^{-3}, then k/GM can be as small as 10^{-5}.

A particle for which k is positive spirals into the sun. A particle for which k is negative is repelled from the solar system. It remains to consider particles for which k is positive but is so small that α/H from eq. (4-95) is appreciably larger than unity. Then the solution to eq. (4-83) may be approximated by

$$u = -\frac{k}{2\alpha^2} \ln \frac{H}{\alpha} + \text{const.} \tag{4-96}$$

The elimination of H from eqs. (4-94) and (4-96) gives

$$\frac{dr}{dt} = -\frac{k}{2\alpha}.$$

The time for the particle to drop from radius r_0 to radius r is

$$t = \frac{2\alpha}{k}(r_0 - r).$$

As k approaches zero, t approaches ∞.

We may summarize the effect of solar radiation on particles in the solar system as follows. (It is assumed that the gravitational effects of the planets are negligible.) The radiation pressure is inversely proportional to the product $a\rho$ of the particle's effective radius a and its density ρ. For the critical value

$$a\rho = 5.7 \times 10^{-5} \text{ gm cm}^{-2},$$

the radiation pressure exactly balances the solar gravitation. For values of $a\rho$ smaller than the critical value, the particle is repelled from the sun. For values of $a\rho$ larger than the critical value (the difference need only be larger than 1 per cent), the particle spirals in toward the sun. As an example, consider particles with density 5.5 gm cm^{-3} (the same as the earth) and initial distance $r_0 = 1$ A.U. The constant α then has the value $4.6 \times 10^{10}a^{-1}$ cm^3 sec^{-1}. Particles with $a = 1$ cm last for 4×10^7 years, and particles with $a = 10^{-3}$ cm last for only 4×10^4 years. The maximum number of revolutions which the particle makes before striking the sun is, from eqs. (4-82) and (4-85),

$$N = \frac{h}{2\pi\alpha} = \frac{\sqrt{kr_0}}{2\pi\alpha} = 2.8 \times 10^7 \, a\rho\sqrt{\frac{kr_0}{GM} \frac{\text{A.U.}}{\text{gm}}} \frac{\text{cm}^2}{}.$$

Thus, for particles with density 5.5 gm cm^{-3} and initial distance 1 A.U., those with $a = 1$ cm have a limit of 1.6×10^8 revolutions, and those with $a = 10^{-3}$ cm have a limit of 1.6×10^5 revolutions.

The Poynting-Robertson effect may be regarded as the dynamic effect of the aberration of sunlight. By the same principle which explains the aberration of starlight, there is a component of the sun's radiation which opposes the particle's motion. Thus the particle continually loses momentum and must therefore spiral into the sun. The energy lost by the particle in its orbit is emitted in the form of radiation. It must be remembered that the particle emits radiation isotropically *only* in its own frame. In any other frame, the emitted radiation has a net momentum.

When the Poynting-Robertson effect was first derived, little was known about the interplanetary medium. The discovery of the *solar wind* has altered our picture of the solar system. The solar wind is a stream of ions, principally protons, which comes from the sun. At the earth's distance from the sun, the ions have an average velocity of 300 to 400 km/sec, but during solar flares and storms the velocity may rise to 2000 km/sec. The ion density is 10 to 20 cm^{-3}, but rises to about 10^4 cm^{-3} during solar activity.

Equation (4-76) may be generalized to apply to a stream of particles with any velocity V:

$$m\frac{du^\mu}{d\tau} = A\rho cw(V^\mu - u^\mu u_\nu V^\nu)\sqrt{1 - \frac{1}{w^2\gamma^2}} \tag{4-97}$$

where $w = u_\alpha V^\alpha$, u^μ is the world-velocity of the particle, γV^μ is the world-velocity of the stream, $V^0 = 1$, and $\rho\gamma^{-2}$ is the proper mass density of the stream particles. Equation (4-97) is clearly a vector equation, since $w\gamma$ is a scalar. Equation (4-97) gives the correct force in proper coordinates. Therefore eq. (4-97) holds in any coordinates. Also, eq. (4-97) reduces to eq. (4-76) for the substitutions $\rho = Uc^{-2}$, $\gamma = \infty$, and $V^\mu = l^\mu$.

But the relativistic form of eq. (4-97) is hardly needed, since the solar-wind velocity is small compared with c. In the approximation $c \gg V \gg v$, the acceleration given by eq. (4-97) is

$$\frac{dv^i}{dt} = \frac{A\rho V}{m} [Vn^i - (n^k v^k)n^i - v^i]$$

where n^i is the unit spatial vector in the direction of the stream.

In order to compare the relative effects of the solar wind and the solar radiation, we will arbitrarily assume that ρ varies as r^{-2} and that V is constant. The equations of motion which then result for the combined forces due to radiation and solar wind show that the parameter α, which determines the *rate* of degeneration of the orbit, depends on the total momentum *density* $Uc^{-1} + \rho V$, while the effective gravitational force k, which determines the critical size-density at which the gravitational and repulsive forces exactly balance each other, depends on the total momentum *flux* $U + \rho V^2$. Since the ratios $\rho Vc/U$ and $\rho V^2/U$ have orders of magnitude 0.5 and 10^{-3}, respectively, for the quiet sun and 10^3 and 20, respectively, for the active sun, it is concluded that solar radiation should determine the critical size-density, but that the solar wind will make an appreciable contribution to the decay of orbits.

The above picture is naturally oversimplified. Not only do the various approximations introduce inaccuracies, but the presence of the interplanetary magnetic field precludes the application of any of the above conclusions to *charged* particles in interplanetary space, which would probably be coerced to move with the solar wind. However, it has been our purpose here to describe radiation pressure, not to give a complete analysis of the interplanetary medium.

One further case of radiation pressure is of special interest. Consider a free particle, of the type used earlier in this section, which travels through *isotropic* radiation of uniform density. Equation (4-76) can be applied individually to the radiation traveling in different directions. Integration over all directions, which is most easily performed in polar coordinates about the particle's direction of motion, yields the result

$$\frac{d}{d\tau}(mu^\mu) = -\frac{4AUu_0}{3c}(u_0 u^\mu - \delta_0^\mu),$$

where u^μ is the world-velocity of the particle, m is its mass, A is its proper cross-sectional area, τ is its proper time, and U is the energy density of the radiation. We make the substitution

$$R = \frac{4AU}{3mc},$$

noting that this R is $\frac{4}{3}$ times the previous R. The equations of motion

$$\frac{du_0}{d\tau} = -Ru_0(u_0^2 - 1)$$

$$\frac{du^i}{d\tau} = -Ru_0^2 u^i$$

have the solution

$$u_0 = \frac{1}{\sqrt{1 - e^{-2R\tau} \tanh^2 k}},$$

$$u^i = \frac{n^i c \tanh k}{\sqrt{e^{2R\tau} - \tanh^2 k}},$$

$$x^i = \frac{n^i c}{R} \left[\sin^{-1} \tanh k - \sin^{-1} \frac{\tanh k}{e^{R\tau}} \right]$$

$$t = \frac{1}{R} [\cosh^{-1} (e^{R\tau} \coth k) - \cosh^{-1} \coth k]$$

where k is a constant of integration and n^i is a unit spatial vector ($n^k n^k = 1$). The quantity $c \tanh k$ is identified as the initial velocity of the particle. In the classical approximation where $k \ll 1$, these solutions reduce to

$$\tau = t,$$

$$\frac{dx^i}{dt} = \frac{n^i ck}{e^{R\tau}},$$

$$x^i = \frac{n^i ck}{R} (1 - e^{-R\tau}).$$

Thus the particle undergoes a deceleration which is proportional to its velocity. It slows down exponentially and traverses a maximum distance ck/R, where ck is the initial velocity of the particle. Without the classical approximation the limiting distance is $(c/R) \sin^{-1} \tanh k$.

4.10 THE LIÉNARD-WIECHERT POTENTIAL

The electromagnetic potential ϕ^μ due to a charged particle in uniform motion, known as the *Liénard-Wiechert potential*, is obtained by transforming from the proper system $\bar{S}$ of the particle. Let x^μ be the coordinates

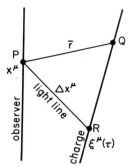

FIGURE 4.2 Potential of moving charge.

of the field event P, and let $\xi^\lambda(\tau)$ be the coordinates of the world-line of the particle, where τ is the proper time of the particle. Let the respective coordinates in $\bar{S}$ be denoted $\bar{x}^\alpha$ and $\bar{\xi}^\alpha(\tau)$.

In the proper system, the potential is given by the simple expression

$$\bar{\phi}^\alpha = \frac{q}{4\pi\epsilon_0 c^2 \bar{r}} \delta^\alpha_0 \tag{4-98}$$

where q is the charge and $\bar{r}$ is the distance in $\bar{S}$ from P to the event Q on the particle's world-line which is simultaneous with P. (See Figure 4.2.) We note that the definition of the 4-vector

$$\Delta x^\mu = x^\mu - \xi^\mu(\tau_R)$$

to P from the event R which lies on the backward light cone of P allows the distance $\bar{r}$ to be written in the form

$$\bar{r} = c\bar{u}_\alpha \Delta x^\alpha$$

where u^μ is the world-velocity $d\xi^\mu/d\tau$ of the particle. Equation (4-98) may therefore be written

$$\bar{\phi}^\alpha = \frac{q\bar{u}^\alpha}{4\pi\epsilon_0 c^3 \bar{u}_\nu \Delta\bar{x}^\nu} . \tag{4-99}$$

Equation (4-99) is immediately transformed into

$$\phi^\mu = \frac{qu^\mu}{4\pi\epsilon_0 c^3 u_\nu \Delta x^\nu} \tag{4-100}$$

for any coordinate system. Equation (4-100) gives the *Liénard-Wiechert potential.*

If the charged particle is not in uniform motion, then the potential at a field event P is still given by eq. (4-100), but the velocity $u^\mu(\tau)$ is evaluated at the event R which lies at the intersection of the particle's world-line with the backward light cone of P. (See Figure 4.3.) That is,

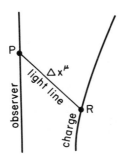

FIGURE 4.3 Potential of accelerated charge.

the potential is given by

$$\phi^\mu = \frac{q\dot\xi^\mu(\tau)}{4\pi\epsilon_0 c^3 \dot\xi_\nu(\tau)[x^\nu - \xi^\nu(\tau)]},\qquad(4\text{-}101)$$

where the proper time τ is that which corresponds to the event R; $\dot\xi^\mu$ denotes $d\xi^\mu/d\tau$. The proof of eq. (4-101), which is based on eqs. (2-12), is straightforward, and need not be given here.

4.11 THE CONSTITUTIVE RELATIONS IN MOVING MEDIA

Up to now we have dealt only with electromagnetic fields in *free space*. The electric displacement **D** and the magnetic field intensity **H** are then the components of the tensor

$$H_{\mu\nu} = \epsilon_0 F_{\mu\nu} = \frac{1}{c^2}\begin{bmatrix} 0 & -D_x & -D_y & -D_z \\ D_x & 0 & c^{-2}H_z & -c^{-2}H_y \\ D_y & -c^{-2}H_z & 0 & c^{-2}H_x \\ D_z & c^{-2}H_y & -c^{-2}H_x & 0 \end{bmatrix}.$$

For the electromagnetic fields in a moving medium, we first choose the proper system in which the element of material under consideration is momentarily at rest. Then Sections 2.1 to 2.3 apply. The tensor $H_{\mu\nu}$ is now defined by the conditions that it be an antisymmetric tensor and that, in the proper system, it be given by

$$H_{0i} = -c^{-2}D_i$$
$$H_{ij} = c^{-4}e(ijk)H_k.$$

With the assumption that the material possesses a *scalar permittivity* ϵ and a *scalar permeability* μ, eqs. (2-4) and (4-9) give

$$H_{0i} = \epsilon F_{0i} \qquad (4\text{-}102)$$
$$H_{ij} = \mu^{-1}c^{-2}F_{ij}.$$

The latter equation can be written

$$H_{ij} = \epsilon F_{ij} - \frac{\epsilon\mu - \epsilon_0\mu_0}{\mu} F_{ij} \tag{4-103}$$

so that eqs. (4-102) and (4-103) can be combined into the single equation

$$H_{\mu\nu} = \epsilon F_{\mu\nu} - \frac{\epsilon\mu - \epsilon_0\mu_0}{\mu} F_{\mu\nu}^{\perp}$$

where $F_{\mu\nu}^{\perp}$ is formed with the projection operator:

$$F_{\mu\nu}^{\perp} = (\delta_{\mu}^{\alpha} - u^{\alpha}u_{\mu})(\delta_{\nu}^{\beta} - u^{\beta}u_{\nu})F_{\alpha\beta}$$

where u^{μ} is the world-velocity of the medium at the given event (which in the proper system is δ_0^{μ}). Thus there results the equation

$$H_{\mu\nu} = \epsilon F_{\mu\nu} - \frac{\epsilon\mu - \epsilon_0\mu_0}{\mu}(\delta_{\mu}^{\alpha} - u^{\alpha}u_{\mu})(\delta_{\nu}^{\beta} - u^{\beta}u_{\nu})F_{\alpha\beta} \tag{4-104}$$

which is valid in the proper system. But eq. (4-104) is clearly in tensor form. Hence it is valid in all inertial systems.

Another form of eq. (4-104) is obtained by multiplying by μ and making use of the antisymmetry of $F_{\mu\nu}$.

$$\mu H_{\mu\nu} = \frac{1}{c^2} F_{\mu\nu} - (\epsilon\mu - \epsilon_0\mu_0)(u_{\mu}F_{\nu\alpha}u^{\alpha} - u_{\nu}F_{\mu\alpha}u^{\alpha}). \tag{4-105}$$

Equation (4-104) or (4-105) is known as the *constitutive relations* in a moving medium which has world-velocity u^{μ}.

The result of Wilson's experiment (see Section 2.5) can now be satisfactorily explained. A thin dielectric slab with metallic-faced surfaces parallel to the x-z plane moves with uniform velocity v in the x-direction in the presence of an external magnetic field $\mathbf{H} = (0, 0, H_0)$. Equations (4-10) may be used to transform field quantities $\mathbf{E}$ and $\mathbf{B}$ from the stationary frame to the slab's frame. In the slab's frame, the fields *outside* the slab are $\mathbf{E} = (0, -\gamma v\mu_0 H_0, 0)$ and $\mathbf{B} = (0, 0, \gamma\mu_0 H_0)$, and hence $\mathbf{D} = (0, -\gamma v\epsilon_0\mu_0 H_0, 0)$ and $\mathbf{H} = (0, 0, \gamma H_0)$, where $\gamma^{-2} = 1 - v^2/c^2$. By eqs. (2-2), since there is no current in the faces, the fields *inside* the slab are $\mathbf{D} = (0, -\gamma v\epsilon_0\mu_0 H_0 - \sigma, 0)$ and $\mathbf{H} = (0, 0, \gamma H_0)$, and hence

$$\mathbf{E} = \left(0, -\frac{\gamma v\epsilon_0\mu_0 H_0 + \sigma}{\epsilon}, 0\right)$$

and $\mathbf{B} = (0, 0, \gamma\mu H_0)$. The surface charge density on the $+y$ face is denoted by σ. This charge is that which lies in the metal; any polarization charge is accounted for by the permittivity of the dielectric. The use of eqs. (4-10) shows that the electric field intensity inside the dielectric in the *stationary* system is

$$\mathbf{E} = \left(0, \gamma^2 v\mu H_0 - \frac{\gamma}{\epsilon}(\gamma v\epsilon_0\mu_0 H_0 + \sigma), 0\right).$$

But this vector must be zero, because Wilson used a wire to short the two faces. Therefore the charge density is given by

$$\sigma = \gamma v H_0(\epsilon\mu - \epsilon_0\mu_0)$$

which is in agreement with the experimental results.

In free space, eq. (4-11) may be written

$$\frac{\partial H^{\mu\nu}}{\partial x^\nu} = J^\mu. \tag{4-106}$$

But then eq. (4-106) must also hold inside a material in the proper frame of the material. And, since $H_{\mu\nu}$ is defined to be a tensor, eq. (4-106) holds in all inertial frames. Thus if we *define*

$$\left.\begin{array}{l} D_i = -c^2 H_{0i} \\ H_i = \tfrac{1}{2}c^4 e(ijk)H_{jk} \end{array}\right\} \tag{4-107}$$

in all inertial frames, then Maxwell's equations (2-2) and (2-3) hold in all inertial frames. The sacrifice that is made is that eqs. (2-4) hold only in the proper frame of the material. If the permittivity and/or the permeability are not scalars, then eq. (4-105) is no longer applicable. However, the other equations—(4-9), (4-12), (4-106), and (4-107)—remain valid.

Ohm's law can similarly be expressed in tensor form. In the proper system, the 3-vector form $\mathbf{J} = \sigma\mathbf{E}$ may be written

$$J^i = \sigma F^{0i} = \sigma F^{\alpha i}u_\alpha \tag{4-108}$$

where u^μ is the world-velocity of the material and σ is the conductivity. The latter is assumed to be a scalar. Equation (4-108) states that the spatial projection of the 4-vector

$$J^\mu - \sigma u_\alpha F^{\alpha\mu}$$

is equal to zero. Hence we have

$$(\delta^\mu_\nu - u^\mu u_\nu)(J^\nu - \sigma u_\alpha F^{\alpha\nu}) = 0$$

or

$$J^\mu - u^\mu u_\nu J^\nu = \sigma u_\nu F^{\nu\mu}. \tag{4-109}$$

Equation (4-109), which is valid in the proper system, is a tensor equation; hence it is valid in all inertial frames.

CHAPTER 5

MATTER

5.1 STRESS-ENERGY TENSOR FOR A PERFECT FLUID

The *stress-energy tensor* $M^{\mu\nu}$ for matter is that tensor which has specified components in the proper system $\bar{x}^\alpha$ of the matter at a given event E. A *perfect fluid* is a fluid in which the only stress is an internal isotropic pressure. The stress-energy tensor for a perfect fluid is defined in the proper system to be

$$\left.\begin{aligned}
\bar{M}^{00} &= \rho_0 \\
\bar{M}^{0i} &= \bar{M}^{i0} = 0 \\
\bar{M}^{ij} &= p_0 \delta^{ij}
\end{aligned}\right\} \tag{5-1}$$

where $\rho_0 c^2$ is the proper density of total energy (this includes *all* energy: rest energy, thermal energy, nuclear energy, etc.) and p_0 is the proper pressure. Since both ρ_0 and p_0 are, by definition, measured in the proper system, they are regarded as scalars. Equation (5-1) may be written in the form

$$\bar{M}^{\alpha\beta} = (\rho_0 + c^{-2}p_0)\bar{u}^\alpha \bar{u}^\beta - c^{-2}p_0\eta^{\alpha\beta} \tag{5-2}$$

since the world-velocity u^μ of the fluid is $\bar{u}^\alpha = \delta_0^\alpha$ in the proper system. But eq. (5-2) is in tensor form, and hence is valid in all inertial frames. Thus the stress-energy tensor at an event E in a perfect fluid is

$$M^{\mu\nu} = (\rho_0 + c^{-2}p_0)u^\mu u^\nu - c^{-2}p\eta^{\mu\nu} \tag{5-3}$$

where ρ_0, p_0, and u^μ are, respectively, the proper density, proper pressure, and world-velocity of the fluid at E.

The most obvious property of $M^{\mu\nu}$ is its symmetry. A less obvious property is that the divergence of $M^{\mu\nu}$ is equal to the force density. Both properties hold even if the matter is not a perfect fluid.

Note that if the *total stress-energy tensor* $T^{\mu\nu}$, defined $T^{\mu\nu} = M^{\mu\nu} + S^{\mu\nu}$ where $S^{\mu\nu}$ is the electromagnetic stress-energy tensor, is postulated to have zero divergence

$$\frac{\partial T^{\mu\nu}}{\partial x^\nu} = 0, \tag{5-4}$$

then eq. (4-16) requires that the matter stress-energy tensor have divergence

$$\frac{\partial M^{\mu\nu}}{\partial x^\nu} = f^\mu, \tag{5-5}$$

where f^μ is the electromagnetic force density. If there were other fields present besides electromagnetism, the negative divergences of their stress-energy tensors would be included on the right-hand side of eq. (5-5).

The divergence of $M^{\mu\nu}$ can be evaluated directly from eq. (5-3):

$$f^\mu = \rho u^\alpha \frac{\partial u^\mu}{\partial x^\alpha} + u^\mu \frac{\partial}{\partial x^\nu}(\rho u^\nu) - \frac{\eta^{\mu\rho}}{c^2}\frac{\partial p_0}{\partial x^\rho} \tag{5-6}$$

where

$$\rho = \rho_0 + p_0 c^{-2}.$$

The first term on the right-hand side of eq. (5-6) is equal to $\rho\, du^\mu/d\tau$, where τ is the proper time. We proceed to solve for $\rho\, du^\mu/d\tau$ in order to obtain the equation of motion. Multiplication of eq. (5-6) by u_μ gives

$$u_\mu f^\mu = \frac{\partial}{\partial x^\nu}(\rho u^\nu) - \frac{u^\rho}{c^2}\frac{\partial p_0}{\partial x^\rho}. \tag{5-7}$$

For electromagnetic forces, the left-hand side of eq. (5-7) will vanish. However, it will not be assumed that f^μ is orthogonal to u^μ in what follows. Elimination of the term $\partial(\rho u^\nu)/\partial x^\nu$ from eq. (5-6) by means of eq. (5-7) then gives the result

$$\rho\frac{du^\mu}{d\tau} = (\eta^{\mu\nu} - u^\mu u^\nu)\left(f_\nu + \frac{1}{c^2}\frac{\partial p_0}{\partial x^\nu}\right). \tag{5-8}$$

We recognize eq. (5-8) as a form of eq. (4-47), with the F^μ/m there replaced by $\rho^{-1}(f^\mu + c^{-2}\eta^{\mu\nu}\,\partial p_0/\partial x^\nu)$ here. Thus the fluid has inertial density ρ and experiences a force density $f^\mu + c^{-2}\eta^{\mu\nu}\,\partial p_0/\partial x^\nu$; the latter is the sum of the electromagnetic force density and the pressure-gradient force density. The spatial part of the pressure term is the classical force density $-\partial p_0/\partial x^i$.

Equation (5-7) may be interpreted as the law of conservation of energy. Consider an infinitesimal spatial vector δx^i, the ends of which are carried

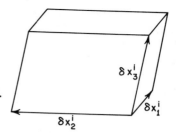

FIGURE 5.1 Volume carried with the fluid.

with the fluid. In a time dt, the vector changes by the amount

$$\frac{\partial v^i}{\partial x^k} \delta x^k \, dt$$

to attain the value

$$\delta x^i + d \, \delta x^i = \delta x^j \left(\delta^i_j + \frac{\partial v^i}{\partial x^j} \, dt \right).$$

We consider the volume δV of the parallelopiped formed by three such vectors δx^i_a ($a = 1, 2, 3,$ *not* a vector index). (See Figure 5.1.) In the time dt, the volume changes from the value $\delta V = |\delta x^i_a|$ to the value

$$\delta V + d \, \delta V = \left| \delta x^j_a \left(\delta^i_j + \frac{\partial v^i}{\partial x^j} \, dt \right) \right| = \delta V \left| \delta^i_j + \frac{\partial v^i}{\partial x^j} \, dt \right|.$$

Thus, to first order in dt, the fractional change in δV is given by

$$\frac{d \, \delta V}{\delta V} = \frac{\partial v^k}{\partial x^k} \, dt. \tag{5-9}$$

Equation (5-7) can be written

$$u_\mu f^\mu = \frac{d\rho_0}{d\tau} + \rho_0 \frac{\partial u^\nu}{\partial x^\nu} + \frac{p_0}{c^2} \frac{\partial u^\sigma}{\partial x^\sigma}$$

which in proper coordinates becomes

$$f^0 = \frac{d\rho_0}{dt} + \rho_0 \frac{\partial v^k}{\partial x^k} + \frac{p_0}{c^2} \frac{\partial v^l}{\partial x^l}.$$

Multiplication by $\delta V \, dt$ and the use of eq. (5-9) gives

$$f^0 \, \delta V \, dt = d(\rho_0 \, \delta V) + \frac{p_0}{c^2} d \, \delta V. \tag{5-10}$$

Equation (5-10) states that $f^0 c^2$ is, in proper coordinates, equal to the sum of the rate of increase of internal energy and the rate at which the pressure does work. For the case of electromagnetism, the orthogonality of u^μ and f^μ requires that f^0 vanish in proper coordinates. Thus electromagnetism does not contribute to the internal energy of the material. This may seem surprising in view of the possibility of the induction of electric or magnetic dipoles within the molecules of the medium. However, it should be recalled that the electromagnetic stress-energy tensor which has been used is the one for *free space*. The inclusion of electric or magnetic dipole densities would necessarily involve using non-zero electric and magnetic susceptibilities.

5.2 FIELD-TO-PARTICLE TRANSITION

The resemblance between eq. (5-8) and eq. (4-47) is an argument for the correctness of eq. (5-4) as a description of the electrodynamics of fluids. However, the presence of $\rho_0 + c^{-2}p_0$ instead of ρ_0 in eq. (5-8) as the inertia density introduces a note of doubt. Therefore it is necessary to prove rigorously that eq. (4-47) follows from eq. (5-5). On the one hand, eq. (5-5) involves two fields—the force density f^μ and the stress-energy tensor $M^{\mu\nu}$ of matter. On the other hand, eq. (4-47) involves corpuscular quantities—the mass and the world-velocity of a particle, and the force exerted on it. The purpose of this section is to obtain the equations of motion of a particle from the conservation law eq. (5-5) for the stress-energy tensor, by going to the limit as the stress-energy tensor can be considered to be localized along a single world-line.

A *congruence* is a bundle of non-intersecting curves. An example of a *time-like congruence* is the bundle of world-lines swept out by the particles of a fluid.

It is assumed that, at least within a region $\mathcal{R}$ of space-time, there exists a congruence. We will consider the tube-like regions of space-time which are defined in the following way. A volume V_1 in the 3-space $t = t_1 = \text{const}$ defines a set of members of the congruence, namely, those members which intersect the space $t = t_1$ in the boundary of the volume V_1. These members intersect another 3-space $t = t_2 = \text{const} > t_1$ in $\mathcal{R}$ in another volume V_2. The tube-like region R of space-time with which we are concerned is the region bounded by V_1, V_2, and the specified members of the congruence. (See Figure 5.2.)

Another tube-like region R' will be said to be *contained in* R if the 3-space volume V' formed by the intersection of R' with a 3-space $t = \text{const}$ is interior to the 3-space volume V formed by the intersection of R with $t = \text{const}$, for all t in the interval $t_1 \leq t \leq t_2$. Similarly, a world-line L will be said to be *contained in* R if the intersection of L with $t = \text{const}$ is an interior point of the volume V formed by the intersection of R with $t = \text{const}$, for all t in the interval $t_1 \leq t \leq t_2$.

It is noted that the quantity $d\Pi$ defined by the expression

$$d\Pi = e_{\mu\nu\rho\sigma} \, dx_0^\mu \, dx_1^\nu \, dx_2^\rho \, dx_3^\sigma \tag{5-11}$$

for an infinitesimal parallelopiped bounded by the vectors dx_0^μ, dx_1^μ, dx_2^μ,

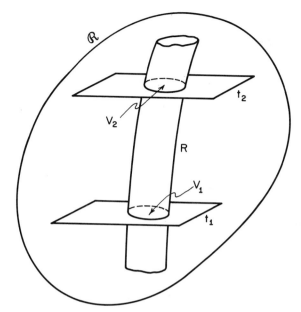

FIGURE 5.2 Definition of region R.

and dx_3^μ is a scalar. It is also noted that if dx_1^μ, dx_2^μ, and dx_3^μ are spatial, then $d\Pi$ has the form

$$d\Pi = dt\, dV \tag{5-12}$$

where $dt = dx_0^0$ and dV is the spatial volume of the spatial cross-section of the parallelopiped:

$$dV = e_{ijk}\, dx_1^i\, dx_2^j\, dx_3^k.$$

Thus an infinitesimally thin, straight, time-like, cylindrical region of the kind described above has, associated with it, the scalar

$$d\Pi = dt\, dV = d\tau\, dV_\pi$$

where dt is the temporal length of the cylinder, dV is its spatial cross-sectional volume, and $d\tau$ and dV_π are, respectively, the corresponding quantities in proper coordinates (with the proper-time axis parallel to the cylinder).

Let us consider now an infinite sequence of tube-like regions R_κ ($\kappa = 1, 2, \ldots$) of space-time, bounded by the spaces $t = t_1$ and $t = t_2$, and having the following three properties. (1) There is a curve C which is contained in all members R_κ of the sequence. (2) Each member R_κ contains in its interior its successor $R_{\kappa+1}$. (3) The volume V_κ and maximum diameter D_κ of the spatial cross-section of R_κ with any space $t = \text{const}$ ($t_1 \leq t \leq t_2$) both tend toward the limit 0 as $\kappa \to \infty$. It is assumed, of course, that the whole construction is within the region $\mathcal{R}$ of space-time in which the congruence exists.

We now have a nested sequence of world-tubes. Each member is within the previous member and, as the index κ approaches ∞, the sequence approaches a curve C. A parameter p which increases monotonically with t may be defined along C, so that C is given parametrically by the coordinates $x^\mu = \xi^\mu(p)$. We then define

$$u^\mu = \frac{d\xi^\mu}{dp}.$$

We next make an assumption about any field quantity $A(x^\mu)$ which will be studied. It does not matter whether A is a component of $M^{\mu\nu}$, a component of f^μ, or anything else. We assume that $A(x^\mu)$ can be replaced within R_1 by successive members of the set $A_\kappa(x^\mu)$ which have the property that $A_\kappa(x^\mu) = 0$ at all events $t_1 \leq t \leq t_2$ *outside* the tube R_κ. It is further assumed that the sequence $A_\kappa(x^\mu)$ is chosen so that for an arbitrary continuous function $w(x^\mu)$, we have

$$\lim_{\kappa \to \infty} \int_{V_\kappa} w(x^\mu) A_\kappa(x^\nu) \, dV = w(t, \xi^i)\alpha(t) \qquad (5\text{-}13)$$

where the volume integral extends over the spatial volume V_κ of the intersection of R_κ with $t = $ const ($t_1 \leq t \leq t_2$), and $x^i = \xi^i$ is the event E where the space $t = $ const intersects C. Differentiability of A is assumed to imply differentiability of $\alpha(t)$.

For the sake of a consistent notation throughout this section, field quantities will be denoted by capital Latin letters, and their limiting quantities in the sense of eq. (5-13) will be denoted by the corresponding lower-case Greek letters. The product of the latter by u^0 will be denoted by the corresponding lower-case Latin letter, e.g., $a = u^0\alpha$.

We must note that a tensorial nature for $A(x^\mu)$ does *not* imply the same tensorial nature for $\alpha(t)$. For example, if A is a scalar, then α is *not* a scalar, because dV is not a scalar. However, as may be seen in eq. (5-12), $dt \, dV/dp$ *is* a scalar. Therefore, $a = u^0\alpha$ would be a scalar. In general, if A is the $\mu\nu\rho \ldots^{\text{th}}$ component of a tensor, then a is also the $\mu\nu\rho \ldots^{\text{th}}$ component of a tensor.

With the preliminaries out of the way, we can proceed to a rapid conclusion. We start with a postulated field equation

$$\frac{\partial A^\mu}{\partial x^\mu} = B \qquad (5\text{-}14)$$

where A^μ and B are field quantities which satisfy the assumptions stated above (but they need *not* be, respectively, vector and scalar). Equation (5-14) is first multiplied by an arbitrary function $w(x^\mu)$ to give

$$\frac{\partial}{\partial x^\mu}(wA^\mu) - w_\mu A^\mu - wB = 0$$

where

$$w_\mu = \frac{\partial w}{\partial x^\mu}.$$

We now take the limit of the above equation in the sense of eq. (5-13) to obtain

$$\lim_{\kappa \to \infty} \int_{V_\kappa} \frac{\partial}{\partial x^\mu} (wA_\kappa^\mu)\, dV - w_\mu \alpha^\mu - w\beta = 0. \qquad (5\text{-}15)$$

The integral in eq. (5-15) may be written

$$\int_{V_\kappa} \frac{\partial}{\partial t} (wA_\kappa^0)\, dV + \int_{V_\kappa} \frac{\partial}{\partial x^i} (wA_\kappa^i)\, dV.$$

The second of the above integrals vanishes by virtue of Gauss' theorem and the assumption that A_κ^i vanishes outside R_κ. Therefore eq. (5-15) becomes

$$\frac{d}{dt}(w\alpha^0) - w_\mu \alpha^\mu - w\beta = 0. \qquad (5\text{-}16)$$

Multiplication of eq. (5-16) by u^0 gives

$$w \frac{d\alpha^0}{dp} + w_\mu u^\mu \alpha^0 - w_\nu a^\nu - wb = 0. \qquad (5\text{-}17)$$

Since $w(x^\mu)$ is an *arbitrary* function, the coefficients of w and w_μ in eq. (5-17) must be set equal to zero *separately*:

$$\frac{d\alpha^0}{dp} = b \qquad\qquad\quad \text{a} \left.\vphantom{\begin{matrix}1\\1\end{matrix}}\right\}$$
$$a^\mu = u^\mu \alpha^0 = u^0 \alpha^\mu. \qquad \text{b} \quad (5\text{-}18)$$

If the field equation is

$$\frac{\partial M^{\mu\nu}}{\partial x^\nu} = F^\mu$$

(note that F^μ is written for f^μ in accordance with the notation convention; and f^μ will be written for F^μ), then eqs. (5-18) become

$$\frac{d\mu^{\mu 0}}{dp} = f^\mu \qquad (5\text{-}19)$$

and

$$m^{\mu\nu} = u^\nu \mu^{\mu 0} = u^0 \mu^{\mu\nu}. \qquad (5\text{-}20)$$

With the definitions $m^\mu = \mu^{\mu 0}$ and $m = u_\mu m^\mu$, eq. (5-20) becomes $m^{\mu\nu} = m^\mu u^\nu$. If $M^{\mu\nu}$ (and hence $m^{\mu\nu}$) is symmetric, then $m^\mu u^\nu = m^\nu u^\mu$. Multiplication by u_μ gives

$$mu^\nu = m^\nu \left(\frac{d\tau}{dp}\right)^2. \qquad (5\text{-}21)$$

If p is identified as the proper time along C, then eqs. (5-19) and (5-21) constitute a description of the motion of a particle:

$$m^\mu = mu^\mu \tag{5-22}$$

$$f^\mu = \frac{dm^\mu}{d\tau} \tag{5-23}$$

$$u^\mu = \frac{d\xi^\mu}{d\tau}.$$

We may interpret f^μ as the force on the particle, m^μ as the particle's momentum, and m as the particle's mass; τ and m are scalars, and f^μ, m^μ, and u^μ are vectors. We also have the expressions

$$m = u_\mu \lim_{V \to 0} \int_V M^{\mu 0} \, dV$$

$$m^\mu = mu^\mu = \lim_{V \to 0} \int_V M^{\mu 0} \, dV$$

$$m^{\mu\nu} = u^\nu m^\mu = u^0 \lim_{V \to 0} \int_V M^{\mu\nu} \, dV.$$

For a perfect fluid, the mass is given by

$$m = \int \rho_0 u^0 \, dV.$$

Note that the condition $M^{\mu\nu}\eta_{\mu\nu} > 0$, which becomes $\rho_0 > 3c^{-2}p_0$ for a perfect fluid, implies $m^{\mu\nu}\eta_{\mu\nu} > 0$; the latter is merely the condition that u^μ be time-like, provided also $m > 0$, since $m^{\mu\nu}\eta_{\mu\nu} = mu^\rho u_\rho$.

We have completed the task of proving that the equation of motion (4-40) results from the field equation (5-5) and the symmetry of the matter stress-energy tensor. Assumptions were made about the process of shrinking to a world-line which state essentially that the limiting process exists. In addition, the assumptions $M^{\mu\nu}\eta_{\mu\nu} > 0$ and

$$u_\mu \lim_{V \to 0} \int_V M^{\mu\nu} \, dV > 0$$

require that the world-line be time-like.

The preceding analysis can be applied to a photon. We start with the electromagnetic stress-energy tensor $S^{\mu\nu}$ and the conditions

$$\frac{\partial S^{\mu\nu}}{\partial x^\nu} = -F^\mu$$

from eq. (4-16), $S^{\mu\nu} = S^{\nu\mu}$, and $S^{\mu\nu}\eta_{\mu\nu} = 0$. Equations (5-18) become

$$\frac{d\sigma^{\mu 0}}{dp} = -f^{\mu} \tag{5-24}$$

$$s^{\mu\nu} = u^{\nu}\sigma^{\mu 0} = u^{0}\sigma^{\mu\nu}. \tag{5-25}$$

With the definition $s^{\mu} = \sigma^{\mu 0}$, eqs. (5-24) and (5-25) become

$$\frac{ds^{\mu}}{dp} = -f^{\mu}$$

and

$$s^{\mu\nu} = u^{\nu}s^{\mu} = u^{0}\sigma^{\mu\nu}.$$

The symmetry of $S^{\mu\nu}$ then requires

$$u^{\mu}s^{\nu} = u^{\nu}s^{\mu}. \tag{5-26}$$

Equation (5-26) requires that s^{μ} be proportional to u^{μ}, since multiplication of eq. (5-26) by any vector a^{μ} not orthogonal to u^{μ} gives $a_{\nu}u^{\nu}s^{\mu} = a_{\sigma}s^{\sigma}u^{\mu}$. If s^{μ} is not proportional to u^{μ}, then $a_{\sigma}s^{\sigma}$ must vanish; hence s^{μ} must vanish. Since the case $s^{\mu} = 0$ is of no physical interest, we must take s^{μ} proportional to u^{μ}:

$$s^{\mu} = su^{\mu}, \tag{5-27}$$

where s is the factor of proportionality. We now have $s^{\mu\nu} = su^{\mu}u^{\nu}$. The property $S^{\mu}_{.\mu} = 0$ requires $su^{\mu}u_{\mu} = 0$. As stated previously, the case $s = 0$ is of no physical interest. Hence we take $u_{\mu}u^{\mu} = 0$, and thus the curve C is a null curve. Further, if f^{μ} vanishes then ds^{μ}/dp also vanishes, indicating that the vector s^{μ} is carried by parallel transport. In ordinary language, we have proved that a photon travels on a null path in any case, and that, in empty space, the path is a straight line.

5.3 GAUSS' THEOREM

Gauss' theorem is independent of the number of dimensions. It was used in its three-dimensional form in the previous section. It will now be proved for four dimensions.

The problem is to evaluate the integral

$$\int \frac{\partial A^{\mu}}{\partial x^{\mu}} \, dx^{0} \, dx^{1} \, dx^{2} \, dx^{3}$$

where the integration extends throughout the interior of a 4-space bounded by the closed 3-space Σ which is given by an equation $F(x^{\mu}) = 0$. Consider first the integral

$$\int \frac{\partial A^{0}}{\partial x^{0}} \, dx^{0} \, dx^{1} \, dx^{2} \, dx^{3}.$$

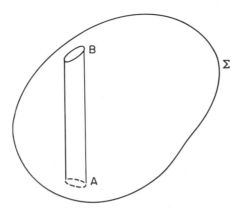

FIGURE 5.3 Proof of Gauss' theorem in four dimensions, with one dimension omitted in the diagram.

The integration over x^0 immediately gives

$$\int (A^0{}_B - A^0{}_A)\, dx^1\, dx^2\, dx^3$$

where A and B denote the ends of the tube generated by the curves $x^1 = $ const, $x^2 = $ const, $x^3 = $ const, with $x^0{}_B > x^0{}_A$. (See Figure 5.3.)

Scalar parameters u^0, u^1, u^2, and u^3 are set up such that $u^0 = 0$ describes Σ with $+u^0$ toward the outside of Σ and in such an order that at B we have

$$dx^1\, dx^2\, dx^3 = \left| \frac{\partial x^i}{\partial u^j} \right|\, du^1\, du^2\, du^3,$$

and at A we have

$$dx^1\, dx^2\, dx^3 = -\left| \frac{\partial x^i}{\partial u^j} \right|\, du^1\, du^2\, du^3.$$

The expression

$$dV_0 = \left| \frac{\partial x^i}{\partial u^j} \right|\, du^1\, du^2\, du^3$$

is recognized as the component of a vector

$$dV_\mu = e_{\mu\nu\rho\sigma} \frac{\partial x^\nu}{\partial u^1} \frac{\partial x^\rho}{\partial u^2} \frac{\partial x^\sigma}{\partial u^3}\, du^1\, du^2\, du^3.$$

The vector nature of dV_μ is verified by substituting

$$\frac{\partial x^\nu}{\partial u^1} = \frac{\partial x^\nu}{\partial \bar{x}^\alpha} \frac{\partial \bar{x}^\alpha}{\partial u^1} \text{ etc.}$$

and using the tensor nature of $e_{\mu\nu\rho\sigma}$. We now have

$$\int \frac{\partial A^0}{\partial x^0}\, dx^0\, dx^1\, dx^2\, dx^3 = \int_\Sigma A^0\, dV_0.$$

Similar expressions can be obtained for the other three components of $\partial A^\mu / \partial x^\mu$. When the four equations are added together, the result is

$$\int \frac{\partial A^\mu}{\partial x^\mu} \, dx^0 \, dx^1 \, dx^2 \, dx^3 = \int A^\nu \, dV_\nu,$$

where the integral on the right-hand side extends over the closed 3-space Σ. It is important to note that the proof is completely independent of any concept of length or time, i.e., independent of what we will later call the *metric* of the space. Furthermore, the number of dimensions is arbitrary; four were chosen only because of the space-time context of the present chapter.

5.4 MECHANICS OF A SYSTEM OF PARTICLES

Consider a distribution of matter whose stress-energy tensor $M^{\mu\nu}$ vanishes outside a sufficiently large spatial sphere. The distribution of matter may then be said to be *isolated*. The sphere sweeps out a cylinder in space-time between two arbitrary 3-spaces A and B, as illustrated in Figure 5.4.

It will be assumed that the stress-energy tensor $M^{\mu\nu}$ is symmetric and has zero divergence (i.e., that there are no external forces acting on the system). Then it can be proved that the quantities

and

$$p^\mu = \int M^{\mu\nu} \, dV_\nu \qquad \text{a}$$

$$l^{\mu\nu} = \int (x^\mu M^{\nu\sigma} - x^\nu M^{\mu\sigma}) \, dV_\sigma \qquad \text{b} \qquad \left.\right\} \quad (5\text{-}28)$$

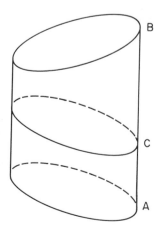

FIGURE 5.4 Cylinder swept out in space-time by a spatial sphere. Time is represented vertically, and one spatial dimension is omitted.

are constant and are, respectively, a vector and a tensor. The integration extends over any 3-space C which intersects the cylinder, and the volume element dV_σ is as defined in Section 5.3.

The vector nature of p^μ and the tensor nature of $l^{\mu\nu}$ follow from the definitions. The constancy of p^μ and $l^{\mu\nu}$ with time is proved by integrating $\partial M^{\mu\nu}/\partial x^\nu$ and $(\partial/\partial x^\rho)(x^\mu M^{\nu\rho} - x^\nu M^{\mu\rho})$, respectively, over the 4-space within the truncated cylinder of Figure 5.4 as follows. In the first case we have, by Gauss' theorem,

$$\int_{\text{cylinder}} \frac{\partial M^{\mu\nu}}{\partial x^\nu} \, dx^0 \, dx^1 \, dx^2 \, dx^3 = \int_B M^{\mu\nu} \, dV_\nu - \int_A M^{\mu\nu} \, dV_\nu, \quad (5\text{-}29)$$

since $M^{\mu\nu}$ vanishes on the "sides" of the cylinder. The right-hand side of eq. (5-29) is $p^\mu(B) - p^\mu(A)$. The left-hand side vanishes because the integrand is zero. Thus $p^\mu(B) = p^\mu(A)$ for arbitrary 3-spaces A and B. For the second case we have, again by Gauss' theorem,

$$\int_{\text{cylinder}} \frac{\partial}{\partial x^\rho} (x^\mu M^{\nu\rho} - x^\nu M^{\mu\rho}) \, dx^0 \, dx^1 \, dx^2 \, dx^3$$

$$= \int_B (x^\mu M^{\nu\rho} - x^\nu M^{\mu\rho}) \, dV_\rho - \int_A (x^\mu M^{\nu\rho} - x^\nu M^{\mu\rho}) \, dV_\rho. \quad (5\text{-}30)$$

The right-hand side of eq. (5-30) is $l^{\mu\nu}(B) - l^{\mu\nu}(A)$. The integrand on the left-hand side is given by the identity

$$\frac{\partial}{\partial x^\rho} (x^\mu M^{\nu\rho} - x^\nu M^{\mu\rho}) = M^{\nu\mu} - M^{\mu\nu} + x^\mu \frac{\partial M^{\nu\rho}}{\partial x^\rho} - x^\nu \frac{\partial M^{\mu\rho}}{\partial x^\rho}$$

which vanishes by virtue of the symmetry and zero-divergence of $M^{\mu\nu}$. Therefore $l^{\mu\nu}(B) = l^{\mu\nu}(A)$ for arbitrary 3-spaces A and B.

For the special case that the 3-space of integration in eqs. (5-28) is normal to the time axis, we have

$$p^\mu = \int M^{\mu 0} \, dV \qquad (5\text{-}31)$$

$$l^{\mu\nu} = \int (x^\mu M^{\nu 0} - x^\nu M^{\mu 0}) \, dV, \qquad (5\text{-}32)$$

where the integration now extends over ordinary spatial volume. It should be kept in mind that p^μ and $l^{\mu\nu}$ are, respectively, vector and tensor, although a particular 3-space has been chosen for the integration.

The vector p^μ is identified as the total linear momentum of the system. The total mass m may then be defined $m^2 = p_\mu p^\mu$, and the world-velocity u^μ of the system is given by

$$p^\mu = m u^\mu. \qquad (5\text{-}33)$$

The mass m is then given by

$$m = u_\mu \int M^{\mu 0} \, dV. \tag{5-34}$$

Note that the center-of-mass velocity u^μ has been defined without using any definition for a center of mass.

The antisymmetric tensor $l^{\mu\nu}$ is identified as the angular momentum, because the definition

$$L_k = e(klm) \int x^l M^{m0} \, dV \tag{5-35}$$

produces the relation

$$l^{ij} = e(ijk)L_k. \tag{5-36}$$

The interpretation is most clearly evident if the distribution of matter is regarded to have an infinitesimal size, i.e., to be a particle. Then eq. (5-35) becomes $L_k = e(klm)x^l p^m$. The temporal components l^{i0} are given by the equation

$$l^{i0} = \int x^i M^{00} \, dV - tp^i \tag{5-37}$$

which, for a particle, states that the particle's position x^i is given by

$$x^i = v^i t + \frac{l^{i0}}{mu^0}$$

where $v^i = u^i/u^0$. Now the constancy of p^μ implies that m and hence u^μ and v^i are constants. Thus the constancy of eq. (5-37) may be interpreted to mean that the center of mass moves with uniform velocity.

It is concluded that an isolated distribution of matter which possesses a symmetric, zero-divergence stress-energy tensor also possesses ten conserved quantities—the four components of p^μ and the six independent, non-zero components of the antisymmetric tensor $l^{\mu\nu}$. The ten constants are: the four components of the total 4-momentum; the three components of the spatial angular momentum; and the three components of the velocity of the center of mass.

5.5 CENTROID AND CENTER OF MASS

We ask whether we can define the center of mass of the isolated system of Section 5.4.

At first sight, the most obvious answer is to define a quantity γ^μ by the relation

$$\gamma^\mu = \frac{\int x^\mu M^{00} \, dV}{\int M^{00} \, dV}, \tag{5-38}$$

where the volume integration extends over a space $t = $ const. The spatial components γ^i are the position vector for what will be called the classical *centroid*. This choice is suggested both by eq. (5-37) and by analogy with electromagnetism where the component $S^{00}c^2$ of the stress-energy tensor is the energy density. However, γ^μ is not a vector. We can force γ^μ to be a vector, but then it is given by eq. (5-38) only in one frame of reference. Let the world-velocity of the latter be denoted n^μ. Then we must write $\gamma^\mu(n^\nu)$, since γ^μ is a function of n^μ. In order to obtain an expression for $\gamma^\mu(n^\nu)$, eq. (5-37) is substituted into eq. (5-38):

$$\gamma^\mu = \frac{p^\mu}{p^0} t + \frac{l^{\mu 0}}{p^0},$$

or, since $n^\mu = \delta^\mu_0$ in the reference frame in which eq. (5-38) holds,

$$\gamma^\mu(n^\nu) = \frac{\tau p^\mu}{n_\alpha p^\alpha} + \frac{l^{\mu\beta}n_\beta}{n_\gamma p^\gamma}. \tag{5-39}$$

Equation (5-39) is now in tensor form and hence holds in all coordinate systems. The parameter τ in eq. (5-39) is arbitrary; therefore $x^\mu = \gamma^\mu$ defines a world-line parallel to p^μ. This line is the world-line of the *centroid* Γ of the system.

The *center of mass* is defined by either of three alternate definitions. The first definition is to set n^α in eq. (5-39) equal to u^α, i.e., to apply eq. (5-38) to the proper frame of the system. Then we have

$$c^\mu = \gamma^\mu(u^\nu) = \frac{\tau p^\mu}{m} + \frac{l^{\mu\beta}p_\beta}{m^2}. \tag{5-40}$$

The second definition is to perform a coordinate transformation to a new origin such that in the new coordinates x'^μ, the relation

$$l'^{\mu\nu}p'_\nu = 0 \tag{5-41}$$

holds. The origin $x'^i = 0$ is then the center of mass. In the translated coordinates $x'^\mu = x^\mu - a^\mu$, we have, from eqs. (5-31) and (5-32), $p'^\mu = p^\mu$ and

$$l'^{\mu\nu} = l^{\mu\nu} - a^\mu p^\nu + a^\nu p^\mu.$$

Hence

$$l'^{\mu\nu}p'_\nu = l^{\mu\nu}p_\nu - m^2 a^\mu + p^\mu a^\nu p_\nu$$

or

$$a^\mu = \frac{p_\nu a^\nu}{m^2} p^\mu + \frac{l^{\mu\nu}p_\nu}{m^2} - \frac{l'^{\mu\nu}p'_\nu}{m^2}.$$

Equation (5-41) then requires that a^μ be equal to the c^μ in eq. (5-40). The relation $m\tau = p_\nu c^\nu$ follows upon multiplying eq. (5.40) by p_μ.

The third definition of c^μ is suggested by the results of the field-to-particle transition of Section 5.2. It was found that the mass of a particle is

$$u_\mu \lim_{V \to 0} \int_V M^{\mu 0} \, dV.$$

Therefore we are led to define

$$c^\mu = \frac{u_\nu \int x^\mu M^{\nu 0} \, dV}{u_\sigma \int M^{\sigma 0} \, dV}$$

where u^μ is given by eq. (5-33). From eqs. (5-33) and (5-34) we then have

$$c^\mu = \frac{p_\nu}{m^2} \int x^\mu M^{\nu 0} \, dV,$$

or, from eq. (5-32),

$$c^\mu = \frac{p_\nu}{m^2} \int x^\nu M^{\mu 0} \, dV + \frac{l^{\mu\nu} p_\nu}{m^2}. \tag{5-42}$$

It is easily verified by the use of eq. (5-31) in proper coordinates (where $p^\mu = m\delta_0^\mu$) that the integral $\int x^\nu M^{\mu 0} \, dV$ has the eigenvector p^μ, i.e., that $p_\nu \int x^\nu M^{\mu 0} \, dV = \lambda p^\mu$. Therefore eq. (5-42) becomes

$$c^\mu = \frac{\lambda p^\mu}{m^2} + \frac{l^{\mu\nu} p_\nu}{m^2}.$$

Comparison with eq. (5-40) shows $\lambda = m\tau$.

Equation (5-40) defines the world-line of the *center of mass* C of the system. The world-line is parallel to p^μ.

The relation between the center of mass C and the centroid Γ is most easily studied in the proper system in which $p^\mu = m\delta_0^\mu$. Equations (5-39) and (5-40) become, respectively,

$$\gamma^\mu = \frac{\tau}{n^0} \delta_0^\mu + \frac{l^{\mu\nu} w_\nu}{m} \tag{5-43}$$

$$c^\mu = \tau\delta_0^\mu + \frac{l^{\mu 0}}{m} \tag{5-44}$$

where $w^\mu = n^\mu/n^0$. The τ's appearing in these two equations are *separately* arbitrary (and hence not necessarily equal). Thus for the points Γ and C in the space $t = 0$ we must have $\gamma^0 = c^0 = 0$ and hence $\tau = m^{-1}l^{0\nu} w_\nu n^0$ in eq. (5-43) and $\tau = 0$ in eq. (5-44). The result is that Γ and C are given by

$$\gamma^i = \frac{l^{i\alpha} w_\alpha}{m} = \frac{l^{i0}}{m} + \frac{l^{ij} w_j}{m}$$

$$c^i = \frac{l^{i0}}{m}.$$

The difference $\sigma^i = \gamma^i - c^i$ is therefore, from eq. (5-36), given by

$$\sigma^i = -\frac{e(ijk)w^j L_k}{mc^2},\tag{5-45}$$

where L_k is the angular momentum defined by eq. (5-35).

Equation (5-45) shows that all possible centroids must, in the proper system, lie within a circular disk with radius L/mc, center at C, and plane perpendicular to L_k.

If M^{00} is non-negative in all possible reference frames, then the disk described above must lie within the system, since, by eq. (5-38), Γ is inside the system. In proper coordinates the system must include the disk in its interior. Therefore a body with angular momentum L and mass m must have its *minimum* diameter perpendicular to L no less than $2L/mc$. For example, the earth which has angular momentum 5.9×10^{33} joule-sec and mass 5.98×10^{24} kg has a minimum equatorial radius of $L/mc = 3.3$ meters.

The concept of the centroid disk gives a surprising result for the electron. The electron has intrinsic angular momentum $h/4\pi = 5.27 \times 10^{-35}$ joule-sec and mass 9.108×10^{-31} kg. Therefore, its minimum radius is $h/4\pi mc = 1.93 \times 10^{-13}$ meter. This length is the same as the uncertainty in distance for an electron whose momentum is uncertain by an amount mc; for by the uncertainty principle of quantum mechanics,

$$\Delta x = \frac{h}{4\pi\,\Delta p} = \frac{h}{4\pi mc}.$$

But the classical electron radius is 2.82×10^{-15} m, about 70 times smaller than the minimum size required by the centroid disk. The classical estimate of the electron's size is obtained by equating the electrostatic field energy outside the electron to its rest mass. We may conclude that if the electron is as small as its classical size indicates, then there exist reference systems in which the electron's centroid is *outside* the electron. But such speculation is useless since, by the uncertainty principle, the separation between the centroid and the center of the electron is too small for measurement.

5.6 INTEGRAL CONSERVATION LAWS

The differential conservation law

$$\frac{\partial T^{\mu\nu}}{\partial x^\nu} = 0\tag{5-4}$$

for a force-free distribution of matter can be put into the integral form

$$\int T^{\mu\nu}\xi_\mu\,dV_\nu = 0\tag{5-46}$$

where the integration extends over the three-dimensional surface of an *arbitrary* four-dimensional region of space-time, and ξ_μ is a suitable vector field. It is desired that eq. (5-46) follow from eq. (5-4) alone. By Gauss' theorem, eq. (5-46) may be rewritten

$$\frac{\partial}{\partial x^\nu}(T^{\mu\nu}\xi_\mu) = 0.$$

The latter relation, in view of eq. (5-4), places a condition on the vector ξ_μ:

$$T^{\mu\nu}\frac{\partial \xi_\mu}{\partial x^\nu} = 0.$$

If the vector ξ_μ is to be independent of the particular $T^{\mu\nu}$ used, then, due to the symmetry of $T^{\mu\nu}$, ξ_μ must satisfy Killing's equation

$$\frac{\partial \xi_\mu}{\partial x^\nu} + \frac{\partial \xi_\nu}{\partial x^\mu} = 0. \tag{5-47}$$

Such a vector in three-dimensional space was encountered in Section 1.6. The method of Section 1.6 can be extended to four-dimensional space-time. An arbitrary transformation between Cartesian coordinates in two inertial frames $\bar{x}^\alpha$ and x^μ must satisfy eq. (3-38). By direct substitution of the infinitesimal transformation

$$\bar{x}^\mu = x^\mu + \xi^\mu(x^\nu)\,\delta t,$$

where t is a transformation parameter, ξ_μ must satisfy eq. (5-47).

The solutions of eq. (5-47) can be obtained by the same method as was used in Section 1.5 for Euclidean three-dimensional space. Equation (3-38) is differentiated, as was eq. (1-15), in such a way as to give the condition

$$\eta_{\alpha\beta}\frac{\partial \bar{x}^\alpha}{\partial x^\rho}\frac{\partial^2 \bar{x}^\beta}{\partial x^\mu\,\partial x^\nu} = 0$$

which, because $\left|\dfrac{\partial \bar{x}^\alpha}{\partial x^\rho}\right| \neq 0$, is the same as

$$\frac{\partial^2 \bar{x}^\alpha}{\partial x^\mu\,\partial x^\nu} = 0$$

which clearly has the linear solution

$$\bar{x}^\alpha = a^\alpha_\mu x^\mu + b^\alpha \tag{5-48}$$

where a^α_μ and b^α are constants. Substitution of eq. (5-48) into eq. (3-38) then yields the condition

$$a^\alpha_\mu a^\beta_\nu \eta_{\alpha\beta} = \eta_{\mu\nu}. \tag{5-49}$$

Upon going to the case of the infinitesimal transformation mentioned previously, we substitute

$$a^\alpha_\mu = \delta^\alpha_\mu + \omega^\alpha_\mu \, \delta t$$

and

$$b^\alpha = \beta^\alpha \, \delta t$$

into eq. (5-48) to obtain

$$\bar{x}^\mu = x^\mu + \xi^\mu(x^\nu) \, \delta t$$

with

$$\xi^\mu = \omega^\mu_\nu x^\nu + \beta^\mu \tag{5-50}$$

and into eq. (5-49) to obtain

$$\omega_{\mu\nu} + \omega_{\nu\mu} = 0$$

where

$$\omega_{\mu\nu} = \omega^\alpha_\nu \eta_{\mu\alpha}.$$

Therefore the solution of eq. (5-47) is eq. (5-50), i.e.,

$$\xi_\mu = \omega_{\mu\nu} x^\nu + \beta_\mu$$

where β_μ and $\omega_{\mu\nu}$ are constants, and $\omega_{\mu\nu}$ is antisymmetric.

There are thus ten independent vector fields ξ_μ corresponding to the ten independent constants β_μ and $\omega_{\mu\nu}$. These ten independent solutions represent the ten coordinate transformations among Cartesian inertial frames: one temporal translation (β_0), three spatial translations (β_i), three spatial rotations (ω_{ij}), and three Lorentz transformations (ω_{0i}).

The conservation equation (5-46) will now be applied to an isolated system. The system is enclosed in a cylindrical space-time region formed by a constant 3-space and the cuts $t = t_1$ and $t = t_2$ (as in Section 5.4). The result is

$$\int_{t_2} T^{\mu 0} \xi_\mu \, dV - \int_{t_1} T^{\mu 0} \xi_\mu \, dV = 0$$

or, more simply,

$$\int T^{\mu 0} \xi_\mu \, dV = \text{const.}$$

The substitution of eq. (5-50) then gives

$$\beta_\mu \int T^{\mu 0} \, dV + \omega_{\mu\nu} \int x^\nu T^{\mu 0} \, dV = \text{const}$$

for *arbitrary* β_μ and $\omega_{\mu\nu} = -\omega_{\nu\mu}$. Consequently, there result two conservation laws

$$\int T^{\mu 0} \, dV = \text{const}$$

$$\int (x^\mu T^{\nu 0} - x^\nu T^{\mu 0}) \, dV = \text{const}$$

which are recognized as the generalized forms of eqs. (5-31) and (5-32) to include the electromagnetic field, since $T^{\mu\nu}$ is the *total* stress-energy tensor. The ten independent ξ_μ correspond to the ten conservation laws: energy (1), linear momentum (3), angular momentum (3), and center-of-mass motion (3). Thus there is a one-to-one correspondence between the coordinate transformations of special relativity and the conservation laws.

With this section we complete a brief description of electromagnetism and dynamics in special relativity. Much more could be said, but Chapters 3 through 5 are sufficient to give the reader the fundamentals of the subject. We pass on to the problem of gravity in special relativity. The question facing us is: Can a suitable field theory be found within the context of special relativity for the description of the phenomenon of gravity?

CHAPTER 6

SPECIAL-RELATIVISTIC GRAVITATION THEORIES

6.1 INTRODUCTION

The special theory of relativity, for which ample verification is found in the studies of fast particles, already has one force field—electromagnetism—incorporated into the theory. Our attention naturally turns to another force field—gravitation—with the hope of incorporating it also into the theory. As we search for the correct formulation of gravitation, it must be kept in mind that the classical formulation, Newtonian gravitation, is probably only an approximation to the correct formulation.

The inconsistency between Newtonian gravity and special relativity is evident from Section 1.12. Equation (1-43) requires that **g** change *instantaneously* for a change in ρ, whereas in special relativity no signal can travel faster than the velocity of light in free space. Further, eq. (1-47) is not invariant under transformations. The substitution $\rho = \rho_0 u^0$, where ρ_0 and u^μ are, respectively, the proper density and the world-velocity of the matter, puts eq. (1-47) into the form

$$\frac{\partial g_k}{\partial x^k} = -4\pi G \rho_0 u^0. \tag{6-1}$$

Straightforward calculation, which need not be given here, shows that eq. (6-1) is not invariant.

In searching for workable revisions of eq. (6-1), particular attention will be paid to the orbits of test particles in the vicinity of a gravitating mass, since the observation of planetary orbits is one of the principal tests for the correctness of a gravitational theory.

6.2 THE ORBIT PROBLEM

In the calculation of the orbit of a satellite revolving around a center of force, the equations of motion

$$\frac{d^2r}{dt^2} - r\left(\frac{d\theta}{dt}\right)^2 = -F(r) \qquad \text{a}$$

$$\left(\frac{dr}{dt}\right)^2 + r^2\left(\frac{d\theta}{dt}\right)^2 = 2J(r) \qquad \text{b} \qquad (6\text{-}2)$$

$$r^2\frac{d\theta}{dt} = H(r) \qquad \text{c}$$

frequently arise. For example, in Newtonian gravity, mF is the force of gravity (with m the mass of the satellite), r is the distance of the satellite from the force center, t is the time, θ is the angle of the radius vector in the orbit plane, H is a constant, and $F(r) = -dJ(r)/dr$.

The orbit produced by eqs. (6-2) will be studied for *arbitrary* functions $F(r)$, $J(r)$, and $H(r)$, and for arbitrary interpretations of r and t. The angle θ will still be considered as the angle in the orbit plane, since its periodic property will be needed.

It is immediately noted that eq. (6-2a) can be derived from eqs. (6-2b) and (6-2c) by the elimination of $d\theta/dt$, differentiation of eq. (6-2b), and division by $2\,dr/dt$. Consequently $F(r)$ is given by

$$F(r) = \frac{H(r)}{r^2}\frac{dH}{dr} - \frac{dJ}{dr}. \qquad (6\text{-}3)$$

The equation for the orbit is obtained from eqs. (6-2) by using eq. (6-2c) to eliminate t and by substituting $r = 1/u$. Equations (6-2a) and (6-2b) then become

$$\frac{d^2u}{d\theta^2} + u = \frac{F}{H^2u^2} - \left(\frac{du}{d\theta}\right)^2\frac{d\ln H}{du}, \qquad (6\text{-}4)$$

$$\left(\frac{du}{d\theta}\right)^2 + u^2 = \frac{2J}{H^2}. \qquad (6\text{-}5)$$

Elimination of $(du/d\theta)^2$ in eq. (6-4) by means of eq. (6-5) gives

$$\frac{d^2u}{d\theta^2} + u = \frac{F}{H^2u^2} - \left(\frac{2J}{H^2} - u^2\right)\frac{d\ln H}{du}. \qquad (6\text{-}6)$$

Equation (6-6) can alternately be obtained by differentiation of eq. (6-5) and the use of eq. (6-3). Equation (6-6) has the form

$$\frac{d^2u}{d\theta^2} + u = N(u) \tag{6-7}$$

where $N(u)$ may be written in either of two ways:

$$N = \frac{F}{H^2u^2} - \left(\frac{2J}{H^2} - u^2\right)\frac{d\ln H}{du} = \frac{1}{H^2}\frac{dJ}{du} - \frac{2J}{H^3}\frac{dH}{du}. \tag{6-8}$$

A circular orbit $u = u_0$ is given by the root of the equation $u_0 = N(u_0)$. From eq. (6-5), this root is also given by $u_0^2 = 2J_0/H_0^2$, where the subscript 0 denotes functions evaluated at $u = u_0$. Any deviation $\eta = u - u_0$ from a circular orbit must satisfy the differential equation

$$\frac{d^2\eta}{d\theta^2} + \left[1 - \left(\frac{dN}{du}\right)_{u_0}\right]\eta = O^2(\eta),$$

which is obtained by substituting $u = u_0 + \eta$ into eq. (6-7). Therefore, to first order in η, the solution is

$$\eta = \alpha\left\{\cos\left[\theta\sqrt{1 - \left(\frac{dN}{du}\right)_{u_0}} + \beta\right]\right\}$$

where α and β are the constants of integration.

The angles of perihelia of the orbit are the angles for which r is minimum and hence u or η is maximum. Therefore, the orbital angle from one perihelion to the next is

$$\phi = \frac{2\pi}{\sqrt{1 - \left(\frac{dN}{du}\right)_{u_0}}} = \frac{2\pi}{1 - \sigma}. \tag{6-9}$$

The quantity σ defined by the above equation will be called the *perihelion advance*. It represents the rate of advance of perihelion. As the satellite advances through θ radians in its orbit, its perihelion advances through $\sigma\theta$ radians. Whenever σ turns out to be negative, the perihelion undergoes a retardation or regression rather than an advance. From eq. (6-9), σ is given by

$$\sigma = 1 - \sqrt{1 - \left(\frac{dN}{du}\right)_{u_0}},$$

or, for small $\left(\frac{dN}{du}\right)_{u_0}$,

$$\sigma = \frac{1}{2}\left(\frac{dN}{du}\right)_{u_0}. \tag{6-10}$$

The function $N(u)$ depends on the functions H and J through eq. (6-8). For the special case that H is a constant, eq. (6-8) becomes

$$\frac{dN}{du} = \frac{1}{H^2} \frac{d}{du} \left(\frac{F}{u^2} \right).$$

Note that for a Newtonian orbit, F is proportional to u^2, and hence eq. (6-10) vanishes. There is then no advance of perihelion.

6.3 ORBIT OF A CHARGED PARTICLE

The similarity between Newton's law of gravitation and Coulomb's law of electrostatics suggests that gravitation may be the temporal component of a 4-vector in exactly the same way that the electrostatic potential is the temporal component of the 4-vector electromagnetic potential. Since the machinery of electromagnetism has already set up, it will be easiest to first do the orbit problem for an atom and then change the name from "electromagnetism" to "gravity."

It was noted in Section 4.6 that the Lagrangian formulation is valid for non-Cartesian coordinates. In particular, we will apply it to spherical polar coordinates.

Consider a charge $-e$ which is free to move in the field of a fixed charge Ze. The particle's orbit is found, by a straightforward calculation which need not be given here, to be planar. In this plane the polar coordinates r, θ are set up about the fixed charge.

The Lagrangian, given by eq. (4-56), is then

$$L = -mc^2\sqrt{\dot{t}^2 - c^{-2}(\dot{r}^2 + r^2\dot{\theta}^2)} + e\phi\dot{t}$$

where the dot indicates differentiation with respect to the proper time τ of the particle, and ϕ is the potential

$$\phi = \frac{Ze}{4\pi\epsilon_0 r}.$$

The conjugate momenta are then

$$p_t = -mc^2\dot{t} + e\phi$$

$$p_r = m\dot{r}$$

$$p_\theta = mr^2\dot{\theta}.$$

Now since neither t nor θ appear explicitly in the Lagrangian, the Lagrangian equations of motion require that p_t and p_θ be constants. We therefore write $p_t = -mc^2A$ and $p_\theta = mh$ where A and h are constants of the motion. The equations of motion are then

$$r^2\dot\theta = h \tag{6-11}$$

$$A = i - \frac{e\phi}{mc^2} = \frac{1}{\sqrt{1 - \frac{v^2}{c^2}}} - \frac{e\phi}{mc^2}. \tag{6-12}$$

It may be noted that in the classical approximation ($v \ll c$) of eq. (6-12), mc^2A is the total energy of the particle:

$$mc^2A = mc^2 + \tfrac{1}{2}mv^2 - \frac{e\phi}{mc^2}.$$

Thus the law of conservation of energy has the form $A = \text{const}$, and the law of conservation of angular momentum has the form $h = \text{const}$.

The Lagrangian equation of motion for r can be obtained by the usual procedure, but that is unnecessary. All the information that is needed is contained in eqs. (6-11), (6-12), and (3-44) which takes the form

$$\dot r^2 + r^2\dot\theta^2 = c^2(i^2 - 1). \tag{6-13}$$

The differentiation of eq. (6-13) and division by $2\dot r$ gives the equation of motion for r. But even this operation is unnecessary, because eqs. (6-11), (6-12), and (6-13) are merely a special case of eqs. (6-2b) and (6-2c). We therefore adopt eqs. (6-7) and (6-8) with the substitutions $H = h$ and

$$J = \frac{c^2}{2}(A^2 - 1) + \frac{AZe^2u}{4\pi\epsilon_0 m} + \frac{Z^2e^4u^2}{32\pi^2\epsilon_0^2 m^2 c^2}.$$

The result is

$$N(u) = c^2h^{-2}(A\mu + \mu^2 u)$$

where

$$\mu = \frac{Ze^2}{4\pi\epsilon_0 mc^2}. \tag{6-14}$$

(This μ, which will be used frequently in orbit problems, should not be confused with magnetic permeability.) Thus the orbit equation is

$$\frac{d^2u}{d\theta^2} + \left(1 - \frac{c^2\mu^2}{h^2}\right)u = \frac{A\mu c^2}{h^2} \tag{6-15}$$

which has the solution

$$u = \frac{A\mu c^2}{h^2 - c^2\mu^2}\left[1 + e\cos\left(\sqrt{1 - \frac{c^2\mu^2}{h^2}}\,\theta + \text{const}\right)\right].$$

This solution represents an ellipse whose axes rotate around the origin. For small μ, the periphelion advance is

$$\sigma = \frac{c^2\mu^2}{2h^2},$$

or

$$\sigma = \frac{\mu}{2p} \tag{6-16}$$

where

$$p = \frac{h^2}{\mu c^2}.$$

Another feature of the equations of motion which must be noted is the behavior of a particle traveling at the speed of light. As the velocity of the test particle is made mathematically to approach the speed of light, the derivatives $\dot{t}$, $\dot{\theta}$, and $\dot{r}$ all tend toward ∞. Thus in eq. (6-15), the left-hand side approaches

$$\frac{d^2u}{d\theta^2} + u$$

and the right-hand side approaches

$$\frac{1}{r^2}\frac{dt}{d\theta} \cdot \frac{\mu c^2}{h}$$

which tends towards zero. Therefore the equation of motion for a particle traveling at the speed of light is

$$\frac{d^2u}{d\theta^2} + u = 0$$

which has the solution $u = \alpha \cos \theta$. The particle therefore will travel in a straight line.

6.4 GRAVITY AS THE TIME COMPONENT OF A VECTOR FIELD

The purpose of this section is to discover the consequences of postulating that the Newtonian gravitational potential is the temporal component of a 4-vector field. The alterations in the electromagnetic theory of the previous section are to replace charge with proper mass and ϵ_0 with $-(4\pi G)^{-1}$. The results of Section 6.3 show that a test particle in orbit around a gravitating center of mass M has a perihelion advance

$$\sigma = \frac{\mu}{2p}. \tag{6-16}$$

The particle which travels with the speed of light is undeflected by gravity.

The length parameter μ defined by eq. (6-14) is now the *gravitational radius*

$$\mu = \frac{GM}{c^2}. \tag{6-17}$$

(The sign remains positive because the particle's negative charge cancels the sign introduced by G.) Any gravitating mass M has a length μ associated with it given by eq. (6-17). For a particle in an orbit of average radius r around the mass, the non-Newtonian features of the vector theory of gravity—and, as we shall see, of the other theories of gravity which will be considered—become important as μ/r ceases to be small compared with unity. For the sun, $\mu = 1.48$ km, and for the earth, $\mu = 4.43$ mm.

Comparison with observation shows the above vector theory to be inadequate. The advance of perihelion is more accurately given by Einstein's formula

$$\sigma = 3\mu/p. \tag{6-18}$$

However, it was assumed only that gravity resembles electromagnetism, which is a special case of possible vector theories. Therefore, we will generalize the vector theory, but before doing so, the simpler case of a *scalar* gravitational theory deserves note.

6.5 SCALAR THEORY OF GRAVITATION

In the remainder of this chapter we will explore various possibilities for describing gravitation in terms of a linear theory. The following two postulates are made.

POSTULATE 1. The potential is determined by a linear second-order differential equation from the quantities (such as ρ, u^μ) which describe the distribution, motion, and stresses of the matter which produces the field.

POSTULATE 2. The acceleration

$$\alpha^\mu = du^\mu/d\tau \tag{6-19}$$

of a test particle is linear and homogeneous in the first derivatives of the potentials.

Now the only scalar invariants of a set of vectors are (1) their self products, (2) their scalar products with each other, and, if there are more than three vectors, (3) their determinant. For example, the scalar invariants of the vectors a^μ, b^μ, c^μ, and d^μ include $a_\mu a^\mu$, $a_\mu b^\mu$, and $e_{\alpha\beta\gamma\delta} a^\alpha b^\beta c^\gamma d^\delta$.

The simplest case is that of a scalar potential Φ. The field equation is assumed to be

$$\Box^2 \Phi = -4\pi G c^2 \rho_0, \tag{6-20}$$

where ρ_0 is the proper density of the matter which produces the field.*
The equation of motion may be obtained by two alternate methods.

In the first method, Postulate 2 is invoked in order to write the equation

$$\alpha^\mu = \Gamma^{\mu\nu} \frac{\partial \Phi}{\partial x^\nu}$$

where the coefficients $\Gamma^{\mu\nu}$ can depend at most on the test particle's world-velocity u^μ. The scalar

$$\Gamma(\mathbf{a}, \mathbf{b}, \mathbf{u}) = \Gamma^{\mu\nu} a_\mu b_\nu$$

which is formed from two *arbitrary* vectors a^μ and b^μ must be a combination of scalar invariants formed from the three vectors a^μ, b^μ, and u^μ, with the condition that a^μ and b^μ each appear to first order. Therefore, we must have

$$\Gamma(\mathbf{a}, \mathbf{b}, \mathbf{u}) = A \cdot (\mathbf{a} \cdot \mathbf{b}) + B \cdot (\mathbf{a} \cdot \mathbf{u}) \cdot (\mathbf{b} \cdot \mathbf{u})$$

where $\mathbf{a} \cdot \mathbf{b}$ denotes $a_\mu b^\mu$, etc., and the coefficients A and B are constant. The requirement that

$$u_\mu \alpha^\mu = u_\mu \frac{du^\mu}{d\tau} = \frac{1}{2}\frac{d}{d\tau}(u_\mu u^\mu) = \frac{1}{2}\frac{d1}{d\tau}$$

vanish imposes the condition

$$0 = \Gamma(\mathbf{u}, \mathbf{b}, \mathbf{u}) = (A + B)(\mathbf{b} \cdot \mathbf{u})$$

for *arbitrary* $\mathbf{b}$. Therefore, $B = -A$, and we find

$$\Gamma(\mathbf{a}, \mathbf{b}, \mathbf{u}) = A[(\mathbf{a} \cdot \mathbf{b} - (\mathbf{a} \cdot \mathbf{u})(\mathbf{b} \cdot \mathbf{u})].$$

The arbitrariness of $\mathbf{a}$ and $\mathbf{b}$ requires

$$\Gamma^{\mu\nu} = A(\eta^{\mu\nu} - u^\mu u^\nu).$$

There results the equation of motion

$$\alpha^\mu = A(\eta^{\mu\nu} - u^\mu u^\nu)\frac{\partial \Phi}{\partial x^\nu}. \qquad (6\text{-}21)$$

In the Newtonian approximation, eqs. (6-20) and (6-21) become, respectively,

$$\nabla^2 \Phi = 4\pi G \rho_0$$

---

* Equation (6-20) is the simplest generalization of eq. (6-1). The more general equation

$$C\frac{\partial^2 \Phi}{\partial x^\mu \partial x^\nu} + D\eta_{\mu\nu}\Box^2\Phi = -4\pi G\rho c^2(E\eta_{\mu\nu} + Fu_\mu u_\nu)$$

where C, D, E, and F are constants, must of necessity reduce to eq. (6-20). For the Newtonian approximation requires $D - E = F = -\frac{1}{3}C$. And, in the Newtonian approximation, the field is over-determined by the equation $\frac{\partial^2 \Phi}{\partial x^i \partial x^j} = \frac{1}{3}\delta_{ij}\nabla^2\Phi$, unless $F = C = 0$. Thus $D = E$, and eq. (6-20) results.

and

$$\alpha^i = -c^2 A \frac{\partial \Phi}{\partial x^i}.$$

Therefore Φ is the Newtonian gravitational potential and A must be chosen equal to c^{-2}. Equation (6-21) then becomes

$$\alpha^\mu = \frac{1}{c^2} (\eta^{\mu\nu} + u^\mu u^\nu) \frac{\partial \Phi}{\partial x^\nu}. \tag{6-22}$$

The second method is the use of intuition to generalize the Newtonian field equations. The field equations are assumed to be

$$\frac{\partial g_\mu}{\partial x^\nu} - \frac{\partial g_\nu}{\partial x^\mu} = 0 \tag{6-23}$$

and

$$\frac{\partial g^\mu}{\partial x^\mu} = -4\pi G \rho_0. \tag{6-24}$$

Equation (6-23) implies that there exists a potential Φ such that g_μ is its gradient:

$$g_\mu = \frac{1}{c^2} \frac{\partial \Phi}{\partial x^\mu}. \tag{6-25}$$

Equation (6-24) then provides the field equation

$$\Box^2 \Phi = -4\pi G \rho_0 c^2.$$

The equation of motion is assumed to be

$$\frac{d}{d\tau} (mu^\mu) = mg^\mu. \tag{6-26}$$

The left-hand side of eq. (6-26) may be expanded to give

$$m \frac{du^\mu}{d\tau} + u^\mu \frac{dm}{d\tau} = mg^\mu. \tag{6-27}$$

Multiplication of eq. (6-27) by u_μ results in the condition

$$\frac{dm}{d\tau} = mg^\mu u_\mu = \frac{m}{c^2} \frac{d\Phi}{d\tau} \tag{6-28}$$

which is easily integrated to give

$$m = m_0 e^{\Phi/c^2}, \tag{6-29}$$

where m_0 is the constant of integration. The substitution of eq. (6-28) back into eq. (6-27) then yields

$$\frac{du^\mu}{d\tau} = g^\nu(\delta^\mu_\nu - u^\mu u_\nu) \tag{6-30}$$

which, in view of eq. (6-25), is identical with eq. (6-22).

Equation (6-29) may seem disconcerting. The particle's proper mass m varies from one event to another. The constant m_0 is the particle's mass in regions where $\Phi = 0$. But it may be noted that eq. (6-29) does give the correct expression for the energy in the limit of large c:

$$\frac{mc^2}{\sqrt{1 - \frac{v^2}{c^2}}} = m_0 c^2 + m_0 \Phi + \tfrac{1}{2} m_0 v^2.$$

It is also noted that the variation in mass arises not from the assumption of a scalar potential but from the assumption of eq. (6-26). An alternate choice for the equation of motion is

$$\frac{d}{d\tau}(m u^\mu) = m(\eta^{\mu\nu} - u^\mu u^\nu) g_\nu$$

which has the more satisfying feature that the proper mass m is a constant; it also leads to eq. (6-30) and hence to eq. (6-22).

The Lagrangian for the test particle's motion is obtained from the equation of motion in the form

$$\frac{du^\mu}{d\tau} + \frac{u^\mu}{c^2} \frac{d\Phi}{d\tau} - \frac{\eta^{\mu\nu}}{c^2} \frac{\partial \Phi}{\partial x^\nu} = 0.$$

Multiplication by e^{Φ/c^2} puts this equation into the form

$$\frac{d}{d\tau}(u^\mu e^{\Phi/c^2}) - \eta^{\mu\nu} \frac{\partial}{\partial x^\nu}(e^{\Phi/c^2}) = 0$$

which is immediately recognized as the Lagrangian equation of motion for the Lagrangian

$$L = e^{\Phi/c^2} \sqrt{\eta_{\mu\nu} u^\mu u^\nu}.$$

This Lagrangian has a simple geometric meaning. Since the Lagrangian equation of motion results from the principle

$$\delta \int L \, d\tau = 0,$$

it follows that the particle's trajectory in space-time is a geodesic, provided that "distance" s is measured by the relation

$$ds = L \, d\tau = e^{\Phi/c^2} \, d\tau. \tag{6-31}$$

The geodesics are in this case maxima, not minima as in Euclidean geometry. The Lagrangian resembles its classical counterpart, because the expansion of $m_0 c^2 L \, d\tau$ is

$$m_0 c^2 e^{\Phi/c^2} \, d\tau = m_0 (c^2 + \Phi - \tfrac{1}{2} v^2) \, dt = m_0 c^2 \, dt - (T - m_0 \Phi) \, dt,$$

where $T = \tfrac{1}{2} m_0 v^2$.

For the orbit problem, a reference frame is chosen in which the gravitating mass M is at rest. From eq. (6-20), the potential is $\Phi = -GM/r$. It is then a straightforward procedure to show that the orbit of a test particle around this mass is planar; the proof need not be given here. With the choice of polar coordinates r, θ in the orbital plane, the equation of motion (6-22) becomes

$$
\left.
\begin{aligned}
\ddot{t} &= -\mu r^{-2}\dot{r}\dot{t} & \text{a} \\[4pt]
\ddot{r} - r\dot{\theta}^2 &= -\mu c^2 r^{-2}(1 + c^{-2}\dot{r}^2) & \text{b} \\[4pt]
\frac{d}{d\tau}(r^2\dot{\theta}) &= -\mu \dot{r}\dot{\theta} & \text{c}
\end{aligned}
\right\} \quad \text{(6-32)}
$$

where μ is the gravitational radius of the mass M defined by eq. (6-17), and the dots indicate differentiation with respect to the proper time of the particle. Equations (6-32a) and (6-32c) can be immediately integrated to give

$$
\dot{t} = ke^{\mu u} \tag{6-33}
$$

and

$$
H = r^2\dot{\theta} = he^{\mu u}, \tag{6-34}
$$

respectively, where $u = 1/r$, k and h are the constants of integration, and H is defined by eq. (6-34). Equations (6-33) and (6-34) can also be obtained from the Lagrangian

$$
L = e^{-\mu/r}\sqrt{\dot{t}^2 - c^{-2}(\dot{r}^2 + r^2\dot{\theta}^2)}.
$$

Since neither t nor θ appear explicitly in the Lagrangian, their conjugate momenta k and $-hc^{-2}$ must be constants. Equations (6-13) and (6-33) now allow $J(u)$ in eq. (6-2b) to be evaluated:

$$
J(u) = \tfrac{1}{2}c^2[k^2e^{2\mu u} - 1].
$$

Equations (6-8) and (6-34) then give

$$
N(u) = \frac{\mu c^2}{h^2}e^{-2\mu u}. \tag{6-35}
$$

The perihelion advance from eq. (6-10) is

$$
\sigma = -\frac{\mu}{p}e^{-2\mu u_0} \simeq -\frac{\mu}{p}
$$

where $p = h^2/\mu c^2$. The perihelion of the orbit regresses, i.e., it moves in the direction opposite the particle's revolution.

For a particle traveling with the speed of light, $h \to \infty$ in eq. (6-35) to give $N = 0$. Hence eq. (6-7) has the solution $u = a \cos \theta$, and the particle follows a straight line.

The non-conservation of rest mass in the theory based on eq. (6-26) gives an interesting but misleading stress-energy tensor $S^{\mu\nu}$ (not to be confused with the one for electromagnetism) for the gravitational field. It is easy enough to find a stress-energy tensor which is consistent with the equation of motion. The definition

$$S^{\mu\nu} = \frac{1}{4\pi G} (g^\mu g^\nu - \tfrac{1}{2}\eta^{\mu\nu} g^\sigma g_\sigma) \tag{6-36}$$

and the postulate

$$\frac{\partial}{\partial x^\nu} (M^{\mu\nu} + S^{\mu\nu}) = 0$$

where

$$M^{\mu\nu} = \rho_0 u^\mu u^\nu$$

reproduce the equation of motion (6-26) by virtue of the field equations (6-23) and (6-24), but it is difficult to interpret the components of $S^{\mu\nu}$.

The Newtonian gravitational energy density is found to be $-g^k g^k / 8\pi G$ in the following way. The density of power generation is found from the equation of motion

$$\frac{dv^k}{dt} = -\frac{\partial \Phi}{\partial x^k},$$

the equation of conservation of mass

$$0 = \frac{\partial \rho}{\partial t} + \frac{\partial}{\partial x^k} (\rho v^k),$$

and the field equation (1-49) to be

$$\rho v^k \frac{dv^k}{dt} = \frac{1}{8\pi G} \frac{\partial}{\partial t} (g^l g^l) - \frac{\partial}{\partial x^m} \left(\rho \Phi v^m + \frac{\Phi}{4\pi G} \frac{\partial^2 \Phi}{\partial x^m \partial t} \right).$$

Upon integrating over all space, the principle of conservation of energy requires that the gravitational field have energy

$$-\frac{1}{8\pi G} \int g^k g^k \, dV.$$

On the other hand, the component $S^{00} c^2$ in eq. (6-36) for a static field is

$$S^{00} c^2 = \frac{1}{8\pi G} g^k g^k.$$

The field energy around two point masses m_1 and m_2 separated by a distance r is found* to be $+Gm_1m_2/r$ in addition to the self-energies. This expression is exactly the *negative* of the potential energy. The discrepancy in sign is due to non-conservation of rest mass. Indeed, without conservation of rest mass it is pointless even to consider finding a stress-energy tensor for the field, because the very concept of energy loses significance.

6.6 VECTOR THEORY OF GRAVITATION

The vector theory of Section 6.4 was a special case in that it was patterned after electromagnetism. In this section we study the most general equation of motion for a vector potential based on Postulate 2 of Section 6.5.

The field equation is assumed to be

$$\Box^2\phi^\mu = -4\pi G\rho_0 c^2 u^\mu \tag{6-37}$$

where ϕ^μ is the vector potential, ρ_0 is the proper density of the matter, and u^μ is its world-velocity. Equation (6-37) is consistent with the result to be obtained later that ϕ^0 corresponds to the Newtonian gravitational potential. The consequences of eq. (6-37) are already familiar from electromagnetism, because eq. (6-37) is exactly analogous to eq. (4-5) with $J^\mu = \rho u^\mu$. Thus the potential due to a point mass M at the origin is

$$\phi^\mu = -\frac{GM}{r}\,\delta_0^\mu. \tag{6-38}$$

The equation of motion

$$\alpha^\mu = \frac{du^\mu}{d\tau} = \Gamma^{\mu\nu\rho}\frac{\partial\phi_\nu}{\partial x^\rho} \tag{6-39}$$

contains coefficients $\Gamma^{\mu\nu\rho}$ which can at most depend on the velocity u^μ. The condition $u_\mu\alpha^\mu = 0$ limits the choice of the $\Gamma^{\mu\nu\rho}$. The scalar

$$\Gamma(\mathbf{a}, \mathbf{b}, \mathbf{c}, \mathbf{u}) = \Gamma^{\mu\nu\rho}a_\mu b_\nu c_\rho$$

---

* The calculation is:

$$\epsilon = \frac{1}{4\pi G}\int g_1^k g_2^k\, dV = -\frac{1}{4\pi G}\int\left[\frac{\partial}{\partial x^k}(g_1^k\Phi_2) - \Phi_2\frac{\partial g_1^k}{\partial x^k}\right]dV$$

$$= -\frac{1}{4\pi G}\int_S g_1^k\Phi_2\, dS^k - \int_V \Phi_2\rho_1\, dV$$

$$\rightarrow \frac{Gm_1m_2}{r}.$$

formed from three arbitrary 4-vectors **a**, **b**, and **c** must have the form

$$\Gamma(\mathbf{a}, \mathbf{b}, \mathbf{c}, \mathbf{u}) = A \cdot (\mathbf{a} \cdot \mathbf{u})(\mathbf{b} \cdot \mathbf{c}) + B \cdot (\mathbf{a} \cdot \mathbf{c})(\mathbf{b} \cdot \mathbf{u})$$
$$+ C(\mathbf{a} \cdot \mathbf{b})(\mathbf{c} \cdot \mathbf{u}) + D(\mathbf{a} \cdot \mathbf{u})(\mathbf{b} \cdot \mathbf{u})(\mathbf{c} \cdot \mathbf{u})$$
$$+ E e_{\alpha\beta\gamma\delta} a^\alpha b^\beta c^\gamma u^\delta, \tag{6-40}$$

where $\mathbf{a} \cdot \mathbf{b} = a_\mu b^\mu$, etc. The condition $\Gamma(\mathbf{u}, \mathbf{b}, \mathbf{c}, \mathbf{u}) = 0$ requires

$$A \cdot (\mathbf{b} \cdot \mathbf{c}) = -(B + C + D)(\mathbf{b} \cdot \mathbf{u})(\mathbf{c} \cdot \mathbf{u})$$

for arbitrary **b** and **c**. Therefore we have $A = 0$ and $B + C + D = 0$. Equation (6-40) becomes

$$\Gamma(\mathbf{a}, \mathbf{b}, \mathbf{c}, \mathbf{u}) = B \cdot (\mathbf{a} \cdot \mathbf{c})(\mathbf{b} \cdot \mathbf{u}) + C(\mathbf{a} \cdot \mathbf{b})(\mathbf{c} \cdot \mathbf{u})$$
$$- (B + C)(\mathbf{a} \cdot \mathbf{u})(\mathbf{b} \cdot \mathbf{u})(\mathbf{c} \cdot \mathbf{u}) + E e_{\alpha\beta\gamma\delta} a^\alpha b^\beta c^\gamma u^\delta.$$

Since the vectors **a**, **b**, and **c** were arbitrary, $\Gamma^{\mu\nu\rho}$ must have the form

$$\Gamma^{\mu\nu\rho} = B\eta^{\mu\rho}u^\nu + C\eta^{\mu\nu}u^\rho - (B + C)u^\mu u^\nu u^\rho + E e^{\mu\nu\rho\sigma}u_\sigma.$$

It is then an easy matter to put eq. (6-39) into the form

$$c^2\alpha^\mu = -\alpha F^\mu_{,\nu}u^\nu + \beta(\eta^{\mu\nu} - u^\mu u^\nu)H_{\nu\rho}u^\rho + \zeta e^{\mu\nu\rho\sigma}u_\sigma F_{\nu\rho}, \tag{6-41}$$

where

$$\alpha = \tfrac{1}{2}(B - C)c^2$$
$$\beta = \tfrac{1}{2}(B + C)c^2$$
$$\zeta = \tfrac{1}{2}Ec^2$$

and

$$F_{\mu\nu} = \frac{\partial \phi_\mu}{\partial x^\nu} - \frac{\partial \phi_\nu}{\partial x^\mu}$$

$$H_{\mu\nu} = \frac{\partial \phi_\mu}{\partial x^\nu} + \frac{\partial \phi_\nu}{\partial x^\mu}.$$

The theory contains the three parameters α, β, and ζ.

Electromagnetism is represented by the field equation (6-37) and the equation of motion (6-41) with $-4\pi G$ replaced by $1/\epsilon_0$, ϕ^μ replaced by $c^2\phi^\mu$, mass replaced by charge, and the parameters α, β, ζ given the values q/m, 0, and 0, respectively. Thus the vector theory of gravity in Section 6.4 was based on the values $\alpha = 1$, $\beta = 0$, and $\zeta = 0$.

In the Newtonian approximation of small velocities and small time derivatives, the equation of motion becomes $\alpha^i = -Bc^2\, \partial\phi_0/\partial x^i$. Thus $Bc^2\phi_0$ is the Newtonian gravitational potential. The choice of the field equation (6-37) now requires us to choose $B = c^{-2}$ or $\alpha + \beta = 1$.

The perihelion advance and the behavior of a particle moving at the velocity of light will now be calculated for arbitrary α and β. We consider a test particle moving around a fixed mass M which has the potential of eq. (6-38). The parameter ζ must be chosen to be zero in order that the orbit be planar and be coplanar with the mass. (See Appendix A.4.) In terms of polar coordinates r, θ in the orbit plane, the equations of motion are

$$
\begin{aligned}
\ddot{r} &= GMr^{-2}\dot{r}(\beta - \alpha - 2\beta\dot{t}^2)c^{-2} && \text{a} \\
\ddot{r} - r\dot{\theta}^2 &= -GMr^{-2}\dot{t}[(\alpha + \beta) + 2\beta\dot{r}^2c^{-2}] && \text{b} \\
\frac{d}{d\tau}(r^2\dot{\theta}) &= -2GM\beta\dot{t}\dot{\theta}\dot{r}c^{-2} && \text{c}
\end{aligned}
\right\} \quad (6\text{-}42)
$$

where the dot denotes differentiation with respect to the proper time τ of the particle. In the Newtonian approximation, eq. (6-42b) requires

$$
\alpha + \beta = 1. \tag{6-43}
$$

There remains therefore only one independent parameter, say β, since $\alpha = 1 - \beta$ and $\zeta = 0$.

In arriving at a solution, use is made of eqs. (6-2) and (6-13). Comparison of eqs. (6-2b) and (6-13) shows that, with τ as the independent variable,

$$
2J = c^2(\gamma^2 - 1) \tag{6-44}
$$

where $\gamma = \dot{t}$. In order to find $N(u)$, we first rewrite eq. (6-42c) in the form

$$
\frac{d \ln H}{du} = 2\mu\beta\gamma \tag{6-45}
$$

where $H = r^2\dot{\theta}$, $\mu = GM/c^2$, and $u = 1/r$. Equation (6-42a) becomes

$$
\frac{d\gamma}{du} = \mu[1 + 2\beta(\gamma^2 - 1)] \tag{6-46}
$$

since $\alpha = 1 - \beta$. Equations (6-44), (6-45), and (6-46) can now be substituted into eq. (6-8) to give

$$
N(u) = \frac{\mu c^2 \gamma(u)}{H^2(u)}. \tag{6-47}
$$

Again, by means of eqs. (6-45) and (6-46), $N(u)$ is found to have the derivative

$$
\frac{dN}{du} = \frac{\mu^2 c^2}{H^2}[1 - 2\beta(\gamma^2 + 1)]. \tag{6-48}
$$

Substitution of eq. (6-48) into eq. (6-10) gives the perihelion advance

$$
\sigma = \frac{\mu}{2p}(1 - 4\beta)
$$

where $p = H^2/\mu c^2$. The case $\beta = 0$ leads to a perihelion advance $\sigma = \dfrac{1}{2}\dfrac{\mu}{p}$, as was found in Section 6.4. The case of a symmetric field tensor with $\alpha = 0$ leads to a perihelion advance of $\sigma = -\dfrac{3}{2}\dfrac{\mu}{p}$. In order to get the Einstein value of $\sigma = 3\dfrac{\mu}{p}$, the parameters α and β must be chosen to be $\frac{9}{4}$ and $-\frac{5}{4}$, respectively. For a particle with the speed of light, we take the limit of eq. (6-47) as all proper-time derivatives approach ∞. In the expression

$$N = \frac{\mu c^2}{r^4 \dot{\theta}}\frac{dt}{d\theta},$$

all quantities remain finite except $\dot{\theta}$ which tends toward ∞. Therefore, N vanishes, and there is no deflection for a particle moving with the speed of light.

To summarize, the most general linear vector-potential equation of motion has three parameters. For a field equation like the one in electro-magnetism, the orbital plane of a particle around a stationary, gravitating mass passes through the mass only if one parameter is zero. The requirement that the theory reduce to Newtonian gravity in the classical approximation pins down the second parameter, leaving only one arbitrary parameter. The perihelion advance is a linear function of the third parameter, and hence can take any value, depending upon the parameter. A particle traveling with the speed of light is not deflected, regardless of the value of the arbitrary parameter. It is concluded that, if the Einstein value for perihelion advance is correct, neither the scalar-potential theory of Section 6.5 nor the vector-potential theory presented here can be valid.

But the vector theory is unsound in another respect. A particle traveling with the speed of light cannot simulate a photon unless $\beta = 0$. On the one hand, Maxwell's equations in special relativity require that light be propagated in free space with an isotropic, constant velocity c. Indeed, this was a postulate in the special theory of relativity. On the other hand, the equation of motion for $\dot{r}$, eq. (6-46), has solutions which allow $\dot{r} = +\infty$ over a *finite* range $0 \leq u < u_0$ only for the value $\beta = 0$. The absurdity of the theory for $\beta \neq 0$ can be seen by following the solution for $\beta = \frac{1}{2}$, $\dot{r} = a/(1 - a\mu u)$, where a is the constant of integration. For a particle falling radially inward from rest at infinity, a is unity, and $\dot{r} = 1/(1 - \mu u)$. The particle's velocity is given by $v/c = \sqrt{2\mu u - \mu^2 u^2}$. By the time the particle reaches a radius μ, it is traveling with the velocity of light. For radii less than μ, $\dot{r}$ is negative! We are not criticizing the vector theory for having an unusual result. A similarly unusual behavior is encountered in Einstein's theory. The criticism is that a particle with the speed of light cannot simulate a photon, unless $\beta = 0$.

6.7 TENSOR THEORY OF GRAVITATION

We will first derive the most general equation of motion for a symmetric second rank tensor potential $\phi^{\mu\nu}$ consistent with Postulate 2 of Section 6.5. The equation of motion is given by

$$\alpha^\mu = \Gamma^{\mu\nu\rho\sigma} \frac{\partial \phi_{\nu\rho}}{\partial x^\sigma}$$

where the $\Gamma^{\mu\nu\rho\sigma}$ can at most depend on the world-velocity u^μ of the test particle. The scalar

$$\Gamma(\mathbf{a}, \mathbf{b}, \mathbf{c}, \mathbf{u}) = \Gamma^{\mu\nu\rho\sigma} a_\mu b_\nu b_\rho c_\sigma$$

formed from three arbitrary vectors $\mathbf{a}, \mathbf{b}, \mathbf{c}$ must be of the form

$$\begin{aligned}
\Gamma(a, b, c, u) = {} & A \cdot (a \cdot b)(b \cdot c) + B \cdot (a \cdot c)(b \cdot b) \\
& + K \cdot (a \cdot u)(b \cdot u)(b \cdot c) + L \cdot (a \cdot u)(b \cdot b)(c \cdot u) \\
& + C \cdot (a \cdot c)(b \cdot u)^2 + D \cdot (a \cdot b)(b \cdot u)(c \cdot u) \\
& + N \cdot (a \cdot u)(b \cdot u)^2(c \cdot u) + E e_{\alpha\beta\gamma\delta} a^\alpha b^\beta c^\gamma u^\delta \cdot (b \cdot u).
\end{aligned}$$

The usual procedure of setting $\mathbf{a} = \mathbf{u}$ and requiring $\Gamma(\mathbf{u}, \mathbf{b}, \mathbf{c}, \mathbf{u}) = 0$, which was used in the two previous sections, introduces the conditions $A + K = 0$, $B + L = 0$, and $C + D + N = 0$. The result is

$$\begin{aligned}
\Gamma(a, b, c, u) = {} & [(a \cdot b) - (a \cdot u)(b \cdot u)][A(b \cdot c) + D(b \cdot u)(c \cdot u)] \\
& + [(a \cdot c) - (a \cdot u)(c \cdot u)][B(b \cdot b) + C(b \cdot u)^2] \\
& + E e_{\alpha\beta\gamma\delta} a^\alpha b^\beta c^\gamma u^\delta \cdot (b \cdot u).
\end{aligned}$$

The equation of motion is therefore

$$\alpha^\mu = (\eta^{\mu\nu} - u^\mu u^\nu)[A\phi^\sigma_{\nu,\sigma} + B\phi^\sigma_{\sigma,\nu} + u^\rho u^\sigma(C\phi_{\rho\sigma,\nu} + D\phi_{\nu\rho,\sigma})] \\ + E e^{\mu\nu\rho\sigma}\phi_{\nu\tau,\rho} u^\tau u_\sigma \quad (6\text{-}49)$$

where the commas denote differentiation. Equation (6-49) is the most general equation of motion which is linear in the first derivatives of a symmetric second-rank tensor potential $\phi^{\mu\nu}$.

The choice of the field equation

$$\Box^2 \phi^{\mu\nu} = 8\pi G c^2 M^{\mu\nu}, \quad (6\text{-}50)$$

where $M^{\mu\nu}$ is the matter stress-energy tensor, leads to the potential

$$\phi^{\mu\nu} = \frac{2GM}{r} \delta^\mu_0 \delta^\nu_0$$

for a stressless point mass at rest at the origin. The equation of motion (6-49) then becomes

$$\left.\begin{array}{rl} \ddot{t} = -2GMr^{-2}\dot{r}\dot{t}[D - B - \dot{t}^2(C + D)] & \qquad \text{a} \\ \ddot{r} - r\dot{\theta}^2 = 2GMc^2r^{-2}\{B + C\dot{t}^2 + c^{-2}\dot{r}^2[B + \dot{t}^2(C + D)]\} & \text{b} \\ \dfrac{1}{r^2}\dfrac{d}{d\tau}(r^2\dot{\theta}) = 2GMr^{-2}\dot{r}\dot{\theta}[B + \dot{t}^2(C + D)]. & \text{c} \end{array}\right\} \qquad (6\text{-}51)$$

We have set $E = 0$ in order that the plane of the orbit be coplanar with the gravitating mass. In order that eq. (6-51b) agree with Newtonian gravity in the non-relativistic approximation, B and C must satisfy the condition $B + C = -1/(2c^2)$. The substitutions

$$\left.\begin{array}{l} \alpha = -2c^2(D - B) \\ \beta = 2c^2B \end{array}\right\} \qquad (6\text{-}52)$$

then put eqs. (6-51a) and (6-51c) into the forms

$$\ddot{t} = \mu r^{-2}\dot{r}\dot{t}\,[\alpha - (\alpha + 1)\dot{t}^2] \qquad (6\text{-}53)$$

$$\frac{d}{d\tau}\ln(r^2\dot{\theta}) = \frac{\mu\dot{r}}{r^2}[\beta - (\alpha + 1)\dot{t}^2] \qquad (6\text{-}54)$$

where as usual $\mu = GM/c^2$. The same analysis as was used in the previous section may be applied to eqs. (6-53), (6-54), and (6-13) to give

$$\frac{d^2u}{d\theta^2} + u = N(u) = -\frac{\mu c^2}{H^2}[\beta - (1 + \beta)\dot{t}^2] \qquad (6\text{-}55)$$

with the by-products

$$\left.\begin{array}{rl} \dfrac{d\dot{t}}{du} = -\mu\dot{t}[\alpha - (\alpha + 1)\dot{t}^2] & \qquad \text{a} \\[2mm] \dfrac{d\ln H}{du} = -\mu[\beta - (\alpha + 1)\dot{t}^2] & \qquad \text{b} \end{array}\right\} \qquad (6\text{-}56)$$

Differentiation of eq. (6-55) with the help of eqs. (6-56) gives

$$\frac{1}{2}\frac{dN}{du} = \frac{\mu^2c^2}{H^2}[-\beta^2 + \dot{t}^2(\beta^2 + 2\beta - \alpha)].$$

For $\dot{t} \simeq 1$, the perihelion advance is

$$\sigma = \frac{\mu}{p}(2\beta - \alpha) \qquad (6\text{-}57)$$

where $p = H^2/\mu c^2$. The deflection of a particle traveling at the speed of light is obtained by taking the limit of eq. (6-55) as $\dot{t}$ and $\dot{\theta}$ both approach ∞. In the limit we have

$$N = \frac{\mu c^2}{r^4} \left(\frac{dt}{d\theta}\right)^2 (1 + \beta).$$

For a particle moving with speed c in a straight line which passes a distance R from the origin, $(dt/d\theta)^2 = r^4/c^2 R^2$. Thus the equation of orbit for the particle is approximately

$$\frac{d^2 u}{d\theta^2} + u = \frac{\mu}{R^2} (1 + \beta).$$

The above equation has the solution

$$u = \frac{1 + e \cos \theta}{p}$$

where now $p = R^2/\mu(1 + \beta)$. Now the asymptotic angle is given by $\cos \theta = -1/e$. Hence the total deflection, if it is small, is $2/e$. Since the perihelion distance is

$$\frac{1 + e}{p} \simeq \frac{1}{R},$$

we can eliminate p and solve for $2/e$:

$$\text{deflection} = \frac{2}{e} = \frac{2\mu}{R} (1 + \beta). \tag{6-58}$$

A gravitational theory with a symmetric tensor potential based on the field equation (6-50) has two arbitrary parameters α and β. The perihelion advance is given by eq. (6-57), and the angular deflection of a particle traveling with the speed of light is given by eq. (6-58). These values can be adjusted to agree with those obtained in Einstein's theory $\left(\sigma = 3\frac{\mu}{p} \text{ and deflection} = 4\frac{\mu}{R}\right)$ by choosing $\alpha = -1$ and $\beta = 1$.

The value $\alpha = -1$ also arises from another consideration. The solution to eq. (6-56a) is

$$\frac{1}{\dot{t}^2} = \frac{1 + \alpha}{\alpha} (1 + Ke^{2\alpha\mu u})$$

where K is the constant of integration. If a particle moving with a velocity c (and hence having $\dot{t} = \infty$) is to maintain the same velocity, then the value of $1/\dot{t}$ must vanish over the range of u through which the particle travels. This in turn requires $1 + \alpha = 0$ or $\alpha = -1$. The same condition also results from the requirement that u^μ appear to no higher than the second power in eq. (6-49), for then $C + D$ and hence $-(\alpha + 1)/2c^2$ must vanish.

Birkhoff[B] proposed a special-relativistic tensor theory of gravity based on specific assumptions about the equation of motion and a different field equation from eq. (6-50). He assumed that the equation of motion (6-49) has to be homogeneous to the second degree in u^μ. Then $C + D = 0$, $A = 0$, and $B = 0$, leaving

$$\alpha^\mu = Du^\rho u^\sigma(\phi^\mu_{\rho,\sigma} - \phi_{\rho\sigma,}{}^\mu).$$

Birkhoff took the field equation to be

$$\Box^2\phi^{\mu\nu} = 8\pi Gc^2 M^{\mu\nu}$$

where *his* $M^{\mu\nu}$ is given by

$$M^{\mu\nu} = \rho u^\mu u^\nu - \tfrac{1}{2}\rho\eta^{\mu\nu}. \tag{6-59}$$

The potential for a stationary point mass is then

$$\phi^{\mu\nu} = \frac{GM}{r}\begin{bmatrix} 1 & 0 & 0 & 0 \\ 0 & c^2 & 0 & 0 \\ 0 & 0 & c^2 & 0 \\ 0 & 0 & 0 & c^2 \end{bmatrix}$$

or

$$\phi_{\mu\nu} = \frac{GM}{r}\begin{bmatrix} 1 & 0 & 0 & 0 \\ 0 & c^{-2} & 0 & 0 \\ 0 & 0 & c^{-2} & 0 \\ 0 & 0 & 0 & c^{-2} \end{bmatrix}.$$

The equations of motion under this potential are

$$\ddot{t} = D\mu c^2 \dot{u}\dot{t} \qquad \text{a}$$
$$\ddot{r} - r\dot{\theta}^2 = -DGMr^{-2}c^2[\dot{t}^2 + c^{-2}r^2\dot{\theta}^2] \qquad \text{b} \quad \Bigg\} \quad (6\text{-}60)$$
$$\frac{1}{r^2}\frac{d}{d\tau}(r^2\dot{\theta}) = -D\mu c^2 \dot{u}\dot{\theta}. \qquad \text{c}$$

Comparison of eq. (6-60b) with Newtonian theory requires $D = c^{-2}$. Equations (6-60a) and (6-60c) then have solutions

$$\dot{t} = ke^{\mu u}$$

and

$$H = r^2\dot{\theta} = he^{-\mu u}$$

where k and h are constants. Calculations similar to those done previously show

$$N(u) = \frac{c^2\mu}{H^2}(2k^2 e^{2\mu u} - 1),$$

for which the perihelion advance is

$$\sigma = 3\frac{\mu}{p}.$$

The deflection of a particle traveling with the speed of light is obtained by taking the limit of $N(u)$ as both k and h tend toward ∞.

$$N = \frac{2c^2\mu}{r^4}\left(\frac{dt}{d\theta}\right)^2.$$

As before, we set $(dt/d\theta)^2 = r^4/c^2R^2$ and find a deflection twice $2\mu/R$, i.e., $4\mu/R$. Thus Birkhoff's theory predicts the same values for the perihelion advance and the deflection of a particle with the speed of light as those obtained in Einstein's theory.

Birkhoff justified his field equation in the following way. In general, the stress-energy tensor for a perfect fluid is given by $M^{\mu\nu} = \rho u^\mu u^\nu - p_0 c^{-2}\eta^{\mu\nu}$ where $\rho = \rho_0 + p_0 c^{-2}$. The equations of motion $\partial M^{\mu\nu}/\partial x^\nu = 0$ for the fluid without external forces yields the relations

$$\frac{\partial(\rho u^\nu)}{\partial x^\nu} = \frac{1}{c^2}\frac{dp_0}{d\tau}$$

$$\rho\frac{du^\mu}{d\tau} = \frac{1}{c^2}(\eta^{\mu\nu} - u^\mu u^\nu)\frac{\partial p_0}{\partial x^\nu}.$$

Consider now small disturbances in a fluid which has an equation of state $p = f(\rho)$. The unperturbed state is taken to be $u^\mu = \delta^\mu_0$, $\rho = \hat\rho$, and $p_0 = \hat p_0 = f(\hat\rho)$. To first order in the deviations $\delta u^\mu = u^\mu - \delta^\mu_0$, $\delta\rho = \rho - \hat\rho$, and $\delta p_0 = p_0 - \hat p_0$, the equations of motion become

$$\hat\rho\frac{\partial\,\delta u^i}{\partial x^i} = \left(\frac{1}{c^2}f' - 1\right)\frac{\partial\,\delta\rho}{\partial t}$$

$$\hat\rho\frac{\partial\,\delta u^i}{\partial t} = -f'\frac{\partial\,\delta\rho}{\partial x^i}$$

where f' denotes the derivative of $f(\rho)$ with respect to its argument. Elimination of δu^i then gives

$$\frac{\partial^2\,\delta\rho}{\partial t^2} - \frac{f'}{1 - c^{-2}f'}\nabla^2\,\delta\rho = 0.$$

The above wave equation implies a wave velocity $\sqrt{f'/(1 - c^{-2}f')}$. Up to this point, the derivation is straightforward. It is at this point that Birkhoff insists that the wave velocity must be equal to c. Then we have $f' = \frac{1}{2}c^2$ which gives $p = \frac{1}{2}c^2\rho$ and hence eq. (6-59).

The special-relativistic gravitational theories have three notable features. (1) There are a large number of theories; we have presented only four. The reader is referred to Whitrow[B] and Morduch's review article on special-relativistic gravitational theories. (2) The Einstein perihelion advance is easy to obtain. (3) The Einstein deflection for a particle traveling with the velocity of light is also not difficult to obtain.

The reader may by now have noticed a glaring discrepancy in connection with particles traveling with the speed of light. On the one hand, *particles* with such a speed may be deflected by gravity in a suitable tensor theory. On the other hand, *photons* must travel in straight lines—this was one of the two postulates of special relativity! Therefore in any special-relativistic theory in which particles traveling with the speed of light are deflected by gravity, such particles cannot simulate photons. Yet observation indicates that photons from distant stars passing near the sun are deflected by the sun's gravity. (See Section 9.5.)

But there is a third crucial test (which, of the three, is verified with the best observational accuracy) that Einstein's theory of gravity passes but that *all* special-relativistic theories of gravity fail. This test is the gravitational redshift.

6.8 GRAVITATIONAL FREQUENCY SHIFT

When we invoke the quantum principle that a photon's energy depends on its frequency, we get into trouble. For example, let a particle of mass m fall from rest at infinity to the surface of a planet of mass M and radius R. Let the particle, which then has total energy $mc^2[1 + (\mu/R) + O^2(\mu/R)]$, where $\mu = GM/c^2$, be converted into a photon. If we follow the usual rule that a photon's energy $\in$ is related to its frequency ν by the formula

$$\in = h\nu, \tag{6-61}$$

then the photon's frequency before leaving the planet is

$$\nu = \frac{mc^2}{h}\left[1 + \frac{\mu}{R} + O^2\left(\frac{\mu}{R}\right)\right].$$

Since all observers in a given reference frame measure the same time interval between any two events, the photon's frequency must remain unchanged as it travels away from the planet. At infinity the photon has energy $mc^2[1 + (\mu/R) + O^2(\mu/R)]$. The net result of the process is to create energy of the amount $mc^2(\mu/R)[1 + O(\mu/R)]$.

Since energy cannot be created, one of the foregoing assumptions must be incorrect. We could attempt to obtain consistency by revising eq. (6-61) to read $\in = h\nu[1 - (\Phi/c^2) + O^2(\Phi/c^2)]$ where Φ is the Newtonian gravitational potential. However, experiment shows that eq. (6-61) is correct; it is the photon's *frequency* which must be altered. In the above example, the photon's energy $h\nu'$ at infinity must, by conservation of energy, be equal to mc^2. Then ν and ν' have the ratio

$$\frac{\nu}{\nu'} = 1 + \frac{\mu}{R} + O^2\left(\frac{\mu}{R}\right).$$

More generally, the change $\Delta\nu$ in the frequency ν of a photon as it travels through a difference $\Delta\Phi$ in gravitational potential is given by

$$\frac{\Delta\nu}{\nu} = -\frac{\Delta\Phi}{c^2} + O^2\left(\frac{\Delta\Phi}{c^2}\right). \qquad (6\text{-}62)$$

Experiment shows eq. (6-62) to be correct. The sign is such that the frequency decreases if the light travels uphill. The frequency shift has been observed both for terrestrial sources and for astronomical sources. The observations will be discussed in Section 9.5c.

The frequency shift described above is a disaster for special-relativistic gravitational theories. The observed frequency for a given spectral line depends on the location of the observer, even though the observer may be stationary relative to the source of light. Such a situation cannot arise in special relativity. For when dx, dy, and dz are set equal to zero in eq. (3-33), the proper time ds is exactly equal to the coordinate time dt. We are forced to conclude that gravitation cannot be incorporated into special relativity.* We therefore turn to the study of non-Euclidean differential geometry in the next chapter.

The preceding discussion provides a clue to the kind of gravitational theory for which we must look. Consider two light signals which travel from a stationary source S to a stationary observer O (see Figure 6.1).

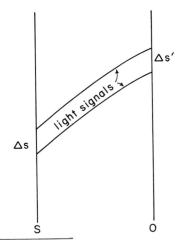

FIGURE 6.1   Frequency shift.

---

* This logical sequence was presented by Alfred Schild at the seminar of the American Mathematical Society at Ithaca, New York, July 24–August 21, 1965.

The time interval between emission of the two signals as measured by S is Δs, and the time interval between reception of the two signals as measured by O is $\Delta s'$. Now the number of waves which leave S in the interval Δs must equal the number of waves which arrive at O in the interval $\Delta s'$. Therefore, the frequency ν of emission and the frequency ν' of reception have the ratio

$$\frac{\nu'}{\nu} = \frac{\Delta s}{\Delta s'}.$$

From eq. (6-62) we then have

$$\frac{\Delta s'}{\Delta s} = 1 + \frac{1}{c^2}(\Phi_0 - \Phi_S) + O^2. \tag{6-63}$$

Equation (6-63) and the boundary condition that space-time be Minkowski in the absence of gravitational fields indicate an equation of the form

$$ds^2 = \left[1 + 2\frac{\Phi}{c^2} + O^2\left(\frac{\Phi}{c^2}\right)\right] dt^2 - \frac{1}{c^2}\left[1 + O\left(\frac{\Phi}{c^2}\right)\right](dx^2 + dy^2 + dz^2)$$

$$+ O\left(\frac{\Phi}{c^2}\right) \cdot dt\, dx^i; \tag{6-64}$$

ds is the time between two events x^μ and $x^\mu + dx^\mu$ measured by an observer whose world-line passes through both events. An expression which, to the order indicated, is identical with eq. (6-64) results from eq. (6-31) in the scalar theory of gravity, if the role of measurement is transferred from $d\tau$ to ds.

6.9 THE EQUIVALENCE PRINCIPLE

Equation (6-62) is a consequence of the *principle of equivalence* which states that gravitation is equivalent to acceleration. More precisely, the principle states that physical experiments performed in a frame in which free particles undergo a common, uniform, constant acceleration cannot distinguish between the following two possibilities or a mixture thereof: (1) the acceleration of the free particles is due to a gravitational field; (2) the acceleration of the free particles is due to an acceleration of the frame. Large-scale experiments can discover the difference, but within a *small* region of space-time, a suitably chosen reference frame can completely eliminate the effects of gravitational acceleration. Let us examine three consequences of the principle of equivalence.

Consider a long, hollow tube of length L with devices for sending light from one end to the other. Let the tube be accelerated in the same direction as the light (Fig. 6.2). The photon which leaves the rear end

FIGURE 6.2 Frequency shift in accelerated system.

when the rear end is stationary reaches the front end when the front end has velocity

$$v = \frac{L}{c} a + O^2\left(\frac{v}{c}\right) \tag{6-65}$$

where a is the acceleration of the tube. The experiment is performed in the absence of any gravitational field. The photon undergoes a Doppler shift given by eq. (3-75)

$$\frac{v'}{v} = 1 - \frac{v}{c} + O^2\left(\frac{v}{c}\right) \tag{6-66}$$

where v' is the frequency of reception and v is the frequency of emission. Elimination of v from eqs. (6-65) and (6-66) gives

$$\frac{\Delta v}{v} = \frac{v' - v}{v} = -\frac{La}{c^2} + O^2\left(\frac{La}{c^2}\right). \tag{6-67}$$

According to the principle of equivalence, the above result must be exactly the same as when the tube is stationary in a gravitational field $g = a$ which points in the direction opposite the light beam. Then La is the difference $\Delta\Phi$ in gravitational potential between the receiver and the emitter. Equation (6-67) becomes eq. (6-62). Thus the gravitational frequency shift described in the previous section is a consequence of the principle of equivalence.

The principle of equivalence also requires that the weights of different objects be proportional to their inertial masses. The ratio of gravitational mass to inertial mass must be a constant which, by appropriate choice of units, can be taken as unity. For example, when an object is weighed in a balance against standard weights and is found to have a gravitational mass m kilograms, the principle of equivalence implies that the object also has an inertial mass equal to m times the inertial mass of the standard kilogram. Such a relation is susceptible to experiment, and experiment indeed shows that, to the accuracy thus far attained, gravitational mass is identical with inertial mass.*

Finally, the principle of equivalence restricts the form of the equation of motion in a gravitational field. The equation of motion

$$\frac{du^\mu}{ds} = \alpha^\mu(x^v, u^\rho)$$

---

* Eötvös[B] et al. found the ratio to be unity to within 10^{-8}. Dicke[B] has pushed this accuracy down to 10^{-9}.

for the trajectory $x^\mu(s)$ of the test particle is assumed to depend only on position and on the world-velocity $u^\mu = dx^\mu/ds$. The parameter s is the test-particle's own time. Upon transformation to a new set of coordinates y^α, we find by differentiation of the relation

$$\frac{dy^\alpha}{ds} = \frac{\partial y^\alpha}{\partial x^\mu} u^\mu$$

that the equation of motion becomes

$$\frac{d^2 y^\alpha}{ds^2} = \frac{\partial y^\alpha}{\partial x^\mu} \alpha^\mu + \frac{\partial^2 y^\alpha}{\partial x^\nu \partial x^\rho} u^\nu u^\rho. \qquad (6\text{-}68)$$

Again according to the principle of equivalence, there must exist, in the neighborhood of any event E, a coordinate system in which the world-velocities of all test particles are constant, independent of the world-velocities. If y^α is the chosen coordinate system, then the left-hand side of eq. (6-68) vanishes. Multiplication by $\partial x^\sigma/\partial y^\alpha$ then gives the result

$$\alpha^\sigma = -\frac{\partial x^\sigma}{\partial y^\alpha} \frac{\partial^2 y^\alpha}{\partial x^\nu \partial x^\rho} u^\nu u^\rho.$$

Therefore the equation of motion for a particle in a gravitational field must have the form

$$\frac{du^\mu}{ds} = -\Gamma^\mu_{\nu\rho}(x^\sigma) u^\nu u^\rho, \qquad (6\text{-}69)$$

where the coefficient $\Gamma^\mu_{\nu\rho}$ is given by

$$\Gamma^\mu_{\nu\rho} = \frac{\partial x^\mu}{\partial y^\alpha} \frac{\partial^2 y^\alpha}{\partial x^\nu \partial x^\rho} \qquad (6\text{-}70)$$

in terms of the frame y^α in which free particles are unaccelerated. The equation of motion is thus *homogeneous to the second order* in the particle's world-velocity. It will be recalled that Birkhoff made this assumption (see Section 6.7). However, his theory was couched in special relativity. We have seen that special relativity is inadequate for gravity. Non-Euclidean geometry is needed, and to this we now turn.

CHAPTER 7

DIFFERENTIAL GEOMETRY

We will proceed by a series of steps to derive certain properties of non-Euclidean differential geometry. The first step is the examination of the geometry of a two-dimensional surface embedded in three-dimensional Euclidean space.

7.1 GEOMETRY ON A SURFACE

Consider a surface embedded in three-dimensional Euclidean space and consider a point P in the surface. The surface is assumed to be smooth in the sense that at each point it possesses a tangent plane. Rectangular Cartesian coordinates x, y, z are then set up by choosing the point P as the origin and the tangent plane at P as the x-y plane. The equation of the surface within a finite region around P is then

$$z = F(x, y), \tag{7-1}$$

where $F(x, y)$ is assumed to be differentiable as many times as needed in the discussion to follow. The particular choice of coordinates described above allows eq. (7-1) to be written

$$z = \tfrac{1}{2}f_{ij}x^i x^j + O^3(x^k) \tag{7-2}$$

where $x^1 = x$, $x^2 = y$, and $f_{ij} = [\partial^2 F/\partial x^i\, \partial x^j]_P$. The indices i, j take the values 1, 2. A vertical plane given by $x^i = a^i \xi$, for constant a^i and arbitrary ξ and z, has, as its intersection with the surface, the curve

$$x^i = a^i \xi \qquad \text{a)}$$
$$z = \tfrac{1}{2} f_{ij} a^i a^j \xi^2 + O^3(\xi). \qquad \text{b)} \qquad (7\text{-}3)$$

We choose a^i to be a *unit* two-dimensional vector, i.e., $a^i a^i = 1$.

The curve given by eqs. (7-3) lies in the plane $x^i = a^i \xi$ and hence can be described by ordinary plane Euclidean geometry. In particular, the curvature κ of the curve $z(\xi)$, defined as the inverse of the radius of the osculating circle, is given by

$$\kappa = \frac{\dfrac{d^2 z}{d\xi^2}}{\left[1 + \left(\dfrac{dz}{d\xi}\right)^2\right]^{\frac{3}{2}}}$$

which, with the substitution of eq. (7-3b), becomes

$$\kappa = f_{ij} a^i a^j \qquad (7\text{-}4)$$

at the point P. Equation (7-4) gives the curvature of the surface at P along the direction a^i.

When considered in the context of two-dimensional geometry, the matrix f_{ij} is a tensor which possesses principal unit vectors (or unit eigenvectors) v_1^i and v_2^i. It is then immediately evident from eq. (7-4) that the eigenvalues of f_{ij} in the directions of the two eigenvectors are respectively the curvatures κ_1 and κ_2 of the surface in those two directions. The eigenvalue equation $|f_{ij} - \Lambda \delta_{ij}| = 0$ yields the roots $\Lambda = \kappa_1, \kappa_2$ given by $\kappa_1 + \kappa_2 = f_{kk}$ and $\kappa_1 \kappa_2 = |f_{ij}|$. The curvatures κ_1 and κ_2 are called the *principal curvatures* of the surface. The principal curvatures are the minimum and maximum curvatures for all directions. If the coordinate axes are chosen to coincide with the directions of the eigenvectors so that $v_k^i = \delta_k^i$, then the tensor f_{ij} is diagonalized, and the curvature in any direction a^i is given by $\kappa = (a^1)^2 \kappa_1 + (a^2)^2 \kappa_2$. The surface itself is then given by $z = \tfrac{1}{2}[\kappa_1(x^1)^2 + \kappa_2(x^2)^2] + O^3(x^i)$.

The *mean curvature M* of the surface is defined

$$M = \tfrac{1}{2}(\kappa_1 + \kappa_2) = \tfrac{1}{2} f_{kk}.$$

The mean curvature is of little importance to us because it does not depend upon the intrinsic geometry of the surface alone. For example, a circular cylinder of radius R has mean curvature $\tfrac{1}{2} R$, but when the same cylinder is unrolled into a plane, its mean curvature becomes zero. Nevertheless, an interesting theorem on mean curvature will be proved later in this section.

On the other hand, the *Gaussian curvature K*, also known as the *total curvature*, defined

$$K = \kappa_1 \kappa_2 = |f_{ij}|,$$

is an intrinsic property of the geometry of the surface. A cylinder has Gaussian curvature zero, regardless of how it is rolled or unrolled.

It is necessary to relate the curvature K to the *metric* of the surface. The Euclidean space in which the surface is embedded has the metric

$$ds^2 = dx^i \, dx^i + dz^2, \tag{7-5}$$

i.e., the distance ds between two nearby points (x, y, z) and $(x + dx, y + dy, z + dz)$ is given by eq. (7-5). Substitution of eq. (7-2) into eq. (7-5) gives

$$ds^2 = g_{ij} \, dx^i \, dx^j \tag{7-6}$$

where

$$g_{ij} = \delta_{ij} + f_{ik} f_{jl} x^k x^l + O^3(x). \tag{7-7}$$

Equation (7-6) is the metric in the surface. If the coordinate axes are along the eigenvectors of f_{ij}, then eq. (7-6) becomes

$$ds^2 = (dx^1)^2 + (dx^2)^2 + (\kappa_1 x^1 \, dx^1 + \kappa_2 x^2 \, dx^2)^2 + O[(x)^3 (dx)^2].$$

The metric must yet be expressed in terms of coordinates which are, as we shall see, intrinsic to the surface. But before doing that, it is of interest to consider the measurement of area on the surface.

Consider an infinitesimal parallelogram on the surface formed by two non-collinear vectors dx^i and δx^i. The angle θ between the vectors in the surface is given by the scalar product

$$d \cdot \delta \cdot \cos \theta = g_{ij} \, dx^i \, \delta x^j$$

where

$$d = \sqrt{g_{ij} \, dx^i \, dx^j}$$
$$\delta = \sqrt{g_{ij} \, \delta x^i \, \delta x^j}.$$

The area dS of the parallelogram is then defined

$$(dS)^2 = (d\delta \sin \theta)^2 = d^2 \delta^2 - (d\delta \cos \theta)^2$$
$$= (g_{ij} g_{kl} - g_{ik} g_{jl}) \, dx^i \, dx^j \, \delta x^k \, \delta x^l. \tag{7-8}$$

Since there are only two dimensions, eq. (7-8) may be written

$$dS = \pm \sqrt{g} (dx^1 \, \delta x^2 - dx^2 \, \delta x^1) \tag{7-9}$$

where $g = |g_{ij}|$. For the special case $dx^i = (dx, 0)$, $\delta x^i = (0, \delta y)$, this reduces to $dS = \sqrt{g} \, dx \, \delta y$.

An interesting property of the mean curvature M is found in the solution of the problem of minimal area. Consider the problem of finding the surface of minimum area which spans a given closed curve C. It will be assumed that the curve C is of such simplicity that the class of desired surfaces can be represented by the equation (7-1). Differentiation of eq. (7-1) and substitution into eq. (7-5) then gives eq. (7-6) where $g_{ij} = \delta_{ij} + F_i F_j$ with $F_i = \partial F/\partial x^i$. The area of the surface is the integral

$$S = \iint \sqrt{g}\, dx\, dy,$$

where g is found by direct evaluation to be $1 + F_k F_k$. The usual variational method, applied to the condition $\delta S = 0$, gives the condition

$$F_{kk} = \frac{F_l F_m F_{lm}}{1 + F_n F_n}$$

where $F_{lm} = \partial^2 F/\partial x^l\, \partial x^m$. This condition must hold at each point of the minimal surface. Upon choosing a point P in the surface and using coordinates at P in which the x-y plane is tangent to the surface, the above condition becomes $f_{kk} = 0$. Thus the minimal surface is one on which the mean curvature M vanishes everywhere.

A *geodesic* is the curve in the surface between two given points which has minimum length. For the metric of eq. (7-7), the length along any curve $x^i(t)$ is

$$s = \int \sqrt{\dot{x}^i \dot{x}^i + (f_{jk} x^k \dot{x}^j)^2 + O[(x)^3 (dx)^2]}\; dt$$

where $\dot{x}^i = dx^i/dt$, and t is any parameter along the curve. The condition that the curve be a geodesic—the condition $\delta s = 0$—becomes the Euler-Lagrange equation which, with t set equal to s, has the form

$$\ddot{x}^i + f_{lm}\dot{x}^l \dot{x}^m f_{ik} x^k + O[(x)^2(\dot{x})^2] = 0. \qquad (7\text{-}10)$$

Equation (7-10), where the dots now indicate differentiation with respect to the distance s along the curve, is the necessary and sufficient condition that the curve be a geodesic.

Consider now a geodesic which passes through the point P and is tangent at P to the plane $x^i = a^i \xi$. The equation $x^i(s)$ for the geodesic, with the distance s as the parameter, may be expanded in a Taylor series about the point P. The use of eq. (7-10) gives

$$x^i(s) = a^i s - \tfrac{1}{6} f_{jk} a^j a^k f_{il} a^l s^3 + O^4(s). \qquad (7\text{-}11a)$$

Geodesic coordinates at P are defined as a coordinate system y^i in which the equation for geodesics through P has the form

$$y^i(s) = a^i(s) + O^4(s). \qquad (7\text{-}11b)$$

Comparison of eqs. (7-11) shows that the geodesic coordinates are given by

$$x^i = y^i - \tfrac{1}{6} f_{ij} f_{kl} y^j y^k y^l + O^4(y).$$

The metric of eqs. (7-6) and (7-7), known as the *line element*, now becomes

$$ds^2 = dy^k \, dy^k + \tfrac{1}{3}(f_{ik}f_{jl} - f_{ij}f_{kl})y^k y^l \, dy^i \, dy^j + O[(y)^3(dy)^2].$$

Note that the second term may be written in the form

$$-\tfrac{1}{3}|f_{ij}| \, (y^1 \, dy^2 - y^2 \, dy^1)^2 \quad \text{or} \quad -\tfrac{1}{3}K(y^1 \, dy^2 - y^2 \, dy^1)^2,$$

so that the line element becomes

$$ds^2 = dy^k \, dy^k - \tfrac{1}{3}K_0(y^1 \, dy^2 - y^2 \, dy^1)^2 + O[(y)^3(dy)^2]. \qquad (7\text{-}12)$$

Equation (7-12) is the line element of the surface at the point P in geodesic coordinates y^1, y^2. The Gaussian curvature K_0 of the surface at the point P (the subscript on K is a reminder that K is evaluated at P) enters eq. (7-12) as the coefficient of the second term, i.e., the first non-Euclidean term in the expansion of ds^2 in powers of y^i.

In polar coordinates ρ, ϕ about the point P, the metric of the surface must have the form

$$ds^2 = C \, d\rho^2 + 2D \, d\rho \, d\phi + E \, d\phi^2$$

where the coefficients C, D, and E are functions of ρ and ϕ.

Geodesic polar coordinates are polar coordinates in which a curve of constant ϕ is also a geodesic and ρ is the distance from P along each geodesic through P. The condition $C = 1$ is immediately imposed. The geodesic condition $\delta \int ds = 0$ applied to the metric in polar coordinates with ρ as the parameter then yields the differential equation

$$\frac{d}{d\rho}\left[\frac{D + E\phi'}{\sqrt{1 + 2D\phi' + E\phi'^2}}\right] - \frac{1}{\sqrt{1 + 2D\phi' + E\phi'^2}}\left[\frac{\partial D}{\partial \phi}\phi' + \frac{1}{2}\frac{\partial E}{\partial \phi}\phi'^2\right] = 0$$

$$(7\text{-}13)$$

where $\phi' = d\phi/d\rho$. The substitution $\phi' = 0$ reduces eq. (7-13) to $\partial D/\partial \rho = 0$. Thus D is a function only of ϕ. The requirement that the line element reduce to the plane Euclidean form $d\rho^2 + \rho^2 \, d\phi^2$ at the origin then fixes the value of D at zero. Thus in geodesic polar coordinates the metric is

$$ds^2 = d\rho^2 + E(\rho, \phi) \, d\phi^2. \qquad (7\text{-}14)$$

The line element of eq. (7-14) may be compared with eq. (7-12) by the substitutions $y^1 = \rho \cos \phi$, $y^2 = \rho \sin \phi$. Equation (7-12) becomes

$$ds^2 = d\rho^2 + \rho^2(1 - \tfrac{1}{3}K\rho^2) \, d\phi^2 + \cdots \qquad (7\text{-}15)$$

where the neglected terms are of order $\rho^3 \, d\rho^2$, $\rho^4 \, d\rho \, d\phi$, and $\rho^5 \, d\phi^2$. Comparison of eqs. (7-14) and (7-15) shows that E is related to K_0 by the expression

$$E(\rho, \phi) = \rho^2(1 - \tfrac{1}{3}K_0\rho^2) + O(\rho^5). \qquad (7\text{-}16)$$

It is easily verified from eq. (7-16) that the curvature K_0 at P is given by

$$K_0 = - \left[\frac{1}{\sqrt{E}} \frac{\partial^2 \sqrt{E}}{\partial \rho^2} \right]_P.$$

It will be proved in Section 8.9 that the curvature at *any* point is given by

$$K = - \frac{1}{\sqrt{E}} \frac{\partial^2 \sqrt{E}}{\partial \rho^2}. \tag{7-17}$$

A *geodesic circle* is the locus of points equidistant from the origin as measured by geodesics in the surface. The circumference of a geodesic circle of radius ρ is found by eq. (7-14) to be

$$\int_0^{2\pi} \sqrt{E} \, d\phi = 2\pi\rho [1 - \tfrac{1}{6} K_0 \rho^2 + O(\rho^3)]$$

and its area is

$$\int_0^\rho \int_0^{2\pi} \sqrt{E} \, d\phi \, d\rho = \pi\rho^2 [1 - \tfrac{1}{12} K_0 \rho^2 + O(\rho^3)].$$

Thus, if there were two-dimensional creatures living in the surface who had no way to detect the third dimension, they could still determine the curvature of their two-dimensional world. They could draw a series of geodesic circles, measure the perimeters $p(\rho)$ or the areas $A(\rho)$, and then apply the formulae

$$K_0 = \lim_{\rho \to 0} \frac{6}{\rho^2} \left(1 - \frac{p}{2\pi\rho} \right) = \lim_{\rho \to 0} \frac{12}{\rho^2} \left(1 - \frac{A}{\pi\rho^2} \right).$$

A *geodesic triangle* is a triangle formed by three geodesics. *Gauss' theorem on integral curvature* states that the surface integral of the Gaussian curvature K over the triangle is equal to the excess of the sum of the interior angles beyond π radians. The theorem is proved as follows. (See Figure 7.1.) One vertex of the triangle is chosen as the origin O for

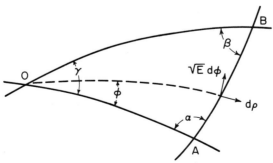

FIGURE 7.1   Gauss' theorem on integral curvature.

geodesic polar coordinates ρ, ϕ. One of the adjacent sides OA is chosen as $\phi = 0$. Equation (7-13) with $D = 0$ becomes

$$\frac{d}{d\rho} \frac{E\phi'}{\sqrt{1 + E\phi'^2}} - \frac{\phi'^2}{2\sqrt{1 + E\phi'^2}} \frac{\partial E}{\partial \phi} = 0. \tag{7-18}$$

With the definition

$$\tan \theta = \sqrt{E} \frac{d\phi}{d\rho} = \sqrt{E}\phi',$$

eq. (7-18) becomes

$$\frac{d}{d\rho}(\sqrt{E} \sin \theta) = \frac{\sin \theta}{2\sqrt{E}} \phi' \frac{\partial E}{\partial \phi}$$

which may be expanded to give

$$\frac{d\theta}{d\rho} = - \frac{d\phi}{d\rho} \frac{\partial \sqrt{E}}{\partial \rho}. \tag{7-19}$$

Equation (7-19) applies to any geodesic, and in particular to the geodesic AB. From eq. (7-9) which applies in any coordinates, the area integral of K is given by

$$I = \iint K\sqrt{E}\, d\phi\, d\rho. \tag{7-20}$$

Substitution of eq. (7-17) into eq. (7-20) and integration over ρ yields

$$I = - \int_{\phi=0}^{\gamma} \left[\left(\frac{\partial \sqrt{E}}{\partial \rho}\right)_{AB} - \left(\frac{\partial \sqrt{E}}{\partial \rho}\right)_0 \right] d\phi = \gamma + \int_{\phi=0}^{\gamma} \frac{d\theta}{d\rho} d\rho.$$

The last term comes from eq. (7-19) and is immediately seen to have the value $\alpha + \beta - \pi$. Hence

$$I = \alpha + \beta + \gamma - \pi,$$

where α, β, and γ are the interior angles of the triangle. For the case of the geometry on the surface of a sphere, the principal curvatures are both equal to the radius of the sphere, and Gauss' theorem on integral curvature reduces to the theorem of spherical excess.

7.2 n-DIMENSIONAL HOMOGENEOUS METRIC

Consider an n-dimensional space in which the metric is given by

$$ds^2 = e^{2F(x^k)} dx^i dx^i, \tag{7-21}$$

where $F(x^k)$ is a function of position and the indices take on the integers 1 to n. (The F in this section should not be confused with the F used in the previous section.) The geodesic condition $\delta \int ds = 0$ now gives the Euler-Lagrange equation

$$\frac{d}{dt} \frac{e^F \dot{x}^i}{\sqrt{\dot{x}^k \dot{x}^k}} - e^F \sqrt{\dot{x}^l \dot{x}^l} F_i = 0$$

where $F_i = \partial F/\partial x^i$, $\dot{x}^i = dx^i/dt$, and t is a parameter along the curve. With the choice $t = s$ we immediately have $\dot{x}^k \dot{x}^k = e^{-2F}$ and

$$\frac{d}{ds}(e^{2F} \dot{x}^i) - F_i = 0$$

or

$$\ddot{x}^i = F_i \dot{x}^k \dot{x}^k - 2F_l \dot{x}^l \dot{x}^i. \tag{7-22}$$

Equation (7-22) is the necessary and sufficient condition for a curve $x^i(s)$ to be a geodesic.

The procedure which was used to obtain geodesic coordinates in Section 7.1 can be used in the present case. The equation $x^i(s)$ for the curve is expanded in a Taylor series about a given point P. For convenience in notation, subscripts on the F will denote its partial differentiation with respect to the corresponding coordinates, and lower case f will indicate the value of F or its derivatives at the point P. The unit vector a^i is defined $\dot{x}^i_P = a^i e^{-f}$. Equation (7-22) and its derivative provide the expressions

$$\ddot{x}^i_P = e^{-2f}(f_i a^k a^k - 2f_l a^l a^i),$$

$$\dddot{x}^i_P = e^{-3f}[(f_{ij} - 4f_i f_j)a^j a^k a^k - 2(f_{lm} - 4f_l f_m)a^i a^l a^m - 2a^i f_n f_n a^p a^p].$$

The Taylor series becomes

$$x^i(s) = x^i_P + e^{-f} a^i s + \tfrac{1}{2} e^{-2f}[f_i a^k a^k - 2f_l a^l a^i]s^2$$
$$+ \tfrac{1}{6} e^{-3f}[(f_{ij} - 4f_i f_j)a^j a^k a^k - 2(f_{lm} - 4f_l f_m)a^i a^l a^m$$
$$- 2a^i f_n f_n a^p a^p]s^3 + O(s^4).$$

Geodesic coordinates y^i about the point P are defined by the relation

$$x^i - x^i_P = e^{-f} y^i + \tfrac{1}{2} e^{-2f}(f_i y^k y^k - 2f_l y^l y^i)$$
$$+ \tfrac{1}{6} e^{-3f}[(f_{ij} - 4f_i f_j)y^j y^k y^k - 2(f_{lm} - 4f_l f_m)y^i y^l y^m$$
$$- 2y^i f_n f_n y^p y^p] + O^4(y),$$

so that the equation of any geodesic through P is

$$y^i(s) = a^i(s) + O^4(s).$$

The line element then takes the form

$$ds^2 = dy^i \, dy^i + \tfrac{1}{3} e^{-2f}[(f_{ij} - f_i f_j)p^{ik}p^{jk} + \tfrac{1}{2} f_k f_k p^{ij} p^{ij}] + O[(y)^3(dy)^2] \tag{7-23}$$

where

$$p^{ij} = y^i \, dy^j - y^j \, dy^i.$$

For two dimensions, eq. (7-23) is

$$ds^2 = dy^i{}^i\, dy + \tfrac{1}{3}e^{-2f}f_{kk}p^2 + O[(y)^3(dy)^2]$$

where $p = y^1\, dy^2 - y^2\, dy^1$. Comparison with eq. (7-12), which is also expressed in geodesic coordinates, shows that the Gaussian curvature at P is

$$K_P = -e^{-2f}f_{kk}. \qquad (7\text{-}24)$$

Since the point P was arbitrary, it follows that the Gaussian curvature at any point is given by

$$K = -e^{-2F}F_{kk}. \qquad (7\text{-}25)$$

7.3 TWO-DIMENSIONAL HEAT METRIC

As an example of a two-dimensional geometry, consider the following situation. A plane metal plate of constant thickness is constrained so that it does not buckle or stretch under the application of differential temperatures. Thus the rectangular Cartesian coordinates x, y of a given point in the plate remain fixed. It is assumed that by the proper use of heat sources and heat sinks we can produce any temperature distribution $T(x, y)$ on the plate consistent with the laws of heat conduction. The heat flow vector $\boldsymbol{\phi}(x, y)$ is related to the temperature by the equation

$$\boldsymbol{\phi} = -k\nabla T, \qquad (7\text{-}26)$$

where k is the constant thermal conductivity. Also, $\boldsymbol{\phi}$ is related to the density $p(x, y)$ of heat application by the equation

$$\nabla \cdot \boldsymbol{\phi} = p. \qquad (7\text{-}27)$$

Elimination of $\boldsymbol{\phi}$ from eqs. (7-26) and (7-27) gives

$$k\nabla^2 T + p = 0. \qquad (7\text{-}28)$$

Measurements are made on the plate by means of a short, graduated metal rod which is allowed to come into thermal equilibrium with the plate. The measured distance ds between two adjacent points (x, y) and $(x + dx, y + dy)$ is then given by

$$ds^2 = \frac{dx^2 + dy^2}{(1 + hT)^2} \qquad (7\text{-}29)$$

where h is the constant coefficient of thermal expansion of the rod. The rod, but not the plate, is allowed to expand or contract under changes in temperature.

We address ourselves to the geometry of the plate as revealed by the measuring rod. Equation (7-29) describes a geometry of the kind studied in the previous section. The $F(x^i)$ of Section 7.2 now becomes

$$F(x, y) = -\ln [1 + hT(x, y)],$$

and eq. (7-25) becomes

$$K = h(1 + hT) \nabla^2 T - h^2 (\nabla T)^2. \qquad (7\text{-}30)$$

The appropriate use of eqs. (7-26) and (7-28) puts eq. (7-30) into the form

$$K = -\frac{h}{k}(1 + hT)p - \left(\frac{h}{k}\right)^2 |\mathbf{\phi}|^2. \qquad (7\text{-}31)$$

Equation (7-31) shows that the curvature of the two-dimensional heat metric depends on both the density p of heat supply and the density $\mathbf{\phi}$ of heat flow.

It may be noted in passing that if the expansion of the measuring rod had been represented by e^{hT} instead of $1 + hT$, then we would have had $F = -hT$ and $K = -\frac{h}{k} e^{2hT} p$. The curvature would then have depended only on p.

Two special cases are of interest to us. The first is the case of a uniform thermal flux vector $\mathbf{\phi}$. The second is the case of circular symmetry and a uniform thermal source density p.

In the case that the flux $\mathbf{\phi}$ is constant, the y-axis may be chosen along $\mathbf{\phi}$ so that $\mathbf{\phi}$ is given by $\mathbf{\phi} = (0, \phi)$, with ϕ constant. Equation (7-26) then has the solution

$$T = -\frac{\phi}{k} y + a \qquad (7\text{-}32)$$

where a is the constant of integration. By the appropriate choice of the x-axis, i.e., of the y origin, the constant a may be taken as $1/h$. Equation (7-30) provides the relation

$$K = -\frac{\phi^2 h^2}{k^2},$$

and eq. (7-29) becomes

$$ds^2 = -\frac{dx^2 + dy^2}{Ky^2}. \qquad (7\text{-}33)$$

The curvature K is a negative constant. Therefore, by a suitable change in the unit of distances, the curvature can be made equal to -1. Equation (7-33) then becomes

$$ds^2 = \frac{dx^2 + dy^2}{y^2}. \qquad (7\text{-}34)$$

7.4 THE POINCARÉ HALF-PLANE

The half-plane $y \geq 0$ having the geometry of the metric (7-34) is known as the *Poincaré half-plane*. The application of the rule $\delta \int ds = 0$ shows that geodesics are given by

$$(x - b)^2 + y^2 = a^2, \tag{7-35}$$

where a and b are arbitrary constants. Equation (7-35) is merely the equation for a circle with radius a and center $(b, 0)$. Thus all geodesics are (in the x, y coordinates) circles which have their centers on the x-axis. Note that if "parallel" means "never meeting," there are an infinite number of geodesics parallel to a given geodesic.

The geodesic distance s between two points x_1, y_1 and x_2, y_2 measured along the geodesic C which passes through the two points is

$$s = \tfrac{1}{2} \ln \frac{(x_2 - x_4)(x_3 - x_1)}{(x_1 - x_4)(x_3 - x_2)} \tag{7-36}$$

where x_3 and x_4 are the x-intercepts of C. (See Figure 7.2.) Equation (7-36) may be abbreviated

$$s = \tfrac{1}{2} \ln R_x(x_1, x_2; x_3, x_4)$$

where R_x is the *cross-ratio* defined

$$R_x(\alpha, \beta; \gamma, \delta) = \frac{(\beta - \delta)(\gamma - \alpha)}{(\alpha - \delta)(\gamma - \beta)}.$$

The condition that two geodesics with x-intercepts x_1, x_2 and x_3, x_4 intersect in a right angle is $R_x(x_1, x_2; x_3, x_4) = -1$.

An object at a point $P(0, y)$ is "seen" (using light rays which follow geodesics PA and PB in Figure 7.3 with the angle BAP a right angle) from the two ends $A(0, a)$ and $B(b, c)$ of a geodesic baseline. The length of the baseline is

$$s = \tfrac{1}{2} \ln \frac{a + b}{a - b} = \tanh^{-1} \sin \phi$$

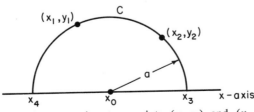

FIGURE 7.2 Geodesic connecting two points (x_1, y_1) and (x_2, y_2) in Poincaré half-plane.

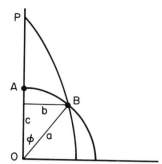

FIGURE 7.3 Parallax in the Poincaré half-plane.

where $\phi = \sin^{-1} b/a$. The angle ϕ has an interesting geometrical interpretation in terms of the metric. The area ABP in the limit $y \to \infty$, i.e., as P recedes to infinity, is from eq. (7-9),

$$\int_{x=0}^{b} \int_{y=\sqrt{a^2-x^2}}^{\infty} \frac{dx\,dy}{-y^2} = \phi.$$

Thus ϕ is the area of the geodesic triangle ABP in the limit as P goes to infinity. It is left to the reader to prove that the relation between the metric distance $AP = s'$ and the parallactic angle $\alpha = 90° - PBA$ is $\tan \alpha \tanh s' = \sinh s$.

The geometry of the Poincaré half-plane can be found on the surface of a pseudosphere. The latter is the figure of revolution formed from a tractrix:

$$\frac{d\eta}{d\xi} = -\frac{\sqrt{1-\xi^2}}{\xi}.$$

(See Figure 7.4.) The metric on the surface of the pseudosphere is

$$ds^2 = d\xi^2\left(1 + \frac{1-\xi^2}{\xi^2}\right) + \xi^2\,d\phi^2 = \frac{dx^2 + dy^2}{y^2}$$

where $y = 1/\xi$ and x is equal to the angle of revolution ϕ.

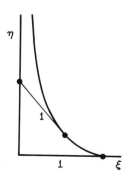

FIGURE 7.4 Tractrix.

7.5 HOT PLATE WITH CIRCULAR SYMMETRY

In the second specific case suggested in Section 7.3, the temperature is assumed to depend only on the radial coordinate r, and the heat-source density p is assumed to be constant. Equation (7-28) becomes

$$\frac{k}{r}\frac{d}{dr}\,r\,\frac{dT}{dr} = -p$$

which has the solution

$$T = T_0 - \frac{pr^2}{4k}, \qquad (7\text{-}37)$$

where T_0 is the constant of integration. (The other constant of integration is eliminated by the requirement that the temperature at the center be finite.) The curvature is now found from eq. (7-30) to be

$$K = -\frac{hp}{k}(1 + hT_0) \qquad (7\text{-}38)$$

and hence constant.

The metric assumes an interesting form. The substitution of eq. (7-37) into eq. (7-29) and the elimination of T_0 by means of eq. (7-38) gives

$$ds^2 = \frac{d\mathfrak{r}^2 + \mathfrak{r}^2\,d\phi^2}{\left(1 + \dfrac{K}{4}\,\mathfrak{r}^2\right)^2} \qquad (7\text{-}39)$$

where

$$\mathfrak{r} = \frac{hp}{k\,|K|}\,r$$

and ϕ is the angular coordinate. If K is negative, then the line element can be written in the form

$$ds^2 = R^2(d\chi^2 + \sinh^2 \chi\, d\phi^2),$$

where

$$R = (-K)^{-\frac{1}{2}}$$

and

$$\tanh \tfrac{1}{2}\chi = \frac{\mathfrak{r}}{2R}.$$

If K is positive, then the line element can be written in the form

$$ds^2 = R^2(d\theta^2 + \sin^2 \theta\, d\phi^2) \qquad (7\text{-}40)$$

where

$$R = K^{-\frac{1}{2}}$$

and

$$\tan \tfrac{1}{2}\theta = \frac{\mathfrak{r}}{2R}. \qquad (7\text{-}41)$$

In either case, R will be called the *radius of curvature* of the space.

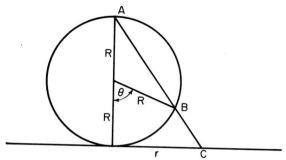

FIGURE 7.5 Stereographic projection of sphere onto plane. The angle ϕ is measured around the vertical axis.

Note that the geometry of eq. (7-40) is the same as the geometry on the surface of a sphere with radius R and spherical polar coordinates θ, ϕ. The transformation of eq. (7-41) is equivalent to the stereographic projection of the sphere onto a plane (see Fig. 7.5). A point B at (R, θ, ϕ) on the sphere is mapped by the line ABC into a point C at (r, ϕ) on the plane. The metric

$$ds^2 = R^2(d\theta^2 + \sin^2 \theta \, d\phi^2)$$

on the sphere becomes

$$ds^2 = \frac{dr^2 + r^2 \, d\phi^2}{\left(1 + \dfrac{r^2}{4R^2}\right)} \tag{7-42}$$

when referred to the coordinates of the plane. That is to say, eq. (7-42) is the metric on the sphere as measured by the coordinates in the plane. In the stereographic projection, a great circle on the sphere with pole at $\theta = \alpha$, $\phi = \beta$ maps into a circle on the plane of radius 2 sec α with center at $r = 2 \tan \alpha$, $\phi = \beta$. The geodesics on the plane are circles; they are projections of great circles on the sphere.

7.6 CURVATURE

We continue our study of the metric of Section 7.2 with the question: Can a curvature be defined for the space? The concept of Gaussian curvature was defined in Section 7.1 only for a two-dimensional surface. Therefore, we construct a two-dimensional surface embedded in the n-dimensional space. We choose the surface which in geodesic coordinates is given by

$$y^i = \lambda a^i + \mu b^i \tag{7-43}$$

where a^i and b^i are constants satisfying the conditions $a^i a^i = 1$, $b^i b^i = 1$, $a^i b^i = 0$; and λ and μ are multipliers. In this two-dimensional space we have

$$dy^i = a^i \, d\lambda + b^i \, d\mu$$

and hence

$$p^{ij} = (a^i b^j - a^j b^i)(\lambda \, d\mu - \mu \, d\lambda).$$

Direct substitution of dy^i and p^{ij} into eq. (7-23) gives

$$ds^2 = d\lambda^2 + d\mu^2 + \tfrac{1}{3} e^{-2f}[(f_{ij} - f_i f_j)(a^i a^j + b^i b^j) + f_{kk}]$$
$$\cdot (\lambda \, d\mu + \mu \, d\lambda)^2 + O(\lambda^3 \, d\lambda^2, \text{ etc.}). \tag{7-44}$$

It should be noted that λ and μ are geodesic coordinates; the geodesics in the surface are given by $y^i = (\alpha a^i + \beta b^i)s + O^4(s)$, and hence by

$$\begin{pmatrix} \lambda = \alpha s + O^4(s) \\ \mu = \beta s + O^4(s) \end{pmatrix}.$$

We now compare eq. (7-44) with eq. (7-12) and identify λ, μ with the y^1, y^2 of Section 7.1. The curvature is then

$$K(P, a^i, b^j) = -e^{-2f}[(f_{kl} - f_k f_l)(a^k a^l + b^k b^l) + f_m f_m]. \tag{7-45}$$

The curvature depends on the origin P of the geodesic coordinates and on the two unit vectors a^i and b^i. We are easily satisfied that for two dimensions with $a^k a^l + b^k b^l = \delta^{kl}$, eq. (7-24) follows.

The average value of K at P will now be calculated—averaged over all two-dimensional surfaces which pass through P. This average is obtained by replacing $a^i a^j$ and $b^i b^j$ in eq. (7-45) with their average δ^{ij}/n:

$$\bar{K}(P) = -\frac{1}{n} e^{-2f}[2f_{kk} + (n-2)f_k f_k]. \tag{7-46}$$

Equation (7-46) gives the curvature at P averaged over all directions. Another kind of average is that in which one vector, say a^i, is held constant, and b^i is allowed to vary. The curvature is then averaged over all surfaces which contain the vector a^i. To find such an average curvature $K(P, a^i)$, we replace $b^i b^j$ in eq. (7-45) with its average $\dfrac{\delta^{ij} - a^i a^j}{n - 1}$.

$$K(P, a^i) = -\frac{1}{n-1} e^{-2f}\{f_{kk} + (n-2)[f_l f_l + (f_{ij} - f_i f_j)a^i a^j]\}.$$

Since K has the dimension of an inverse square length, we can define the *radius of curvature* R of the space as $R = |K|^{-\frac{1}{2}}$. The radius of curvature is frequently a useful concept. For example, it was seen in Section 7.5 that a two-dimensional space with constant curvature $+R^{-2}$ has the same geometry as the surface of a three-dimensional sphere of radius R.

It can be proved that if $K(P, a^i, b^j)$ is everywhere independent of a^i and b^j, then K is a constant. First, it is noted from eq. (7-45) that in order for K to be independent of a^i and b^i, the coefficient of $a^k a^l + b^k b^l$, namely $f_{kl} - f_k f_l$, must be a multiple of δ_{kl}. We thus obtain the condition

$$\frac{\partial^2 \phi}{\partial x^i \, \partial x^j} = \mathscr{F} \cdot \phi \, \delta_{ij}$$

where $\phi = e^{-F}$ and $-\mathscr{F}$ is the factor of proportionality. (F is used instead of f because we are not restricted to any one point.) Since $\partial^2 \phi / \partial x^i \, \partial x^j$ vanishes for $i \neq j$, the solution must be of the form $\phi = \Sigma_i \phi^i(x^i)$, i.e., the variables are separated. The equation

$$\frac{d^2 \phi^i(x^i)}{(dx^i)^2} = \mathscr{F}\phi, \quad \text{(no sum on } i)$$

which shows that $\mathscr{F}\phi$ is a constant, say $2A$, may be integrated to give

$$\phi^i(x^i) = A(x^i)^2 + B_i x^i + C_i \quad \text{(no sum on } i).$$

Thus ϕ is given by

$$\phi = A r^2 + \Sigma_i B_i x^i + C$$

where A, B_i, and C are constants, and $r^2 = x^k x^k$. Direct substitution of $F = -\ln \phi$ and $F_{kl} - F_k F_l = -\mathscr{F}\delta_{kl}$ into eq. (7-45) gives

$$K = 4AC - B_k B_k.$$

Therefore, the curvature K is a constant.

In order to examine the form of the line element

$$ds^2 = \frac{dx^i \, dx^i}{\phi^2} \tag{7-47}$$

for the ϕ given above, each of several cases may be taken in turn.

If $A \neq 0$, then by a suitable translation of coordinates we may choose $B_i = 0$. The curvature is then $K = 4AC$. Two subcases must be examined. If $C = 0$, then $K = 0$ and an inversion (see Section 3.2) puts eq. (7-47) into the Cartesian Euclidean form. If $C \neq 0$, then either the dilatation $x^i = C\bar{x}^i$ or the inversion $x^i = \dfrac{\bar{x}^i}{A\bar{r}^2}$ puts eq. (7-47) into the form

$$ds^2 = \frac{d\bar{x}^i \, d\bar{x}^i}{\left(1 + \dfrac{K}{4} \bar{r}^2\right)^2}. \tag{7-48}$$

If $A = 0$, then ϕ has the linear form $\phi = B_k x^k + C$, and the curvature is $K = -B_k B_k$. For real B_k the curvature is non-positive. If K is zero, then the B_k all vanish, ϕ is a constant, and eq. (7-47) becomes the Cartesian

Euclidean metric. If $K < 0$, then by a suitable rotation we can obtain coordinates in which $B_i = B\delta_i^1$. Equation (7-47) then becomes

$$ds^2 = \frac{dx^i\, dx^i}{-K \cdot (x^1)^2}.$$

But even the above form (it will be seen in Sections 8.10 and 13.8) can be put into the form of eq. (7-48) by a suitable transformation.

Thus eq. (7-48) is common to all cases of constant curvature.

7.7 SPACE OF CONSTANT CURVATURE

Consider an n-dimensional space having a curvature K which is constant in both direction and position. We have just seen that the metric can be put into the form of eq. (7-48):

$$ds^2 = \frac{dx^i\, dx^i}{\left(1 + \dfrac{Kr^2}{4}\right)^2}. \tag{7-49}$$

Polar coordinates r, θ_2, θ_3, $\ldots$, θ_n are defined in terms of the rectangular, locally Cartesian coordinates x^i of eq. (7-49) by the relations:

$$x^n = r\cos\theta_2$$
$$x^{n-1} = r\sin\theta_2\cos\theta_3$$
$$x^{n-2} = r\sin\theta_2\sin\theta_3\cos\theta_4$$
$$\cdots$$
$$x^2 = r\sin\theta_2\sin\theta_3\cdots\sin\theta_{n-1}\cos\theta_n$$
$$x^1 = r\sin\theta_2\sin\theta_3\cdots\sin\theta_{n-1}\sin\theta_n$$
$$0 \le \theta_\alpha \le \pi \qquad \alpha = 2, 3, \ldots, n-1$$
$$0 \le \theta_n < 2\pi.$$

We find $r^2 = x^i x^i$ and

$$dx^i\, dx^i = dr^2 + r^2\{d\theta_2^2 + \sin^2\theta_2[d\theta_3^2 + \sin^2\theta_3 \cdot$$
$$(d\theta_4^2 + \cdots \sin^2\theta_{n-1}\, d\theta_n^2)]\}$$

so that eq. (7-49) becomes

$$ds^2 = \frac{dr^2 + r^2\{d\theta_2^2 + \sin^2\theta_2[d\theta_3^2 + \cdots + \sin^2\theta_{n-1}\, d\theta_n^2]\}}{\left(1 + \dfrac{K}{4}r^2\right)^2} \tag{7-50}$$

which agrees with eq. (7-39) for $n = 2$.

The further transformations on the radial coordinate which were made in Section 7.5 can also be made here.

If $K = 0$, then eq. (7-50) gives the n-dimensional, Euclidean, polar-coordinate metric.

If $K > 0$, then the definitions $K = R^{-2}$ and $r = 2R \tan \frac{1}{2}\theta_1$ put eq. (7-50) into the form

$$ds^2 = R^2\{d\theta_1^2 + \sin^2 \theta_1[d\theta_2^2 + \sin^2 \theta_2(d\theta_3^2 + \cdots + \sin^2 \theta_{n-1} \, d\theta_n^2)]\}.$$

(7-51)

The geometry for this case is the same as for the n-dimensional surface of a sphere of radius R in $(n + 1)$-dimensional Euclidean space.

If $K < 0$, then the definitions $K = -R^{-2}$ and $r = 2R \tanh \frac{1}{2}\theta_1$ put eq. (7-50) into the form

$$ds^2 = R^2\{d\theta_1^2 + \sinh^2 \theta_1[d\theta_2^2 + \sin^2 \theta_2(d\theta_3^2 + \cdots + \sin^2 \theta_{n-1} \, d\theta_n^2)]\}.$$

A *geodesic sphere* with radius ρ and center P is the locus of all points which lie a geodesic distance ρ from P. It is clear from eq. (7-50) that the $(n - 1)$-dimensional *area* $A_n(\rho)$ of a geodesic sphere in a space of constant curvature K is the integral of

$$\frac{r^{n-1}}{\left(1 + \dfrac{Kr^2}{4}\right)^{n-1}} \sin^{n-2} \theta_2 \sin^{n-3} \theta_3 \cdots \sin \theta_{n-1} \, d\theta_2 \, d\theta_3 \cdots d\theta_n$$

which is found to give

$$A_n(\rho) = \frac{nC_n r^{n-1}}{\left(1 + \dfrac{Kr^2}{4}\right)^{n-1}}$$

where $r(\rho)$ is given by

$$\rho = \int_0^r \frac{dr}{1 + \frac{1}{4}Kr^2}$$

and C_n is given by

$$C_n = \begin{cases} = \dfrac{\pi^{\frac{n}{2}}}{\left(\dfrac{n}{2}\right)!} & n \text{ even} \\[3em] = \dfrac{2^n \pi^{\frac{n-1}{2}} \left(\dfrac{n-1}{2}\right)!}{n!} & n \text{ odd.} \end{cases}$$

The area $A_n(\rho)$ can be expanded in a power series:

$$A_n = nC_n \rho^{n-1}\left[1 - \frac{n-1}{6} K\rho^2 + O^4(\rho)\right].$$

(7-52a)

The volume $V_n(\rho)$ of the sphere found from the definition

$$V_n(\rho) = \int_0^\rho A_n(\rho)\, d\rho$$

is

$$V_n = C_n \rho^n \left[1 - \frac{n(n-1)}{6(n+2)} K\rho^2 + O^4(\rho) \right]. \qquad (7\text{-}52b)$$

If our three-dimensional space, for example, had a non-zero curvature K, we could measure K by constructing sufficiently large spheres. The departure of the areas or volumes from the Euclidean values would then, by eqs. (7-52), provide a determination of K. Such methods are, however, highly impractical because of the small value of K. Less direct but more feasible methods will be discussed in the study of cosmology.

7.8 THREE-DIMENSIONAL HEAT METRIC

As an example of a non-Euclidean three-dimensional geometry, we will consider again the heat metric of Section 7.3. With complete disregard for the practical difficulties involved in measuring the metric inside the block of metal, we add a third dimension to the line element:

$$ds^2 = \frac{dx^2 + dy^2 + dz^2}{(1 + hT)^2}. \qquad (7\text{-}53)$$

Equations (7-26), (7-27), and (7-28) become

$$\boldsymbol{\phi} = -k\,\nabla T \qquad (7\text{-}54)$$

$$\nabla \cdot \boldsymbol{\phi} = p$$

$$k\,\nabla^2 T + p = 0. \qquad (7\text{-}55)$$

The results of Section 7.6 may be applied to the metric of eq. (7-53). In particular, the substitution* $a^i a^j + b^i b^j = \delta^{ij} - c^i c^j$ in eq. (7-45) shows that the curvature at a point P in the surface having the unit normal c^i $(c^k c^k = 1)$ is

$$K(P, c^i) = h(1 + hT)T_{kk} - h^2 T_i T_i - h(1 + hT)T_{mn}c^m c^n. \qquad (7\text{-}56)$$

In three dimensions, a surface is specified by its normal as well as by two non-collinear vectors lying in it. The mean curvature $\bar{K}(P)$ at P averaged

---

* The relation $a^i a^j + b^i b^j = \delta^{ij} - c^i c^j$ is proved by noting that it is a tensor equation (in Cartesian Euclidean space) and that it holds in the coordinate system in which the axes are parallel to the vectors a^i, b^i, and c^i.

over all surfaces which pass through P will be used in what follows. The average curvature $\bar{K}(P)$ may be obtained either from eq. (7-56) by substituting $c^i c^j = \frac{1}{3}\delta^{ij}$ or from eq. (7-46) by substituting $F = -\ln(1 + hT)$:

$$\bar{K}(P) = \frac{2}{3}h(1 + hT)\nabla^2 T - h^2(\nabla T)^2. \tag{7-57}$$

Elimination of T by means of eqs. (7-54) and (7-55) then gives

$$\bar{K}(P) = -\frac{2}{3}\frac{h}{k}(1 + hT)p - \left(\frac{h}{k}\right)^2 |\phi|^2. \tag{7-58}$$

Consider the case of spherical symmetry in which the heat-source density p is zero everywhere except at a point P. Let the rate of supply of heat (in calories per second) at P be denoted Q. If r is the radial coordinate from P, the temperature, from eq. (7-55), is given by $T = \alpha/hr$ where $\alpha = Qh/4\pi k$. The metric is now

$$ds^2 = \frac{dx^2 + dy^2 + dz^2}{\left(1 + \dfrac{\alpha}{r}\right)^2} \tag{7-59}$$

and the curvature from eq. (7-56) is

$$K(r, c) = \alpha r^{-3}\left[1 - 3\left(1 + \frac{\alpha}{r}\right)(c_r)^2\right]$$

where c_r is the radial component of the unit normal to the surface in which K is the curvature. The curvature ranges between a minimum of $-\alpha r^{-3}\left(2 + 3\dfrac{\alpha}{r}\right)$ and a maximum of $+\alpha r^{-3}$, depending on the direction of c. The average curvature is

$$\bar{K} = -\alpha^2 r^{-4}.$$

Numerical evaluation of the above example gives an appreciation for the values which are involved. We take a steel plate with $k = 0.11$ cal cm^{-1} sec^{-1} deg^{-1}, a heat source $Q = 1$ cal sec^{-1}, and a steel measuring rod with $h = 0.11 \times 10^{-4}$ deg^{-1}. Then $h/k = 10^{-4}$ cm sec cal^{-1}, and $\alpha = 8 \times 10^{-6}$ cm $= 0.08$ micron. The mean curvature at a point 1 cm from the origin is -6×10^{-11} cm^{-2}; the corresponding radius of curvature is about a kilometer. The maximum curvature at the same point is 8×10^{-6} cm^{-2}; the corresponding radius of curvature is 3.5 meters.

A second case serves to illustrate the constant-curvature metric of eq. (7-49). Again, spherical symmetry is assumed, but this time the heat source is assumed to be uniformly distributed throughout a sphere of radius r_1. The solutions of eq. (7-55) with $p = $ const > 0 for $0 \le r \le r_1$

and $p = 0$ for $r > r_1$ are

$$T = T_0 - \frac{pr^2}{6k} \qquad 0 \le r \le r_1 \tag{7-60}$$

$$T = T_0 - \frac{pr_1^2}{2k} + \frac{pr_1^3}{3kr} \qquad r \ge r_1$$

where $T_0 = T(0)$. The geometry outside the boundary $r = r_1$ was considered in the previous example. The curvature *inside* the boundary has the value

$$K = -\frac{2hp}{3k}(1 + hT_0) \tag{7-61}$$

from eq. (7-56). Note that the curvature is both independent of direction and, as required by the theorem of Section 7.6, constant. When we substitute eq. (7-60) into eq. (7-53), make the dilatation $x^i = (1 + hT_0)\bar{x}^i$, and use eq. (7-61), the metric takes the form

$$ds^2 = \frac{d\bar{x}^i \, d\bar{x}^i}{\left(1 + \dfrac{K}{4}\bar{r}^2\right)^2} \tag{7-62}$$

as required by eq. (7-49).

The geometry for the case $1 + hT(r_1) = 0$ is particularly interesting. The central temperature is given by $1 + hT_0 = hpr_1^2/6k$. (We have by now completely lost sight of the initial practical thermal considerations in order to study the geometry for its own sake.) The curvature is negative; and the introduction of the radius of curvature $R = |K|^{-\frac{1}{2}}$ puts the metric of eq. (7-62) into the form

$$ds^2 = \frac{d\bar{x}^i \, d\bar{x}^i}{\left(1 - \dfrac{\bar{r}^2}{4R^2}\right)^2}. \tag{7-63}$$

The boundary is given by $\bar{r}_1 = 2R$. In terms of the metric of eq. (7-63), the distance from the origin to the Cartesian radius $2R$ is infinite! The metric distance to a radius $\bar{r}$ ($<2R$) is $2R \tanh^{-1}(\bar{r}/2R)$.

As a preparation for the next section, it is noted that the change of variable

$$e^F = (1 + hT)^{-1} = W^2 \tag{7-64}$$

puts the curvature as given by eq. (7-57) into the form

$$K = -\frac{4}{3}\frac{\nabla^2 W}{W^5}. \tag{7-65}$$

We thus eliminate the gradient but retain the Laplacian.

7.9 GEOMETRIZATION OF THE FIELD EQUATION

We set ourselves to the task of geometrizing the field equations for two theories: the three-dimensional heat metric of Section 7.8 and the scalar gravitational theory of Section 6.5. The verb *geometrize* means to put the theory into the form of a relation between the geometry and the sources rather than between the field and the sources.

For the problem of thermal conduction, we hope to obtain a law which relates the curvature $\bar{K}$ to the source density p. This is almost the case in eq. (7-58). Indeed, for small T, eq. (7-58) is

$$\bar{K}(P) = -\frac{2}{3}\frac{hp}{k}. \tag{7-66}$$

Equation (7-66) has the desired property, because it expresses the curvature in terms of the source density.

We will now *postulate* eq. (7-66). Equation (7-58) is then regarded as an approximation to the new theory. (This investigation is pursued for its geometrical interest, apart from any experimental considerations.) We now regard T as being defined by eq. (7-53) or by eq. (7-57)—the latter follows directly from the former. With the introduction of the variable W by means of eq. (7-64), the elimination of $\bar{K}$ between eqs. (7-65) and (7-66) gives

$$\frac{\nabla^2 W}{W^5} = \frac{hp}{2k}. \tag{7-67}$$

One further change must be made; p is the source density in Cartesian volume. If q is the source density in metric volume, equal to pW^{-6}, then eq. (7-67) becomes

$$\nabla^2 W = \frac{h}{2k} qW^{11} \tag{7-68}$$

and the metric is

$$ds^2 = W^4(dx^2 + dy^2 + dz^2). \tag{7-69}$$

The theory is now geometrized; $W(x, y, z)$ is determined strictly in terms of the source density by means of eq. (7-68).

The spherically symmetric solution to eq. (7-68) for a point source is $W = A + B/r$, where A and B are the constants of integration. The condition that the geometry be Euclidean at infinity requires that A be unity. To first order in $1/r$, eq. (7-69) becomes

$$ds^2 = \left(1 + \frac{4B}{r}\right)(dx^2 + dy^2 + dz^2).$$

Equation (7-59) to the same accuracy is

$$ds^2 = 1 - \frac{2\alpha}{r}(dx^2 + dy^2 + dz^2).$$

Therefore we make the identification

$$B = -\frac{\alpha}{2} = -\frac{Qh}{8\pi k},$$

and the metric becomes

$$ds^2 = \left(1 - \frac{\alpha}{2r}\right)^4 (dx^2 + dy^2 + dz^2). \tag{7-70}$$

The difference between eqs. (7-59) and (7-70) is due to the difference between the field equations.

In the case of the scalar theory of gravitation, a geometrical interpretation was obtained from the Lagrangian analysis. The Lagrangian for a test particle was found to be

$$L = e^{\frac{\Phi}{c^2}}\sqrt{\eta_{\mu\nu}\dot{x}^\mu \dot{x}^\nu}$$

where Φ is the scalar potential and $\dot{x}^\mu = dx^\mu/d\tau$. The variational principle $\delta \int L\, d\tau = 0$ then implies that, for the purpose of describing a particle's trajectory, space-time possesses a metric

$$ds^2 = e^{\frac{2\Phi}{c^2}}\eta_{\mu\nu}\, dx^\mu\, dx^\nu. \tag{7-71}$$

A test particle follows a path which is geodesic in this metric. (The principle $\delta \int ds = 0$ gives a maximum rather than a minimum, because the diagonal components of $\eta_{\mu\nu}$ do not have the same sign.)

The mean curvature $\bar{K}$ for the metric of eq. (7-71) is obtained by an obvious generalization of eq. (7-46):

$$\bar{K} = -\frac{1}{2c^2}e^{-\frac{2\Phi}{c^2}}\eta^{\alpha\beta}\left[\frac{\partial^2 \Phi}{\partial x^\alpha\, \partial x^\beta} + \frac{1}{c^2}\frac{\partial \Phi}{\partial x^\alpha}\frac{\partial \Phi}{\partial x^\beta}\right]. \tag{7-72}$$

Equation (7-72) can be rigorously verified by the application of eq. (8-54) in the next chapter. Substitution of the field equation (6-20) and eq. (6-25) into eq. (7-72) gives

$$\bar{K} = e^{-\frac{2\Phi}{c^2}}[2\pi G\rho - \tfrac{1}{2}g^\alpha g_\alpha], \tag{7-73}$$

where ρ is the proper density.

We now *postulate* the field equation

$$\bar{K} = 2\pi G\rho \tag{7-74}$$

as the replacement for the old equation (7-73). The curvature is thus a function only of the density of matter, not the gravitational field intensity.

Equation (7-71) gives the metric. Equation (7-72) is still correct, because it depends only on the geometry. What is different is that the old field equation (6-20) is replaced by the new field equation (7-74) which is in geometrical form. The substitution

$$Y = e^{\frac{\Phi}{c^2}} \tag{7-75}$$

(which takes the place of the W in the thermal case) into eq. (7-72) yields the relation

$$\bar{K} = -\frac{\Box^2 Y}{2Y^3}. \tag{7-76}$$

The elimination of $\bar{K}$ from eqs. (7-76) and (7-74) gives the result

$$\Box^2 Y = -4\pi G\rho Y^3. \tag{7-77}$$

As part of the postulate of eq. (7-74) we may choose ρ to be the proper density in terms of *metric* distances (i.e., according to ds). The metric is now

$$ds^2 = Y^2 \eta_{\mu\nu}\, dx^\mu\, dx^\nu. \tag{7-78}$$

Equations (7-77) and (7-78) constitute the geometrized scalar theory of gravitation.

The theory suggested above is satisfactory in every way except for lack of agreement with observation. The problem of orbital motion is solved by a series of steps. First we take the spherically symmetric solution for a point mass M. As in the thermal case, the solution must have the form $Y = 1 + B/r$. From eq. (7-75) and the Newtonian approximation $\Phi = -GM/r$, the constant B must be equal to $-\mu = -GM/c^2$. The field Y is thus equal to $1 - \mu/r$. Note that, due to the equivalence of gravitational and inertial mass, all trace of the test particle has vanished from eq. (7-77) in contrast with the thermal case. (The expansion coefficient h enters eq. (7-68).)

The equations of motion for a test particle are found by using the geodesic condition $\delta \int ds = 0$. The latter condition is the same as using the Lagrangian

$$L = \sqrt{ Y^2(r)\left\{ \left(\frac{dt}{ds}\right)^2 - \frac{1}{c^2}\left[\left(\frac{dr}{ds}\right)^2 + r^2\left(\frac{d\theta}{ds}\right)^2 \right] \right\} }$$

with metric length s as the independent variable. It is immediately evident that the momenta conjugate to t and θ are constants:

$$Y\frac{dt}{ds} = k$$

$$Yr^2\frac{d\theta}{ds} = h,$$

where k and h are constants. Upon switching to τ given by $d\tau^2 = dt^2 - c^{-2}(dr^2 + r^2\,d\theta^2)$ as the independent variable, the preceding equations become

$$\dot{t} = \frac{k}{Y}$$

$$r^2\dot{\theta} = \frac{h}{Y}$$

$$\dot{r}^2 + r^2\dot{\theta}^2 = c^2(\dot{t}^2 - 1).$$

The dots indicate differentiation with respect to τ. The application of the results of Section 6.2 gives the orbit equation

$$\frac{d^2u}{d\theta^2} + u = N(u) = \frac{c^2\mu Y}{h^2} = \frac{c^2\mu}{h^2}(1 - \mu u).$$

Hence the perihelion advance is $\sigma = -\mu/2p$. A light ray is not deflected because, with either s or τ identified as the proper time of the particle, we must take the limit $N \to 0$ for $h \to \infty$.

The geometrized scalar gravitational theory presented above fails on the perihelion and light-deflection tests. However, the theory does pass the test for gravitational frequency shift—something that no special-relativistic theory could ever do. The reason is that the geometrized scalar gravitational theory need not be restricted to special-relativistic space-time. We may postulate, if we wish, that it is ds and not $d\tau$ that measures proper times and proper distances. The similarity between the scalar-theory metric and the metric required by the gravitational frequency shift, noted in Section 6.8, then guarantees that the gravitational frequency shift follows from the theory.

CHAPTER 8

RIEMANNIAN GEOMETRY

In Chapter 7 it was assumed that an n-dimensional space contains the metric given by eq. (7-21). The more general case now comes under study. It is assumed that for any two neighboring points with coordinates x^i and $x^i + dx^i$, there exists a scalar metric ds^2 which may be written

$$ds^2 = g_{ij}\, dx^i\, dx^i \qquad i, j = 1, 2, \ldots, n. \qquad (8\text{-}1)$$

The coefficient matrix g_{ij} is assumed to be symmetric in its indices, to possess a non-zero determinant, and to be differentiable to any order needed.

8.1 PROPERTIES OF THE METRIC TENSOR

It is easily verified from the definition of g_{ij} and eq. (3-37a) that g_{ij} is a second rank covariant tensor. Hence g_{ij} will be known as the *metric tensor*.

The inverse of the metric tensor will be denoted g^{ij}; it is defined $g^{ij}g_{jk} = \delta^i_k$ and is a symmetric contravariant tensor. It follows that if $\xi_i = g_{ij}\xi^j$, then $\xi^i = g^{ij}\xi_j$.

Let a^i be a contravariant vector. An example is the coordinate differential dx^i. Then the quantity $a_i = g_{ij}a^j$ is a covariant vector, as may be verified by the use of eq. (3-35). Note that a^i can be obtained from a_i by the relation $a^i = g^{ij}a_j$. In general, the lower indices are covariant indices and the upper indices are contravariant indices. If b^i is a second vector, then the scalar product of the vectors a^i and b^i is $g_{ij}a^ib^j$. If this product vanishes, then the vectors a^i and b^i are said to be *orthogonal* to each other. A *null* vector is one which is orthogonal to itself.

The tensorial nature of g^{ij} is evident from the scalar product of two arbitrary vectors a^i and b^i. Their scalar product $g_{ij}a^ib^j$ is a scalar because g_{ij} is a tensor. But by *lowering* the index of a^i and b^i, i.e., writing $a^i = g^{ij}a_j$, etc., the scalar product becomes $g^{ij}a_ib_j$. Upon transforming to new coordinates $\bar{x}^r$, we have

$$g^{ij}a_ib_j = \bar{g}^{rs}\bar{a}_r\bar{b}_s = \bar{g}^{rs}\frac{\partial x^i}{\partial \bar{x}^r}\frac{\partial x^j}{\partial \bar{x}^s}a_ib_j$$

which gives

$$\left(g^{ij} - \bar{g}^{rs}\frac{\partial x^i}{\partial \bar{x}^r}\frac{\partial x^j}{\partial \bar{x}^s}\right)a_ib_j = 0.$$

Since the vectors a^i and b^i are arbitrary, it follows that g^{ij} obeys the transformation of eq. (3-37b) for a second-rank tensor.

Thus the raising and lowering of indices and the formation of scalar products of vectors are performed in the same way as was done in special relativity, with g_{ij} taking the place of $\eta_{\mu\nu}$. An important distinction between special relativity and what we are now pursuing is that the $\eta_{\mu\nu}$ are constant while g_{ij} is in general a function of position. Also, we were restricted to rectangular Cartesian coordinates in special relativity, but now *any* continuous coordinate system is admissible.

8.2 GEODESICS

We now seek the necessary and sufficient condition analogous to eq. (7-22) that a curve $x^i(t)$ between two given points A and B be a geodesic. It will be assumed that the points A and B lie in such a relation to each other that there exists a family of curves joining them, and that everywhere on each member $C:x^i(t)$ of the family the scalar $g_{ij}\,dx^i\,dx^j$ formed from the differential $dx^i = (dx^i/dt)\,dt$ is positive. The condition that one member of the family be a geodesic is that the integral

$$s = \int_A^B ds$$

along it be invariant to first order under the change to a nearby member; i.e., $\delta s = 0$. With the use of eq. (8-1), this condition becomes

$$0 = \delta \int_A^B \sqrt{g_{ij}\frac{dx^i}{dt}\frac{dx^j}{dt}}\,dt \tag{8-2}$$

where t is any monotonic parameter along the curve.

The *acceleration vector* α_i arises from the evaluation of the right-hand side of eq. (8-2). We find

$$\delta \int_A^B \sqrt{g_{ij} \frac{dx^i}{dt} \frac{dx^j}{dt}} \, dt = - \int_A^B \alpha_i \, \delta x^i \, dt \qquad (8\text{-}3)$$

where

$$\alpha_i = \frac{d}{dt} \left(\frac{g_{ij} \dfrac{dx^j}{dt}}{\sqrt{g_{mn} \dfrac{dx^m}{dt} \dfrac{dx^n}{dt}}} \right) - \frac{1}{2} \frac{\dfrac{\partial g_{kl}}{\partial x^i} \dfrac{dx^k}{dt} \dfrac{dx^l}{dt}}{\sqrt{g_{pq} \dfrac{dx^p}{dt} \dfrac{dx^q}{dt}}}. \qquad (8\text{-}4)$$

The covariant-vectorial nature of α_i is seen in eq. (8-3) which is a scalar equation. Under a coordinate transformation $\bar{x}^r = \bar{x}^r(x^i)$, the right-hand side becomes

$$\int \alpha_i \, \delta x^i \, dt = \int \bar{\alpha}_r \, \delta \bar{x}^r \, dt = \int \bar{\alpha}_r \frac{\partial \bar{x}^r}{\partial x^i} \, \delta x^i \, dt.$$

Since this relation must hold for arbitrary δx^i, it follows that α_i transforms as a covariant vector: $\alpha_i = (\partial \bar{x}^r / \partial x^i) \bar{\alpha}_r$.

The condition that the curve be a geodesic is, from eq. (8-3), the condition $\alpha_i = 0$. Having obtained this condition, we now set t equal to s along the geodesic and use the notation $\dot{x}^i = dx^i/ds$. Equation (8-4) becomes

$$\alpha_i = \frac{d}{ds} (g_{ij} \dot{x}^j) - \frac{1}{2} \frac{\partial g_{kl}}{\partial x^i} \dot{x}^k \dot{x}^l$$

or

$$\alpha_i = g_{ij} \ddot{x}^j + [kl, i] \dot{x}^k \dot{x}^l \qquad (8\text{-}5)$$

where

$$[jk, i] = \frac{1}{2} \left(\frac{\partial g_{ji}}{\partial x^k} + \frac{\partial g_{ki}}{\partial x^j} - \frac{\partial g_{jk}}{\partial x^i} \right). \qquad (8\text{-}6)$$

The latter quantity is known as the *Christoffel symbol of the first kind.* It is symmetric in the first two indices jk. Multiplication of eq. (8-5) by g^{im} gives

$$\alpha^m = \ddot{x}^m + \left\{ \begin{matrix} m \\ jk \end{matrix} \right\} \dot{x}^j \dot{x}^k \qquad (8\text{-}7)$$

where

$$\left\{ \begin{matrix} m \\ jk \end{matrix} \right\} = g^{mi}[jk, i]. \qquad (8\text{-}8)$$

The latter quantity is known as the *Christoffel symbol of the second kind,* and is symmetric in the lower two indices.

The transformation law for the Christoffel symbol of the second kind is obtained by using the vector nature of α^i. Under a coordinate transformation $\bar{x}^r(x^i)$, we have on the one hand

$$\alpha^i = \frac{\partial x^i}{\partial \bar{x}^r}\,\bar{\alpha}^r = \frac{\partial x^i}{\partial \bar{x}^r}\left[\ddot{\bar{x}}^r + \begin{Bmatrix} r \\ st \end{Bmatrix}\dot{\bar{x}}^s\dot{\bar{x}}^t\right]$$

and on the other hand

$$\alpha^i = \frac{d}{ds}\left(\frac{\partial x^i}{\partial \bar{x}^r}\,\dot{\bar{x}}^r\right) + \begin{Bmatrix} i \\ jk \end{Bmatrix}\frac{\partial x^j}{\partial \bar{x}^s}\frac{\partial x^k}{\partial \bar{x}^t}\dot{\bar{x}}^s\dot{\bar{x}}^t.$$

Note that although $\dot{x}^i$ is a vector, $\ddot{x}^i$ is not a vector, and $\begin{Bmatrix} i \\ jk \end{Bmatrix}$ is not a tensor. We have

$$\left.\begin{aligned}
\begin{Bmatrix} r \\ tu \end{Bmatrix} &= \frac{\partial \bar{x}^r}{\partial x^i}\frac{\partial x^j}{\partial \bar{x}^t}\frac{\partial x^k}{\partial \bar{x}^u}\begin{Bmatrix} i \\ jk \end{Bmatrix} + \frac{\partial^2 x^l}{\partial \bar{x}^t \partial \bar{x}^u}\frac{\partial \bar{x}^r}{\partial x^l} \qquad\qquad \text{a} \\[2mm]
\begin{Bmatrix} r \\ tu \end{Bmatrix} &= \frac{\partial \bar{x}^r}{\partial x^i}\frac{\partial x^j}{\partial \bar{x}^t}\frac{\partial x^k}{\partial \bar{x}^u}\begin{Bmatrix} i \\ jk \end{Bmatrix} - \frac{\partial^2 \bar{x}^r}{\partial x^l \partial x^m}\frac{\partial x^l}{\partial \bar{x}^t}\frac{\partial x^m}{\partial \bar{x}^u}. \qquad \text{b}
\end{aligned}\right\} \quad (8\text{-}9)$$

Equations (8-9) are the rules for transforming the Christoffel symbol of the second kind from one coordinate system to another.

The acceleration vector α^i for any curve $x^i(s)$ is given by eq. (8-7). But only for a geodesic is α^i zero everywhere along the curve:

$$0 = \ddot{x}^i + \begin{Bmatrix} i \\ jk \end{Bmatrix}\dot{x}^j\dot{x}^k. \qquad\qquad (8\text{-}10)$$

EXAMPLE. In spherical polar coordinates, the metric for three-dimensional Euclidean geometry is

$$ds^2 = dr^2 + r^2(d\theta^2 + \sin^2\theta\,d\phi^2),$$

i.e.,

$$g_{ij} = \begin{bmatrix} 1 & 0 & 0 \\ 0 & r^2 & 0 \\ 0 & 0 & r^2\sin^2\theta \end{bmatrix}$$

for the coordinates $x^1 = r$, $x^2 = \theta$, $x^3 = \phi$. Calculation shows that the only non-vanishing Christoffel symbols of the first kind are

$[22, 1] = -r$ $\qquad\qquad$ $[12, 2] = [21, 2] = r$

$[33, 1] = -r\sin^2\theta$ $\qquad$ $[13, 3] = [31, 3] = r\sin^2\theta$

$[33, 2] = -r^2\sin\theta\cos\theta$ $\qquad$ $[23, 3] = [32, 3] = r^2\sin\theta\cos\theta.$

The acceleration vector is thus

$$\alpha_1 = \ddot{r} - r(\dot{\theta}^2 + \sin^2\theta\dot{\phi}^2)$$

$$\alpha_2 = \frac{d}{ds}(r^2\dot{\theta}) - r^2\sin\theta\cos\theta\dot{\phi}^2$$

$$\alpha_3 = \frac{d}{ds}(r^2\sin^2\theta\dot{\phi}).$$

The Cartesian components a_i of the acceleration are given by $a_i = \sqrt{\alpha_i\alpha^i}$ (no sum on i):

$$a_r = \ddot{r} - r(\dot{\theta}^2 + \sin^2\theta\dot{\phi}^2)$$

$$a_\theta = \frac{1}{r}\left[\frac{d}{ds}(r^2\dot{\theta}) - r^2\sin\theta\cos\theta\dot{\phi}^2\right]$$

$$a_\phi = \frac{1}{r\sin\theta}\frac{d}{ds}(r^2\sin^2\theta\dot{\phi}).$$

8.3 GEODESIC COORDINATES

Geodesic coordinates are defined in the same way as in Chapter 7. First we expand the equation $x^i(s)$ for a geodesic about a given point P in a Taylor series:

$$x^i(s) = x^i_P + \dot{x}^i_P s + \tfrac{1}{2}\ddot{x}^i_P s^2 + \tfrac{1}{6}\dddot{x}^i_P s^3 + O^4(s). \tag{8-11}$$

Then the coefficients in eq. (8-11) are evaluated by the use of eq. (8-10). Equation (8-10) immediately gives

$$\ddot{x}^i_P = -\begin{Bmatrix} i \\ jk \end{Bmatrix}_P a^j a^k$$

where $a^i = \dot{x}^i_P$. In order to obtain $\dddot{x}^i_P$, eq. (8-10) must be differentiated with respect to s. The result is

$$\dddot{x}^i = -\begin{Bmatrix} i \\ jkl \end{Bmatrix}\dot{x}^j\dot{x}^k\dot{x}^l$$

where

$$\begin{Bmatrix} i \\ jkl \end{Bmatrix} = \underset{jkl}{S}\left[\frac{\partial}{\partial x^l}\begin{Bmatrix} i \\ jk \end{Bmatrix} - \begin{Bmatrix} i \\ mj \end{Bmatrix}\begin{Bmatrix} m \\ kl \end{Bmatrix} - \begin{Bmatrix} i \\ mk \end{Bmatrix}\begin{Bmatrix} m \\ jl \end{Bmatrix}\right].$$

The symbol $\underset{jkl}{S}$ denotes the part which is symmetric in the indices j, k, l. For three indices, as in this case, the symmetric part of a matrix is equal to one-sixth of the sum of the terms formed by all permutations of the indices. In the present case we have

$$\underset{jkl}{S}\frac{\partial}{\partial x^l}\begin{Bmatrix} i \\ jk \end{Bmatrix} = \frac{1}{3}\left[\frac{\partial}{\partial x^l}\begin{Bmatrix} i \\ jk \end{Bmatrix} + \frac{\partial}{\partial x^j}\begin{Bmatrix} i \\ kl \end{Bmatrix} + \frac{\partial}{\partial x^k}\begin{Bmatrix} i \\ lj \end{Bmatrix}\right].$$

Equation (8-11) for a geodesic thus becomes

$$x^i(s) = x^i_P + a^i s - \frac{1}{2}\begin{Bmatrix} i \\ jk \end{Bmatrix}_P a^j a^k s^2 - \frac{1}{6}\begin{Bmatrix} i \\ lmn \end{Bmatrix}_P a^l a^m a^n s^3 + O^4(s). \quad (8\text{-}12)$$

Geodesic coordinates y^i about P are defined by the equation

$$x^i = x^i_P + y^i - \frac{1}{2}\begin{Bmatrix} i \\ jk \end{Bmatrix}_P y^j y^k - \frac{1}{6}\begin{Bmatrix} i \\ lmn \end{Bmatrix} y^l y^m y^n + O^4(y) \quad (8\text{-}13)$$

so that the geodesic is given by

$$y^i(s) = a^i s + O^4(s). \quad (8\text{-}14)$$

Several properties of geodesic coordinates are here noted for later reference. First, comparison of eqs. (8-12) and (8-14) shows that in geodesic coordinates around a point P, all $\begin{Bmatrix} i \\ jk \end{Bmatrix}$ and all $\begin{Bmatrix} i \\ jkl \end{Bmatrix}$ vanish at P. But in general we have from eqs. (8-6) and (8-8) the relations

$$[jk, i] = g_{il}\begin{Bmatrix} l \\ jk \end{Bmatrix}$$

and

$$\frac{\partial g_{ij}}{\partial x^k} = [ik, j] + [jk, i]. \quad (8\text{-}15)$$

Therefore all $[jk, i]$ and all first derivatives of the metric tensor vanish at P. Second, when eqs. (8-9) are applied to the case that $\bar{x}^r$ are geodesic coordinates and x^i are arbitrary coordinates, we immediately have

$$\begin{Bmatrix} i \\ jk \end{Bmatrix} = \frac{\partial x^i}{\partial \bar{x}^r}\frac{\partial^2 \bar{x}^r}{\partial x^j \partial x^k} = -\frac{\partial \bar{x}^r}{\partial x^j}\frac{\partial \bar{x}^s}{\partial x^k}\frac{\partial^2 x^i}{\partial \bar{x}^r \partial \bar{x}^s}. \quad (8\text{-}16)$$

It must be emphasized that in geodesic coordinates at P, the first derivatives of the metric tensor, although they vanish at P, do not in general vanish elsewhere. Therefore, in geodesic coordinates the second derivatives of the metric tensor do not necessarily vanish.

Throughout the remainder of this chapter, bars will denote geodesic coordinates or values in geodesic coordinates thus: $\bar{x}^r$, $\bar{g}^{rs}$, etc.

8.4 PARALLEL DISPLACEMENT

A contravariant vector ξ^i_Q at a point $Q(x^i + dx^i)$ is said to be *parallel* to a contravariant vector ξ^i_P at the point $P(x^i)$ if the components of ξ^i_Q and ξ^i_P are identical in geodesic coordinates constructed at P:

$$\bar{\xi}^r_Q = \bar{\xi}^r_P. \quad (8\text{-}17)$$

When eq. (8-17) is written in terms of an arbitrary coordinate system x^i, the equation

$$\xi_Q^i = \left(\frac{\partial x^i}{\partial \bar{x}^r}\right)_Q \left(\frac{\partial \bar{x}^r}{\partial x^j}\right)_P \xi_P^j$$

may be expanded by the use of the Taylor series

$$\left(\frac{\partial x^i}{\partial \bar{x}^r}\right)_Q = \left(\frac{\partial x^i}{\partial \bar{x}^r}\right)_P + \left(\frac{\partial^2 x^i}{\partial \bar{x}^r \partial \bar{x}^s}\right)_P \left(\frac{\partial \bar{x}^s}{\partial x^k}\right)_P dx^k + O^2(dx)$$

to give, with the substitution of eq. (8-16),

$$\xi_Q^i = \xi_P^i - \left\{\begin{matrix} i \\ jk \end{matrix}\right\}_P \xi_P^j \, dx^k + O[\xi, (dx)^2]. \tag{8-18}$$

Equation (8-18) is the condition that a vector ξ_Q^i at Q be parallel to a vector ξ_P^i at P. For a contravariant vector η_i, the corresponding relation is found to be

$$\eta_{iQ} = \eta_{iP} + \left\{\begin{matrix} j \\ ik \end{matrix}\right\} \eta_{jP} \, dx^k + O[\eta, (dx)^2]. \tag{8-19}$$

If a contravariant vector ξ^i and a covariant vector η_i are given at one point P on a curve $x^i(p)$, then they can be carried by *parallel displacement* along the curve by the use of eqs. (8-18) and (8-19). To carry the vectors from $x^i(p)$ to $x^i(p + dp)$ requires a change in their components given by

$$d\xi^i = -\left\{\begin{matrix} i \\ jk \end{matrix}\right\} \xi^j \frac{dx^k}{dp} dp$$

$$d\eta_i = \left\{\begin{matrix} j \\ ik \end{matrix}\right\} \eta_j \frac{dx^k}{dp} dp,$$

where p is a parameter along the curve. Therefore the resulting vectors $\xi^i(p)$ and $\eta_i(p)$ must satisfy the equations

$$\frac{d\xi^i}{dp} + \left\{\begin{matrix} i \\ jk \end{matrix}\right\} \xi^j \frac{dx^k}{dp} = 0 \tag{8-20}$$

$$\frac{d\eta_i}{dp} - \left\{\begin{matrix} j \\ ik \end{matrix}\right\} \eta_j \frac{dx^k}{dp} = 0. \tag{8-21}$$

Equations (8-20) and (8-21) are the conditions for vectors ξ^i and η_i to be carried along a curve $x^i(p)$ by parallel displacement.

It can be verified without difficulty that the forms $\xi_i = g_{ij}\xi^j$ and $\eta^i = g^{ij}\eta_j$ are also carried by parallel displacement, and that the scalar product $\xi^i\eta_i$ is constant along the curve. It follows that the magnitude of each vector $\xi^i\xi_i$ and $\eta^i\eta_i$ is constant, as is also the quantity*

$$\cos \theta = \frac{\xi^i \eta_i}{\sqrt{|\xi^j \xi_j \eta^k \eta_k|}}. \tag{8-22}$$

---

* The possibility that $\cos \theta$ may exceed unity need not detain us, since we are defining $\cos \theta$ instead of θ.

Thus two vectors carried along a curve by parallel displacement maintain a constant "angle" between each other.

Note from eqs. (8-20) and (8-10) that the condition for the parallel displacement of the tangent dx^i/ds of the curve $x^i(s)$, where s is the metric distance defined by eq. (8-1), is identical with the condition for a geodesic. Thus we obtain an alternate definition for a geodesic: *a geodesic is a curve whose tangent is carried by parallel displacement along it.* It also follows that a vector carried along a *geodesic* by parallel transport makes a constant angle with the geodesic in the sense of eq. (8-22). More will be said about the definition of geodesics in Section 8.14.

It is important to realize that when a vector is carried by parallel displacement from one point to another point, the resulting vector depends on the curve that is used. A vector which is carried around a closed curve and back to the starting point does not in general have the same components as when it started out. Consider a closed curve Γ: $x^i(p)$ and a point P: $x^i(0)$ on Γ. The parameter p on Γ runs from 0 to p_0 so that $x^i(p_0) = x^i(0)$. A vector ξ^i is carried by parallel displacement from P once around Γ back to P again, and becomes ξ'^i, different from ξ^i. The difference $\Delta\xi^i = \xi'^i - \xi^i$ is given by the integral

$$\Delta\xi^i = \int_\Gamma \frac{d\xi^i}{dp}\, dp$$

taken around Γ. By eq. (8-20), we have

$$\Delta\xi^i = -\int_\Gamma \left\{ {i \atop jk} \right\} \xi^j\, dx^k. \tag{8-23}$$

Equation (8-23) is in the form of a circuit integral. If the integrand $A_l^i = \left\{ {i \atop jl} \right\} \xi^j$ were a unique function of position over a two-dimensional surface S having Γ as its boundary, then by Stokes' theorem eq. (8-23) can be converted into a surface integral. This, however, cannot be done in general, because parallel displacement is not in general integrable. The function A_l^i indicated above is not a unique function, since ξ^i is not unique.

However, if we are interested in only an approximate answer, then we may proceed to use Stokes' theorem. A digression is in order to state Stokes' theorem in n-dimensions.

Stokes' theorem in n-dimensional space is proved as follows. We are given a closed curve Γ and a two-dimensional surface S having Γ as its boundary. We are also given functions $f_i(x^j)$ which are not necessarily a vector. A set of two coordinates u, v is constructed in S so that S has the parametric form $x^i(u, v)$. Then the integral

$$I = \int_\Gamma f_i(x^j)\, dx^i$$

around Γ becomes

$$I = \int_\Gamma \left(f_i \frac{\partial x^i}{\partial u} \, du + f_i \frac{\partial x^i}{\partial v} \, dv \right).$$ (8-24)

The surface S is divided into a grid of infinitesimal quadrilaterals by the curves $u = $ const and $v = $ const. We add to eq. (8-24) the total of the line integrals back and forth on each such grid line, which of course is zero:

$$I = \sum_{\substack{\text{grid} \\ \text{areas}}} \int \left(f_i \frac{\partial x^i}{\partial u} \, du + f_i \frac{\partial x^i}{\partial v} \, dv \right).$$

But for each grid area, the integral is

$$\iint \left[-\frac{\partial}{\partial v}\left(f_i \frac{\partial x^i}{\partial u} \right) + \frac{\partial}{\partial u}\left(f_i \frac{\partial x^i}{\partial v} \right) \right] du \, dv$$

$$= \iint \left[-\frac{\partial f_i}{\partial v} \frac{\partial x^i}{\partial u} + \frac{\partial f_i}{\partial u} \frac{\partial x^i}{\partial v} \right] du \, dv$$

$$= \iint \frac{\partial f_i}{\partial x^j} \left[-\frac{\partial x^j}{\partial v} \frac{\partial x^i}{\partial u} + \frac{\partial x^j}{\partial u} \frac{\partial x^i}{\partial v} \right] du \, dv.$$

Therefore, if we denote

$$dS^{ij} = \left[\frac{\partial x^i}{\partial u} \frac{\partial x^j}{\partial v} - \frac{\partial x^j}{\partial u} \frac{\partial x^i}{\partial v} \right] du \, dv,$$

the integral of eq. (8-24) becomes

$$I = \iint_S \frac{\partial f_j}{\partial x^i} \, dS^{ij} = \frac{1}{2} \iint_S \left(\frac{\partial f_j}{\partial x^i} - \frac{\partial f_i}{\partial x^j} \right) dS^{ij}.$$

Note that no metric is assumed. Thus we have proved Stokes' theorem

$$\int_\Gamma f_i(x^j) \, dx^i = \iint_S \frac{\partial f_j}{\partial x^i} \, dS^{ij}.$$

We return to the integral of eq. (8-23) and propose to evaluate it by converting it into a surface integral over a two-dimensional surface S bounded by Γ. By eq. (8-18), the vector ξ^i at any point $x^i = x^i_P + \Delta x^i$ on S obtained by parallel displacement over any reasonable path is

$$\xi^i = \xi^i_P - \left\{ \begin{matrix} i \\ jk \end{matrix} \right\} \xi^j_P \, \Delta x^k + O^2(\Delta x).$$ (8-25)

The substitution of eq. (8-25) into eq. (8-23) now gives us

$$\Delta \xi^i = -\int A^i_k \, dx^k + O^3(\Delta x)$$

where

$$A_k^i = \xi_P^j \left[\begin{Bmatrix} i \\ jk \end{Bmatrix} - \begin{Bmatrix} i \\ km \end{Bmatrix} \begin{Bmatrix} m \\ jl \end{Bmatrix} \Delta x^l \right].$$

Note that A_k^i is here a unique function of position on S. Hence Stokes' theorem can be applied to give

$$\Delta \xi^i = -\frac{1}{2} \iint_S \left(\frac{\partial A_l^i}{\partial x^k} - \frac{\partial A_k^i}{\partial x^l} \right) dS^{kl} + O^3(\Delta x)$$

or

$$\Delta \xi^i = -\frac{1}{2} \iint_S R^i{}_{jkl} \xi_P^j \, dS^{kl} + O^3(\Delta x) \qquad (8\text{-}26)$$

where

$$R^i{}_{jkl} = \frac{\partial \begin{Bmatrix} i \\ jl \end{Bmatrix}}{\partial x^k} - \frac{\partial \begin{Bmatrix} i \\ jk \end{Bmatrix}}{\partial x^l} + \begin{Bmatrix} i \\ km \end{Bmatrix} \begin{Bmatrix} m \\ jl \end{Bmatrix} - \begin{Bmatrix} i \\ lm \end{Bmatrix} \begin{Bmatrix} m \\ jk \end{Bmatrix}. \qquad (8\text{-}27)$$

Equation (8-26) gives the total change in the vector ξ^i due to its parallel displacement around a closed curve which bounds the surface S. For the special case that Γ is the parallelogram formed by two differentials dx^i and δx^i, we have

$$\Delta \xi^i = -\tfrac{1}{2} R^i{}_{jkl} \xi^j \, \Delta S^{kl} + O^3(dx, \delta x),$$

with

$$\Delta S^{kl} = dx^k \, \delta x^l - \delta x^k \, dx^l. \qquad (8\text{-}28)$$

Owing to the antisymmetry $R^i{}_{jkl} = -R^i{}_{jlk}$, this becomes

$$\Delta \xi^i = -R^i{}_{jkl} \xi^j \, dx^k \, \delta x^l + O^3(dx, \delta x). \qquad (8\text{-}29)$$

The direction of the circuit is in the sense: $dx^k, \delta x^k, -dx^k, -\delta x^k$.

It has been proved that when a vector ξ^i is moved by parallel displacement around an infinitesimal closed circuit in the form of a parallelogram formed by the vectors dx^i, δx^i, the change in ξ^i when it reaches the starting point is given by eq. (8-29). The quantity $R^i{}_{jkl}$ which is defined by eq. (8-27) is a tensor and is known as the *Riemann-Christoffel tensor*.

8.5 THE RIEMANN-CHRISTOFFEL TENSOR

The tensorial nature of $R^i{}_{jkl}$ follows from eq. (8-29) where $\Delta \xi^i$ is a vector (the difference between two vectors) and ξ^i, dx^i, and δx^i are arbitrary vectors. The contravariant and covariant indices are upper and lower, respectively, in accordance with the customary notation. The upper index may be lowered by the usual process of multiplying by the metric tensor: $R_{ijkl} = g_{im}R^m{}_{jkl}$. We will now consider the properties of the fourth-rank covariant tensor R_{ijkl}.

Since R_{ijkl} is a tensor, its properties may be studied in any coordinate system. In particular, we will use geodesic coordinates about an arbitrary point P. The vanishing of the Christoffel symbols then reduces eq. (8-27) to

$$\bar{R}^i{}_{jkl} = \frac{\partial}{\partial \bar{x}^k}\left\{\overline{\begin{matrix}i\\jl\end{matrix}}\right\} - \frac{\partial}{\partial \bar{x}^l}\left\{\overline{\begin{matrix}i\\jk\end{matrix}}\right\}. \tag{8-30}$$

Equation (8-30) may be expanded with the use of the definition of the Christoffel symbols and then simplified by recalling that the first derivatives of the metric tensor all vanish. The result is

$$\bar{R}_{ijkl} = \frac{1}{2}\left[\frac{\partial^2 \bar{g}_{il}}{\partial \bar{x}^j \, \partial \bar{x}^k} + \frac{\partial^2 \bar{g}_{jk}}{\partial \bar{x}^i \, \partial \bar{x}^l} - \frac{\partial^2 \bar{g}_{ik}}{\partial \bar{x}^j \, \partial \bar{x}^l} - \frac{\partial^2 \bar{g}_{jl}}{\partial \bar{x}^i \, \partial \bar{x}^k}\right]. \tag{8-31}$$

Equation (8-31) shows that $\bar{R}_{ijkl}$ is antisymmetric in each pair of the indices ij and kl, and is symmetric in the interchange of the two pairs:

$$\bar{R}_{ijkl} = -\bar{R}_{ijlk} = -\bar{R}_{jikl} = \bar{R}_{klij}.$$

Another symmetry property is the cyclic property

$$\bar{R}_{ijkl} + \bar{R}_{iklj} + \bar{R}_{iljk} = 0.$$

Since these symmetry properties have the form of tensor relations which hold in one coordinate system, they hold in all coordinate systems.

$$\left.\begin{matrix}R_{ijkl} = -R_{ijlk} = -R_{jikl} = R_{klij}\\ R_{ijkl} + R_{iklj} + R_{iljk} = 0.\end{matrix}\right\} \tag{8-32}$$

In eqs. (8-30) and (8-31), $\bar{R}_{ijkl}$ was expressed in terms of the first derivatives of the Christoffel symbols and in terms of the second derivatives of the metric tensor. It is also possible to do the reverse, i.e., express the first derivatives of the Christoffel symbols and the second derivatives of the metric tensor in terms of the Riemann-Christoffel tensor:

$$\frac{\partial \overline{[jl, i]}}{\partial \bar{x}^k} = \tfrac{1}{3}[\bar{R}_{ijkl} + \bar{R}_{ilkj}] \tag{8-33}$$

$$\frac{\partial^2 \bar{g}_{ij}}{\partial \bar{x}^k \, \partial \bar{x}^l} = \tfrac{1}{3}[\bar{R}_{iklj} + \bar{R}_{jkli}]. \tag{8-34}$$

Equation (8-33) is proved by using the relation $\left\{\begin{matrix}i\\jkl\end{matrix}\right\} = 0$ or

$$\underset{jkl}{S}\frac{\partial \overline{[jk, i]}}{\partial \bar{x}^l} = 0 \tag{8-35}$$

which holds in geodesic coordinates. Equation (8-34) follows from eq. (8-33) with the use of eq. (8-15).

Although the Riemann-Christoffel tensor has n^4 components, it is clear from eqs. (8-32) that these components are not independent of each other. The number of independent relations among the set of eqs. (8-32) turns out to be $\dfrac{n^2(11n^2 + 1)}{12}$, leaving only $\dfrac{n^2(n^2 - 1)}{12}$ independent components of R_{ijkl}. Now if there existed any other symmetry equations for R_{ijkl}, then the actual number N of independent components of R_{ijkl} is smaller than $\dfrac{n^2(n^2 - 1)}{12}$. But N can be calculated from the derivatives of the metric tensor in the following way.

By means of eq. (8-31), $\bar{R}_{ijkl}$ is a linear function of the second derivatives of the metric tensor. Therefore, if N' is the number of linearly independent second derivatives of the metric tensor, $N \le N'$. But on the other hand, eq. (8-34) gives the second derivatives of the metric tensor linearly in terms of $\bar{R}_{ijkl}$. Therefore N is equal to N'. We have therefore to find the number of independent second derivatives of the metric tensor in geodesic coordinates. The only condition on the second derivatives of the metric tensor is provided by eq. (8-35) which constitutes $\dfrac{n^2(n + 1)(n + 2)}{6}$ conditions. Thus the number of independent second derivatives of the metric tensor is $[\tfrac{1}{2}n(n + 1)]^2 - \dfrac{n^2(n + 1)(n + 2)}{6}$ or $\dfrac{n^2(n^2 - 1)}{12}$. Therefore we have

$$N = \frac{n^2(n^2 - 1)}{12}$$

for the number of linearly independent components of the Riemann-Christoffel curvature tensor in n-dimensional space. As a by-product of this derivation, we conclude from the argument of the preceding paragraph that there can exist no further symmetry conditions on R_{ijkl} beside those contained in eqs. (8-32).

For future reference we note here that by contraction of indices in the Riemann-Christoffel tensor, the symmetric second-rank *Ricci tensor* can be formed:

$$R_{ij} = R^k{}_{ijk}. \tag{8-36}$$

Further contraction yields the scalar

$$R = g^{ij} R_{ij}.$$

The *Einstein tensor* G_{ij} is defined

$$G_{ij} = R_{ij} - \tfrac{1}{2} R g_{ij}. \tag{8-37}$$

The Ricci tensor has $\frac{1}{2}n(n + 1)$ independent components; for $n = 4$, the number is 10.

8.6 TENSOR DERIVATIVES

Consider a vector field $A^i(x)$ which is defined throughout a given region of n-dimensional space and is differentiable. If the components of the field at a point P: x^i are $A^i(x) = A^i(P)$, then the components of the field at a nearby point Q: $x^i + dx^i$ are

$$A^i_Q = A^i_P + \left(\frac{\partial A^i}{\partial x^j}\right)_P dx^j + 0^2(dx).$$

In order to compare A^i_Q with A^i_P, the vector A^i_P is moved by parallel displacement from P to Q and becomes A'^i_Q given by

$$A'^i_Q = A^i_P - \begin{Bmatrix} i \\ jk \end{Bmatrix}_P A^k_P \, dx^j + 0^2(dx).$$

The *absolute change* in the vector $A^i(x)$ in going from P to Q is defined as the difference

$$\Delta A^i = A^i_Q - A'^i_Q = \left[\left(\frac{\partial A^i}{\partial x^j}\right)_P + \begin{Bmatrix} i \\ jk \end{Bmatrix}_P A^k_P\right] dx^j + 0^2(dx). \quad \text{(8-38)}$$

The *covariant derivative* of $A^i(x)$ with respect to x^k is defined

$$A^i_{,k} = \frac{\partial A^i}{\partial x^k} + \begin{Bmatrix} i \\ jk \end{Bmatrix} A^j$$

so that eq. (8-38) becomes

$$\Delta A^i = A^i_{,k} \, dx^k + 0^2(dx).$$

The covariant derivative is a tensor, as may be verified by using the transformation properties of the Christoffel symbol or, more simply, by noting that eq. (8-38) is a vector for arbitrary values of the vector dx^k. For a covariant vector field $A_i(x)$, the covariant derivative is defined

$$A_{i,k} = \frac{\partial A_i}{\partial x^k} - \begin{Bmatrix} j \\ ik \end{Bmatrix} A_j$$

and is also a tensor.

It should be noted that in general the ordinary derivative $\partial A^i/\partial x^k$ does not transform as a tensor. Thus the covariant derivative, or *tensor derivative* as it is also called, is needed not only in order to compare the vector field at two points but also in order to provide a derivative which transforms as a tensor.

For a tensor $T^{abc\cdots e}_{ijk\cdots m}$ of any rank, with the indicated contravariant and covariant indices, the tensor derivative with respect to x^h is defined

$$T^{abc\cdots e}_{ijk\cdots m,h} = \frac{\partial T^{abc\cdots e}_{ijk\cdots m}}{\partial x^h} + \begin{Bmatrix} a \\ hu \end{Bmatrix} T^{ubc\cdots e}_{ijk\cdots m} + \cdots$$

$$+ \begin{Bmatrix} e \\ hu \end{Bmatrix} T^{abc\cdots u}_{ijk\cdots m} - \begin{Bmatrix} u \\ hi \end{Bmatrix} T^{abc\cdots e}_{ujk\cdots m} - \cdots$$

$$- \begin{Bmatrix} u \\ hm \end{Bmatrix} T^{abc\cdots e}_{ijk\cdots u},$$

and is also a tensor but of one higher rank. We now examine the properties of the tensor derivative.

It is evident that in geodesic coordinates, in which the Christoffel symbols vanish, the tensor derivative is merely the ordinary derivative. Thus an alternate definition of the tensor derivative is that it be (1) a tensor and (2) the ordinary derivative in geodesic coordinates. Since the first derivatives of the metric tensor vanish in geodesic coordinates, it is evident that the metric tensor acts as a constant under tensor differentiation. We have, for example,

$$A^i{}_{,k} = (g^{ij}A_j){}_{,k} = g^{ij}A_{j,k}.$$

The tensor derivative follows the usual rule for differentiation by parts:

$$(A^iB_j){}_{,k} = A^i{}_{,k}B_j + A^iB_{j,k}$$

$$(SA^i){}_{,k} = S_{,k}A^i + SA^i{}_{,k}.$$

In the latter example, the covariant derivative $S_{,k}$ of a scalar S is identical with the ordinary derivative $\partial S/\partial x^k$ and is a covariant vector.

Tensor derivatives, unlike ordinary derivatives, do not commute. The commutator of the second derivatives of a contravariant vector field $A^i(x)$ is given by

$$A^i{}_{,jk} - A^i{}_{,kj} = -R^i{}_{ljk}A^l \tag{8-39}$$

where $A^i{}_{,jk} = (A^i{}_{,j}){}_{,k}$. Equation (8-39) is proved as follows. The first and second tensor derivatives are defined

$$A^i{}_{,j} = \frac{\partial A^i}{\partial x^j} + \begin{Bmatrix} i \\ jl \end{Bmatrix} A^l$$

$$A^i{}_{,jk} = \frac{\partial A^i{}_{,j}}{\partial x^k} + \begin{Bmatrix} i \\ kl \end{Bmatrix} A^l{}_{,j} - \begin{Bmatrix} l \\ jk \end{Bmatrix} A^i{}_{,l}.$$

Now in geodesic coordinates, all undifferentiated Christoffel symbols vanish. Therefore, when $A^i{}_{,j}$ is substituted into $A^i{}_{,jk}$, all that remains in geodesic coordinates is

$$\overline{A^i}_{,jk} = \frac{\partial^2 \overline{A}_i}{\partial \bar{x}^k \partial \bar{x}^j} + \overline{A}^l \frac{\partial}{\partial \bar{x}^k}\left\{ \begin{matrix} i \\ jl \end{matrix} \right\}.$$

The commutation of the ordinary derivatives and the use of eq. (8-30) then gives eq. (8-39) which is a tensor equation and hence valid in any system of coordinates. For a covariant vector A_i the relation is

$$A_{i,jk} - A_{i,kj} = R^l{}_{ijk} A_l.$$

And in general for any tensor $T^{abc\cdots}_{ijk\cdots}$ the rule is

$$T^{abc\cdots}_{ijk\cdots,st} - T^{abc\cdots}_{ijk\cdots,ts} = -R^a{}_{mst} T^{mbc\cdots}_{ijk\cdots}$$
$$- R^b{}_{mst} T^{amc\cdots}_{ijk\cdots} - \cdots + R^m{}_{ist} T^{abc\cdots}_{mjk\cdots}$$
$$+ R^m{}_{jst} T^{abc\cdots}_{imk\cdots} + \cdots. \quad (8\text{-}40)$$

8.7 THE BIANCHI IDENTITY

When eq. (8-27) is evaluated in geodesic coordinates at an arbitrary point P, we have

$$\frac{\partial \overline{R}^i{}_{jkl}}{\partial \bar{x}^m} = \frac{\partial^2}{\partial \bar{x}^m \partial \bar{x}^k}\left\{ \begin{matrix} i \\ jl \end{matrix} \right\} - \frac{\partial^2}{\partial \bar{x}^m \partial \bar{x}^l}\left\{ \begin{matrix} i \\ jk \end{matrix} \right\}.$$

From this it is obvious that, since the ordinary derivative is the tensor derivative in geodesic coordinates, there exists an identity among the tensor derivatives of the Riemann-Christoffel tensor:

$$\overline{R}_{ijkl,m} + \overline{R}_{ijlm,k} + \overline{R}_{ijmk,l} = 0. \quad (8\text{-}41)$$

Equation (8-41) is a tensor equation valid in one coordinate system and hence valid in all coordinate systems. We have then the identity

$$R_{ijkl,m} + R_{ijlm,k} + R_{ijmk,l} = 0 \quad (8\text{-}42)$$

which is known as the *Bianchi identity*.

Multiplication of eq. (8-42) by $g^{il} g^{jm}$ gives $R^m{}_{k,m} = \frac{1}{2} R_{,k}$, or, in terms of the Einstein tensor defined by eq. (8-37),

$$G^{ij}{}_{,j} = 0. \quad (8\text{-}43)$$

Equation (8-43) is known as the *Ricci identity*. Both the Bianchi identity and the Ricci identity are true identities independent of the specific form of either the metric tensor g_{ij} or the Riemann-Christoffel tensor R_{ijkl}.

The Riemann-Christoffel tensor which continually emerges in various geometrical considerations—e.g., eqs. (8-29) and (8-40)—is related to the Gaussian curvature in n-dimensional space. We now proceed to the task of discovering this relationship.

8.8 GEOMETRICAL CONCEPTS

The geometrical concepts of the magnitude of a vector and the orthogonality of two vectors must be explored at some length due to the arbitrary nature of the metric of eq. (8-1). For an arbitrary coordinate system x^i, the metric tensor g_{ij} at a point P contains $\frac{1}{2}n(n + 1)$ independent components. However, a set of coordinates x'^r can be found such that at P the metric tensor g'_{rs} is diagonalized and further that each diagonal component is ± 1. The transformation matrices $a_r^i = \partial x^i / \partial x'^r$ are clearly given by the equation

$$a_r^i a_s^j g_{ij} = g'_{rs}. \tag{8-44}$$

Equation (8-44) constitutes $\frac{1}{2}n(n + 1)$ equations for the n^2 unknowns a_r^i. Therefore there remain $\frac{1}{2}n(n - 1)$ degrees of freedom in choosing the a_r^i. The point is that there exists a set of coordinate systems x'^r such that at P the metric tensor assumes the special form

$$a_r^i a_s^j g_{ij} = g'_{rs} = \eta_{rs} = \epsilon_r \, \delta_{rs} \quad \text{(no sum on r)}. \tag{8-45}$$

The symbol η_{rs} denotes a diagonal matrix whose non-zero components ϵ_r are $+1$ or -1. The order in which the $+1$'s and -1's appear in η_{rs} can be changed, but the total number of $+1$'s and of -1's cannot be changed. These numbers are the *signature* of the metric. For example, in special relativity, where the metric (for $x^i = cx'^i$) was

$$\eta_{rs} = \begin{bmatrix} +1 & 0 & 0 & 0 \\ 0 & -1 & 0 & 0 \\ 0 & 0 & -1 & 0 \\ 0 & 0 & 0 & -1 \end{bmatrix},$$

the signature was $+ - - -$ or $+1, -3$.

If the signature of the metric is all positive (or, which amounts to the same thing, all negative), the concept of vectors is qualitatively similar to vectors in Euclidean space. For example, a vector is never orthogonal to itself.

However, if the signature of the metric has mixed sign, then three types of vectors exist according as the scalar self product

$$\mathbf{a} \cdot \mathbf{a} = g_{ij} a^i a^j \tag{8-46}$$

of the vector a^i is positive, negative, or zero. Since eq. (8-46) is a scalar, a vector can only belong to one type. If eq. (8-46) is zero, then the vector is said to be a *null* vector. We will define the quantity $\epsilon(\mathbf{a})$ for any vector a^i

by the expressions

$$\epsilon(\mathbf{a}) = \begin{cases} = 0 & \text{if } \mathbf{a} \text{ is null} \\ = \dfrac{\mathbf{a} \cdot \mathbf{a}}{|\mathbf{a} \cdot \mathbf{a}|} & \text{if } \mathbf{a} \text{ is not null.} \end{cases}$$

Then $\epsilon(\mathbf{a})$ is $+1$, -1, and 0, respectively, for the three types of vectors named above. Note that $\epsilon(\mathbf{a})$ is a scalar.

A vector $\mathbf{a}$ is said to be a *unit vector* if $|\mathbf{a} \cdot \mathbf{a}| = 1$. For a metric with a signature of mixed sign, this provides the possibility for unit vectors having infinite components! For example in the Minkowski metric (that of special relativity), the vectors $x^r = (\cosh u, \sinh u, 0, 0)$ and $y^r = (\sinh u, \cosh u, 0, 0)$ are both unit vectors and are orthogonal to each other, even though u may be made as large as we please.

Some further relations between g_{ij}, η_{rs}, and a_r^i will be needed. If $\breve{a}_i^r$ is the inverse of a_r^i and η^{rs} is the inverse of η_{rs}, then the following relations hold:

$$\breve{a}_i^r = g_{ij}\eta^{rs}a_s^j \qquad \text{a}$$

$$\eta^{rs} = \breve{a}_i^r\breve{a}_j^s g^{ij} \qquad \text{b}$$

$$g^{ij} = a_r^i a_s^j \eta^{rs} \qquad \text{c} \qquad \qquad \text{(8-47)}$$

$$g_{ij} = \breve{a}_i^r\breve{a}_j^s \eta_{rs} \qquad \text{d}$$

$$|a_r^i| = \frac{1}{\sqrt{g}} \Pi\epsilon_s \qquad \text{e}$$

$$|a_i^r| = \sqrt{g}\,\Pi\epsilon_s. \qquad \text{f}$$

The determinant of the metric tensor g_{ij} is denoted g; and $\Pi\epsilon_s$ denotes the product of the n ϵ_s which are defined by eq. (8-45). Each of the above equations is easily verified by the techniques of matrix algebra.

A system of n mutually orthogonal vectors a_α^i ($\alpha = 1, 2, \ldots, n$; i is the vector index) can be set up at any point P in an n-dimensional space which possesses the metric of eq. (8-1). The individual vectors will be labeled with Greek letters, and the vector indices will be denoted by Latin letters. Such a system of vectors is known as an *orthogonal ennuple* or, for brevity, an *ennuple*. (In four dimensions the term *tetrad* is often used.) From the definition of the ennuple there follow the relations

$$g_{ij}a_\alpha^i a_\beta^j = \begin{cases} 0 & \alpha \neq \beta \\ \pm 1 & \alpha = \beta. \end{cases} \qquad (8\text{-}48)$$

Comparison of eq. (8-48) with eq. (8-45) shows that the unit vectors a_α^i are identical with the transformation matrices which put the metric tensor in the special form η_{rs}. Thus eqs. (8-45) and (8-47) apply to the ennuple vectors. The only difference is that in eq. (8-47a), for example, the quantity $g_{ij}a_\alpha^i$ is interpreted as the covariant form $a_{\alpha i}$ of the vector a_α^i. The components $\breve{a}_i^\alpha$ of the inverse matrix are merely, from eqs. (8-47a) and (8-45), $\breve{a}_i^\alpha = \epsilon_\alpha a_{\alpha i}$ (no sum on α). Note that ϵ_α is the same as $\epsilon(\mathbf{a}_\alpha)$, because $\mathbf{a}_\alpha$ is a unit vector. Note also that none of the ennuple vectors can be a null vector.

8.9 RIEMANNIAN CURVATURE

In the Taylor expansion of the metric tensor near a point P in geodesic coordinates based at P, the first derivatives vanish and the second derivatives may be expressed in terms of the Riemann-Christoffel tensor by means of eq. (8-34) with the result

$$\bar{g}_{ij}(\bar{x}) = \bar{g}_{ij}(0) + \tfrac{1}{6}(\bar{R}_{iklj} + \bar{R}_{jkli})\bar{x}^k\bar{x}^l + O^3(\bar{x}).$$

The line element in geodesic coordinates is therefore

$$ds^2 = \bar{g}_{ij}(\bar{x})\,d\bar{x}^i\,d\bar{x}^j = \bar{g}_{ij}(0)\,d\bar{x}^i\,d\bar{x}^j + \tfrac{1}{12}\bar{R}_{iklj}p^{ik}p^{jl} + O[(\bar{x})^3(d\bar{x})^2] \quad \text{(8-49)}$$

where

$$p^{ik} = \bar{x}^i\,d\bar{x}^k - \bar{x}^k\,d\bar{x}^i.$$

We now set up two vectors a^i and b^i which are unit vectors and are orthogonal to each other at P—but otherwise arbitrary. Then the equation

$$\bar{x}^i = \lambda\bar{a}^i + \mu\bar{b}^i \quad \text{(8-50)}$$

describes a two-dimensional surface about P. The line element in this surface, obtained by substituting eq. (8-50) into eq. (8-49) for constant a^i and b^i, is

$$ds^2 = \epsilon(\mathbf{a})\,d\lambda^2 + \epsilon(\mathbf{b})\,d\mu^2 - \tfrac{1}{3}\bar{R}_{ikjl}\bar{a}^i\bar{b}^k\bar{a}^j\bar{b}^l$$
$$\cdot\,(\lambda\,d\mu - \mu\,d\lambda)^2 + O(\lambda^3\,d\lambda^2,\ \text{etc.}). \quad \text{(8-51)}$$

Equation (8-51) gives the line element in the surface defined by the two orthogonal vectors a^i and b^i in terms of coordinates λ and μ in the surface.

Following the method which was used in Section 7.6, we identify eq. (8-51) with eq. (7-12). By an obvious generalization of the concept of Gaussian curvature to a space of arbitrary curvature, we may write

$$K(P;\mathbf{a},\mathbf{b}) = \bar{R}_{ikjl}\bar{a}^i\bar{b}^k\bar{a}^j\bar{b}^l\epsilon(\mathbf{a})\epsilon(\mathbf{b}). \quad \text{(8-52)}$$

Since the right-hand side of eq. (8-52) is a scalar, the equation is valid in any coordinate system.

$$K(x^m;\mathbf{a},\mathbf{b}) = R_{ikjl}a^ib^ka^jb^l\epsilon(\mathbf{a})\epsilon(\mathbf{b}). \quad \text{(8-53)}$$

Equation (8-53) gives the Gaussian curvature at a point x^m in the two-dimensional space formed by two vectors a^i and b^i. Thus the Riemann-Christoffel tensor represents the curvature of the n-dimensional space. The tensor R_{ijkl} is therefore usually called the *Riemann curvature tensor*, or simply the *Riemann tensor*.

An orthogonal ennuple may be constructed at P having a^i and b^i as two of its members. Equation (8-53) applies to *any* two members **a**, **b** of the ennuple. The average value of $K(x; \mathbf{a}, \mathbf{b})$ averaged over all directions **b** orthogonal to **a** is defined as $(n - 1)^{-1}$ times the sum of the values assumed by $K(x; \mathbf{a}, \mathbf{b})$ when **b** is each of the $n - 1$ ennuple vectors different from **a**. That is

$$K(x; \mathbf{a}) = \frac{1}{n - 1} R_{ikjl} a^i a^j \epsilon(\mathbf{a}) \sum_{a_\alpha^i \neq a^i} a_\alpha^k a_\alpha^l \epsilon(\mathbf{a}_\alpha),$$

or, using eq. (8-47c) and the symmetry properties of R_{ijkl},

$$K(x; \mathbf{a}) = - \frac{1}{n - 1} R_{ij} a^i a^j \epsilon(\mathbf{a})$$

where R_{ij} is the Ricci tensor defined in eq. (8-36). The average $\bar{K}(x)$ of $K(x; \mathbf{a})$ over all directions **a** is defined as $1/n$ times the sum of the values assumed by $K(x; \mathbf{a})$ when **a** is each of the vectors of the ennuple. That is,

$$\bar{K}(x) = - \frac{1}{n(n - 1)} R_{ij} \sum_\alpha a_\alpha^i a_\alpha^j \epsilon(\mathbf{a}_\alpha)$$

which by eq. (8-47c) becomes

$$\bar{K}(x) = - \frac{R(x)}{n(n - 1)}. \tag{8-54}$$

Thus the Gaussian curvature is equal to $- \dfrac{1}{n(n - 1)}$ times the scalar $R = g^{ij} R_{ij}$. For this reason R is called the *curvature scalar*.

As an example of Riemannian curvature, we will calculate R in a two-dimensional space using geodesic polar coordinates. The metric tensor from eq. (7-14) is

$$g_{ij} = \begin{bmatrix} 1 & 0 \\ 0 & E(\rho, \phi) \end{bmatrix}$$

with $x^1 = \rho$, $x^2 = \phi$. The non-vanishing Christoffel symbols of the second kind are

$$\begin{Bmatrix} 1 \\ 22 \end{Bmatrix} = -\sqrt{E}\, \frac{\partial \sqrt{E}}{\partial \rho},$$

$$\begin{Bmatrix} 2 \\ 12 \end{Bmatrix} = \begin{Bmatrix} 2 \\ 21 \end{Bmatrix} = \frac{1}{\sqrt{E}} \frac{\partial \sqrt{E}}{\partial \rho},$$

$$\begin{Bmatrix} 2 \\ 22 \end{Bmatrix} = \frac{1}{\sqrt{E}} \frac{\partial \sqrt{E}}{\partial \phi},$$

and the non-vanishing components of the Riemann tensor are

$$R_{1212} = R_{2121} = -R_{1221} = -R_{2112} = -\sqrt{E}\,\frac{\partial^2\sqrt{E}}{\partial\rho^2}.$$

The Ricci tensor is

$$R_{11} = \frac{1}{\sqrt{E}}\frac{\partial^2\sqrt{E}}{\partial\rho^2} \qquad R_{22} = \sqrt{E}\,\frac{\partial^2\sqrt{E}}{\partial\rho^2} \qquad R_{12} = R_{21} = 0,$$

and the curvature scalar is

$$R = \frac{2}{\sqrt{E}}\frac{\partial^2\sqrt{E}}{\partial\rho^2}.$$

The Gaussian curvature from eq. (8-54) is therefore

$$K = -\frac{1}{\sqrt{E}}\frac{\partial^2\sqrt{E}}{\partial\rho^2}. \tag{8-55}$$

Equation (8-55) was used in proving Gauss' theorem on integral curvature in Section 7.1.

Consider two arbitrary non-collinear, non-null vectors α^i and β^i at a point P. We ask for the Gaussian curvature at P in the two-dimensional surface through P which contains the directions α^i and β^i. All that is necessary is to choose two orthogonal unit vectors a^i and b^i in the surface for use in eq. (8-53). In particular, we can choose

$$a^i = \frac{\alpha^i}{\sqrt{|\alpha\cdot\alpha|}}$$

$$b^i = \frac{\beta^i - \dfrac{\alpha\cdot\beta}{\alpha\cdot\alpha}\alpha^i}{\sqrt{\left|\beta\cdot\beta - \dfrac{(\alpha\cdot\beta)^2}{\alpha\cdot\alpha}\right|}}.$$

Equation (8-53) then becomes

$$K(x;\alpha,\beta) = \frac{R_{ikjl}\alpha^i\beta^k\alpha^j\beta^l}{(g_{mn}g_{pq} - g_{mq}g_{pn})\alpha^m\beta^p\alpha^n\beta^q}$$

or

$$[R_{ikjl} - K(g_{ij}g_{kl} - g_{il}g_{kj})]\alpha^i\beta^k\alpha^j\beta^l = 0.$$

For convenience in referring to the above equation, we write it in the form

$$S_{ikjl}\alpha^i\beta^k\alpha^j\beta^l = 0 \qquad\qquad\text{a}$$

where

$$S_{ikjl} = R_{ikjl} - K(x;\alpha,\beta)(g_{ij}g_{kl} - g_{il}g_{kj}). \qquad\text{b}$$

$$\left.\right\}\ (8\text{-}56)$$

8.10 SPACE OF CONSTANT CURVATURE

A space with $n \geq 3$ dimensions in which the curvature K is independent of direction has constant curvature. This theorem, known as Schur's theorem, is proved as follows. From eq. (8-56b), S_{ikjl} has the same symmetry properties as R_{ikjl}. Therefore we can write

$$S_{ijlk} + S_{ijkl} = 0 \qquad \text{a}$$
$$2S_{ikjl} + 2S_{iklj} = 0 \qquad \text{b} \qquad \text{(8-57)}$$
$$-S_{iljk} - S_{ijkl} - S_{iklj} = 0. \qquad \text{c}$$

If $K(x; \boldsymbol{\alpha}, \boldsymbol{\beta})$ is independent of the vectors $\boldsymbol{\alpha}$ and $\boldsymbol{\beta}$, then, in particular, eq. (8-56a) with β^i arbitrary requires that S_{ikjl} be antisymmetric in its second and fourth indices. Thus we have

$$S_{ikjl} + S_{iljk} = 0. \qquad \text{d} \qquad \text{(8-57)}$$
$$-S_{iklj} - S_{ijlk} = 0. \qquad \text{e}$$

The sum of eqs. (8-57) is $3S_{ikjl} = 0$ or simply $S_{ikjl} = 0$. Therefore, from eq. (8-56b) we have

$$R_{ikjl} = K \cdot (g_{ij}g_{kl} - g_{il}g_{jk}) \qquad \text{(8-58)}$$

in a space in which K is independent of direction. The Einstein tensor is then $G^{ij} = \frac{1}{2}(n - 1)(n - 2)Kg^{ij}$, and the Ricci identity (8-43) gives $(n - 1)(n - 2)K_{,i} = 0$. For $n \geq 3$ we have immediately $\partial K/\partial x^i = 0$. Therefore, K and R are constants, R_{ikjl} is given by eq. (8-58), and R_{ij} is equal to $-(n - 1)Kg_{ij}$.

We have just proved that if the curvature is independent of direction, then eq. (8-58) holds, which in turn implies that K is constant. Conversely, it is clear from eqs. (8-56) that if R_{ikjl} is a multiple of $(g_{ij}g_{kl} - g_{il}g_{jk})$, then the multiplier is the Gaussian curvature which is independent of direction. Thus eq. (8-58) is the necessary and sufficient condition that the Gaussian curvature be independent of direction and, further, K is the Gaussian curvature.

For a space having a Gaussian curvature which is independent of direction, there exists a *canonical* form for the metric. But before exhibiting this form, it is necessary to first prove the uniqueness theorem that there is only one metric for such a space—i.e., that all possible metrics are obtained from each other by coordinate transformations.

Given two metrics $g_{ij}(x^k)$ and $g'_{rs}(x'^t)$ in two coordinate systems x^i and x'^r, respectively, in n-dimensional space, and the two equations

$$R_{ijkl} = K \cdot (g_{ik}g_{jl} - g_{il}g_{jk}) \qquad \text{a}$$
$$R'_{rstu} = K \cdot (g'_{rt}g'_{su} - g'_{ru}g'_{st}), \qquad \text{b} \qquad \text{(8-59)}$$

we are to prove that there exists a transformation $x'^r = x'^r(x^i)$ such that we have

$$g_{ij}(x^k) = g'_{rs}[x'^t(x^k)] \frac{\partial x'^r}{\partial x^i} \frac{\partial x'^s}{\partial x^j}. \tag{8-60}$$

Define

$$p_i^r = \frac{\partial x'^r}{\partial x^i}.$$

A necessary condition for eq. (8-60) to hold is

$$\frac{\partial p_j^r}{\partial x^k} = \left\{ \begin{matrix} i \\ jk \end{matrix} \right\} p_i^r - \left\{ \begin{matrix} r \\ st \end{matrix} \right\}' p_j^s p_k^t \tag{8-61}$$

from eq. (8-9b). Equation (8-61) implies that $g_{ij} - g'_{rs} p_i^r p_j^s$ is constant, and as initial conditions we may choose

$$[g_{ij} - g'_{rs} p_i^r p_j^s]_P = 0 \tag{8-62}$$

at some point P. Then eqs. (8-61) and (8-62) have as their solution eq. (8-60). Our task therefore reduces to proving that *there exist* solutions to eq. (8-61). The necessary and sufficient condition for the existence of solutions to eq. (8-61) is the satisfaction of the integrability condition

$$\frac{\partial^2 p_j^r}{\partial x^l \partial x^k} = \frac{\partial^2 p_j^r}{\partial x^k \partial x^l}. \tag{8-63}$$

But eq. (8-63) may be written

$$p_i^r R^i{}_{jkl} - p_j^s p_k^t p_l^u R''{}^r{}_{stu} = 0$$

which is satisfied by virtue of eqs. (8-59). Therefore the solutions p_i^r exist and involve $\frac{1}{2}n(n+1)$ arbitrary constants—the number of $(p_i^r)_P$ plus the number of $x_P'^r$ minus the number of conditions of eq. (8-62).

Any space with Gaussian curvature K independent of direction has coordinates x^i in which the metric takes the form

$$ds^2 = \frac{\eta_{ij} dx^i dx^j}{\left[1 + \dfrac{K}{4} \eta_{kl} x^k x^l \right]^2}, \tag{8-64}$$

where η_{ij} is the diagonal matrix whose non-zero elements are ± 1. The proof is simple. Calculation of the Riemann curvature tensor for the metric of eq. (8-64) with constant K gives eq. (8-58). Thus eq. (8-64) is the metric for at least one space of constant curvature. But by the uniqueness theorem which was just proved, there is no other metric for such a space.* Equation (8-64) will be known as the *canonical* form of the metric of a space of constant curvature.

---

* By restricting ourselves to *real* coordinates, we must make the distinction that the metrics for spaces with the same constant curvature and the *same signatures* are transformable into each other.

If the curvature is non-zero, the x^i in eq. (8-64) can be replaced by $x^i/\sqrt{|K|}$ to give

$$ds^2 = S^2 \frac{\eta_{ij}\, dx^i\, dx^j}{\left[1 + \dfrac{k}{4}\eta_{kl}x^k x^l\right]^2} \tag{8-65}$$

where k is ± 1 and S is the radius of curvature $|K|^{-\frac{1}{2}}$. Equation (8-65) holds for any curvature $K = k/S^2$ provided S is taken as an arbitrary constant for the case $k = 0$.

8.11 SPACE OF ZERO CURVATURE

It is clear from the definition of the Riemann curvature tensor that it vanishes everywhere if there exists a coordinate system in which the Christoffel symbols vanish everywhere. We will now prove the converse: if the Riemann curvature tensor vanishes everywhere in an n-dimensional space, then there exists a coordinate system in which the Christoffel symbols vanish everywhere.

A vector field $A^i(x)$ is constructed such that it is everywhere parallel to itself. The condition for parallelism is $A^i_{,k} = 0$ or

$$\frac{\partial A^i}{\partial x^k} = -\left\{\begin{matrix} i \\ jk \end{matrix}\right\} A^j. \tag{8-66}$$

The integrability condition

$$\frac{\partial^2 A^i}{\partial x^l \partial x^k} - \frac{\partial^2 A^i}{\partial x^k \partial x^l} = 0$$

may then, from eq. (8-39), be written in the form

$$A^j R^i_{jkl} = 0. \tag{8-67}$$

Equation (8-67) may also be interpreted as the condition that, upon carrying the vector A^i around any closed curve by parallel displacement, it must return to its initial value. The vanishing of the Riemann curvature tensor satisfies eq. (8-67) and thus ensures the existence of the field $A^i(x)$. In fact, there are n linearly independent fields of parallel vectors which we will denote $A^i_\alpha(x)$. (The upper index is the vector index; the lower index is the family index.)

A new coordinate system $x'^r(x^i)$ is defined by the relation

$$\frac{\partial x^i}{\partial x'^r} = A^i_r(x).$$

The integrability condition

$$\frac{\partial^2 x^i}{\partial x'^r \, \partial x'^s} - \frac{\partial^2 x^i}{\partial x'^s \, \partial x'^r} = \begin{Bmatrix} i \\ jk \end{Bmatrix}\left(A_s^k \frac{\partial x^j}{\partial x'^r} - A_r^k \frac{\partial x^j}{\partial x'^s} \right)$$

is then automatically satisfied, ensuring the existence of the new coordinates. By the rule for vector transformation, the vector $A_\alpha^i(x)$ in the new coordinates is $A_\alpha'^r = \delta_\alpha^r$. Therefore the derivatives of $A_\alpha'^r$ vanish, which, in eq. (8-66), implies that all Christoffel symbols in the x'^r coordinates vanish.

8.12 GEOMETRICAL INTERPRETATION OF CURVATURE

In Section 8.4, a vector ξ^i was carried by parallel displacement around a closed circuit. The change $\Delta \xi^i$ when the vector returns to its starting point is given by eq. (8-29) for the parallelogram circuit formed by the two coordinate displacements dx^i, δx^i taken in the sequence dx^i, δx^i, $-dx^i$, $-\delta x^i$. For the case $\xi^i = dx^i = a^i$ and $\delta x^i = b^i$, eq. (8-28) becomes

$$\Delta S^{kl} = a^k b^l - a^l b^k,$$

and eq. (8-29) becomes

$$\Delta a^i = -R^i_{jkl} a^j a^k b^l.$$

With the use of eq. (8-56) we find

$$b_i \, \Delta a^i = K(\mathbf{a}, \mathbf{b})[(\mathbf{a} \cdot \mathbf{a})(\mathbf{b} \cdot \mathbf{b}) - (\mathbf{a} \cdot \mathbf{b})^2]. \tag{8-68}$$

From the definition

$$S^2 = \tfrac{1}{2} \, \Delta S_{kl} \, \Delta S^{kl} = (\mathbf{a} \cdot \mathbf{a})(\mathbf{b} \cdot \mathbf{b}) - (\mathbf{a} \cdot \mathbf{b})^2$$

eq. (8-68) becomes

$$b_i \, \Delta a^i = S^2 K(\mathbf{a}, \mathbf{b}). \tag{8-69}$$

Equation (8-69) can be interpreted in terms of angles. The angle θ between the vectors a^i and b^i is defined by eq. (8-22). The change in angle $\Delta\theta$ which results from carrying $\mathbf{a}$ (but not $\mathbf{b}$) around the circuit is given by

$$\cos(\theta + \Delta\theta) = \frac{\mathbf{b} \cdot (\mathbf{a} + \Delta\mathbf{a})}{\sqrt{(\mathbf{a} \cdot \mathbf{a})(\mathbf{b} \cdot \mathbf{b})}}.$$

Thus $\Delta\theta$ is related to K by the equation

$$\Delta\theta = -SK(P; \mathbf{a}, \mathbf{b}), \tag{8-70}$$

which is known as *Pérès' formula*. Equation (8-70) gives the change in the angle θ between two vectors when one vector, but not the other, is carried around an infinitesimal circuit of area S by parallel displacement.

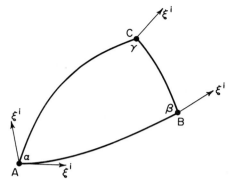

FIGURE 8.1 Gauss' integral curvature theorem for infinitesimal triangle.

Equation (8-70) can, by suitable generalizations, be proved for any two vectors in the plane of the circuit.

Gauss' curvature theorem of Section 7.1 can now be proved for an arbitrary two-dimensional space. The theorem states that the sum of the interior angles of a geodesic triangle is equal to $\pi + \int K \, dS$ where $\int K \, dS$ is the integral of the Gaussian curvature over the area of the triangle. The geodesic triangle is divided into infinitesimal geodesic triangles. For a typical infinitesimal triangle ABC (see Fig. 8.1), a vector ξ^i which is initially at A parallel to the geodesic AB is moved by parallel displacement to B. The vector remains parallel to AB, so that at B it makes an angle $\pi - \beta$ with the geodesic BC. The vector ξ^i is carried by parallel displacement along the geodesic BC, maintaining a constant angle with BC. When it arrives at C, the vector makes an angle $\gamma + \beta - \pi$ with the geodesic CA. The vector is then carried by parallel displacement from C to A. Upon returning to A after being moved by parallel displacement around the triangle, the vector ξ^i makes an angle $\alpha + \beta + \gamma - \pi$ with its original direction. By eq. (8-70) this angle* is $+KS$. Therefore

$$\alpha + \beta + \gamma = \pi + KS. \tag{8-71}$$

Although there is an accuracy of $O^3(\Delta x)$ in eq. (8-71), the result from summing over all the infinitesimal triangles is

$$\alpha + \beta + \gamma = \pi + \int K \, dS \tag{8-72}$$

for a finite triangle. The extra term $\Sigma O^3(\Delta x)$ goes to zero as the sizes of the infinitesimal triangles go to zero. The area dS in eq. (8-72) is defined

---

* The change in sign comes because eq. (8-70) is actually the change in the angle between ξ^i and the tangent to AC at A.

for a parallelogram dx^i, δx^i by

$$dS^2 = dx_i\, dx^i\, \delta x_j\, \delta x^j - (dx_k\, \delta x^k)^2.$$

Curvature of space reveals itself in the change in direction of a vector transported by parallel displacement around a closed circuit. In a two-dimensional space, the curvature makes itself felt in the difference between the sum of the interior angles of a geodesic triangle and the straight angle of π radians. Note that the two-dimensional space for which Gauss' integral curvature theorem has been proved can be a subspace of an n-dimensional space. It must be cautioned, however, that the circuits and areas used in the proofs of the relevant theorems were in one sense not completely general; their surfaces did not contain any null vectors.

8.13 THE PERMUTATION SYMBOL

In special relativity, the four-index permutation symbol $e(\mu\nu\rho\sigma)$ was used as a fourth-rank tensor which was either completely covariant (written $e_{\mu\nu\rho\sigma}$) or completely contravariant (written $e^{\mu\nu\rho\sigma}$). For a general metric in n-dimensional space, the n-index permutation symbol $e(ijk\cdots)$ is no longer a tensor. However, the quantities $\epsilon_{ijk\ldots}$ and $\epsilon^{ijk\cdots}$ defined

$$\epsilon_{ijk\ldots} = \sqrt{|g|}\, e(ijk\cdots)$$

$$\epsilon^{ijk\cdots} = \frac{1}{\sqrt{|g|}}\, e(ijk\cdots),$$

where g is the determinant of g_{ij}, are n-th rank covariant and contravariant tensors, respectively. Their tensorial nature is proved by the use of the transformation equations for both the n-th rank tensor and the metric tensor. Upon transformation from one system x^i to another system x'^r, $\epsilon'_{rst}\ldots$ is given by

$$\epsilon_{ijk\ldots}\frac{\partial x^i}{\partial x'^r}\frac{\partial x^j}{\partial x'^s}\cdots = \sqrt{|g|}\, e(ijk\cdots)\frac{\partial x^i}{\partial x'^r}\frac{\partial x^j}{\partial x'^s}\cdots = \sqrt{|g|}\left|\frac{\partial x^i}{\partial x'^p}\right| e(rst\cdots).$$

$$(8\text{-}73)$$

From the equation

$$g'_{rs}(x') = g_{ij}(x)\frac{\partial x^i}{\partial x'^r}\frac{\partial x^j}{\partial x'^s}$$

for transforming the metric tensor we have immediately

$$g' = g\left|\frac{\partial x^i}{\partial x'^r}\right|^2.$$

The positive root of the determinant of the transformation matrix is to be taken in order that the transformation be the sum of infinitesimal transformations—reflections are excluded. Therefore eq. (8-73) becomes $\epsilon_{rst} \ldots$. Thus $\epsilon_{ijk} \ldots$ is a covariant tensor. Similarly it can be proved that $\epsilon^{ijk} \cdots$ is a contravariant tensor.

The relation

$$\left\{ \begin{matrix} i \\ ik \end{matrix} \right\} = \frac{\partial}{\partial x^k} \ln \sqrt{|g|} \tag{8-74}$$

will be useful in later applications. Equation (8-74) is proved in the form

$$gg^{ij} \frac{\partial g_{ij}}{\partial x^k} = \frac{\partial g}{\partial x^k}$$

by noting that the quantity on the left-hand side is the sum of the products of the derivative of g_{ij} with the cofactor of g_{ij}. The quantity on the right is again the same thing, and hence there is equality.

Equation (8-74) is particularly useful for expressing the covariant divergence of a vector A^i in terms of the ordinary derivative:

$$A^i_{,i} = \frac{1}{\sqrt{|g|}} \frac{\partial}{\partial x^i} (A^i \sqrt{|g|}). \tag{8-75}$$

8.14 DEFINITION OF GEODESICS

Two definitions have been given for a geodesic: (1) A geodesic is a curve between two points such that the integral of ds in eq. (8-1) is an extremum (see Section 8.2); (2) A geodesic is a curve $x^i(s)$ such that the tangent $u^i = dx^i/ds$, where s is defined by eq. (8-1), is carried by parallel displacement along the curve (see Section 8.4).

In this section we will examine a third, more comprehensive definition: (3) A geodesic is a curve along which there exists a parameter p such that the equation $x^i(p)$ for the curve satisfies the condition

$$\frac{d^2 x^i}{dp^2} + \left\{ \begin{matrix} i \\ jk \end{matrix} \right\} \frac{dx^j}{dp} \frac{dx^k}{dp} = 0. \tag{8-76}$$

It will be convenient to define

$$a^i(q) = \frac{d^2 x^i}{dq^2} + \left\{ \begin{matrix} i \\ jk \end{matrix} \right\} \frac{dx^j}{dq} \frac{dx^k}{dq}$$

on any curve $x^i(q)$, where q is any scalar parameter along the curve. When a coordinate transformation is made, the use of eq. (8-9b) shows that

$a^i(q)$ is a vector. The change from one parameter q to another r is expressed by the formula

$$a^i(q) = \left(\frac{dr}{dq}\right)^2 a^i(r) + \frac{dx^i}{dq}\frac{d}{dq}\ln\frac{dr}{dq}. \tag{8-77}$$

If the curve is a geodesic by definition (3), then there exists a parameter p, which we will call the *preferred parameter*, such that $a^i(p)$ vanishes everywhere on the curve.

First we must prove that definition (3) specifies a unique curve. We choose q in eq. (8-77) to be any one of the coordinates which are not constant along the curve, say x^a. Then we have

$$\left\{\begin{matrix} a \\ jk \end{matrix}\right\}\frac{dx^j}{dq}\frac{dx^k}{dq} = \left(\frac{dr}{dq}\right)^2 a^a(r) + \frac{d}{dq}\ln\frac{dr}{dq}. \tag{8-78}$$

The quantity $\dfrac{d}{dq}\ln\dfrac{dr}{dq}$ can be eliminated from eqs. (8-77) and (8-78) to give

$$\frac{d^2x^i}{dq^2} = \left[\frac{dx^i}{dq}\left\{\begin{matrix} a \\ jk \end{matrix}\right\} - \left\{\begin{matrix} i \\ jk \end{matrix}\right\}\right]\frac{dx^j}{dq}\frac{dx^k}{dq} + \left(\frac{dr}{dq}\right)^2\left[a^i(r) - \frac{dx^i}{dq}a^a(r)\right]. \tag{8-79}$$

Since the parameter r appears only in the second term on the right-hand side of eq. (8-79), that term must be independent of the parameter. Thus if the curve possesses a preferred parameter, then the second term vanishes identically for all parameters. But then the second-derivative on the left is a function only of position and the first-derivatives. Differentiation of eq. (8-79) will consequently give *all* derivatives d^nx^i/dq^n in terms of position and first-derivatives. By expanding $x^i(q)$ in a Taylor series about any point P, the tangent dx^i/dq at P specifies a unique curve through P. Therefore definition (3) is unambiguous.

The next question to be answered is whether definition (3) is consistent with definitions (1) and (2). Define

$$\phi = \left(\frac{ds}{dq}\right)^2 = g_{ij}\frac{dx^i}{dq}\frac{dx^j}{dq}$$

and differentiate ϕ with respect to q:

$$\frac{d\phi}{dq} = 2g_{ij}\frac{dx^i}{dq}a^j(q). \tag{8-80}$$

Equation (8-80) shows that if the curve is a geodesic by definition (3) and p is the preferred parameter, then ds/dp is a constant. If ds is not zero along the geodesic, then ds/dp is a non-zero constant, and eq. (8-76) reduces to eq. (8-10). Thus definition (1) is the non-null case of definition (3). Since definition (2) follows from definition (1), we have proved the consistency of the three definitions. The condition in Section 8.2 that $g_{ij}\,dx^i\,dx^j$

be positive includes the case that it is negative merely by reversing the signs of all the g_{ij}; the real restriction was $g_{ij}\,dx^i\,dx^j \neq 0$.

A *null geodesic* is a curve which has a null tangent and which is a geodesic according to definition (3). Equation (8-80) guarantees that if a geodesic has a null tangent at one point, then the tangent is everywhere null. Since the metric quantity s does not vary along a null geodesic, the preferred parameter cannot be chosen to be s as in the case of non-null geodesics.

It is interesting to note that if r in eq. (8-77) is the preferred parameter p for a geodesic, then

$$a^i(q) = \frac{dx^i}{dq}\frac{d}{dq}\ln\frac{dp}{dq}. \tag{8-81}$$

Thus any curve $x^i(q)$ such that $a^i(q)$ is parallel to dx^i/dq is a geodesic. Further, if the preferred parameter is not known, it can be found by the following method. First we establish any parameter q along the curve. Then we write down

$$a^i(q) = \frac{dx^i}{dq}\,\psi(q) \tag{8-82}$$

and solve for $\psi(q)$. Note that eq. (8-82) cannot be written down unless the curve is a geodesic. Comparison of eqs. (8-81) and (8-82) shows that the preferred parameter p is given by

$$p = \int e^{\int \psi\,dq}\,dq.$$

8.15 VOLUME

The n-dimensional parallelopiped defined by n linearly independent infinitesimal vectors dx^i_α ($\alpha = 1, 2, \ldots, n$) in n-dimensional space has a *volume*

$$dV = \epsilon_{ijk\ldots r}\,dx^i_1\,dx^j_2\cdots dx^r_n. \tag{8-83}$$

The reason for the definition of eq. (8-83) is two-fold. First, it is clearly a scalar since it is the product of an n-th rank covariant tensor with n contravariant vectors. Second, eq. (8-83) reduces to the Euclidean definition of volume in three-dimensional Euclidean space. There may be an ambiguity in the sign of dV, but this is due to the choice which one has in ordering the vectors dx^i_α.

CHAPTER 9

GENERAL
RELATIVITY

9.1 SPACE-TIME

We regard space-time as a four-dimensional Riemannian space possessing a metric

$$ds^2 = g_{\mu\nu}\, dx^\mu\, dx^\nu. \tag{9-1}$$

(Greek indices run over 0, 1, 2, 3. Latin indices will run over 1, 2, 3.) Points in this space-time will be called *events*, in accordance with the terminology of special relativity. According to the discussion of Section 8.8, there exists at any event P: x_P^μ a transformation $\bar{x}^\alpha = \bar{x}^\alpha(x^\mu)$ such that the new metric tensor

$$\eta_{\alpha\beta} = \bar{g}_{\alpha\beta}(P) = g_{\mu\nu}(P)\frac{\partial x^\mu}{\partial \bar{x}^\alpha}\frac{\partial x^\nu}{\partial \bar{x}^\beta} \tag{9-2}$$

is diagonalized and has the values ± 1 on the diagonal. Since the metric tensor is continuous (due to its assumed differentiability) and the metric in regions free of a gravitational field is that of special relativity, it follows that the signature of the metric is $+\ -\ -\ -$ and that eq. (9-2) is the Minkowski metric. We need not be concerned about whether the spatial components of $\eta_{\alpha\beta}$ should be -1 or $-c^{-2}$, since one form is obtained from the other merely by the transformation $x'^i = cx^i$. Indeed, on occasion it will be convenient to regard the units of distance and time to be so chosen that c is unity.

Note that if geodesic coordinates are constructed at P and, in particular, those geodesic coordinates are chosen in which the metric at P is Minkowski, then the metric is Minkowski in the *neighborhood* of P.

According to eq. (8-49), the metric ds^2 deviates from $\bar{g}_{\mu\nu}(P)\,d\bar{x}^\mu\,d\bar{x}^\nu$ only by terms which are quadratic in the coordinates. We are familiar with the way in which the quadratic nature of a sphere allows any small part of it to be approximated by a plane. In the same way, any small region of space-time may be approximated by Minkowski space-time.

Since eq. (9-1) is a scalar, the following special-relativistic concepts may be immediately carried over into general relativity. Light rays follow null curves, i.e., curves having null tangent vectors. There exists at each event a null cone containing the tangents of all possible light rays through the event. Two neighboring events are separated by a time-like, null, or space-like interval according as ds^2 is greater than, equal to, or less than zero. And in general, a vector V^μ is said to be time-like, null, or space-like according as $g_{\mu\nu}V^\mu V^\nu$ is positive, zero, or negative. Furthermore, ds measures proper time along a time-like interval. If s is the proper time of a particle having a world-line $x^\mu(s)$ which is everywhere time-like, then its world-velocity is

$$u^\mu = \frac{dx^\mu}{ds}$$

and satisfies the identity $1 = g_{\mu\nu}u^\mu u^\nu$ from eq. (9-1). The world-velocity is a vector, since it transforms according to eq. (3-36). For two events separated by a space-like interval dx^μ, the proper distance of separation is $c\sqrt{-g_{\mu\nu}\,dx^\mu\,dx^\nu}$.

Proper coordinates for a particle at an event P on the particle's world-line are coordinates in which (1) the particle is stationary, i.e., its world-velocity is $u^\mu = \delta_0^\mu$; (2) the metric is Minkowski; and (3) the Christoffel symbols vanish. The difference between geodesic coordinates and proper coordinates is that geodesic coordinates can be constructed about any event; proper coordinates can only be constructed about an event on a world-line, and the metric must be Minkowski. Furthermore, the third-order terms in eq. (8-11) are specified for geodesic coordinates and not for proper coordinates.

It will be assumed that the metric in a nearly empty universe is nearly Minkowski. Thus in the case of an isolated object, we will require the boundary condition that $g_{\mu\nu}$ at spatial infinity be $\eta_{\mu\nu}$.

The stress-energy tensor for matter or for electromagnetism is defined as that tensor which, in geodesic coordinates, is given by the special-relativistic definition. If, in geodesic coordinates, the total stress-energy tensor $T^{\mu\nu}$ is postulated to have zero divergence, then the conservation law in general coordinates becomes

$$T^{\mu\nu}{}_{,\nu} = 0. \tag{9-3}$$

The stress-energy tensor for a perfect fluid is

$$T^{\mu\nu} = (\rho + c^{-2}p)u^\mu u^\nu - c^{-2}pg^{\mu\nu}, \tag{9-4}$$

where ρ is the proper density and p is the proper pressure. (The subscript 0 which was used in Chapter 5 will hereafter be omitted.)

9.2 EQUATION OF MOTION

Equation (6-69) is the equation of motion for a free particle in a gravitational field. But the coefficient $\Gamma^{\mu}_{\nu\rho}$ is given by eq. (6-70) in terms of the coordinates y^{α} in which free particles have special-relativistic straight-line motion. Thus we can identify the y^{α} coordinates as geodesic coordinates. Then eq. (8-16) requires that the coefficient $\Gamma^{\mu}_{\nu\rho}$ be identical with the Christoffel symbol $\begin{Bmatrix} \mu \\ \nu\rho \end{Bmatrix}$. Therefore the equation of motion becomes the geodesic equation (8-10). Free particles follow geodesics in space-time. The equation of motion for a free particle is*

$$\frac{d^2x^{\mu}}{ds^2} + \begin{Bmatrix} \mu \\ \nu\rho \end{Bmatrix} \frac{dx^{\nu}}{ds} \frac{dx^{\rho}}{ds} = 0 \qquad (9\text{-}5)$$

where s is the proper time along the geodesic. An important result to be proved in Section 12.1 is that eq. (9-5) is a consequence of eq. (9-3) for the case of a zero-pressure perfect fluid; a less rigorous derivation is provided by replacing the ordinary derivatives in Section 5.1 with covariant derivatives.

In order to compare eq. (9-5) with the Newtonian equation of motion, the approximation is made that $g_{\mu\nu}$ differs very little from the Minkowski metric:

$$g_{\mu\nu} = \eta_{\mu\nu} + h_{\mu\nu}.$$

Upon neglecting terms of higher than the first order in $h_{\mu\nu}$, it is found that eq. (9-5) reduces to the Newtonian equation of motion provided

$$g_{00} = 1 + 2\Phi c^{-2}$$
$$g_{0i} = 0$$
$$g_{ij} = -c^{-2}\delta_{ij}$$

where Φ is the Newtonian gravitational potential. Thus, upon neglecting terms of order higher than Φc^{-2} or $v^2 c^{-2}$ where v is a velocity characteristic of the particles in the system, we have

$$ds^2 = \left(1 + 2\frac{\Phi}{c^2}\right) dt^2 - \frac{1}{c^2}(dx^2 + dy^2 + dz^2).$$

---

* On occasion it is more convenient to use this equation of motion in its Lagrangian form of eq. (8-2): $0 = \delta \int \sqrt{g_{\mu\nu} \dfrac{dx^{\mu}}{ds} \dfrac{dx^{\nu}}{ds}}\, ds.$

Division by dt^2 gives

$$\left(\frac{ds}{dt}\right)^2 = 1 + 2\frac{\Phi}{c^2} - \frac{v^2}{c^2}. \tag{9-6}$$

We regard Φc^{-2} and $v^2 c^{-2}$ as of the same order, and denote this order of magnitude by the symbol O. The terms $h_{0i}\dfrac{dx^i}{dt}$ and $h_{ij}\dfrac{dx^i}{dt}\dfrac{dx^j}{dt}$ do not appear in eq. (9-6), implying that these terms must be of higher order, namely O^2. Thus we have $h_{0i} = O^{\frac{3}{2}}c^{-1}$ and $h_{ij} = O^1 \cdot c^{-2}$.

To summarize, the equation of motion (9-5) reduces to the Newtonian equation of motion provided the metric tensor is given by

$$\left.\begin{array}{l} g_{00} = 1 + 2\Phi c^{-2} + O^2 \\ g_{0i} = O^{\frac{3}{2}}c^{-1} \\ g_{ij} = -c^{-2}\delta_{ij} + Oc^{-2} \end{array}\right\}. \tag{9-7}$$

The same results were obtained in Section 6.8 on the basis of the gravitational frequency shift. This is not simply a fortuitous coincidence. Equation (9-5) was obtained from eq. (6-69); and both the latter and the frequency shift were found to be consequences of the principle of equivalence.

9.3 THE FIELD EQUATION

For the metric tensor of eq. (9-7), the Christoffel symbols are

$$\begin{Bmatrix} 0 \\ 00 \end{Bmatrix} = \frac{1}{c^2}\frac{\partial \Phi}{\partial t} + \cdots, \qquad \begin{Bmatrix} i \\ 00 \end{Bmatrix} = \frac{\partial \Phi}{\partial x^i} + \cdots$$

$$\begin{Bmatrix} 0 \\ 0i \end{Bmatrix} = \frac{1}{c^2}\frac{\partial \Phi}{\partial x^i} + \cdots, \qquad \begin{Bmatrix} i \\ 0j \end{Bmatrix} = \frac{c}{L} O^{\frac{3}{2}}$$

$$\begin{Bmatrix} 0 \\ ij \end{Bmatrix} = \frac{1}{cL} O^{\frac{3}{2}}, \qquad \begin{Bmatrix} i \\ jk \end{Bmatrix} = \frac{1}{L} \cdot O$$

where $1/L$ denotes the order of magnitude of differentiation with respect to a spatial coordinate; differentiation with respect to time then has order of magnitude v/L, i.e., $(c/L)O^{\frac{1}{2}}$. The Riemann curvature tensor is then

$$R^0{}_{000} = O$$

$$R^0{}_{ij0} = \frac{1}{c^2}\frac{\partial^2 \Phi}{\partial x^i \partial x^j} + \frac{O^2}{L^2}$$

$$R^0{}_{ijk} = \frac{1}{cL} O^{\frac{3}{2}}$$

$$R^i{}_{jkl} = \frac{O}{L^2}$$

and the Ricci tensor is

$$R_{00} = -\frac{\partial^2 \Phi}{\partial x^i \, \partial x^i} + \frac{O^2 c^2}{L^2}$$

$$R_{0i} = \frac{c}{L^2} O^{\frac{3}{2}}$$

$$R_{ij} = \frac{O}{L^2}.$$

We wish to relate the curvature of space-time to the presence of matter, since gravity appears in the neighborhood of matter. In Section 7.9 an attempt was made to put the curvature proportional to the density of matter. Such a train of thought naturally leads us to relate the Riemann curvature to the density of matter. The Riemann tensor cannot be proportional to the density of matter in any way, or else the Riemann tensor would vanish in empty space. This in turn would imply that gravity does not act in empty space, contrary to observation. We next consider how the Ricci tensor might be related to the density of matter. The Ricci tensor has 10 independent components. These 10 components are to be determined by a relation with the matter that is present. In the foregoing approximation, we find $R_{00} = -\nabla^2 \Phi$. In Newtonian gravity, we had $\nabla^2 \Phi = 4\pi G \rho$. We are therefore led to consider the equation $R_{00} = -4\pi G \rho$ which can be generalized into the tensor form

$$R_{\mu\nu} = -4\pi G T_{\mu\nu} \tag{9-8}$$

where $T_{\mu\nu}$ is the total stress-energy tensor for matter and radiation. Equation (9-8) could be adopted as the gravitational field equation, except for one difficulty. The conservation law (9-3) imposes the four conditions $R^{\mu\nu}{}_{,\nu} = 0$ which, together with the 10 conditions of eq. (9-8), constitute 14 conditions for determining the 10 $g_{\mu\nu}$. The latter are consequently overdetermined. Therefore, eq. (9-8) cannot be used.

It is noticed that, since the divergence of the Einstein tensor $G_{\mu\nu}$ is identically zero, a field equation of the form

$$G_{\mu\nu} = -\kappa T_{\mu\nu}, \tag{9-9}$$

where κ is a constant, has the advantage that it imposes no additional conditions on $G_{\mu\nu}$ in consequence of the vanishing of the divergence of $T_{\mu\nu}$. Indeed, if eq. (9-9) is taken as the field equation, then the vanishing of the divergence of $G_{\mu\nu}$ as a mathematical identity implies the vanishing of the divergence of $T_{\mu\nu}$. However, we immediately encounter a difficulty if we attempt to evaluate $G_{\mu\nu}$ to the accuracy which was used for $R_{\mu\nu}$. The curvature scalar R cannot be calculated in terms of Φ.

The above difficulty is avoided if use is made of the property that the equation

$$R_{\mu\nu} - \tfrac{1}{2}Rg_{\mu\nu} = -\kappa T_{\mu\nu} \tag{9-9}$$

is the same as the equation

$$R_{\mu\nu} = -\kappa(T_{\mu\nu} - \tfrac{1}{2}Tg_{\mu\nu}) \tag{9-10}$$

where

$$T = g^{\mu\nu}T_{\mu\nu}.$$

Multiplication of any tensor by the square of the operator $\delta^{\mu}_{\alpha}\delta^{\nu}_{\beta} - \tfrac{1}{2}g^{\mu\nu}g_{\alpha\beta}$ reproduces the original tensor. Equation (9-10) can now be readily checked in the Newtonian approximation. We take $T_{\mu\nu} = \rho u_{\mu}u_{\nu}$ with $u^{\mu} = \delta^{\mu}_{0}$ to obtain

$$T_{00} = \rho, \qquad T_{0i} = 0, \qquad T_{ij} = 0, \qquad T = \rho.$$

According to eq. (9-10), the Ricci tensor is then

$$R_{00} = -\tfrac{1}{2}\kappa\rho, \qquad R_{0i} = 0, \qquad R_{ij} = \tfrac{1}{2}\kappa\rho\eta_{ij}.$$

These values agree with the forms obtained previously, provided κ is taken equal to $8\pi G$.

$$\kappa = 8\pi G. \tag{9-11}$$

We therefore postulate eq. (9-9), with κ given by eq. (9-11), as the gravitational field equation. It constitutes 10 equations for the 10 unknowns $g_{\mu\nu}$. The Bianchi identity implies the conservation equation (9-3).

The zero-divergence property of the field equation is unaffected if any tensor with identically zero divergence is added to eq. (9-9). Such a term is $\Lambda g_{\mu\nu}$, where Λ is a constant. Thus the field equation could be taken as

$$G_{\mu\nu} + \Lambda g_{\mu\nu} = -\kappa T_{\mu\nu}. \tag{9-12}$$

Equation (9-12) is equivalent to

$$R_{\mu\nu} = -\kappa(T_{\mu\nu} - \tfrac{1}{2}Tg_{\mu\nu}) + \Lambda g_{\mu\nu};$$

which in the Newtonian approximation becomes

$$-\nabla^{2}\Phi = -\tfrac{1}{2}\kappa\rho + \Lambda. \tag{9-13}$$

Since Newtonian gravity is known to act throughout the solar system (diameter 1.2×10^{10} km) and is thought to act throughout the galaxy (diameter 10^{18} km), $|\Lambda|$ can be no larger than the order of 10^{-25} sec^{-2}. Equation (9-13) shows that Λ, known as the *cosmological constant*, is equivalent to a uniform negative mass density.

The theory of gravity in which eq. (9-12) is the field equation is known as the *general theory of relativity*, abbreviated *general relativity*, originally proposed by Einstein. It should be noted that eq. (9-12) implies eq. (9-3) and hence the equation of motion (9-5) for a free particle. Thus general relativity, compared with other field theories, has the distinctive feature that the equation of motion is contained in the field equation. But it should also be pointed out that eq. (9-12) is only a gravitational theory whereas eqs. (9-5) and (9-7) are based on the principle of equivalence and are therefore more universal. Thus any alternative to Einstein's theory must be based on a four-dimensional metric in which eqs. (9-5) and (9-7) hold.

We will now examine some consequences of Einstein's gravitational theory.

9.4 FIELD OF A POINT MASS

The gravitational field *around* an isolated point mass M is determined by the field equation $G_{\mu\nu} = -\Lambda g_{\mu\nu}$. The cosmological constant will be neglected, and the field equation becomes

$$G_{\mu\nu} = 0. \tag{9-14}$$

The boundary condition on the $g_{\mu\nu}$ is $g_{\mu\nu} \to \eta_{\mu\nu}$ at spatial infinity. From the previous discussion of the Newtonian approximation, it is expected that g_{00} will be asymptotic to $1 - 2\mu/r$ as $r \to \infty$, where μ is the gravitational radius defined by eq. (6-17).

The condition of spherical symmetry places certain restrictions on the metric tensor. We begin by setting up a coordinate system in the following way. Spherical polar angles θ and ϕ are defined around the point mass which itself follows a geodesic. The angles are carried along the geodesic by parallel displacement. A light ray to or from the mass then follows a path of constant θ and ϕ due to symmetry. An event E is described by two light paths, one which leaves the mass at time t_1 and arrives at E, and one which leaves E and arrives at the mass at time t_2 ($> t_1$). The coordinates of E are then taken as the times t_1 and t_2 and the angles θ and ϕ which are followed by the light rays.

Spherical symmetry requires that the line element not vary when θ or ϕ are varied. Therefore θ and ϕ can appear in the line element only in the form $d\theta^2 + \sin^2 \theta \, d\phi^2$, and in no other part of the line element. Thus the line element has the form

$$ds^2 = g'_{11} \, dt_1^2 + 2g'_{12} \, dt_1 \, dt_2 + g'_{22} \, dt_2^2 + g'_{33}(d\theta^2 + \sin^2 \theta \, d\phi^2),$$

where g'_{11}, g'_{12}, g'_{22}, and g'_{33} are independent of θ and ϕ.

Since the conditions $d\theta = 0$, $d\phi = 0$, and *either* $dt_1 = 0$ or $dt_2 = 0$ must describe a light ray for which $ds = 0$, it is necessary that g'_{11} and g'_{22} vanish. The line element is then

$$ds^2 = 2g'_{12} \, dt_1 \, dt_2 + g'_{33}(d\theta^2 + \sin^2 \theta \, d\phi^2).$$

New coordinates t, r are defined by the two conditions: (1) $r = c\sqrt{-g'_{33}}$; (2) there be no term $dr\,dt$ in the line element. The latter condition takes the form

$$\frac{\partial R}{\partial t_2}\frac{\partial T}{\partial t_1} + \frac{\partial R}{\partial t_1}\frac{\partial T}{\partial t_2} = 0$$

where $r = R(t_1, t_2)$, $t = T(t_1, t_2)$. The line element in the new coordinates t, r, θ, ϕ is then

$$ds^2 = g_{00}\,dt^2 + g_{11}\,dr^2 - c^{-2}r^2(d\theta^2 + \sin^2\theta\,d\phi^2) \qquad (9\text{-}15)$$

where t is given by

$$dt = \varphi\left(\frac{\partial R}{\partial t_1}\,dt_1 - \frac{\partial R}{\partial t_2}\,dt_2\right)$$

and φ is the integrating factor

$$\varphi = \frac{\dfrac{\partial T}{\partial t_1}}{\dfrac{\partial R}{\partial t_1}} = -\frac{\dfrac{\partial T}{\partial t_2}}{\dfrac{\partial R}{\partial t_2}}.$$

It will be convenient to denote g_{00} by e^ν and g_{11} by $-c^2 e^\lambda$. Thus eq. (9-15) is

$$ds^2 = e^{\nu(r,t)}\,dt^2 - c^{-2}[e^{\lambda(r,t)}\,dr^2 + r^2(d\theta^2 + \sin^2\theta\,d\phi^2)]. \qquad (9\text{-}16)$$

The non-vanishing Christoffel symbols are:

$$\begin{Bmatrix}0\\00\end{Bmatrix} = \frac{1}{2}\frac{\partial\nu}{\partial t} \qquad \begin{Bmatrix}0\\11\end{Bmatrix} = \tfrac{1}{2}e^{\lambda-\nu}c^{-2}\frac{\partial\lambda}{\partial t} \qquad \begin{Bmatrix}1\\11\end{Bmatrix} = \frac{1}{2}\frac{\partial\lambda}{\partial r}$$

$$\begin{Bmatrix}1\\00\end{Bmatrix} = \tfrac{1}{2}c^2 e^{\nu-\lambda}\frac{\partial\nu}{\partial r} \qquad \begin{Bmatrix}1\\22\end{Bmatrix} = -re^\lambda \qquad \begin{Bmatrix}2\\33\end{Bmatrix} = -\sin\theta\cos\theta$$

$$\begin{Bmatrix}0\\01\end{Bmatrix} = \frac{1}{2}\frac{\partial\nu}{\partial r} \qquad \begin{Bmatrix}1\\33\end{Bmatrix} = -r\sin^2\theta e^{-\lambda} \qquad \begin{Bmatrix}3\\13\end{Bmatrix} = \frac{1}{r}$$

$$\begin{Bmatrix}1\\01\end{Bmatrix} = \frac{1}{2}\frac{\partial\lambda}{\partial t} \qquad \begin{Bmatrix}2\\12\end{Bmatrix} = \frac{1}{r} \qquad \begin{Bmatrix}3\\23\end{Bmatrix} = \cot\theta$$

The Einstein tensor for eq. (9-16) is found to be

$$G_0^0 = \frac{c^2}{r^2}[e^{-\lambda}(1 - r\lambda') - 1] \qquad\qquad \text{a}$$

$$G_1^1 = G_0^0 + \frac{c^2}{r}e^{-\lambda}(\nu' + \lambda') \qquad\qquad \text{b} \left.\vphantom{\begin{matrix}a\\b\\c\end{matrix}}\right\} \quad (9\text{-}17)$$

$$G_1^0 = -\frac{1}{c^2}e^{\lambda-\nu}G_0^1 = -\frac{1}{r}e^{-\nu}\dot\lambda. \qquad\qquad \text{c}$$

In addition there are G_2^2 and G_3^3, but they will not be written down because they are not needed. All other components of G_μ^ν vanish. In eqs. (9-17), the prime denotes differentiation with respect to r and the dot denotes differentiation with respect to t. The numbering of coordinates 0, 1, 2, 3 is in the order t, r, θ, ϕ. Up to this point only the condition of spherical symmetry has been used.

The field equation (9-14) now implies

$$
\begin{aligned}
\dot{\lambda} &= 0 & &\text{a} \\
\lambda' + \nu' &= 0 & &\text{b} \\
e^{-\lambda}(1 - r\lambda') &= 1. & &\text{c}
\end{aligned}
\quad (9\text{-}18)
$$

Equation (9-18a) requires that $\lambda(r)$ be independent of t. Equation (9-18c) requires

$$
e^{-\lambda} = 1 - \frac{\text{const}}{r}. \qquad (9\text{-}19)
$$

Equation (9-18b) requires that $\lambda + \nu$ be independent of r: $\lambda + \nu = f(t)$, where $f(t)$ is some function of t. A new coordinate $\bar{t}$ is defined

$$
\bar{t} = \int e^{\frac{1}{2}f(t)}\, dt
$$

with the result

$$
e^\nu\, dt^2 = e^{-\lambda}\, d\bar{t}^2.
$$

Thus the line element becomes

$$
ds^2 = e^{-\lambda}\, dt^2 - c^{-2}[e^\lambda\, dr^2 + r^2(d\theta^2 + \sin^2\theta\, d\phi^2)] \qquad (9\text{-}20\text{a})
$$

where the bar has been dropped from the t. The boundary condition which was stated at the beginning of this section requires that the constant in eq. (9-19) have the value 2μ. Thus λ is given by

$$
e^{-\lambda} = 1 - \frac{2\mu}{r}. \qquad (9\text{-}20\text{b})
$$

Calculation shows that G_2^2 and G_3^3 for the metric of eq. (9-20) vanish.

It is concluded that there exists a set of coordinates t, r, θ, ϕ such that eq. (9-20) describes the metric in the space around an isolated point mass $M = \mu c^2/G$. Equation (9-20) is known as the *Schwarzschild line element*. The mass M is the effective gravitational mass (not necessarily the same as either the inertial mass or the total proper mass).

The Schwarzschild line element has at the radius 2μ a singularity known as the *Schwarzschild singularity*. The reader may well object that eq. (9-20) was based on the assumption that light rays could leave and arrive at the central point mass. Further, the metric is supposed to be differentiable everywhere. These difficulties are avoided by choosing a spherically symmetric mass which has a radius larger than twice its gravitational radius μ. The metric in the empty space outside the mass is then given by eq. (9-20). The metric in the interior will be examined in Section 9.7.

But there remains the nagging question of the Schwarzschild singularity. Suppose that there existed an object which was smaller than its Schwarzschild radius 2μ. There are no known objects with so small a size (see Table 9.1), but suppose that somehow a star or a galaxy had

TABLE 9.1   RATIO OF GRAVITATIONAL RADIUS TO RADIUS

Object	$\dfrac{\mu}{R}$
Proton	1.0×10^{-39}
Metal sphere with radius 1 meter	3×10^{-23}
Earth	6.95×10^{-10}
Sun	2.12×10^{-6}
Certain white dwarf stars	2.5×10^{-4}
Galactic nucleus	3×10^{-7}

collapsed to a size smaller than its Schwarzschild radius. The curious properties of the metric for such a case will be examined in Section 9.6.

It is important to note that the coefficients in eq. (9-20a) depend on the coordinates that are used. The definition of a new radial coordinate $\mathfrak{r}$ by the relation

$$r = \mathfrak{r}\left(1 + \frac{\mu}{2\mathfrak{r}}\right)^2$$

for $r \geq 2\mu$ and $\mathfrak{r} \geq \frac{1}{2}\mu$ puts the line element (9-20) into the form

$$ds^2 = \left(\frac{1 - \dfrac{\mu}{2\mathfrak{r}}}{1 + \dfrac{\mu}{2\mathfrak{r}}}\right)^2 dt^2 - \frac{1}{c^2}\left(1 + \frac{\mu}{2\mathfrak{r}}\right)^4 [d\mathfrak{r}^2 + \mathfrak{r}^2(d\theta^2 + \sin^2\theta\, d\phi^2)]$$

which is known as the *isotropic* form of the Schwarzschild line element. Cartesian-like coordinates $x = \mathfrak{r}\sin\theta\cos\phi$, $y = \mathfrak{r}\sin\theta\sin\phi$, and $z = \mathfrak{r}\cos\theta$ can then be introduced if desired.

The equation of motion (8-2) for a test particle in the metric of eq. (9-20) becomes

$$\delta\int \sqrt{e^{-\lambda}\dot{t}^2 - c^{-2}[\dot{r}^2 e^{\lambda} + r^2(\dot{\theta}^2 + \sin^2\theta\,\dot{\phi}^2)]}\; ds = 0 \qquad (9\text{-}21)$$

where the dot denotes d/ds. It may be verified that the orbit is planar; hence we set $\theta = \dfrac{\pi}{2}$ and use ϕ as the angular coordinate. Since neither

t nor ϕ appear explicitly in eq. (9-21), their conjugate momenta are constant:

$$e^{-\lambda}\dot{t} = A = \text{const.} \qquad \left.\begin{array}{c} a \\ \\ b \end{array}\right\} \quad (9\text{-}22)$$
$$r^2\dot{\phi} = h = \text{const.}$$

The line element in eq. (9-20) provides the equation of motion for r:

$$\dot{r}^2 + e^{-\lambda}r^2\dot{\phi}^2 = e^{-\lambda}c^2(e^{-\lambda}\dot{t}^2 - 1). \qquad (9\text{-}23)$$

Substitution of $\dot{t}$ and $\dot{\phi}$ from eqs. (9-22) into (9-23) gives

$$\dot{r}^2 + e^{-\lambda}\frac{h^2}{r^2} = c^2(A^2 - e^{-\lambda}). \qquad (9\text{-}24)$$

The change in variable $r = 1/u$ and the substitutions $d/ds = hu^2\, d/d\phi$ and $e^{-\lambda} = 1 - 2\mu u$ put eq. (9-24) into the form

$$\left(\frac{du}{d\phi}\right)^2 + u^2 = \frac{c^2}{h^2}(A^2 - 1) + \frac{2\mu c^2}{h^2}u + 2\mu u^3. \qquad (9\text{-}25)$$

Equation (9-25) differs from the corresponding Newtonian orbit equation only in the presence of the term $2\mu u^3$ on the right-hand side.

The constant A is the energy per unit mass of the test particle. Consider an observer who is stationary at $\left(r, \dfrac{\pi}{2}, \phi\right)$ and who measures his own time τ as given by

$$\frac{dt}{d\tau} = e^{\frac{1}{2}\lambda}.$$

As the test particle passes the observer, he interprets the dilation of the test particle's time to be due to its velocity v relative to him, in accordance with the special-relativistic formula

$$\frac{ds}{d\tau} = \sqrt{1 - \frac{v^2}{c^2}}.$$

We then have from eq. (9-22a)

$$A = e^{-\frac{1}{2}\lambda}\left(1 - \frac{v^2}{c^2}\right)^{-\frac{1}{2}}$$

which is approximately the same as

$$A = 1 + \frac{1}{c^2}\left(\frac{v^2}{2} - \frac{\mu c^2}{r}\right).$$

The terms in parentheses are respectively the kinetic energy per unit mass and the Newtonian gravitational energy per unit mass. Thus Ac^2 is the *total* energy per unit mass, i.e., the sum of rest-mass energy, kinetic energy, and potential energy of the test particle. In Section 9.6 it will be convenient to regard the quantity

$$\mathcal{E} = \tfrac{1}{2}c^2(A^2 - 1) \qquad (9\text{-}26)$$

as the energy, thus excluding rest mass.

9.5 EINSTEIN'S THREE CLASSICAL TESTS

The observational tests which Einstein proposed for his theory of gravity were measurements of: the perihelion advance for the planet Mercury; the deflection of light which passes close to the sun; and the redshift in the spectral lines of white dwarf stars. Each of these effects will be considered separately.

a. Perihelion Advance. Equation (9-25) can be differentiated with respect to ϕ and divided by $2\,du/d\phi$ to give

$$\frac{d^2u}{d\phi^2} + u = \frac{\mu c^2}{h^2} + 3\mu u^2 = N(u). \qquad (9\text{-}27)$$

The use of eq. (6-10) then gives the perihelion advance

$$\sigma = \frac{3\mu}{p}.$$

For Mercury's orbit around the sun, this fraction is 8×10^{-8}, which gives a perihelion advance of $43''$ per century. This figure is of course only the perihelion precession due to the higher-order term of order $u\mu/r$ in eq. (9-27). There are in addition the gravitational effects upon Mercury due to the presence of other planets and the oblateness of the sun.

The observational data are summarized in Table 9.2, which is quoted from the work of G. M. Clemence[B]. The first column is the source of the perturbation, and the second and third columns give the theoretical advance of perihelion in $''$ per century for Mercury and the earth, respectively. All entries except the relativity entry are based on Newtonian

TABLE 9.2 *PERIHELION ADVANCE*

CAUSE OF PERTURBATION	MERCURY	EARTH
Mercury	$0''.025 \pm 0''.00$	$-13''.75 \pm 2''.3$
Venus	277.856 ± 0.27	345.49 ± 0.3
Earth	90.038 ± 0.08	
Mars	2.536 ± 0.00	97.69 ± 0.1
Jupiter	153.584 ± 0.00	696.85 ± 0.0
Saturn	7.302 ± 0.01	18.74 ± 0.0
Uranus	0.141 ± 0.00	0.57 ± 0.0
Neptune	0.042 ± 0.00	0.18 ± 0.0
Sun's oblateness	0.010 ± 0.02	0.00 ± 0.0
Moon		7.68 ± 0.0
Relativity	43.03 ± 0.03	3.8 ± 0.0
General precession	5025.645 ± 0.30	5025.65 ± 0.3
Sum	5600.21 ± 0.4	6182.9 ± 2.3
Observed motion	5599.74 ± 0.41	6183.7 ± 1.1
Difference	-0.47 ± 0.57	$+0.8 \pm 2.5$

gravity. The last three lines at the bottom of the table show respectively the total predicted precessions, the observed precessions, and the differences. The latter are within the limits of error.

b. Deflection of Light. In the general theory of relativity, as contrasted with some of the special-relativistic gravitational theories of Chapter 6, the behavior of a photon is identical with the behavior of a particle traveling with the speed of light. The reason is that in both cases the particle follows a null curve. It will be proved in Section 12.3, from the nature of the electromagnetic stress-energy tensor, that a photon follows a null curve which, in the absence of external forces, is a null geodesic. Thus we may take the orbit equation (9-27) in the limit $h \to \infty$ to describe either a photon or a particle traveling with the speed of light:

$$\frac{d^2u}{d\phi^2} + u = 3\mu u^2. \tag{9-28}$$

In the lowest approximation in which the term on the right is neglected, the solution is a straight line

$$u = \frac{\cos \phi}{R}, \tag{9-29}$$

where R is the distance of closest approach to the mass. In the next approximation, eq. (9-29) is used on the right-hand side of eq. (9-28) to give the differential equation

$$\frac{d^2u}{d\phi^2} + u = \frac{3\mu}{R^2} \cos^2 \phi = \frac{3\mu}{2R^2}(1 + \cos 2\phi)$$

which has the solution

$$u = \frac{\cos \phi}{R} + \frac{3\mu}{2R^2}(1 - \tfrac{1}{3} \cos 2\phi). \tag{9-30}$$

Equation (9-30) gives the solution for $u(\phi)$ to terms of order μ/R^2. The light ray comes in from infinity at the asymptotic angle $\phi = -\left(\frac{\pi}{2} + \epsilon\right)$ and goes out to infinity at an asymptotic angle $\phi = \frac{\pi}{2} + \epsilon$, where ϵ is of order μ/R. The angle ϵ is obtained by substituting $\phi = \frac{\pi}{2} + \epsilon$, $u = 0$ into eq. (9-30):

$$\epsilon = \frac{2\mu}{R} + O^2\left(\frac{\mu}{R}\right).$$

Thus the total angle of deflection 2ϵ of the light ray is

$$2\epsilon = \frac{4\mu}{R}.$$

For a light ray which skims the sun's limb, the deflection is $1''.75$.

The observational verification of the gravitational deflection of light passing close to the sun is difficult for practical reasons. The method, in principle, is to photograph the stars around the sun during a total solar eclipse. The first difficulty is the need to wait for a total solar eclipse which is visible on a land area which is accessible with scientific equipment. Second, the eclipse lasts only a few minutes. Third, in an eclipse there are not always bright stars near the sun's position on the celestial sphere. Fourth, the sun's corona may produce a slight dilatation of the photographic plate, thus masking the effect sought for. The latest determination (from the eclipse of 1952) gives a deflection at the sun's limb of $1.''70 \pm 0.''10$.*

c. Gravitational Redshift. Consider the frequency ν at which an observer at infinity receives light emitted at a frequency ν_0 by an atom on the surface of a star. Since the metric of eq. (9-20) applies to the space outside the star, the proper time s at the atom is given by

$$ds = \sqrt{1 - \frac{2\mu}{R}}\, dt,$$

where R is the radius of the star, and the proper time s' for the observer at infinity is given by

$$ds' = dt.$$

Because the number of waves of light is conserved, we have the relation $\nu\, ds = \nu'\, ds'$ which immediately gives the result

$$\frac{\nu'}{\nu} = \sqrt{1 - \frac{2\mu}{R}}.$$

Thus there is a predicted redshift

$$\frac{\Delta\lambda}{\lambda} = \frac{\lambda' - \lambda}{\lambda} \simeq \frac{\mu}{R}. \tag{9-31}$$

It may be recalled from Section 6.9 that the gravitational redshift is a consequence only of the principle of equivalence, not of the gravitational field equation.

White dwarf stars are useful as a test of eq. (9-31) because they have the largest ratio μ/R (see Table 9.1). The white dwarf 40 Eridani B has a mass $0.43 \pm 0.04 M_\odot$ and a radius $0.016 \pm 0.002 R_\odot$†; the latter is estimated from its effective temperature and its absolute magnitude.

---

* See McVittie[B] and Klüber[B] for a discussion of the observations.
† The symbol $\odot$ denotes the sun or solar quantities.

Equation (9-31) predicts

$$c\frac{\Delta\lambda}{\lambda} = 17 \pm 3 \frac{km}{sec}.$$

Measurement (see Popper[B]) gives

$$c\frac{\Delta\lambda}{\lambda} = 21 \pm 4 \frac{km}{sec}.$$

The white dwarf Sirius B is difficult to observe because of its nearness to the extremely bright Sirius A. Adam's[B] observation indicates a redshift of

$$c\frac{\Delta\lambda}{\lambda} = 21 \frac{km}{sec},$$

which was in agreement with the theoretical value in 1925 but is in disagreement with the theoretical value of 79 km/sec for a mass of $1M_{\odot}$ and a radius of $0.008R_{\odot}$ given by McVittie[B]. However, Kuiper in unpublished work quoted by McVittie felt that the observed redshift should be corrected up to 60 to 80 km/sec. Adams assumed a radius of $0.03R_{\odot}$.

It is easier to confirm the gravitational redshift in terrestrial experiments. Pound[B] and Snider used the 14.4-kev γ-rays from Fe^{57} produced by the Mössbauer effect. The γ-rays traversed a vertical distance of 22.5 meters. The predicted fractional frequency shift is $\Delta\nu/\nu = 2.5 \times 10^{-15}$. Pound and Snider found the ratio of the observed shift to the theoretical shift to be 0.997 ± 0.008.

A comment should be made about *redshifts* in general. The wavelengths or the frequencies of spectral lines are changed by a ratio which is uniform throughout the spectrum, whether the change is due to gravity or to motion. Observational results are usually given in the form

$$z = \frac{\text{observed wavelength} - \text{normal wavelength}}{\text{normal wavelength}}$$

This ratio, denoted by z, is constant from one spectral line to another for a given source. Although both violet shifts ($z < 0$) and redshifts ($z > 0$) are observed for various sources, it is the objects with redshifts which are of interest in the context of this book, because gravitational effects and, as will be seen later, cosmological effects give rise only to redshifts.

9.6 SCHWARZSCHILD ORBITS

The orbits of particles in the Schwarzschild field deserve further study in order to see how they differ from Newtonian orbits. With the substitutions of eqs. (9-20b) and (9-26), eq. (9-24) becomes

$$\left(\frac{dr}{ds}\right)^2 = 2\epsilon + \frac{2\mu c^2}{r} - \frac{h^2}{r^2} + \frac{2h^2\mu}{r^3}. \tag{9-32}$$

The length 2μ and the time $2\mu/c$ will be adopted, respectively, as the unit of length and time, so that $2\mu = 1$ and $c = 1$. Equation (9-32) becomes

$$\left(\frac{dr}{ds}\right)^2 = 2\epsilon + \frac{1}{r} - \frac{h^2}{r^2} + \frac{h^2}{r^3}, \qquad (9\text{-}33)$$

where h is the angular momentum per unit mass. Equation (9-33) differs from the corresponding Newtonian equation of motion only in the presence of the last term. With $h = 0$ both the Newtonian and Einsteinian equations of motion are the same:

$$\left(\frac{dr}{ds}\right)^2 = 2\epsilon + \frac{1}{r}. \qquad (9\text{-}34)$$

It must be kept in mind that in Einstein's theory the coordinates take on a special meaning. The r appearing in eq. (9-33) is defined in such a way that a sphere in both the Newtonian and Einstein theories has area $4\pi r^2$. But only in the Newtonian theory is r also the radial distance. Similarly the s appearing in eq. (9-33) is the time of the test particle in both theories, but only in the Newtonian theory is it also the time for other observers.

For $h \neq 0$, the Newtonian and Einsteinian equations of motion are different. It is convenient to regard eq. (9-33) as a one-dimensional energy equation:

$$\epsilon = \tfrac{1}{2}\left(\frac{dr}{ds}\right)^2 + V(r) \qquad \text{a}$$

where the potential energy $V(r)$ per unit mass is given by

$$V(r) = \tfrac{1}{2}\left[-\frac{1}{r} + \frac{h^2}{r^2} - \frac{h^2}{r^3}\right]. \qquad \text{b}$$

(9-35)

In the Newtonian case the potential consists of a negative $1/r$ term and a positive $1/r^2$ term. Thus $V(r)$ is a curve shown qualitatively in Figure 9.1.

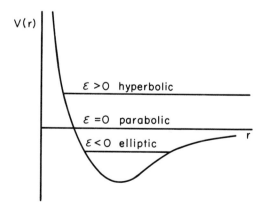

FIGURE 9.1 Newtonian orbits around point mass.

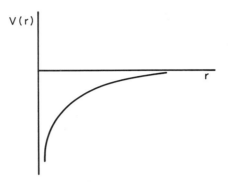

FIGURE 9.2 Einstein motion for $h < \sqrt{3}$.

There is a minimum at $r = 2h^2$. The curve approaches $V = 0$ at $r = \infty$ and $V = +\infty$ at $r = 0$. The kinetic energy is represented graphically by the vertical distance at a given radius r between the curve $V(r)$ and the horizontal line which represents the total energy of the test particle. Many of the orbital characteristics can be read from such a diagram. For example, if $\epsilon < 0$, then the intersections of the curve $V = V(r)$ with the line $V = \epsilon$ give the maximum and minimum distances of the particle from the mass.

For Einsteinian motion of a test particle where all the terms in eq. (9-35b) are used, five different cases must be distinguished (Figs. 9.2 to 9.6).

$\boxed{h < \sqrt{3}}$ The function $V(r)$ increases monotonically from $V = -\infty$ at $r = 0$ to $V = 0$ at $r = \infty$. Bound states exist, and all states (bound or unbound) pass through the origin.

$\boxed{h = \sqrt{3}}$ The function $V(r)$ has an inflection at $(3, -\frac{1}{18})$, but otherwise increases monotonically from $V = -\infty$ at $r = 0$ to $V = 0$ at $r = \infty$. This case is similar to the previous case except that an unstable circular orbit with radius $r = 3$ is possible for $\epsilon = -\frac{1}{18}$.

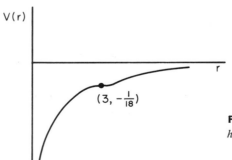

$(3, -\frac{1}{18})$

FIGURE 9.3 Einstein motion for $h = \sqrt{3}$.

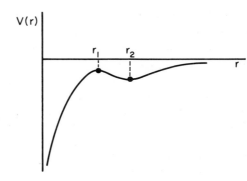

FIGURE 9.4 Einstein motion for $\sqrt{3} < h < 2$.

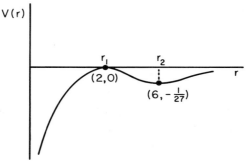

FIGURE 9.5 Einstein motion for $h = 2$.

$\boxed{h > \sqrt{3}}$ $V(r)$ has a maximum at $r_1 = h^2 - h\sqrt{h^2 - 3}$ and a minimum at $r_2 = h^2 + h\sqrt{h^2 - 3}$. $\boxed{h < 2}$ The maximum $V(r_1)$ is negative. Hence three different kinds of bound motion exist, one of which is the analogue of Keplerian ellipses. A particle with positive energy passes through the origin. $\boxed{h = 2}$ The maximum $V(r_1)$ is zero. Two kinds of bound motion exist, one of which is the analogue of Keplerian ellipses. $\boxed{h > 2}$ The maximum $V(r_1)$ is positive. Particles with energy less than

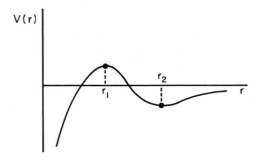

FIGURE 9.6 Einstein motion for $h > 2$.

$V(r_1)$ will not reach the origin. There are two kinds of bound motion, one of which is the analogue of Keplerian ellipses.

It is of interest to note how r_1 and r_2 vary with h. As h increases beyond $\sqrt{3}$, r_1 moves inward and r_2 moves outward. In the limit $h \to \infty$, $r_2 \to \infty$ but $r_1 \to \frac{3}{2}$. Thus there is always bound motion inside r_1, no matter how large h may be. Another curious feature is that a particle with sufficient energy can always reach the origin, regardless of the magnitude of h—a feat impossible in Newtonian gravitation!

The nature of the Schwarzschild singularity at $r = 1$ can best be studied by considering test particles and photons which travel radially inward or radially outward. For a particle with energy ε, the equations of motion are eq. (9-34)

$$\left(\frac{dr}{ds}\right)^2 = 2\varepsilon + \frac{1}{r} \tag{9-34}$$

and eq. (9-22a)

$$\frac{dt}{ds} = \frac{Ar}{r-1} \tag{9-36}$$

where the constants ε and A are related by eq. (9-26). For a particle of extremely high energy we may take $2\varepsilon = A^2$. Thus for a photon, the quotient of the square root of eq. (9-34) by eq. (9-36) becomes

$$\frac{dr}{dt} = \pm \frac{r-1}{r}. \qquad \text{Photon} \tag{9-37}$$

The upper sign is for an outgoing photon and the lower sign is for an incoming photon. For the case of a particle which falls in from rest at infinity (or moves out so as to reach rest at infinity), we set $\varepsilon = 0$ and $A = 1$; eqs. (9-34) and (9-36) become

$$\frac{dr}{ds} = \pm \frac{1}{\sqrt{r}} \qquad\qquad \text{a}$$

$$\left.\begin{array}{l}\\ \\ \\ \\ \end{array}\right\} \text{Particle} \quad (9\text{-}38)$$

$$\frac{dr}{dt} = \pm \frac{r-1}{r^{\frac{3}{2}}}. \qquad\qquad \text{b}$$

The upper sign is for an outgoing particle, and the lower sign is for an incoming particle.

The particle motion represented by eqs. (9-38) is known as the *parabolic pendlebahn*, abbreviated in this section PP. The integral of eq. (9-38a) has the simple form

$$s = \pm \tfrac{2}{3} r^{\frac{3}{2}} + \text{const.}$$

In order to integrate eq. (9-38b), it is necessary to introduce the function

$$f(r) = 2\sqrt{r} + \ln \left|\frac{\sqrt{r}-1}{\sqrt{r}+1}\right| \tag{9-39}$$

which has the derivative

$$\frac{df}{dr} = \frac{\sqrt{r}}{r-1}.$$

The function $\frac{2}{3}r^{\frac{3}{2}} + f(r)$ then has the derivative $r^{\frac{3}{2}}(r-1)^{-1}$. Therefore the integral of eq. (9-38b) is

$$t = \pm[\tfrac{2}{3}r^{\frac{3}{2}} + f(r)] + \text{const.} \qquad (9\text{-}40)$$

It is however necessary to verify that eq. (9-40) gives the correct integral when r crosses the singularity at $r = 1$. First we regard the correct solution to eq. (9-38b) for $r < 1$, if it exists, to be given by

$$t(b) - t(a) = \lim_{\epsilon \to 0}\left[\int_a^{1-\epsilon} \frac{r^{\frac{3}{2}}}{r-1}\,dr + \int_{1+\epsilon}^b \frac{r^{\frac{3}{2}}}{r-1}\,dr\right] \qquad a < 1, \qquad b > 1$$

or

$$t(b) - t(a) = \lim_{\epsilon \to 0}\{[\tfrac{2}{3}r^{\frac{3}{2}} + f(r)]_a^{1-\epsilon} + [\tfrac{2}{3}r^{\frac{3}{2}} + f(r)]_{1+\epsilon}^b\}.$$

Calculation shows that the above expression is equal to $[\tfrac{2}{3}r^{\frac{3}{2}} + f(r)]_a^b$. Hence eq. (9-40) is the correct integral when continued across the singularity. If s is chosen to be zero at $r = 0$, then the PP is given by

$$s = \pm\tfrac{2}{3}r^{\frac{3}{2}} \qquad\qquad\qquad \left.\begin{array}{l} \text{a)} \\[1.2em] \text{b)} \end{array}\right\} \text{PP} \quad (9\text{-}41)$$
$$t(r) = \pm[\tfrac{2}{3}r^{\frac{3}{2}} + f(r)] + t(0)$$

where $f(r)$ is given by eq. (9-39).

For a photon, eq. (9-37) is easily integrated to give

$$t(r) = \pm[r + \ln|r-1|] + t(0). \qquad \text{Photon} \qquad (9\text{-}42)$$

The continuation across the singularity can be verified for eq. (9-42) in the same way as for eq. (9-41b).

Figure 9.7 represents the function $f(r)$ and Figure 9.8 shows the function $t(r)$ for the outgoing and incoming PP in eq. (9-41b) with $t(0) = 0$. The behavior of the trajectories inside the singularity is remarkable. The "incoming" particle begins at the origin at $t = 0$ and moves outward to meet itself coming in from the outside at $t = \infty$, $r = 1$. The "outgoing" particle separates at $t = -\infty$, $r = 1$, and one of itself moves inward to the origin while the other moves outward.

Incoming and outgoing photons show the same kind of behavior. Figure 9.9, where the dashed curves are the PP of Figure 9.8, show eq. (9-42) for $t(0) = 0$.

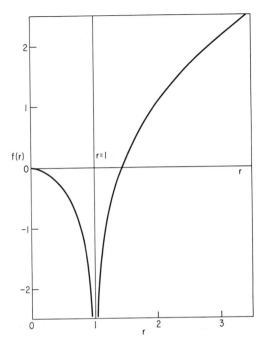

FIGURE 9.7 The function
$$f(r) = 2\sqrt{r} + \ln\left|\frac{\sqrt{r} - 1}{\sqrt{r} + 1}\right|.$$

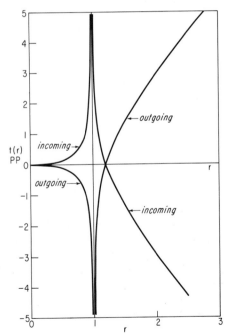

FIGURE 9.8 Parabolic pendlebahn $t(r)$.

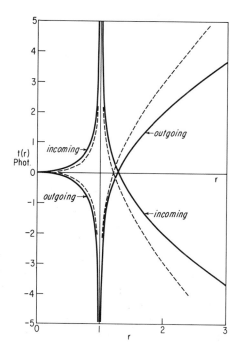

FIGURE 9.9 Photon in Schwarzschild field.

The strange behavior inside the singularity is to be expected, because the metric inside the singularity

$$ds^2 = -\frac{1-r}{r}\,dt^2 + \frac{r}{1-r}\,dr^2 - r^2(d\theta^2 + \sin^2\theta\,d\phi^2)$$

has signature $- + - -$ rather than $+ - - -$.

It is illuminating to introduce new coordinates τ, ρ as follows.

$$\tau = t + f(r) \qquad\qquad\qquad\quad \text{a)}$$
$$\tfrac{2}{3}\rho^{\frac{3}{2}} = \tfrac{2}{3}r^{\frac{3}{2}} + f(r) + t. \qquad \text{b)} \qquad \text{(9-43)}$$

Three features of the new coordinates should be noted. First, comparison of eqs. (9-43b) and (9-41b) shows that the incoming PP is described by $\rho = $ const. Second, comparison of eqs. (9-43a) and (9-41) shows that the incoming PP has proper time $\tau - t(0)$. Third, at a given event the vector δx^μ which is tangent to $\tau = $ const is orthogonal to the vector dx^μ which is tangent to $\rho = $ const. This relation is verified by constructing the vectors in question:

$$\frac{\delta t}{\delta r} = -\frac{r^{\frac{1}{2}}}{r-1} \qquad\qquad \frac{dt}{dr} = -\frac{r^{\frac{3}{2}}}{r-1}$$

$$\delta\theta = 0 \qquad\qquad\qquad d\theta = 0$$

$$\delta\phi = 0 \qquad\qquad\qquad d\phi = 0.$$

Then we have $g_{\mu\nu}\,\delta x^\mu\,dx^\nu = 0$. This means that the metric in terms of τ, ρ, θ, ϕ

$$ds^2 = d\tau^2 - \frac{\rho}{r}\,d\rho^2 - r^2(d\theta^2 + \sin^2\theta\,d\phi^2)$$

contains no $d\tau\,d\rho$ term. The metric is unchanged by the group of transformations

$$\tau' = \tau - a$$
$$\rho' = [\rho^{\frac{3}{2}} - \tfrac{3}{2}a]^{\frac{2}{3}}$$

where a is a constant.

The metric in terms of τ and r assumes an interesting form.

$$ds^2 = \frac{r-1}{r}\,d\tau^2 - \frac{2}{\sqrt{r}}\,d\tau\,dr - [dr^2 + r^2(d\theta^2 + \sin^2\theta\,d\phi^2)].$$

The spatial part of the metric is Euclidean! The physical interpretation of this is that if a large number of particles fall from rest at infinity with their proper times τ synchronized at infinity, then the space $\tau = $ const is Euclidean, even for $r < 1$.

To summarize the equations of motion for the PP and for photons, eqs. (9-41) and (9-42) are listed below, along with their representations in terms of τ and ρ.

$$t + \tfrac{2}{3}r^{\frac{3}{2}} + f(r) = \text{const}$$
$$\tau + \tfrac{2}{3}r^{\frac{3}{2}} = \text{const}$$
$$\rho = \text{const}$$
$$s - \tau = \text{const}$$

$\left.\right\}$ Incoming PP

$$t - \tfrac{2}{3}r^{\frac{3}{2}} - f(r) = \text{const}$$
$$\tau - 2f(r) - \tfrac{2}{3}r^{\frac{3}{2}} = \text{const}$$
$$\tfrac{2}{3}\rho^{\frac{3}{2}} - \tfrac{4}{3}r^{\frac{3}{2}} - 2f(r) = \text{const}$$
$$s - \tfrac{2}{3}r^{\frac{3}{2}} = \text{const}$$

$\left.\right\}$ Outgoing PP

$$t + r + \ln|r - 1| = \text{const}$$
$$\tau + r - 2\sqrt{r} + 2\ln|\sqrt{r} + 1| = \text{const}$$

$\left.\right\}$ Incoming Photon

$$t - r - \ln|r - 1| = \text{const}$$
$$\tau - r - 2\sqrt{r} - 2\ln|\sqrt{r} - 1| = \text{const}$$

$\left.\right\}$ Outgoing Photon

Note that in terms of τ and r there is no singularity for an incoming PP or photon. Similar behavior for the outgoing PP and photon is obtained by reversing the sign of $f(r)$ in eq. (9-43a) and the sign of t in eq. (9-43b). The curves represented by the above equations are shown in Figure 9.10.

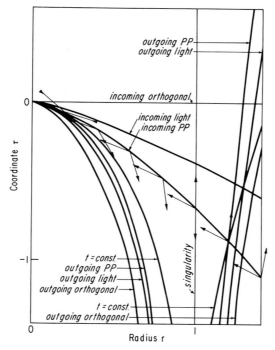

FIGURE 9.10 Trajectories $\tau(r)$ near Schwarzschild singularity. Light cones are designated by arrows.

The curve labeled incoming (outgoing) orthogonal is the curve whose tangent is orthogonal to the incoming (outgoing) PP's.

It is interesting to determine what an observer fixed at $r = r_0$ would see as the particle on the incoming PP falls toward the origin. An atomic clock on the particle would measure the proper time s of the particle as it falls inward. It is supposed that light signals from the particle reach the observer so that the observer is able to follow the particle's proper time $s(T)$, coordinate distance $r(T)$, coordinate time $t(T)$, and redshift $z(T)$ as functions of the time T at which the observer receives the light signals (T is the observer's proper time). It is assumed that both the coordinate time t and the particle's proper time s are calibrated so that the particle reaches the origin at $t = s = 0$. It is then a straightforward task to write down the necessary equations. Equations (9-41) and (9-42) give

$$s(T) = -\tfrac{2}{3}[r(T)]^{\frac{3}{2}}$$
$$t(T) = s(T) - f[r(T)]$$
$$s(T) - r(T) - 2\sqrt{r(T)} - 2\ln|\sqrt{r(T)} - 1| =$$
$$\sqrt{\frac{r_0}{r_0 - 1}}\,T - r_0 - \ln|r_0 - 1|. \tag{9-44}$$

Differentiation of eq. (9-44) with respect to T gives

$$\frac{dT}{ds} = 1 + z = \sqrt{\frac{r_0 - 1}{r_0}} \; \frac{1}{1 - \dfrac{1}{\sqrt{r(T)}}}. \qquad (9\text{-}45)$$

Equation (9-44) shows that, as the particle approaches the Schwarzschild radius $r = 1$, i.e., $s \to -\frac{2}{3}$, the observer's time T of observation approaches $+\infty$. The observer never sees the particle reach $r = 1$, although the particle passes $r = 1$ and reaches $r = 0$ in a finite proper time! Equation (9-45) shows that the light from the particle is redshifted more and more; as the particle approaches $r = 1$, z approaches ∞.

9.7 THE INTERIOR SCHWARZSCHILD SOLUTION

In Section 9.4 the gravitational field of a point mass was derived. In this section the gravitational field for a static sphere of fluid will be derived, both inside and outside the sphere. A static, spherical distribution of perfect fluid with radius a is assumed to be spherically symmetric about its center and to be isolated in an otherwise empty universe. Such a system can serve, for example, as a model for a non-convective, non-rotating star.

The line element of eq. (9-16) is applicable both inside and outside the sphere, because its derivation was based only on the assumption of spherical symmetry. The coordinate r which appears in eq. (9-16) is chosen as the measurement of radius, and the boundary of the fluid is denoted $r = a$.

The stress-energy tensor for a perfect fluid given by eq. (9-4) is substituted into the conservation law (9-3) with

$$u^\mu = e^{-\nu/2}\delta_0^\mu$$

to give

$$\frac{dp}{dr} + \tfrac{1}{2}(\rho c^2 + p)\frac{d\nu}{dr} = 0. \qquad (9\text{-}46)$$

The proper density ρ, the proper pressure p, and the metric exponents ν and λ are functions only of r. If the equation of state $p(\rho)$ were known, eq. (9-46) could be integrated to give ν:

$$-\frac{\nu}{2} = \int_0^p \frac{dp}{\rho c^2 + p} + \text{const.}$$

However, since we do not know the equation of state, we are forced to turn to the field equation.

Equation (9-12) will be used as the field equation in order to see the effect of the cosmological constant. Inside the sphere, the field equation, with the substitutions of eqs. (9-4) and (9-17), becomes

$$\kappa\rho + \Lambda = \frac{c^2}{r^2}\left[1 - \frac{d}{dr}(re^{-\lambda})\right] \tag{9-47}$$

$$\kappa\left(\rho + \frac{p}{c^2}\right) = \frac{c^2}{r}e^{-\lambda}\frac{d}{dr}(\nu + \lambda) \tag{9-48}$$

$$\frac{\partial\lambda}{\partial t} = 0. \tag{9-49}$$

There is also the field equation $G_2^2 = G_3^3 = \kappa c^{-2}p - \Lambda$, but it is redundant. The field equation (9-12) for a spherically symmetric, perfect fluid with a static line element is identically satisfied for the components G_2^2 and G_3^3 by virtue of the Bianchi identity (9-46) and the field-equation components G_0^0 and G_1^1. Equation (9-49) shows that λ is independent of t, as expected for a static line element. Equation (9-47) can be immediately integrated to give

$$e^{-\lambda(r)} = 1 - \frac{\kappa}{rc^2}\int_0^r \rho r^2\,dr - \frac{\Lambda r^2}{3c^2}. \tag{9-50}$$

Outside the sphere, eq. (9-50) becomes

$$e^{-\lambda} = 1 - \frac{2\mu}{r} - \frac{\Lambda r^2}{3c^2}$$

where

$$\mu = \frac{4\pi G}{c^2}\int_0^a \rho r^2\,dr.$$

Equation (9-48) requires that $\nu + \lambda$ be a function of t; and by a suitable redefinition of t, this function can be chosen to be zero. We then have, in the space outside the sphere,

$$e^\nu = e^{-\lambda} = 1 - \frac{2\mu}{r} - \frac{\Lambda r^2}{3c^2}.$$

The cosmological constant enters eq. (9-20b) as an additional term $-\Lambda r^2/3c^2$. It is curious that the quantity $M = \mu c^2/G$ which is identified by an observer in a planetary orbit around the sphere as the gravitational mass of the sphere is different from the total proper mass of the sphere

$$M_0 = \int_0^a 4\pi\rho e^{\lambda/2} r^2\,dr.$$

In order to obtain specific expressions for $\lambda(r)$ and $\nu(r)$ inside the sphere, it is necessary to resort to a specific assumption about the equation of state of the fluid. The simplest assumption is that the proper density ρ is constant throughout the fluid. Such an equation of state necessitates a certain pressure distribution, but the pressure as well as the metric exponents can be obtained from the system of equations (9-46), (9-48), and (9-50). Equation (9-46) gives

$$e^{\nu/2}\left(\rho + \frac{p}{c^2}\right) = D \tag{9-51}$$

where D is the constant of integration. Equation (9-50) gives

$$e^{-\lambda} = 1 - \frac{r^2}{R^2} \tag{9-52}$$

where

$$R = \sqrt{\frac{3c^2}{\kappa\rho + \Lambda}}. \tag{9-53}$$

Equations (9-51) and (9-52) are then used in eq. (9-48) to give

$$e^{\nu/2} = A - B\sqrt{1 - \frac{r^2}{R^2}} \tag{9-54}$$

where

$$A = \frac{\kappa DR^2}{2c^2} = \frac{4\pi GDR^2}{c^2}$$

and B is the constant of integration. By using eqs. (9-53) and (9-54) to eliminate ρ and ν from eq. (9-51) we obtain the proper pressure p:

$$\frac{\kappa p}{c^2} = \Lambda + \frac{c^2}{R^2} \cdot \frac{3B\sqrt{1 - \dfrac{r^2}{R^2}} - A}{A - B\sqrt{1 - \dfrac{r^2}{R^2}}}. \tag{9-55}$$

Equations (9-52), (9-54), and (9-55) give the solutions for λ, ν, and p inside a sphere of perfect fluid with constant density ρ. The constants of integration are B and D.

The boundary conditions $p(a) = 0$ and $\nu(a-) = \nu(a+)$ are sufficient to determine the two constants of integration. The boundary conditions represent, respectively, the assumption that the pressure drops to zero at the surface and the condition that the metric tensor is continuous across the boundary. (The Riemann metric is supposed to be differentiable. Therefore surfaces and interfaces in general relativity must be regarded as limits of continuous distributions of matter.) For simplicity the cosmological constant will be neglected. From eq. (9-55) we have $A = 3B\sqrt{1 - a^2/R^2}$. Equation (9-54) then gives

$$e^{\nu(a)} = 1 - \frac{a^2}{R^2} = 4B^2\left[1 - \frac{a^2}{R^2}\right].$$

Therefore $B = \frac{1}{2}$, the exponent v is given by

$$e^{v/2} = \frac{1}{2}\left[3\sqrt{1 - \frac{a^2}{R^2}} - \sqrt{1 - \frac{r^2}{R^2}}\right],$$

and the pressure is given by

$$\frac{\kappa p}{c^2} = \frac{c^2}{R^2} \frac{\sqrt{1 - \frac{r^2}{R^2}} - \sqrt{1 - \frac{a^2}{R^2}}}{\sqrt{1 - \frac{a^2}{R^2}} - \frac{1}{3}\sqrt{1 - \frac{r^2}{R^2}}}.$$

The constants μ, M, and R are given in terms of ρ and a by the relations

$$M = \tfrac{4}{3}\pi a^3 \rho, \qquad \mu = \frac{GM}{c^2}, \qquad \left(\frac{R}{a}\right)^2 = \frac{a}{2\mu}.$$

Thus for $a \gg \mu$ we have $R \gg a$. Note that in order for v and λ to be real and for p to be neither negative nor infinite, the radius a must be larger than $\frac{9}{4}\mu$. Thus a sphere made of incompressible fluid cannot have a radius smaller than $\frac{9}{4}\mu$.

9.8 WEAK-FIELD SOLUTIONS

The interior and exterior Schwarzschild solutions to the field equation of general relativity are exact solutions. But because the field equations are non-linear in the field variables $g_{\mu\nu}(x^\rho)$, it is extremely difficult to find other exact solutions. The obvious alternative is to use approximation methods, the simplest of which is the weak-field approximation.

A background Minkowski metric is assumed, and the actual metric tensor $g_{\mu\nu}$ is regarded as differing only slightly from the Minkowski metric tensor $\eta_{\mu\nu}$. We therefore define

$$h_{\mu\nu} = g_{\mu\nu} - \eta_{\mu\nu}$$

and retain only terms of first order in $h_{\mu\nu}$. The Riemann curvature tensor is

$$R_{\kappa\lambda\mu\nu} = \frac{1}{2}\left[\frac{\partial^2 h_{\kappa\nu}}{\partial x^\lambda \, \partial x^\mu} + \frac{\partial^2 h_{\lambda\mu}}{\partial x^\kappa \, \partial x^\nu} - \frac{\partial^2 h_{\kappa\mu}}{\partial x^\lambda \, \partial x^\nu} - \frac{\partial^2 h_{\lambda\nu}}{\partial x^\kappa \, \partial x^\mu}\right] + O^2(h). \quad (9\text{-}56)$$

Covariant derivatives of $h_{\mu\nu}$ become ordinary derivatives because the Christoffel symbols are of order $h_{\mu\nu}$ and hence are neglected. In fact, the $h_{\mu\nu}(x^\rho)$ may be regarded as a linear field in purely Minkowski space. The Ricci tensor is

$$R_{\mu\nu} = \tfrac{1}{2}\Box^2 h_{\mu\nu} - \frac{1}{2}\frac{\partial \gamma_\nu}{\partial x^\mu} - \frac{1}{2}\frac{\partial \gamma_\mu}{\partial x^\nu} \qquad (9\text{-}57)$$

where

$$\gamma_\mu = \frac{\partial h_\mu^\lambda}{\partial x^\lambda} - \frac{1}{2}\frac{\partial h_\lambda^\lambda}{\partial x^\mu}.$$

(Indices are raised and lowered by means of the Minkowski metric tensor.)

The quantity γ_μ can, by a suitable choice of coordinates, be made to vanish. The new coordinates x'^μ are defined $x'^\mu = x^\mu + f^\mu(x^\nu)$ where f^μ is a small quantity of the same order as $h_{\mu\nu}$ and is chosen to satisfy the condition

$$\Box^2 f_\mu = \gamma_\mu. \tag{9-58}$$

With the definition $h'_{\mu\nu} = g'_{\mu\nu} - \eta_{\mu\nu}$, $h'_{\mu\nu}$ is found from the tensor transformation of the metric tensor to be

$$h'_{\mu\nu} = h_{\mu\nu} - \frac{\partial f_\mu}{\partial x^\nu} - \frac{\partial f_\nu}{\partial x^\mu}.$$

Hence

$$\gamma'_\mu = \gamma_\mu - \Box^2 f_\mu. \tag{9-59}$$

Equation (9-58) then implies the vanishing of γ'_μ.

It has been proved that a coordinate system x^μ can be chosen so that the Ricci tensor is

$$R_{\mu\nu} = \tfrac{1}{2}\Box^2 h_{\mu\nu} \tag{9-60}$$

and the $h_{\mu\nu}$ satisfy the *normalization condition*

$$\frac{\partial h_\mu^\lambda}{\partial x^\lambda} - \frac{1}{2}\frac{\partial h_\lambda^\lambda}{\partial x^\mu} = 0. \tag{9-61}$$

From the analogy with electromagnetism, the integral of eq. (9-60) is seen to be

$$h_{\mu\nu} = \frac{1}{2\pi c^2}\int \frac{[R_{\mu\nu}]}{[r]} dV \tag{9-62}$$

where the brackets indicate that the retarded values are to be taken. The linear-theory field equation has become

$$\Box^2 h_{\mu\nu} = -2\kappa(T_{\mu\nu} - \tfrac{1}{2}\eta_{\mu\nu}T_\alpha^\alpha). \tag{9-63}$$

The relation between a slowly moving perfect fluid and the field quantities $h_{\mu\nu}$ produced by the fluid is found by collecting eqs. (9-4), (9-10), and (9-62). The contraction of eq. (9-4) gives $T = T_\alpha^\alpha = \rho - 3pc^{-2}$. For a slowly moving fluid, the distinctions between proper density and coordinate density and between world-velocity and coordinate velocity v^i

disappear. We have

$$T_{00} - \tfrac{1}{2}Tg_{00} = \tfrac{1}{2}(\rho + 3pc^{-2})$$

$$T_{0i} - \tfrac{1}{2}Tg_{0i} = -c^{-2}\rho v^i$$

$$T_{ij} - \tfrac{1}{2}Tg_{ij} = c^{-4}[\rho(v^i v^j + \tfrac{1}{2}c^2\delta_{ij}) - \tfrac{1}{2}p\delta_{ij}]$$

by neglecting terms of order $h_{\mu\nu}$ and of order higher than p and v^2. Equations (9-10) and (9-62) now give

$$h_{00} = -\frac{2G}{c^2}\int \frac{\rho + 3pc^{-2}}{r}\, dV$$

$$h_{0i} = \frac{4G}{c^4}\int \frac{\rho v^i}{r}\, dV \qquad\qquad (9\text{-}64)$$

$$h_{ij} = -\frac{2G}{c^6}\int \frac{1}{r}\,[\rho(\delta_{ij}c^2 + 2v^i v^j) - p\,\delta_{ij}]\, dV.$$

It can be verified by direct substitution into eq. (9-61) that the normalization condition is satisfied. Thus $c^2 h_{00}$ is twice the Newtonian potential Φ with an additional term due to pressure; h_{0i} is similar in form to the electromagnetic vector potential; h_{ij} contains a term $\Phi c^{-4}\delta_{ij}$ plus terms due to pressure and the velocities (with the latter in quadratic form). For future reference we note the following forms.

$$\left.\begin{aligned}
g_{00} &= 1 + 2\frac{\Phi}{c^2} + O\!\left(\frac{\Phi}{c^2}\frac{p}{\rho c^2}\right) \\[2mm]
g_{0i} &= \frac{1}{c}\,O\!\left(\frac{\Phi}{c^2}\frac{v}{c}\right) \\[2mm]
g_{ij} &= -\frac{1}{c^2}\delta_{ij}\!\left(1 - 2\frac{\Phi}{c^2}\right) + \frac{1}{c^2}\!\left[O\!\left(\frac{\Phi}{c^2}\frac{v^2}{c^2}\right) + O\!\left(\frac{\Phi}{c^2}\frac{p}{\rho c^2}\right)\right].
\end{aligned}\right\} \qquad (9\text{-}65)$$

The effective gravitational mass density is seen in eq. (9-64) to be not merely ρ but $\rho + 3pc^{-2}$. It is for this reason that isotropic electromagnetic radiation for which $p = \tfrac{1}{3}\rho c^2$ has a gravitational mass which is twice the mass equivalent of its energy.

The equation of motion for the linear approximation to general relativity might at first sight seem to be simply the expression of eq. (9-5) to first order in $h_{\mu\nu}$. However, this approach is incorrect due to the presence of the general-relativistic metric s in eq. (9-5). If the background metric is to be taken as the Minkowski metric, then the independent variable in the equation of motion must be taken to be the s given by eq. (3-33). For an *arbitrary* parameter s, eq. (9-5) becomes

$$\frac{d^2x^\mu}{ds^2} = -\left\{\begin{matrix}\mu\\\nu\rho\end{matrix}\right\}\frac{dx^\nu}{ds}\frac{dx^\rho}{ds} + \frac{1}{2}\frac{dx^\mu}{ds}\frac{d}{ds}\ln\left(g_{\mu\nu}\frac{dx^\mu}{ds}\frac{dx^\nu}{ds}\right). \tag{9-66}$$

With the requirement that s satisfy the relation $1 = \eta_{\mu\nu}\dfrac{dx^\mu}{ds}\dfrac{dx^\nu}{ds}$, eq. (9-66)* may be written

$$\frac{d^2x^\mu}{ds^2} = -\left\{\begin{matrix}\nu\\\rho\sigma\end{matrix}\right\}\frac{dx^\rho}{ds}\frac{dx^\sigma}{ds}\left(\delta_\nu^\mu - \eta_{\nu\tau}\frac{dx^\tau}{ds}\frac{dx^\mu}{ds}\right) \tag{9-67}$$

where s is now the Minkowski metric. The Christoffel symbol entering eq. (9-67) is still the general-relativistic quantity.

Upon retaining only terms of first order in $h_{\mu\nu}$, eq. (9-67) becomes

$$\frac{du^\mu}{ds} = (\eta^{\mu\nu} - u^\mu u^\nu)u^\rho u^\sigma\left(\frac{1}{2}\frac{\partial h_{\rho\sigma}}{\partial x^\nu} - \frac{\partial h_{\nu\rho}}{\partial x^\sigma}\right), \tag{9-68}$$

where $u^\mu = dx^\mu/ds$. Equation (9-68) corresponds to eq. (6-49) for the parameters $A = 0$, $B = 0$, $E = 0$, $C = \frac{1}{2}$, $D = -1$.

With the definition of the field potential

$$\phi_{\mu\nu} = h_{\mu\nu} - \tfrac{1}{2}\eta_{\mu\nu}\eta^{\alpha\beta}h_{\alpha\beta}$$

we may fit the weak-field approximation into the context of the special-relativistic theory of Section 6.7. The equation of motion (9-68) becomes

$$\frac{}{ds} = (\eta^{\mu\nu} - u^\mu u^\nu)\left[-\frac{1}{4}\frac{\partial\phi_\sigma^\sigma}{\partial x^\nu} + u^\rho u^\sigma\left(\frac{1}{2}\frac{\partial\phi_{\rho\sigma}}{\partial x^\nu} - \frac{\partial\phi_{\nu\rho}}{\partial x^\sigma}\right)\right]$$

which corresponds to eq. (6-49) for the parameters $A = 0$, $B = 1/2c^2$, $C = -1/c^2$, $D = 2/c^2$, and $E = 0$. The extra factor of $-2/c^2$ is needed to make the field equation

$$\Box^2\phi_{\mu\nu} = -2\kappa T_{\mu\nu}$$

for the $\phi_{\mu\nu}$ used here correspond to eq. (6-50).

The advance of perihelion and the deflection of a particle with the speed of light can now be calculated for the linear approximation to general relativity. From eqs. (6-52) and (6-57) the perihelion advance is

$$\sigma = \frac{5\mu}{p}$$

which is $\frac{5}{3}$ the Einstein value. The deflection of a particle with the speed of light is, from eq. (6-58), $4\mu/R$—the same as that in the exact theory.

The linear theory outlined above cannot really be regarded as a special-relativistic gravitational theory because light rays propagate neither

---

* Multiplication of eq. (9-66) by $\eta_{\mu\lambda}\dfrac{dx^\lambda}{ds}$ allows evaluation of the logarithm term.

rectilinearly nor with a constant coordinate velocity c—one of the two basic postulates of special relativity. The linear approximation to general relativity is an approximation to a theory in which a light ray is *exactly* described by the condition $ds^2 = 0$, and in which both a photon and a particle with speed of light behave identically. The deflection of light predicted by the linear theory violates the rectilinear propagation postulate of special relativity. As for the velocity of light, in the lowest approximation where the metric is

$$ds^2 = \left(1 + \frac{2\Phi}{c^2}\right) dt^2 - \frac{1}{c^2}\left(1 - \frac{2\Phi}{c^2}\right)(dx^2 + dy^2 + dz^2),$$

the coordinate velocity of light is clearly $c(1 + 2\Phi/c^2)$.

It may be remarked that the metric

$$ds^2 = \left(1 - \frac{2\mu}{r}\right) dt^2 - \frac{1}{c^2}\left(1 + \frac{2\mu}{r}\right)(dx^2 + dy^2 + dz^2),$$

when treated *exactly*, gives the equations of motion

$$\dot{t} = \frac{k}{1 - \dfrac{2\mu}{r}}, \qquad r^2\dot{\theta} = \frac{h}{1 + \dfrac{2\mu}{r}}$$

which lead to a perihelion advance of $\sigma = 4\mu/p$ and a deflection for light of $4\mu/R$.

9.9 GRAVITATIONAL WAVES

According to the weak-field approximation to general relativity which was outlined in the previous section, there should exist in empty space gravitational waves propagated with velocity c. The field equation (9-10) for empty space in the linear approximation, $\Box^2 h_{\mu\nu} = 0$, has the plane wave as the simplest solution. With the x-axis chosen in the direction of propagation, $h_{\mu\nu}$ depends only upon $t - x$. (We choose $c = 1$ for convenience.) The normalization condition (9-61) becomes

$$\left.\begin{aligned}
\dot{h}_{00} + 2\dot{h}_{01} + \dot{h}_{11} &= 0 \\
\dot{h}_{22} + \dot{h}_{33} &= 0 \\
\dot{h}_{02} + \dot{h}_{12} &= 0 \\
\dot{h}_{03} + \dot{h}_{13} &= 0
\end{aligned}\right\} \tag{9-69}$$

where the dot indicates differentiation with respect to $t - x$.

The only non-vanishing components of the Riemann curvature tensor obtained from eqs. (9-56) and (9-69) are

$$R_{0202} = R_{1212} = R_{0221} = -\tfrac{1}{2}\ddot{h}_{22}$$
$$R_{0303} = R_{1313} = R_{0331} = -\tfrac{1}{2}\ddot{h}_{33}$$
$$R_{0203} = R_{0321} = R_{0231} = R_{1213} = -\tfrac{1}{2}\ddot{h}_{23}$$

and those components which can be obtained from these by the symmetry conditions. The fact that only h_{22}, h_{23}, and h_{33} appear in the Riemann curvature tensor indicates that only h_{22}, h_{23}, and h_{33} have physical reality. The other components of $h_{\mu\nu}$ can be eliminated by means of an appropriate coordinate transformation. That transformation is in fact given by

$$x'^{\mu} = x^{\mu} + F^{\mu}(x) \tag{9-70}$$

where the $F^{\mu}(x)$ are of order $h_{\mu\nu}$ and are given by Table 9.3. The trans-

TABLE 9.3 *TRANSFORMATION OF GRAVITATIONAL WAVES TO SIMPLIFIED FORM*

		$\nu = 0$	1	2	3
	$\mu = 0$	$\tfrac{1}{2}h_{00}$	$\tfrac{1}{2}h_{01} + \tfrac{1}{4}h_{11} - \tfrac{1}{4}h_{00}$	0	0
$\dfrac{\partial F_{\mu}}{\partial x^{\nu}} =$	1	$\tfrac{1}{2}h_{01} - \tfrac{1}{4}h_{11} + \tfrac{1}{4}h_{00}$	$\tfrac{1}{2}h_{11}$	$\tfrac{1}{2}(h_{12} + h_{02})$	$\tfrac{1}{2}(h_{13} + h_{03})$
	2	h_{02}	$\tfrac{1}{2}(h_{12} - h_{02})$	$\tfrac{1}{4}(h_{22} + h_{33})$	0
	3	h_{03}	$\tfrac{1}{2}(h_{13} - h_{03})$	0	$\tfrac{1}{4}(h_{22} + h_{33})$

formation of Table 9.3 is equivalent to two transformations, one in which F^{μ} is a function only of $t - x$ and is given by

$$\dot{F}_{\mu} = (\tfrac{1}{2}h_{00}, -\tfrac{1}{2}h_{11}, h_{02}, h_{03}) \tag{9-71}$$

and a transformation given by

$$\left.\begin{aligned}
\bar{t} &= t + \tfrac{1}{2}\alpha x \\
\bar{x} &= x + \tfrac{1}{2}\alpha t + \tfrac{1}{2}\beta y + \tfrac{1}{2}\gamma z \\
\bar{y} &= y(1 + \tfrac{1}{2}\delta) + \tfrac{1}{2}\beta x \\
\bar{z} &= z(1 + \tfrac{1}{2}\delta) + \tfrac{1}{2}\gamma x
\end{aligned}\right\} \tag{9-72}$$

where the quantities

$$\alpha = h_{01} + \tfrac{1}{2}(h_{11} + h_{00})$$
$$\beta = h_{02} + h_{12}$$
$$\gamma = h_{03} + h_{13}$$
$$\delta = \tfrac{1}{2}(h_{22} + h_{33})$$

are, by eqs. (9-69), constants. It is necessary that the function $F^{\mu}(x)$ which is used in eq. (9-70) satisfy the condition

$$\Box^{2}F_{\mu} = 0 \tag{9-73}$$

in order that the normalization condition remain valid. But it is obvious that eq. (9-73) is satisfied because the part of F_μ given by eq. (9-71) is itself a solution of the wave equation, and the part given by eqs. (9-72) contains no powers of the coordinates higher than the first. The resulting line element is

$$ds^2 = dt^2 - dx^2 - (1 - h_{22})\, dy^2 - (1 + h_{22})\, dz^2 + 2h_{23}\, dy\, dz. \quad (9\text{-}74)$$

It has been proved that to first order the line element for a plane gravitational wave, propagated in the direction of the x-axis, is, by a suitable choice of coordinates, given by eq. (9-74). Note that a rotation in the y-z plane by an amount θ gives new values:

new	old	old

$$h_{22} = h_{22} \cos 2\theta + h_{23} \sin 2\theta$$
$$h_{23} = h_{23} \cos 2\theta - h_{22} \sin 2\theta.$$

Thus it is possible to find y- and z-axes such that either h_{22} or h_{23} vanishes. In the latter case the axes are called the *principal axes* of the wave. A rotation of any integer multiple of $\dfrac{\pi}{2}$ radians brings the axes again to principal axes. A rotation of $\dfrac{\pi}{4}$ radians puts the axes in such a position that $h_{22} = 0$ and $h_{23} \neq 0$.

The double-angled behavior of the plane gravitational wave is seen more clearly in an example. In electromagnetism, a sinusoidal plane-front wave

$$E_y = A \cos \omega(t - x)$$
$$E_z = B \cos [\omega(t - x) + \kappa]$$

is circularly polarized if and only if $E_y^2 + E_z^2$ is constant. But then it follows that for the non-trivial case $E_y^2 + E_z^2 > 0$, we must have

$$E_y = A \cos \omega(t - x)$$
$$E_z = \pm A \sin \omega(t - x).$$

The angle ϕ between the E vector and the y-axis, given by

$$\tan \phi = \frac{E_z}{E_y},$$

is therefore

$$\phi = \pm \omega(t - x).$$

At a given location, the electric vector swings around at an angular velocity

$$\frac{\partial \phi}{\partial t} = \pm \omega.$$

In the case of gravitational waves, we define the amplitude H of the wave by

$$H^2 = \tfrac{1}{2} h^{\mu\nu} h_{\mu\nu}.$$

For a plane wave propagated along the x-axis, this becomes

$$H^2 = \mu^2 + \nu^2$$

where $\mu = h_{22}$, $\nu = h_{23}$. For a sinusoidal wave we take

$$\mu = A \cos \omega(t - x)$$
$$\nu = B \cos [\omega(t - x) + \kappa].$$

If it is required that H be constant and non-zero, then by a treatment similar to the electromagnetic case we find

$$\mu = A \cos \omega(t - x)$$
$$\nu = \pm A \sin \omega(t - x).$$

The angle ϕ to the principal axis is given by

$$\tan 2\phi = \frac{h_{23}}{h_{22}} = \frac{\nu}{\mu} = \pm \tan \omega(t - x).$$

Therefore

$$\phi = \pm \tfrac{1}{2} \omega(t - x).$$

Thus the principal axes of a circularly polarized gravitational wave rotate with angular velocity

$$\frac{\partial \phi}{\partial t} = \pm \tfrac{1}{2} \omega.$$

CHAPTER 10

SELECTED TOPICS IN GENERAL RELATIVITY

10.1 SECOND-ORDER THEORY

The linear approximation of Section 9.8 was based on the retention of only the terms of first order in the deviation $h_{\mu\nu}$ of the metric from the Minkowski metric. It was found that the metric has the form given by eq. (9-65) where Φ is the Newtonian potential. In applications to planetary motion, the Newtonian potential is of the same order as the squares of the velocities. We will therefore regard both Φ/c^2 and v^2/c^2 as of the same order, denoted by O, as in Section 9.2. The velocities of both the sources and the test particles are taken to be of the same order. Hence we have, from eq. (9-65), $h_{0i} = c^{-1}O^{\frac{3}{2}}$. Note also that some terms in g_{ij} in eq. (9-65) are of order O^2 and hence are useless unless the theory is carried to third order. Furthermore, the time derivative $\partial/\partial t$ is of order $cO^{\frac{1}{2}}$ compared with the spatial derivative $\partial/\partial x^i$.

Since the line element has the form

$$ds^2 = dt^2\left[1 + 2\frac{\Phi}{c^2} + 2h_{0i}v^i - c^{-2}v^k v^k\left(1 - 2\frac{\Phi}{c^2}\right) + O^2(h)\right]$$

where $v^i = dx^i/dt$, the second order is obtained merely by working out g_{00} to second order; g_{0i} and g_{ij} may be left in their first-order form.

263

Our starting point is the metric

$$g_{00} = 1 + h_{00}$$

$$g_{0i} = \frac{1}{c} 0^{\frac{3}{2}}(h_{00})$$

$$g_{ij} = -\frac{\delta_{ij}}{c^2} + \frac{\delta_{ij}h_{00}}{c^2} + \frac{1}{c^2} 0^2(h_{00}).$$

Calculation of the Ricci tensor for the above metric gives the result

$$R_{00} = -\tfrac{1}{2}c^2\nabla^2 h_{00} + \tfrac{1}{2}c^2(\nabla h_{00})^2 - \tfrac{1}{2}c^2 h_{00}\nabla^2 h_{00}$$

$$-\frac{3}{2}\frac{\partial^2 h_{00}}{\partial t^2} + c^2\frac{\partial^2 h_{0k}}{\partial t\,\partial x^k} + 0^3. \tag{10-1}$$

However, the temporal component of the normalization condition is, to first order,

$$c^2\frac{\partial h_{0k}}{\partial x^k} = 2\frac{\partial h_{00}}{\partial t}.$$

Therefore the last two terms in eq. (10-1) may be combined to give

$$R_{00} = -\tfrac{1}{2}c^2\nabla^2{}_{00} + \tfrac{1}{2}c^2(\nabla h_{00})^2 - \tfrac{1}{2}c^2 h_{00}\nabla^2 h_{00}$$

$$+\frac{1}{2}\frac{\partial^2 h_{00}}{\partial t^2} + 0^3. \tag{10-2}$$

The ∇ operator is the usual one; i.e., $\nabla_i = \partial/\partial x^i$ and $(\nabla h_{00})^2 = (\nabla_k h_{00})(\nabla_k h_{00})$.

The field equation

$$R_{00} = -8\pi G(T_{00} - \tfrac{1}{2}Tg_{00})$$

is now used. Since we are working to second order, we must express $T_{\mu\nu}$ to first order in h_{00}. With the substitutions

$$T_{\mu\nu} = (\rho + pc^{-2})u_\mu u_\nu - pc^{-2}g_{\mu\nu}$$

$$(u_0)^2 = 1 + h_{00} + v^2/c^2 + 0^2$$

$$c^2 h_{00}\nabla^2 h_{00} = 8\pi G h_{00}\rho$$

which come, respectively, from the assumption of a perfect fluid, the condition $1 = g_{\mu\nu}u^\mu u^\nu$, and the first-order solution, we obtain from eq. (10-2)

$$\nabla^2 h_{00} = \frac{8\pi G}{c^2}\rho + \frac{16\pi G}{c^4}\rho v^2 + \frac{1}{c^2}\frac{\partial^2 h_{00}}{\partial t^2} + (\nabla h_{00})^2 + \frac{24\pi G}{c^4}p. \tag{10-3}$$

It is clear from eq. (10-3) that h_{00} to second-order accuracy is given by

$$h_{00} = h_{00}^{\textcircled{1}} + h_{00}^{\textcircled{2}} + h_{00}^{\textcircled{3}} + h_{00}^{\textcircled{4}} + h_{00}^{\textcircled{5}}$$

and the field equations

$$\nabla^2 h_{00}^{\textcircled{1}} = \frac{8\pi G}{c^2} \rho \qquad\qquad \text{a}$$

$$\nabla^2 h_{00}^{\textcircled{2}} = \frac{16\pi G}{c^4} \rho v^2 \qquad\qquad \text{b}$$

$$\nabla^2 h_{00}^{\textcircled{3}} = \frac{1}{c^2} \frac{\partial^2 h_{00}}{\partial t^2} \qquad\qquad \text{c} \qquad (10\text{-}4)$$

$$\nabla^2 h_{00}^{\textcircled{4}} = (\nabla h_{00})^2 \qquad\qquad \text{d}$$

$$\nabla^2 h_{00}^{\textcircled{5}} = \frac{24\pi G}{c^4} p. \qquad\qquad \text{e}$$

The integral of eq. (10-4a) is

$$h_{00}^{\textcircled{1}} = -\frac{2G}{c^2} \int \frac{\rho}{r} \, dV. \qquad (10\text{-}5)$$

However, care must be exercised in evaluating the integral because ρ is the *proper* density but dV is the *coordinate* volume. Thus the combination $\rho \, dV$ is *not* proper mass. In order to convert from coordinate volume dV to proper volume dV_π, we must make use of the concept of four-dimensional volume in Section 8.15. The four-dimensional volume of the parallelopiped formed by the four vectors

$$dx_0^\mu = u^\mu \, ds, \qquad dx_1^\mu = \delta_1^\mu \, dx, \qquad dx_2^\mu = \delta_2^\mu \, dy, \qquad dx_3^\mu = \delta_3^\mu \, dz$$

is

$$dV_4 = \sqrt{-g} \, \epsilon(\mu\nu\rho\sigma) \, dx_0^\mu \, dx_1^\nu \, dx_2^\rho \, dx_3^\sigma = \sqrt{-g} \, u^0 \, ds \, dV$$

since $dV = dx \, dy \, dz$. On the other hand, in the proper coordinates, the same four-dimensional volume is merely $ds \, dV_\pi$. Therefore we have the relation

$$dV = \frac{dV_\pi}{\sqrt{-g} \, u^0},$$

which to our accuracy becomes

$$dV = dV_\pi \left(1 + \tfrac{3}{2} h_{00} - \frac{1}{2} \frac{v^2}{c^2} + 0^2\right).$$

Equation (10-5) becomes

$$h_{00}^{\textcircled{1}} = -\frac{2G}{c^2} \int \frac{dm}{r} \left(1 + \tfrac{3}{2} h_{00} - \frac{1}{2} \frac{v^2}{c^2}\right).$$

Equation (10-4b) has the integral

$$h_{00}^{\textcircled{2}} = -\frac{4G}{c^4} \int \frac{\rho v^2}{r} \, dV.$$

Since this term is already of second order, we may identify $\rho \, dV$ with proper mass:

$$h_{00}^{\textcircled{2}} = -\frac{4G}{c^4} \int \frac{v^2}{r} \, dm.$$

Equation (10-4c) is most easily solved with the use of an intermediary function χ. We define

$$\nabla^2 \chi = \frac{h_{00}}{c^2}. \qquad (10\text{-}6)$$

Then $h_{00}^{\textcircled{3}}$ is given by

$$h_{00}^{\textcircled{3}} = \frac{\partial^2 \chi}{\partial t^2}.$$

Since we are dealing with second-order quantities, there is sufficient accuracy in using Newtonian gravitation, including the principle of superposition. For each element of mass dm, eq. (10-6) becomes, in polar coordinates around the mass,

$$\frac{1}{r^2} \frac{\partial}{\partial r} r^2 \frac{\partial \chi}{\partial r} = -\frac{2G \, dm}{c^4 r}$$

which has the solution

$$\chi = -\frac{G}{c^4} r \, dm.$$

Retracing our steps back to $h_{00}^{\textcircled{3}}$, we have

$$h_{00}^{\textcircled{3}} = -\frac{G}{c^4} \int \frac{d^2 r}{dt^2} \, dm$$

where by d^2r/dt^2 is meant the second time-rate of change of the distance between the field point (as fixed) and the moving element dm of fluid.

Equation (10-4d) is solved by noting that the right-hand side is identical with $\frac{1}{2} \nabla^2 (h_{00}^2) - h_{00} \nabla^2 h_{00}$ and by using the first-order substitution of eq. (10-4a) for the $\nabla^2 h_{00}$. We then have

$$\nabla^2 (h_{00}^{\textcircled{4}} - \tfrac{1}{2} h_{00}^2) = -\frac{8\pi G}{c^2} \rho h_{00}$$

which has the solution

$$h_{00}^{\textcircled{4}} = \tfrac{1}{2} h_{00}^2 + \frac{2G}{c^2} \int \frac{h_{00} \, dm}{r}.$$

Finally, eq. (10-4e) has the integral

$$h_{00}^{\textcircled{5}} = -\frac{6G}{c^4} \int \frac{p \, dV}{r}.$$

Collecting the five terms, we have for h_{00} to second order the expression

$$h_{00} = h + \tfrac{1}{2}h^2 + \frac{G}{c^2}\int dm\left[-\frac{3}{r}\frac{v^2}{c^2} - \frac{h}{r} - \frac{1}{c^2}\frac{d^2r}{dt^2}\right] \tag{10-7}$$

where

$$h = -\frac{2G}{c^2}\int\frac{dm}{r} - \frac{6G}{c^4}\int\frac{p\,dV}{r}.$$

The pressure is regarded as a first-order effect, i.e., $p/\rho c^2 = O^1$.

The equation of motion for a test particle is eq. (9-5), which is the geodesic condition for a curve in space-time. It will be more convenient to use the coordinate time t rather than the proper time s as the independent variable. Equation (8-79) may be used to convert from s to t with the result

$$\frac{d^2x^\mu}{dt^2} = \left[\frac{dx^\mu}{dt}\begin{Bmatrix}0\\\nu\rho\end{Bmatrix}\right] - \begin{Bmatrix}\mu\\\nu\rho\end{Bmatrix}\frac{dx^\nu}{dt}\frac{dx^\rho}{dt}.$$

This expression will be used as the equation of motion.

To sufficient order, the Christoffel symbols are

$$\begin{Bmatrix}0\\00\end{Bmatrix} = \frac{1}{2}\frac{\partial h}{\partial t} + O^{\frac{5}{2}}$$

$$\begin{Bmatrix}i\\00\end{Bmatrix} = c^2\left[\frac{1}{2}\frac{\partial h}{\partial x^i} + \frac{1}{2}\frac{\partial\theta}{\partial x^i} + \frac{1}{2}h\frac{\partial h}{\partial x^i} - \frac{\partial h_{0i}}{\partial t}\right] + O^3$$

$$\begin{Bmatrix}0\\0j\end{Bmatrix} = \frac{1}{2}\frac{\partial h}{\partial x^j} + O^2$$

$$\begin{Bmatrix}i\\0j\end{Bmatrix} = -\frac{1}{2}\delta_{ij}\frac{\partial h}{\partial t} - \frac{c^2}{2}\left(\frac{\partial h_{0i}}{\partial x^j} - \frac{\partial h_{0j}}{\partial x^i}\right) + O^{\frac{5}{2}}$$

$$\begin{Bmatrix}0\\jk\end{Bmatrix} = O^{\frac{3}{2}}$$

$$\begin{Bmatrix}i\\jk\end{Bmatrix} = \frac{1}{2}\left[\delta_{jk}\frac{\partial h}{\partial x^i} - \delta_{ij}\frac{\partial h}{\partial x^k} - \delta_{ik}\frac{\partial h}{\partial x^j}\right] + O^2$$

where $\theta = h_{00} - h$. Substitution of the Christoffel symbols gives the equation of motion

$$\frac{dv^i}{dt} + \frac{c^2}{2}\frac{\partial h}{\partial x^i} = -\tfrac{1}{2}c^2\frac{\partial\theta}{\partial x^i} - \tfrac{1}{2}c^2h\frac{\partial h}{\partial x^i} + c^2\frac{\partial h_{0i}}{\partial t}$$

$$+ \tfrac{3}{2}v^i\frac{\partial h}{\partial t} + 2v^iv^k\frac{\partial h}{\partial x^k} - \tfrac{1}{2}v^kv^k\frac{\partial h}{\partial x^i}$$

$$+ c^2v^k\left[\frac{\partial h_{0i}}{\partial x^k} - \frac{\partial h_{0k}}{\partial x^i}\right] \tag{10-8}$$

where $v^i = dx^i/dt$.

10.2 THE PROBLEM OF N BODIES

We will apply the results of the preceding section to the case of N point particles which interact with each other through gravity. The field is given by eq. (10-7) which for point masses becomes

$$h_{00} = h + \tfrac{1}{2}h^2 + \sum_{\beta=1}^{N}\left[-\frac{3\mu_\beta v_\beta^2}{r_\beta c^2} + 2\frac{\mu_\beta}{r_\beta}\sum_{\gamma \neq \beta}\frac{\mu_\gamma}{r_{\beta\gamma}} - \frac{\mu_\beta}{c^2}\frac{d^2 r_\beta}{dt^2}\right] \qquad \text{a}$$

where

$$(10\text{-}9)$$

$$h = -2\sum_{\beta=1}^{N}\frac{\mu_\beta}{r_\beta}; \qquad \text{b}$$

μ_β is G/c^2 times the mass of the βth particle (including the first-order pressure correction), v_β is the velocity of the βth particle, r_β is the distance between the field point and the βth particle, and $r_{\beta\gamma}$ is the distance between the βth and γ^{th} particles.

We are concerned with the motion, not of a test particle, but of one of the N particles, say the αth particle. The differentiations indicated in eq. (10-8) are to be applied to eq. (10-9) and to

$$h_{0i} = \frac{4}{c^2}\sum_{\beta=1}^{N}\frac{\mu_\beta v_\beta^i}{r_\beta} \qquad \text{c} \quad (10\text{-}9)$$

where v_β^i is the velocity of the βth particle. It is easy enough to differentiate r_β, for we have

$$r_\beta^2 = (x_\alpha^i - x_\beta^i)(x_\alpha^i - x_\beta^i) \quad \text{(no sum on } \alpha, \beta)$$

where x_β^i is the coordinate of the βth particle. The left-hand side of eq. (10-8) becomes the expression

$$\frac{dv_\alpha^i}{dt} + c^2\sum_{\beta \neq \alpha}\frac{\mu_\beta}{r_\beta^3}(x_\alpha^i - x_\beta^i)$$

which in the Newtonian approximation is equal to zero. Note that the αth particle must be omitted from the sums in eqs. (10-9) because we seek the effect of the *other* particles on it.

The differentiations on the right-hand side of eq. (10-8) can be carried out by straightforward calculation. There arise two terms (one from $\partial h_{0i}/\partial t$ and one from $d^2 r_\beta/dt^2$ in θ) which contain the acceleration dv_β/dt of the βth particle. Since the terms are of second order, we are justified in using the first-order solution

$$\frac{dv_\beta^i}{dt} = -c^2\sum_{\gamma \neq \beta}\frac{\mu_\gamma}{r_{\beta\gamma}^3}(x_\beta^i - x_\gamma^i).$$

A comment must be made about the second term in brackets in eq. (10-9a). This term was originally $\mu_\beta h(x_\beta)/r_\beta$; it contained the gravitational field at the βth particle due to the *other* particles. Note that the latter includes the αth particle. However, in differentiating this term with respect to x_α^i, we may differentiate the $1/r_\beta$ but not the $h(x_\beta)$, even though the latter contains a term $-2\mu_\alpha/r_\beta$. The reason is that we must regard the product $\mu_\beta h(x_\beta)$ as a property of the βth particle which is not subject to variation of the field point. This situation is clarified by remembering that the equation of motion was originally that of a test particle which did not contribute to the field.

The result of the calculation described above is

$$\frac{dv_\alpha^i}{dt} + c^2 \sum_{\beta \neq \alpha} \frac{\mu_\beta}{r_\beta^3}(x_\alpha^i - x_\beta^i)$$

$$= \sum_{\beta \neq \alpha} \frac{\mu_\beta}{r_\beta^3}(x_\alpha^i - x_\beta^i)\left[5\frac{\mu_\alpha c^2}{r_\beta} + 4\sum_{\gamma \neq \alpha}\frac{\mu_\gamma c^2}{r_\gamma}\right.$$

$$+ \sum_{\gamma \neq \beta, \alpha} \frac{\mu_\gamma c^2}{r_{\gamma\beta}} - \tfrac{1}{2}(x_\alpha^k - x_\beta^k)\sum_{\gamma \neq \beta, \alpha}\frac{\mu_\gamma c^2}{r_{\gamma\beta}^3}(x_\beta^k - x_\gamma^k)$$

$$+ v_\alpha^k v_\alpha^k - 2(v_\alpha^k - v_\beta^k)(v_\alpha^k - v_\beta^k) + \left.\frac{3}{2}\frac{1}{r_\beta^2}[v_\beta^k(x_\alpha^k - x_\beta^k)]^2\right]$$

$$+ \sum_{\beta \neq \alpha}\frac{\mu_\beta}{r_\beta^3}(x_\alpha^k - x_\beta^k)[4(v_\alpha^i - v_\beta^i)(v_\alpha^k - v_\beta^k) + v_\beta^k(v_\alpha^i - v_\beta^i)]$$

$$- \frac{7}{2}\sum_{\beta \neq \alpha}\sum_{\gamma \neq \beta, \alpha}\frac{\mu_\beta \mu_\gamma c^2}{r_\beta r_{\beta\gamma}^3}(x_\beta^i - x_\gamma^i). \qquad \text{(no sum on } \alpha) \qquad (10\text{-}10)$$

10.3 THE TWO-BODY PROBLEM

The equations of motion for two point masses m_1 and m_2 are, from eq. (10-10),

$$\left.\begin{aligned}
\frac{d^2\xi_1^i}{dt^2} - \frac{\mu_2 c^2}{r^3}x^i &= -\frac{\mu_2 x^i}{r^3}\left[5\frac{\mu_1 c^2}{r} + 4\frac{\mu_2 c^2}{r} + \dot\xi_1^k\dot\xi_1^k - 2v^k v^k\right. \\
&\quad + \left.\frac{3}{2}\frac{1}{r^2}(\dot\xi_2^k x^k)^2\right] - \frac{\mu_2 v^i}{r^3}x^k(4v^k - \dot\xi_2^k) \\
\frac{d^2\xi_2^i}{dt^2} + \frac{\mu_1 c^2}{r^3}x^i &= \frac{\mu_1 x^i}{r^3}\left[5\frac{\mu_2 c^2}{r} + 4\frac{\mu_1 c^2}{r} + \dot\xi_2^k\dot\xi_2^k - 2v^k v^k\right. \\
&\quad + \left.\frac{3}{2}\frac{1}{r^2}(\dot\xi_1^k x^k)^2\right] + \frac{\mu_1 v^i}{r^3}x^k(4v^k + \dot\xi_1^k)
\end{aligned}\right\} \qquad (10\text{-}11)$$

where ξ^i_α is the coordinate of the αth particle, the dot indicates time differentiation, and the following definitions are made:

$$x^i = \xi^i_2 - \xi^i_1$$

$$r^2 = x^i x^i$$

$$v^i = \frac{dx^i}{dt}$$

$$\mu_\alpha = \frac{Gm_\alpha}{c^2}.$$

New coordinates x^i, α^i will be introduced in place of ξ^i_1 and ξ^i_2. The x^i are defined above; the α^i are defined thus:

$$\alpha^i = \frac{\mu_1 \xi^i_1 + \mu_2 \xi^i_2}{\mu}$$

where $\mu = \mu_1 + \mu_2$.

In the first-order approximation, which may be freely substituted into the second-order terms, we may choose the original coordinates ξ^i_α in such a way that the center of mass is stationary:

$$\dot{\xi}^i_1 = -\frac{\mu_2}{\mu} v^i, \qquad \dot{\xi}^i_2 = \frac{\mu_1}{\mu} v^i.$$

Then by suitably adding and subtracting eqs. (10-11) with factors μ_1 or μ_2 when needed, as in the classical treatment, we obtain the equations of motion

$$\ddot{x}^i + \frac{\mu c^2}{r^3} x^i = Cx^i + D\dot{x}^i \qquad (10\text{-}12)$$

$$\ddot{\alpha}^i = Ax^i + B\dot{x}^i \qquad (10\text{-}13)$$

where the coefficients A, B, C, and D are given by

$$A = \frac{\mu_1\mu_2(\mu_2 - \mu_1)c^2}{2\mu r^3}\left(\frac{4}{r} - \frac{1}{a} - \frac{3p}{r^2}\right)$$

$$B = -\frac{\mu_1\mu_2(\mu_2 - \mu_1)}{\mu^2 r^2}\dot{r}$$

$$C = \frac{c^2}{a r^3}\left\{\mu^2 + \frac{3}{2}\mu_1\mu_2 + \frac{a}{r}(2\mu^2 - \mu_1\mu_2) - \frac{3}{2}\frac{ap}{r^2}\mu_1\mu_2\right\}$$

$$D = \frac{2}{\mu r^2}(2\mu^2 - \mu_1\mu_2)\dot{r}.$$

The quantities a and p appearing in the above expressions are the semi-major axis and the semi-latus rectum, respectively, for the classical orbit

$1/r = (1/p)[1 + e \cos (\phi + \omega)]$ which has been substituted into the second-order terms. Thus we have two equations of motion—one for the center of mass α^i and one for the relative separation x^i.

The two-body problem in general relativity has immediate application to astronomy. There may exist double stars in which the ratio of mass to separation is large enough for there to be observable effects of general relativity. The equations of motion are given to second order by eqs. (10-12) and (10-13). They show that the orbit is planar to at least the second approximation. Equation (10-12) can be solved for the relative orbit. The angular momentum $H = r^2\dot{\phi}$ for the relative orbit is given by the differential equation

$$\frac{dH}{dt} = -\frac{2}{\mu}(2\mu^2 - \mu_1\mu_2)H\dot{u}$$

which has the solution

$$H = he^{-\frac{2}{\mu}(2\mu^2 - \mu_1\mu_2)u}$$

where $u = 1/r$. The radial equation

$$\ddot{r} - r\dot{\phi}^2 + \frac{\mu c^2}{r^2} = Cr + D\dot{r}$$

can then be solved by approximation methods to find the orbit $r(\phi)$. The perihelion advance of the *relative orbit* is given by

$$\sigma = \frac{3\mu}{p}.$$

This is the same as for a test particle going around a stationary mass. The μ here is the total mass of both particles (multiplied by G/c^2).

The equation of motion for the center of mass must be examined rather closely. In the classical approximation, α^i is the coordinate of the center of mass. However, we saw in Chapter 5 the difficulty of defining center of mass even in special relativity. Therefore no attempt will be made here to give an exact definition for center of mass in general relativity. Nevertheless, merely the fact that α^i is, to first order, the coordinate of the center of mass tells us something. If α^i were to change by an amount of order p, then we could say that the system is moving through space. We should not be surprised to find $\ddot{\alpha}^i$ *not* zero to second order, because we have not tried to define α^i as the center of mass to second order. However, it would be surprising if it were found that the *average* $\ddot{\alpha}^i$ were not zero. This would mean that the double-star system is accelerating through space. The momentum reaction would presumably be taken up by gravitational waves emitted in the opposite direction. Now the average $\ddot{\alpha}^i$ perpendicular to the orbit is obviously zero. The average $\ddot{\alpha}^i$ along the minor axis of the orbit is quickly seen by symmetry to be zero. But what of the component of $\ddot{\alpha}^i$ along the major axis? An integration of $\ddot{\alpha}^i$ over one period must be performed. The results, based on eq. (10-13), are zero. Therefore a double star should have uniform translational motion to second order. Different results by other authors are due principally to failure to recognize what was explained in the last discussion paragraph of Section 10.2.

10.4 ROTATIONAL SYMMETRY

The Schwarzschild line element is an exact solution of the field equation based on spherical symmetry. The assumption of rotational symmetry leads to a more general solution which includes the Schwarzschild solution as a special case.

The principal steps of the derivation will be given here. The reader may consult the literature for a fuller treatment.* The line element is assumed to be static (invariant under temporal translations), rotationally symmetric (invariant under angular translations), and invariant under reversal of time or angle. It follows that the line element must be of the form

$$ds^2 = g_{00}\, dt^2 + (g_{11}\, dx_1^2 + 2g_{12}\, dx_1\, dx_2 + g_{22}\, dx_2^2) + g_{33}\, d\phi^2$$

where ϕ is the angle about the axis of symmetry, x_1 and x_2 are coordinates in the meridianal plane $\phi = $ const, and all $g_{\mu\nu}$ are independent of both t and ϕ. It is then possible to transform to coordinates in which $g_{12} = 0$ and $g_{11} = g_{22}$. But then the sum $G_1^1 + G_2^2$ of two components of the Einstein tensor becomes a multiple of

$$\left(\frac{\partial^2}{\partial x_1^2} + \frac{\partial^2}{\partial x_2^2}\right)\sqrt{g_{00}g_{33}}.$$

The assumption $G_1^1 + G_2^2 = 0$ allows the further transformation from x_1, x_2 to r, z such that $r = c\sqrt{-g_{00}g_{33}}$ and the line element contains dr, dz only in the form $dr^2 + dz^2$. The line element has thus, by the appropriate choice of coordinates and by the assumption $G_1^1 + G_2^2 = 0$, been reduced to the form

$$ds^2 = e^{2\nu}\, dt^2 - \frac{1}{c^2} e^{-2\nu}[e^{2\gamma}(dz^2 + dr^2) + r^2\, d\phi^2] \qquad (10\text{-}14)$$

where ν and γ are functions only of z and r.

---

* See References in Section B. 2.

The Einstein tensor for the metric of eq. (10-14) is given by

$$G_1^1 = -G_2^2 = c^2 e^{2(\nu-\gamma)}\left(\nu_2^2 - \nu_1^2 - \frac{1}{r}\gamma_2\right) \qquad a$$

$$G_2^1 = G_1^2 = c^2 e^{2(\nu-\gamma)}\left(-2\nu_1\nu_2 + \frac{1}{r}\gamma_1\right) \qquad b \Bigg\} \quad (10\text{-}15)$$

$$G_3^3 = c^2 e^{2(\nu-\gamma)}(\gamma_{11} + \gamma_{22} + \nu_1^2 + \nu_2^2) \qquad c$$

$$G_3^3 - G_0^0 = 2c^2 e^{2(\nu-\gamma)}\nabla^2\nu \qquad d$$

where

$$\nabla^2\nu = \frac{1}{r}\frac{\partial}{\partial r}\left(r\frac{\partial \nu}{\partial r}\right) + \frac{\partial^2\nu}{\partial z^2}$$

and the subscripts 1 and 2 indicate partial differentiation with respect to z and r, respectively. The other components of G_μ^ν vanish identically. The vacuum condition $G_\mu^\nu = 0$ implies

from eq. (10-15a),

$$\frac{\partial\gamma}{\partial r} = r(\nu_2^2 - \nu_1^2) \Bigg\}$$

$$\frac{\partial\gamma}{\partial z} = 2r\nu_1\nu_2 \qquad (10\text{-}16)$$

from eq. (10-15b), and

$$\nabla^2\nu = 0 \qquad (10\text{-}17)$$

from eq. (10-15d). From eqs. (10-16) we see that the differential of γ is

$$d\gamma = 2r\nu_1\nu_2\,dz + r(\nu_2^2 - \nu_1^2)\,dr. \qquad (10\text{-}18)$$

The condition of integrability for γ is

$$\frac{\partial}{\partial z}\left(\frac{\partial\gamma}{\partial r}\right) = \frac{\partial}{\partial r}\left(\frac{\partial\gamma}{\partial z}\right)$$

which, with the substitution of eqs. (10-16), reduces to $r\nu_1\,\nabla^2\nu = 0$. Thus eq. (10-18) is integrable by virtue of eq. (10-17). Also, by virtue of eqs. (10-16), eq. (10-15c) becomes

$$G_3^3 = 2c^2 e^{2(\nu-\gamma)}r\nu_2\nabla^2\nu$$

which, because of eq. (10-17), vanishes. Our task thus reduces to finding a solution of eq. (10-17).

Equation (10-17) is familiar to us from classical gravitation. The Newtonian potential Φ in a vacuum satisfies the same equation. Therefore for each Newtonian solution $\Phi(z, r)$ there exists a corresponding general-relativistic solution $\nu(z, r) = \Phi/c^2$. It must be kept in mind that the

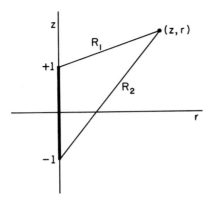

FIGURE 10.1 Potential of line mass.

coordinates z, r do not retain their Euclidean meaning and that the mass distribution in the general-relativistic case will not be the same as in the Newtonian case.

Let us consider first the case where Φ is the Newtonian potential due to a line mass of length $2l$ and uniform density $2l/M$. With the line mass placed on the z-axis so that its ends are at $z = \pm l$ (see Figure 10.1), the potential is

$$\Phi(z, r) = -\frac{GM}{2l} \ln \frac{R_1 + R_2 + 2l}{R_1 + R_2 - 2l},$$

where

$$R_1^2 = (z - l)^2 + r^2$$
$$R_2^2 = (z + l)^2 + r^2.$$

Upon identifying Φ with νc^2 and z, r with the coordinates of eq. (10-14), we have immediately a solution to the general-relativistic problem of the gravitational field due to a line mass. We do not know the mass distribution along the line without carrying out a calculation to find it, but it is clear from the Newtonian approximation that M is the total effective gravitational mass in the general-relativistic case.

The special case $l = \mu = GM/c^2$ is of particular interest. The metric is given by

$$\nu = \frac{1}{2} \ln \frac{R_1 + R_2 - 2\mu}{R_1 + R_2 + 2\mu}$$

and

$$\gamma = \frac{1}{2} \ln \frac{(R_1 + R_2)^2 - 4\mu^2}{4R_1 R_2}$$

where

$$R_1^2 = (z - \mu)^2 + r^2$$
$$R_2^2 = (z + \mu)^2 + r^2.$$

Equation (10-14) becomes

$$ds^2 = \frac{R_1 + R_2 - 2\mu}{R_1 + R_2 + 2\mu} dt^2 - \frac{(R_1 + R_2 + 2\mu)^2}{4c^2 R_1 R_2}(dr^2 + dz^2)$$

$$- \frac{R_1 + R_2 + 2\mu}{R_1 + R_2 - 2\mu}\frac{r^2}{c^2} d\phi^2.$$

Transformation of the above metric to new coordinates ρ, θ defined by

$$\rho = \frac{R_1 + R_2 + 2\mu}{2}$$

$$\cos\theta = \frac{R_2 - R_1}{2\mu}$$

or by

$$\left. \begin{aligned} z &= (\rho - \mu)\cos\theta \\ r &= \sqrt{\rho^2 - 2\mu\rho}\,\sin\theta \end{aligned} \right\} \tag{10-19}$$

puts the line element into the Schwarzschild form of eq. (9-20), where the r there is the ρ here. Thus the case under consideration is the field of a point mass! But then how did we start out with a line mass? The answer lies in the choice of coordinates. Equations (10-19) show that the Schwarzschild singularity $\rho = 2\mu$ transforms into the *line* $r = 0$, $|z| < \mu$. Furthermore, the transformation is such that the singular region $\rho < 2\mu$ does not exist in the z, r coordinates. Surfaces of constant ρ become ellipsoids in the z, r coordinates, and surfaces of constant θ become hyperboloids of revolution.

In the more general case where l is not equal to μ, the exponents ν and γ are, respectively, equal to μ/l and $(\mu/l)^2$ times the corresponding values in the Schwarzschild case.*

---

* That is

$$\nu = \frac{\mu}{2l}\ln\frac{R_1 + R_2 - 2l}{R_1 + R_2 + 2l}$$

$$\gamma = \frac{1}{2}\left(\frac{\mu}{l}\right)^2 \ln\frac{(R_1 + R_2)^2 - 4l^2}{4R_1 R_2},$$

or, in coordinates ξ, η more suited to the problem, defined by $R_1 + R_2 = 2l\cosh\xi$, $R_2 - R_1 = 2l\cos\eta$,

$$\nu = \frac{\mu}{l}\ln\tanh\frac{\xi}{2}$$

$$\gamma = \frac{1}{2}\left(\frac{\mu}{l}\right)^2 \ln\frac{\sinh^2\xi}{\cosh^2\xi - \cos^2\eta}.$$

The line element is

$$ds^2 = c^2\left(\tanh\frac{\xi}{2}\right)^{2\psi} dt^2 - l^2\left(\coth\frac{\xi}{2}\right)^{2\psi}[(\sinh\xi)^{2\psi^2}$$

$$\times (\sinh^2\xi + \sin^2\eta)^{1-\psi^2}(d\xi^2 + d\eta^2) + \sinh^2\xi\sin^2\eta\,d\phi^2]$$

where $\psi = \mu/l$.

When one calculates the *metric* length of the mass by taking the limit of the metric for small r and $|z| < l$, it is found that the metric length is either zero or infinite unless $l = \mu$ (in which case the length is $2\pi\mu$, as can be obtained from the Schwarzschild metric).

Since a single line mass in the z, r coordinates with mass M and "length" $2\mu = 2GM/c^2$ represents a single point particle, it seems reasonable to expect two such line masses to represent two point particles. Consider two line masses on the z-axis having masses M and M' and "lengths" 2μ and $2\mu'$, where μ and μ' are the gravitational lengths. Let $2D$ be their separation (see Figure 10.2). The exponent ν for the line element of eq. (10-14) is easily found to be given by

$$e^{2\nu} = \frac{R_1 + R_2 - 2\mu}{R_1 + R_2 + 2\mu} \cdot \frac{R_3 + R_4 - 2\mu'}{R_3 + R_4 + 2\mu'}$$

where the R's are the distances of the field point from the ends of the masses based on the Pythagorean theorem in z, r coordinates. Extensive calculation shows that the other exponent γ from eq. (10-18) is given by

$$e^{2\gamma} = \frac{(R_1 + R_2)^2 - 4\mu^2}{4R_1R_2} \cdot \frac{(R_3 + R_4)^2 - 4\mu'^2}{4R_3R_4}$$
$$\cdot \left[\frac{(\mu' + D)R_1 + (\mu + \mu' + D)R_2 - \mu R_4}{DR_1 + (\mu + D)R_2 - \mu R_3}\right]^2 \left(\frac{D}{D + \mu'}\right)^2.$$

The constant of integration has been chosen so that $\gamma \to 0$ at large distances from the system, and, in particular, so that $\gamma = 0$ along the z-axis above and below both masses.

We must exercise care in interpreting the results of these calculations. We started with the assumption of a static line element. Then we introduced two masses. But two masses in otherwise empty space must either revolve around each other or fall toward each other—a situation which is obviously not static. Therefore we expect the line element for the two

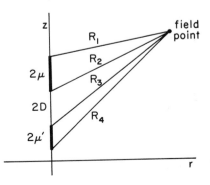

FIGURE 10.2 Two point masses.

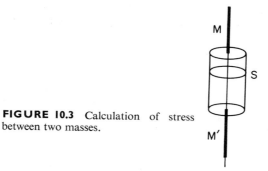

FIGURE 10.3 Calculation of stress between two masses.

masses to exhibit a curious behavior of some kind. Now the only place where the line element can exhibit a singular behavior is along the z-axis between the outer ends of the masses. The singularities along the masses themselves are understandable. But what about the space between the masses? Examination of the line element shows that there is a singularity along the z-axis *between* the masses which corresponds to a line compression. Thus the calculation of the line element shows that two static masses have some kind of medium between them which transmits the compressional force necessary to keep the masses apart.

The singularity appears in the exponent γ. On the z-axis between the masses, γ has the value

$$\gamma = \ln\left[1 - \frac{\mu\mu'}{(D + \mu)(D + \mu')}\right].$$

For the case of a large separation $D \gg \mu, \mu'$, this becomes

$$\gamma \approx -\frac{\mu\mu'}{D^2}.$$

The spatial part of the line element in a plane $z = $ const has the metric $e^{2\gamma} dr^2 + r^2 d\phi^2$. Thus a small circle of coordinate radius r around the z-axis between the masses has a ratio of metric circumference to metric radius of $2\pi e^{-\gamma}$. This is the same kind of geometry as on a cone of half-angle $\sin^{-1}e^{-\gamma}$ except that here $\gamma < 0$ and the angle is imaginary.

In order to find the state of stress along the singularity, we will replace the singularity by a cylinder of coordinate radius a which contains no singularities. Then we will take the limit as $a \to 0$. (See Figure 10.3.) It will be assumed that G_μ^ν vanishes everywhere outside the cylinder and outside the line masses. However, we will retain the assumption $G_1^1 + G_2^2 = 0$ which was necessary in setting up the coordinates z, r. The cylinder has coordinate radius a and lies between the inner ends of the line masses. It is assumed that no singularities exist inside the cylinder.

The total stress F exerted across any plane S given by $z = $ const inside the cylinder is calculated as follows. From the stress-energy tensor, F is given by

$$F = c^2 \int T_1^1 \, dS$$

where

$$dS = e^{\gamma - 2\nu} r \, dr \, d\phi.$$

But the substitution of the field equation $T_1^1 = -\dfrac{1}{\kappa} G_1^1$ and the use of eq. (10-15a) give

$$F = \frac{c^4}{4G} \int_0^a e^{-\gamma} \left(\nu_1^2 - \nu_2^2 + \frac{\gamma_2}{r} \right) r \, dr.$$

The part of the integral which contains the ν's is of order a. Since we are interested in taking the limit $a \to 0$, this part of the integral will be neglected, leaving the part which depends on γ:

$$F = \frac{c^4}{4G} (e^{-\gamma(0)} - e^{-\gamma(a)}). \tag{10-20}$$

In order to avoid having the metric be singular along the z-axis, $\gamma(0)$ must vanish. Furthermore, γ is assumed to be continuous so that for small a we have

$$e^{-\gamma(a)} = \frac{1}{1 - \dfrac{\mu\mu'}{(D + \mu)(D + \mu')}}.$$

Therefore in the limit $a \to 0$, eq. (10-20) becomes

$$F = -\frac{c^4}{4G} \frac{\mu\mu'}{D(D + \mu + \mu')} = -\frac{GMM'}{(2D)^2} \frac{1}{1 + \dfrac{\mu + \mu'}{D}}.$$

The above calculation shows that the z-axis between the two line masses contains a compression which, in the Newtonian limit $D \gg \mu, \mu'$, is merely the Newtonian force of attraction $GMM'/(2D)^2$.

10.5 FIELD OF VARIABLE MASS

We ask the question: what is the general-relativistic perturbation on a planetary orbit around a *variable* mass? It will be assumed that a spherically symmetric star loses mass in the form of electromagnetic radiation so that the mass $M(t)$ is a function of time. Spherical symmetry is presumed to hold for all physical quantities, so that the line element of eq. (9-16) applies. For the sake of greater simplicity, it will be assumed that the star maintains a constant coordinate radius a and does not emit any solar wind.

The study in Section 4.4 showed that, at least in special relativity, the electromagnetic stress-energy tensor for radiation has the form $S^{\mu\nu} = \lambda^\mu \lambda^\nu$ where λ^μ is a null vector whose spatial part is in the direction of propagation. But this is a tensor property, and hence may be carried over into general relativity. In the present problem, the vector λ^μ has the form

$$\lambda^\mu = \lambda^0[1, ce^{\frac{1}{2}(\nu-\gamma)}, 0, 0].$$

The proper energy density $U(t, r)$ for a stationary observer is obtained by transforming to local proper coordinates $\Delta \bar{x}^\alpha$ in which the local metric is Minkowski:

$$\Delta \bar{t} = e^{\frac{1}{2}\nu} \Delta t$$
$$\Delta \bar{x} = e^{\frac{1}{2}\lambda} \Delta r$$
$$\Delta \bar{y} = r \Delta \theta$$
$$\Delta \bar{z} = r \sin \theta \, \Delta \phi.$$

(The bar is omitted from the U for convenience.) Thus we find $U = S^{00}c^2 e^\nu = (\lambda^0)^2 c^2 e^\nu$. Therefore the electromagnetic stress-energy tensor is given by

$$S^{\mu\nu} = \frac{U}{c^2} \begin{bmatrix} e^{-\nu} & ce^{-\frac{1}{2}(\nu+\lambda)} & 0 & 0 \\ ce^{-\frac{1}{2}(\nu+\lambda)} & c^2 e^{-\lambda} & 0 & 0 \\ 0 & 0 & 0 & 0 \\ 0 & 0 & 0 & 0 \end{bmatrix}.$$

The only non-vanishing components of S^ν_μ are

$$S^0_0 = Uc^{-2}$$
$$S^1_1 = -Uc^{-2}$$
$$S^0_1 = -Uc^{-3}e^{\frac{1}{2}(\lambda-\nu)}$$
$$S^1_0 = Uc^{-1}e^{\frac{1}{2}(\nu-\lambda)}.$$

The field equation $G^\nu_\mu = -\kappa S^\nu_\mu$ outside the star supplies the conditions

$$G^0_0 = -\kappa Uc^{-2}$$
$$G^0_1 = \kappa Uc^{-3}e^{\frac{1}{2}(\lambda-\nu)}$$
$$G^1_0 = -\kappa Uc^{-1}e^{\frac{1}{2}(\nu-\lambda)}$$
$$G^1_1 - G^0_0 = 2\kappa Uc^{-2}$$
$$G^2_2 = 0$$
$$G^3_3 = 0$$

which with eqs. (9-17) gives

$$
\left.
\begin{aligned}
\frac{\partial}{\partial t}(re^{-\lambda}) &= \frac{\kappa r^2}{c^3} U e^{\frac{1}{2}(\nu-\lambda)} \\[2mm]
\frac{\partial}{\partial r}(re^{-\lambda}) &= 1 - \frac{\kappa r^2}{c^4} U \\[2mm]
\frac{\partial}{\partial r}(\nu+\lambda) &= \frac{2\kappa r}{c^4} U e^{\lambda}.
\end{aligned}
\right\} \tag{10-21}
$$

The field equation outside the star and the Bianchi identity provide the condition $S^{\nu}_{\mu,\nu} = 0$ which to lowest order, i.e., with ν and λ zero, becomes

$$
\frac{\partial}{\partial t}(r^2 U) + c\frac{\partial}{\partial r}(r^2 U) = 0. \tag{10-22}
$$

The solution to eq. (10-22) is

$$
r^2 U(t, r) = f\left(t - \frac{r}{c}\right)
$$

where f is an arbitrary function. But the rate at which mass is lost is

$$
-\frac{dM}{dt} = (4\pi r^2 U)_{r=a} \cdot \frac{1}{c}.
$$

Therefore we have the boundary condition

$$
f\left(t - \frac{a}{c}\right) = -\frac{c}{4\pi}\dot{M}(t)
$$

which fixes the function f in terms of the time derivative $\dot{M}$ of the mass $M(t)$. Therefore in general $f\left(t - \dfrac{r}{c}\right)$ is equal to $-(c/4\pi)\dot{M}\left(t - \dfrac{r}{c} + \dfrac{a}{c}\right)$, and $U(t, r)$ is given by

$$
U = -\frac{c}{4\pi r^2}\dot{M}\left(t - \frac{r}{c} + \frac{a}{c}\right).
$$

Equations (10-21) then give

$$
\left.
\begin{aligned}
\frac{\partial}{\partial t}(re^{-\lambda}) &= -2\dot{\mu}\left(t - \frac{r}{c} + \frac{a}{c}\right) & \quad\text{a} \\[2mm]
\frac{\partial}{\partial r}(re^{-\lambda}) &= 1 + \frac{2}{c}\dot{\mu}\left(t - \frac{r}{c} + \frac{a}{c}\right) & \quad\text{b} \\[2mm]
\frac{\partial}{\partial r}(\nu+\lambda) &= -\frac{4}{cr}\dot{\mu}\left(t - \frac{r}{c} + \frac{a}{c}\right) & \quad\text{c}
\end{aligned}
\right\} \tag{10-23}
$$

where $\mu(t) = GM(t)/c^2$. Equations (10-23) are the first-order equations for v and λ. Equations (10-23a) and (10-23b) have the integral

$$e^{-\lambda} = 1 - \frac{2}{r}\mu\left(t - \frac{r}{c} + \frac{a}{c}\right).$$

Thus the value of $e^{-\lambda}$ is given to first order by eq. (9-20b), provided that μ is evaluated at the time when the light signal passing through (t, r) left the star. Note that the gradient of λ is

$$\frac{\partial \lambda}{\partial r} = -\frac{2\mu}{r^2} - \frac{2\dot{\mu}}{cr},$$

so that eq. (10-23c) becomes

$$\frac{\partial v}{\partial r} = \frac{2}{r^2}\mu\left(t - \frac{r}{c} + \frac{a}{c}\right) - \frac{2}{cr}\dot{\mu}\left(t - \frac{r}{c} + \frac{a}{c}\right). \qquad (10\text{-}24)$$

The Newtonian potential, given by $\Phi = vc^2/2$, has a gradient from eq. (10-24) of

$$-\frac{\partial \Phi}{\partial r} = -\frac{G}{r^2}M\left(t - \frac{r}{c} + \frac{a}{c}\right) + \frac{G}{cr}\dot{M}\left(t - \frac{r}{c} + \frac{a}{c}\right).$$

The first term is to be expected; it is merely the Newtonian gravitational field due to the mass at the time when the light ray through (t, r) left the object. The second term is the relativistic correction. However, in comparison with the first term, the second term has the same magnitude as the fraction of mass lost in a time r/c. For the earth's distance from the sun, this magnitude is 10^{-18}—utterly negligible.

Although the result has little importance for astronomy, the derivation of the result provides an example of the use of the electromagnetic stress-energy tensor for radiation in the context of general relativity. The same method is used in Section A.3 in connection with cosmology.

CHAPTER 11

INERTIAL FRAMES

11.1 COORDINATES

Coordinates x^μ about a given time-like geodesic Γ are chosen in the following way. An event O on Γ is selected as the origin, and a space-like hypersurface* Σ is constructed through O orthogonal to Γ. We construct any congruence of time-like geodesics such that the members intersect Σ and such that Γ is that member which passes through O (Fig. 11.1). Coordinates x^i ($i = 1, 2, 3$) are established in Σ by any convenient means. The coordinates x^0, x^1, x^2, x^3 of an event P are then defined as follows. The member Γ' of the congruence which passes through P intersects Σ at Q. Then x^0 is the proper time along Γ' from Q to P, and x^i is the location of Q in Σ.

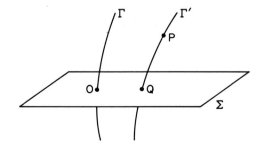

FIGURE 11.1 Construction of coordinates in Section 11.1.

---

* A *hypersurface* is an $(n - 1)$-dimensional space embedded in an n-dimensional space.

282

The above choice of coordinates results in a simplification of the metric tensor. First, the orthogonality of Σ and Γ at O requires $g_{0i}(0) = 0$. Second, the condition that $x^0 = s$ and $x^i = $ const designate geodesics (the members of the congruence) requires

$$g_{00}(x^\mu) = 1 \qquad (11\text{-}1)$$

and, for members of the congruence, $d^2x^\mu/ds^2 = 0$. Finally, the latter condition in turn implies $\begin{Bmatrix} \mu \\ 00 \end{Bmatrix} = 0$ which implies

$$[00, \mu] = 0. \qquad (11\text{-}2)$$

Equations (11-1) and (11-2) require $\partial g_{0i}/\partial x^0 = 0$. Therefore g_{0i} is independent of x^0 and is zero along Γ. With $t = x^0$ the metric is

$$ds^2 = dt^2 + 2g_{0i}(x^l)\, dt\, dx^i + g_{jk}(x^\mu)\, dx^j\, dx^k. \qquad (11\text{-}3)$$

(Latin indices as usual will run over 1, 2, 3, and Greek indices will run over 0, 1, 2, 3.) In addition there are the conditions

$$g_{0i}(0) = 0 \qquad (11\text{-}4)$$

and $\begin{Bmatrix} 0 \\ 0i \end{Bmatrix} = 0$ along Γ.

11.2 LOCAL CARTESIAN COORDINATES

An orthogonal ennuple $\lambda_\alpha^\mu(\sigma)$ is erected at any event $\Pi(\sigma, 0, 0, 0)$ on the geodesic Γ of the previous section. (See Figure 11.2.) From the definition of an orthogonal ennuple comes the relations

$$g_{\mu\nu}[x^\rho(\sigma)]\lambda_\alpha^\mu(\sigma)\lambda_\beta^\nu(\sigma) = \eta_{\alpha\beta} \qquad (11\text{-}5)$$

$$g_{\mu\nu}[x^\rho(\sigma)] = \eta_{\alpha\beta}\check{\lambda}_\mu^\alpha(\sigma)\check{\lambda}_\nu^\beta(\sigma) \qquad (11\text{-}6)$$

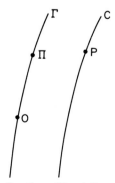

FIGURE 11.2 Erection of local Cartesian coordinates.

where $\breve{\lambda}^{\alpha}_{\mu}$ is the inverse of λ^{μ}_{α}. The ennuple is chosen so that $\lambda^{\mu}_0(\sigma) = \delta^{\mu}_0$ and so that the $\lambda^{\mu}_{\alpha}(\sigma)$ are continuous functions of σ having second derivatives. It follows from eq. (11-5) that $\lambda^0_a(\sigma) = 0$.

Consider a curve C in the neighborhood of Γ defined parametrically by the equations

$$t = \sigma, \qquad x^i = \lambda^i_a(\sigma)\xi^a(\sigma) \tag{11-7}$$

where $\xi^a(\sigma)$ are continuous functions of σ having second derivatives. Substitution of eq. (11-7) into eq. (11-3), the use of eq. (11-4) in the form $g_{0i} = O(\xi)$, and the condition

$$\frac{d\xi^a}{d\sigma} = O(\xi) \tag{11-8}$$

give

$$\left(\frac{ds}{d\sigma}\right)^2 = 1 + O^2(\xi). \tag{11-9}$$

The absolute acceleration of the world-line C is defined by eq. (8-7):

$$A^{\mu} = \frac{d^2 x^{\mu}}{ds^2} + \left\{ \begin{matrix} \mu \\ \nu\rho \end{matrix} \right\} \frac{dx^{\nu}}{ds}\frac{dx^{\rho}}{ds}.$$

Since C is not necessarily a geodesic, A^{μ} may not be zero. It follows from eqs. (11-8) and (11-9) that A^{μ} is given by

$$A^{\mu} = \frac{d^2 x^{\mu}}{d\sigma^2} + \left\{ \begin{matrix} \mu \\ \nu\rho \end{matrix} \right\} \frac{dx^{\nu}}{d\sigma}\frac{dx^{\rho}}{d\sigma} + O^2(\xi).$$

Substitution of eqs. (11-7) and subsequent expansion gives $A^0 = O^2(\xi)$ and

$$A^i = \lambda^i_a \frac{d^2\xi^a}{d\sigma^2} + 2\Lambda^i_a \frac{d\xi^a}{d\sigma} + L^i_a\xi^a + R^i_{0j0}\lambda^j_a\xi^a + O^2(\xi) \tag{11-10}$$

where

$$\Lambda^i_a = \frac{d\lambda^i_a}{d\sigma} + \left\{ \begin{matrix} i \\ 0j \end{matrix} \right\} \lambda^j_a \tag{11-11}$$

$$L^i_a = \frac{d\Lambda^i_a}{d\sigma} + \left\{ \begin{matrix} i \\ 0j \end{matrix} \right\} \Lambda^j_a.$$

Due to the special nature of the coordinates which are being used, Λ^i_a is the absolute rate of change of λ^i_a along Γ. Thus if the vectors λ^i_a are carried by parallel displacement along Γ, then Λ^i_a, and consequently L^i_a vanishes.

Multiplication of eq. (11-10) by $\breve{\lambda}^b_i$ gives

$$\frac{d^2\xi^a}{d\sigma^2} = \breve{\lambda}^a_i A^i - 2\breve{\lambda}^a_i\Lambda^i_b \frac{d\xi^b}{d\sigma} - \breve{\lambda}^a_i L^i_b\xi^b + \breve{\lambda}^a_i R^i_{00j}\lambda^j_b\xi^b + O^2(\xi). \tag{11-12}$$

Equation (11-12) is the generalized form of eq. (1-41). The Cartesian nature of the coordinates ξ^a results from the use of an *orthogonal* ennuple.

The various terms here may be interpreted as in Chapter 1. The force term of eq. (1-41) is here split into a non-gravitational term $\check{\lambda}_i^a A^i$ and gravitational term involving the Riemann curvature tensor. It is evident that the Coriolis effect, the centrifugal force, and the d'Alembert terms must be included in the second and third terms on the right-hand side of eq. (11-12).

In order to identify the Coriolis effect in eq. (11-12), it is first noted that $\eta_{\alpha\gamma}\check{\lambda}_\mu^\gamma \Lambda_\beta^\mu$ is antisymmetric in α, β. This is proved by covariantly differentiating eq. (11-5) with respect to x^ρ, multiplying by dx^ρ/ds, and substituting eq. (11-6) to eliminate $g_{\mu\nu}$. In particular, we find that $\eta_{ac}\check{\lambda}_i^c \Lambda_b^i$ or $-c^{-2}\check{\lambda}_i^a \Lambda_b^i$ is antisymmetric in a, b. Therefore a quantity ω^k may be defined: $\check{\lambda}_i^a \Lambda_b^i = e(akb)\omega^k$. Then Λ_b^i is given by $\Lambda_b^i = e(akb)\omega^k\lambda_a^i$, and the second term in eq. (11-12) becomes

$$-2\check{\lambda}_i^a \Lambda_b^i \frac{d\xi^b}{d\sigma} = -2e(akb)\omega^k \frac{d\xi^b}{d\sigma}$$

which has the same form as the Coriolis term of eq. (1-41).

The third term of eq. (11-12) can also be analyzed, but we will not do so here because it is not of interest.

In the Newtonian approximation, the fourth term in eq. (11-12) is the difference in gravitational acceleration between C and Γ. In the weak-field approximation (Section 9.3), the Riemann tensor is

$$R^i{}_{00j} = -\frac{\partial^2 \Phi}{\partial x^i \partial x^j},$$

where Φ is the Newtonian potential. Therefore, with the coordinates x^i chosen* so that $\lambda_a^i = \delta_a^i$, the fourth term of eq. (11-12) is

$$\xi^b \frac{\partial}{\partial \xi^b} \left(-\frac{\partial \Phi}{\partial \xi^a} \right).$$

Note that if C is a geodesic and the ennuple vectors are carried along Γ by parallel displacement, eq. (11-12) becomes

$$\frac{d^2 \xi^a}{d\sigma^2} = \check{\lambda}_i^a R^i{}_{00j} \lambda_b^j \xi^b + O^2(\xi)$$

or, in coordinates in which $\lambda_a^i = \delta_a^i$,

$$\frac{d^2 \xi^a}{d\sigma^2} = R^a{}_{00b} \xi^b + O^2(\xi).$$

---

* These special coordinates are obtained by choosing x^i so that $g_{ij}(\Pi) = \eta_{ij}$, and then orienting λ_a^i so that $\lambda_a^i = \delta_a^i$.

11.3 ROTATION OF A CONGRUENCE OF GEODESICS

If the world-line C of Section 11.2 is regarded as a geodesic of the congruence of Section 11.1, then C is given by $x^i = $ const, i.e.,

$$\lambda_a^i(\sigma)\xi^a(\sigma) = \text{const.} \tag{11-13}$$

Differentiation of eq. (11-13) and the use of the condition that the λ_a^i be carried by parallel displacement give

$$\lambda_a^i \frac{d\xi^a}{d\sigma} = \begin{Bmatrix} i \\ 0j \end{Bmatrix} \lambda_a^j \xi^a$$

or, in coordinates in which $\lambda_a^i = \delta_a^i$ and $g_{ij} = \eta_{ij}$ at the event of interest,

$$\frac{d\xi^a}{d\sigma} = \begin{Bmatrix} a \\ 0b \end{Bmatrix} \xi^b = -c^2[0b, a]\xi^b.$$

Expansion then gives the result

$$\frac{d\xi^a}{d\sigma} = \frac{c^2}{2}\left(\frac{\partial g_{0b}}{\partial x^a} - \frac{\partial g_{0a}}{\partial x^b}\right)\xi^b - \frac{c^2}{2}\frac{\partial g_{ab}}{\partial t}\xi^b$$

or

$$\frac{d\xi^a}{d\sigma} = e(abc)\omega^b\xi^c - \frac{c^2}{2}\frac{\partial g_{ab}}{\partial t}\xi^b \tag{11-14}$$

where

$$\omega^i = -\frac{c^2}{2}e(ijk)\frac{\partial g_{0k}}{\partial x^j}. \tag{11-15}$$

This ω^i is not the same as the ω^i in Section 11.2.

The first term on the right-hand side of eq. (11-14) indicates that the geodesics are rotating with the angular velocity ω^i given by eq. (11-15). Physically, this means that when coordinates are constructed (in accordance with the procedure of Section 11.1) from a system of non-interacting particles in free motion, the rotation of the particles relative to a reference frame in which Coriolis forces vanish (i.e., $\Lambda_a^i = 0$) is given by eq. (11-15), where g_{0i} is the metric tensor in the chosen coordinates. A congruence of geodesics is *rotational* if ω^i is non-zero and *irrotational* if ω^i vanishes.

If now in any coordinate system it happens that the curl $e(ijk)\,\partial g_{0k}/\partial x^j$ vanishes and g_{0i} is a function only of the spatial coordinates, then there exists an irrotational congruence of geodesics and a coordinate system in which $g_{0i} = 0$. To prove this, it is necessary only to note that the given condition implies that g_{0i} is a gradient: $g_{0i} = \partial\phi(x^k)/\partial x^i$. The line element then becomes

$$ds^2 = [d(t + \phi)]^2 + \left(g_{ij} - \frac{\partial\phi}{\partial x^i}\frac{\partial\phi}{\partial x^j}\right)dx^i\,dx^j$$

so that the transformation $t = \bar{t} - \phi$, $x^i = \bar{x}^i$ puts the metric into the form

$$ds^2 = d\bar{t}^2 + \bar{g}_{ij}\, d\bar{x}^i\, d\bar{x}^j$$

in which the time-space term $\bar{g}_{0i}$ is suppressed. It is now easy to see that the Christoffel symbols $\begin{Bmatrix} \mu \\ 00 \end{Bmatrix}$ vanish. Therefore the members of the congruence, $\bar{x}^i = \text{const}$, satisfy the geodesic equation, and hence are geodesics. The coordinates $\bar{x}^\mu$ are then the Section 11.1 type of coordinate based on this congruence. The congruence is irrotational because the angular velocity of eq. (11-15) vanishes.

It is always possible to find an irrotational congruence of geodesics, and hence to find a coordinate system for which the time-space term in the line element vanishes. The construction of the coordinates is carried out in the same way as in Section 11.1, except that the geodesics are chosen to intersect Σ orthogonally. For then not only do the conditions $g_{00} = 1$ and $\partial g_{0i}/\partial x^0 = 0$ hold, but also $g_{0i} = 0$ everywhere on Σ. Therefore $g_{0i} = 0$ everywhere, and the line element is

$$ds^2 = dt^2 + g_{ij}\, dx^i\, dx^j.$$

The congruence is clearly irrotational. It is also said to be *normal* because there exists a set of spaces $t = \text{const}$ which are orthogonal to the geodesics. The coordinates so constructed are called *Gaussian* coordinates.

11.4 ROTATION OF AN INERTIAL FRAME

An *inertial frame* for an observer in geodesic motion is a frame in which the Coriolis effect vanishes. The reference axes in the inertial frame are therefore the vectors λ_a^i as used in Section 11.2, with the inclusion of the condition of parallel displacement:

$$0 = \frac{d\lambda_a^i}{d\sigma} + \begin{Bmatrix} i \\ 0j \end{Bmatrix}\lambda_a^j. \tag{11-16}$$

Direct evaluation of the Christoffel symbol here, as was done in the previous section, leads to the formula

$$\frac{d\lambda_a^i}{d\sigma} = -e(ijk)\omega^j\lambda_a^k + \frac{c^2}{2}\frac{\partial g_{ij}}{\partial t}\lambda_a^j, \tag{11-17}$$

where ω^i is given by eq. (11-15). The inertial axes thus appear to rotate with an angular velocity $-\omega^i$ relative to the coordinates.

In general coordinates, eq. (11-16) becomes

$$0 = \frac{d\lambda_\alpha^\mu}{ds} + \begin{Bmatrix} \mu \\ \nu\rho \end{Bmatrix}\lambda_\alpha^\nu u^\rho, \tag{11-18}$$

where the vector $u^p = dx^p/ds$ is the world-velocity of the observer. If the observer is in geodesic motion, we may choose $\lambda_0^\mu = u^\mu$ for the time-like ennuple vector. It is well to keep in mind that eq. (11-18) holds in *any* coordinates, not necessarily those of Section 11.1.

The foregoing analysis will be applied to two examples: the rotating shell and the geodesic effect.

11.5 ROTATING SPHERICAL SHELL

Consider the following problem. A spherical shell of radius a and uniform mass M, with its center at the origin of rectangular Cartesian coordinates, rotates about the z-axis with a constant angular velocity Ω. The problem is to calculate the first-order coefficients $h_{\mu\nu}$ of the weak-field line element inside the sphere.

Two approximations will be made. First, we will use the weak-field approximation to general relativity which was presented in Section 9.8. This is equivalent to assuming $a \gg \mu$ where $\mu = GM/c^2$. Second, only terms of first order in Ω will be retained. Since the stresses which hold the sphere together against centrifugal forces vary with Ω^2, they are completely neglected.

The stress-energy tensor $T^{\mu\nu}$ which enters the right-hand side of the field equation (9-63) is equal to $\rho u^\mu u^\nu$, where u^μ is the world-velocity of a point on the sphere. The latter has a velocity $v^i = e(ijk)\Omega^j x^k$, and the approximations allow us to write $u^0 = 1$, $u^i = v^i$. Therefore the field equation is

$$\Box^2 h_{00} = -\kappa\rho$$
$$\Box^2 h_{0i} = 2\kappa c^{-2}\rho v^i$$
$$\Box^2 h_{ij} = -\kappa c^{-2}\rho\delta_{ij}.$$

The components h_{00} and h_{ij} are constant inside the sphere, and we have the surprising result that the space-time inside a non-rotating spherical shell is Minkowski. The field equation for h_{0i} is $\nabla^2 h_{0i} = -2\kappa c^{-4}\rho v^i$ which has the solution

$$h_{0i} = \frac{4}{3}\frac{\mu\Omega}{ac^2}(-y, x, 0) \qquad r \leq a$$

$$h_{0i} = \frac{4}{3}\frac{\mu\Omega a^2}{r^3 c^2}(-y, x, 0). \qquad r \geq a$$

The weak-field equation of motion (9-68) becomes

$$\frac{d^2 x^i}{dt^2} = -2e(ijk)\omega^j \frac{dx^k}{dt},$$

where

$$\omega^i = -\frac{c^2}{2} e(ijk) \frac{\partial h_{0k}}{\partial x^j} = -\frac{4\mu}{3a} \Omega^i.$$

Therefore an observer inside the sphere would claim that he is in a rotating system, because he observes a Coriolis effect—in spite of the fact that the coordinates x, y, z are inertial coordinates at spatial infinity! The interior observer will assert that the coordinate axes are rotating relative to an inertial frame with angular velocity ω^i.

The same conclusion is reached when eq. (11-17), valid to our approximation, is applied to the interior of the shell:

$$\frac{d\lambda_a^i}{dt} = -e(ijk)\omega^j\lambda_a^k.$$

Thus the axes of the inertial frame rotate with angular velocity

$$-\omega^i = \frac{4\mu}{3a} \Omega^i$$

relative to the coordinate axes. The inertial frame inside the shell is dragged by the shell with an angular velocity equal to $4\mu/3a$ times that of the shell.

II.6 THE GEODESIC EFFECT

In the previous section it was found to be possible for inertial axes of a test particle to rotate relative to an *a priori* coordinate system, even though the coordinates may be inertial at infinity. The case where the metric is constant in time and the test particle returns to its initial location is of special interest. The rotation of the inertial axes of the particle during its journey is called the *geodesic effect*. Examples include the earth revolving around the sun and a satellite revolving around the earth.

The geodesic effect will be calculated for a satellite revolving in a circular orbit around a point mass M. The orbit equations of Section 9.4 become

$$\frac{dt}{ds} = \frac{A}{1 - \frac{2\mu}{r}} \qquad A = \text{const}$$

$$\frac{d\phi}{ds} = \frac{h}{r^2} \qquad h = \text{const}$$

$$\left(1 - \frac{2\mu}{r}\right) \frac{h^2}{c^2 r^2} = A^2 - 1 + \frac{2\mu}{r}$$

$$\frac{1}{r} = \frac{\mu c^2}{h^2} + \frac{3\mu}{r^2}$$

where $\mu = GM/c^2$. Solution for $A(\mu, r)$ and $h(\mu, r)$ yields

$$A = \frac{1 - \dfrac{2\mu}{r}}{\sqrt{1 - \dfrac{3\mu}{r}}}, \qquad h = \sqrt{\frac{\mu c^2 r}{1 - \dfrac{3\mu}{r}}}.$$

Thus the angular velocity Ω of the satellite's revolution with respect to coordinate time is

$$\Omega = \frac{d\phi}{dt} = \sqrt{\frac{\mu c^2}{r^3}}.$$

The difference between Ω and the angular velocity $d\phi/ds$ with respect to proper time is responsible for the geodesic effect.

Equation (11-18) is now applied. The coordinates are spherical polar: t, r, θ, ϕ. The orbit lies in the plane $\theta = \dfrac{\pi}{2}$. The world-velocity of the satellite is

$$u^\mu = \frac{1}{\sqrt{1 - \dfrac{3\mu}{r}}}(1, 0, 0, \Omega),$$

and the metric is eq. (9-20). Equation (11-18) becomes

$$\left.\begin{array}{ll}
\dfrac{d\lambda^0}{ds} + \dfrac{\mu}{r^2}\dfrac{1}{1 - \dfrac{2\mu}{r}}\lambda^1 u^0 = 0 & \quad\text{a} \\[2em]
\dfrac{d\lambda^1}{ds} + \left(1 - \dfrac{2\mu}{r}\right)\dfrac{\mu c^2}{r^2}\lambda^0 u^0 - \left(1 - \dfrac{2\mu}{r}\right)r\lambda^3 u^3 = 0 & \quad\text{b} \\[2em]
\dfrac{d\lambda^2}{ds} = 0 & \quad\text{c} \\[2em]
\dfrac{d\lambda^3}{ds} + \dfrac{\lambda^1 u^3}{r} = 0 & \quad\text{d}
\end{array}\right\} \quad \text{(11-19)}$$

Equation (11-19c) integrates immediately to give $\lambda^2 = \text{const}$, which indicates that the rotation of the inertial axes is around the axis of revolution. The fact that the satellite's world-line is a geodesic requires that $\lambda^\mu = u^\mu$ be a solution. The latter is of no interest, however, because we are concerned with the inertial axes which are orthogonal to the satellite's world-velocity. The orthogonality condition $0 = g_{\mu\nu}\lambda^\mu u^\nu$ becomes

$$\lambda^0 = \frac{\Omega r^2}{c^2\left(1 - \dfrac{2\mu}{r}\right)}\lambda^3. \qquad (11\text{-}20)$$

Equation (11-20) makes eqs. (11-19a) and (11-19d) identical, and eq. (11-19b) becomes

$$\frac{d\lambda^1}{ds} - \frac{\Omega r \lambda^3}{u^0} = 0. \qquad \text{a}$$

Equation (11-19d) may be rewritten

$$\frac{d}{ds}(r\lambda^3) + \Omega u^0 \lambda^1 = 0. \qquad \text{b}$$

(11-21)

The solution to eqs. (11-21) is clearly

$$u^0 \lambda^1 = \sin \Omega s$$

$$r\lambda^3 = \cos \Omega s.$$

The above equations show that the inertial axes rotate about the polar axis in the negative ϕ direction with angular velocity (per unit proper time) Ω relative to the radius vector. On the other hand, the satellite revolves with angular velocity $u^0\Omega$. Therefore the inertial axes of the satellite rotate with angular velocity $\Omega(u^0 - 1)$ in the positive ϕ direction relative to inertial axes at infinity. In one revolution, the inertial axes rotate through an angle

$$2\pi\left[1 - \sqrt{1 - \frac{3\mu}{r}}\right]$$

or approximately $3\pi\mu/r$ radians. The satellite must revolve through an additional angle $\delta\phi \approx 3\pi\mu/r \approx 3\mu\phi/2r$ in order for the inertial axes to come back to their initial angles with the radius vector.

Thus the earth rotates through an angle $3\pi\mu/r$ per revolution due to general relativity. This amounts to only $0.''019$ per year, which is too small for observation. For an artificial satellite skimming the earth's surface, the precession is $1.''35 \times 10^{-3}$ per revolution or $8.''5$ per year. There is hope that this precession can be observed, perhaps by means of a gyroscope in an artificial satellite.

The precession due to the geodesic effect may be contrasted with the Thomas precession as follows. The geodesic precession depends on the metric and appears even in a particle following geodesic motion. The Thomas precession depends on the particle's absolute acceleration and thus vanishes for a particle in geodesic motion. Inertial precession is a sensitive measure of the choice of interpreting gravity as in general relativity or as an extra force field; the latter gives $+\frac{1}{3}$ of the precession of the former.

11.7 EFFECT OF THE ROTATING EARTH

In Section 11.5, the line element outside a rotating spherical shell was found to be given by

$$h_{0i} = \frac{4\mu a^2}{3c^2 r^3} e(ijk)\Omega^j x^k$$

where $\mu c^2/G$ is the mass and Ω^i is the angular velocity. The effect of a solid sphere having spherical symmetry is then

$$h_{0i} = \frac{2IG}{c^4 r^3} e(ijk)\Omega^j x^k,$$

where I is the moment of inertia. The other components of the metric, in the weak-field approximation, are given by

$$h_{00} = -\frac{2\mu}{r}$$

$$h_{ij} = \frac{1}{c^2} h_{00}\delta_{ij},$$

where $\mu c^2/G$ is the total mass of the body.

The equation of motion (9-68) for slow velocities contains a term $c^2 e(ijk)v^k e(jlm)\,\partial h_{0m}/\partial x^l$ which in the present context becomes

$$\frac{2IG}{c^2 r^5} e(ijk)v^k (3\Omega^l x^l x^j - \Omega^j r^2).$$

For a satellite in an equatorial orbit around the central body, the equations of motion in polar coordinates r, θ to terms of first order in the velocity, are

$$\frac{d^2 r}{dt^2} - r\left(\frac{d\theta}{dt}\right)^2 = -\frac{GM}{r^2} + \frac{2IG\Omega}{c^2 r^2}\frac{d\theta}{dt}$$

$$\frac{1}{r}\frac{d}{dt}\left(r^2 \frac{d\theta}{dt}\right) = -\frac{2IG\Omega}{c^2 r^3}\frac{dr}{dt}. \tag{11-22}$$

The integral of eq. (11-22) is

$$r^2 \frac{d\theta}{dt} = h + \frac{2IG\Omega}{c^2 r}$$

where h is a constant, and $F(r)$ in eq. (6-2a) is

$$F(r) = \frac{\mu c^2}{r^2} - \frac{2IG\Omega h}{c^2 r^4}.$$

or

$$F(u) = \mu c^2 u^2 - \frac{2IG\Omega h}{c^2} u^4.$$

The term of order Ω^2 has been dropped because the metric is not known to this accuracy. The $H(r)$ in eq. (6-2c) is

$$H(u) = h + \frac{2IG\Omega}{c^2} u.$$

Equation (6-3) gives $J = \mu c^2 u + k$, where k is a constant. Equation (6-8) then gives

$$N(u) = \frac{\mu c^2}{h^2}\left[1 - \frac{4IG\Omega k}{\mu c^4 h} - \frac{8IG\Omega}{c^2 h} u + 0^2(u) + 0^2(\Omega)\right]$$

which leads to a perihelion advance

$$\sigma = -\frac{4\mu IG\Omega}{h^3}. \tag{11-23}$$

For application to the case of an artificial satellite around the earth, eq. (11-23) is put into the form

$$\sigma = -\frac{4\mu}{r}\frac{R^2}{r^2}\frac{\Omega}{\omega}\frac{I}{MR^2}$$

where R is the earth's radius, M is the earth's mass, I is the earth's moment of inertia, Ω is the earth's angular velocity of rotation, ω is the satellite's angular velocity of revolution, and r is the radius of the satellite's orbit. For a satellite skimming the earth's surface,

$$\frac{\mu}{r} = 7.0 \times 10^{-10}, \qquad \frac{R}{r} = 1, \qquad \frac{\Omega}{\omega} = \frac{1}{17.3}, \qquad \frac{I}{MR^2} = 0.33$$

to give $\sigma = -5.3 \times 10^{-11} = -6.''9$ per century. This may be compared with the Einstein precession of $3\mu/r$ or 2.1×10^{-9}.

11.8 GENERAL METRIC FOR A MASS POINT

The purpose of this section is to develop the equations of motion in the neighborhood of a point mass *without* reference to the field equations for the metric. In Section 9.4, the line element, under the assumption of spherical symmetry, was found to be eq. (9-16). It will be assumed that both e^ν and e^λ are independent of t and can be expanded in powers of μ/r:

$$e^{\nu(r)} = 1 - 2\alpha\frac{\mu}{r} + 2\beta\left(\frac{\mu}{r}\right)^2 + \cdots$$

$$e^{\lambda(r)} = 1 + 2\gamma\frac{\mu}{r} + \cdots. \tag{11-24}$$

The geodesic equation of motion $\delta \int ds = 0$ or

$$\delta \int \sqrt{e^{\nu}\dot{t}^2 - c^{-2}[e^{\lambda}\dot{r}^2 + r^2(\dot{\theta}^2 + \sin^2\theta\dot{\phi}^2)]} \, dp = 0$$

with $\dot{x}^{\mu} = dx^{\mu}/dp$ gives, with the subsequent identification $p = s$, the equations of motion

$$\frac{d}{ds}(e^{\nu}\dot{t}) = 0$$

$$\frac{d}{ds}(r^2\dot{\theta}) = r^2 \sin\theta \cos\theta \dot{\phi}^2$$

$$\frac{d}{ds}(r^2 \sin^2\theta\dot{\phi}) = 0$$

$$e^{\nu}\dot{t}^2 - c^{-2}[e^{\lambda}\dot{r}^2 + r^2(\dot{\theta}^2 + \sin^2\theta\dot{\phi}^2)] = 1.$$

The orbital plane is chosen to be $\theta = \dfrac{\pi}{2}$ so that the equations of motion become

$$\frac{d}{ds}(e^{\nu}\dot{t}) = 0$$

$$\frac{d}{ds}(r^2\dot{\phi}) = 0$$

$$e^{\nu}\dot{t}^2 - c^{-2}(e^{\lambda}\dot{r}^2 + r^2\dot{\phi}^2) = 1.$$

The integrals of the first two equations are $e^{\nu}\dot{t} = k = $ const and $r^2\dot{\phi} = h = $ const, and the third equation becomes

$$e^{\lambda}\dot{r}^2 + h^2 r^{-2} = c^2(k^2 e^{-\nu} - 1). \tag{11-25}$$

Equation (11-25) may be differentiated and divided by $2\dot{r}$ to give

$$\ddot{r} + \frac{c^2}{2} e^{\nu - \lambda} \nu' \dot{t}^2 + \tfrac{1}{2}\lambda'\dot{r}^2 - r e^{-\lambda}\dot{\phi}^2 = 0 \tag{11-26}$$

where the prime denotes differentiation with respect to r.

The geodesic effect will be studied first. For a circular orbit $r = a = $ const, we may write $\dot{x}^{\mu} = \dot{t}(1, 0, 0, \Omega)$ where, from eq. (11-26),

$$\Omega = \frac{d\phi}{dt} = \sqrt{\frac{c^2}{2a} e^{\nu}\nu'}. \tag{11-27}$$

The non-vanishing Christoffel symbols are

$$\begin{Bmatrix} 0 \\ 01 \end{Bmatrix} = \tfrac{1}{2}\nu'$$

$$\begin{Bmatrix} 1 \\ 00 \end{Bmatrix} = \tfrac{1}{2}c^2 e^{\nu-\lambda}\nu'$$

$$\begin{Bmatrix} 1 \\ 11 \end{Bmatrix} = +\tfrac{1}{2}\lambda'$$

$$\begin{Bmatrix} 1 \\ 22 \end{Bmatrix} = \begin{Bmatrix} 1 \\ 33 \end{Bmatrix} = -re^{-\lambda}$$

$$\begin{Bmatrix} 2 \\ 21 \end{Bmatrix} = \begin{Bmatrix} 3 \\ 31 \end{Bmatrix} = 1/r.$$

The condition (11-18) for parallel displacement becomes

$$\begin{aligned}
\dot{\lambda}^0 + \tfrac{1}{2}\nu'\dot{t}\lambda^1 &= 0 & &\text{a} \\
\dot{\lambda}^1 + \tfrac{1}{2}c^2 e^{\nu-\lambda}\nu'\dot{t}\lambda^0 - ae^{-\lambda}\dot{\phi}\lambda^3 &= 0 & &\text{b} \\
\dot{\lambda}^2 &= 0 & &\text{c} \qquad (11\text{-}28) \\
\dot{\lambda}^3 + \frac{1}{a}\dot{\phi}\lambda^1 &= 0. & &\text{d}
\end{aligned}$$

With the orthogonality condition $0 = g_{\mu\nu}\lambda^\mu \dot{x}^\nu$ or

$$\lambda^0 = \frac{a^2}{c^2}\,\Omega e^{-\nu}\lambda^3,$$

eqs. (11-28a) and (11-28d) become identical, namely

$$\frac{d}{d\phi}(a\lambda^3) + \lambda^1 = 0 \qquad\qquad \text{a}$$

and eq. (11-28b) becomes

$$\frac{d\lambda^1}{d\phi} - K^2 a\lambda^3 = 0 \qquad\qquad \text{b}$$

$$\left.\begin{aligned}&\\&\\&\end{aligned}\right\} \quad (11\text{-}29)$$

where

$$K^2 = e^{-\lambda}(1 - \tfrac{1}{2}a\nu').$$

Equations (11-29) have the solution

$$\lambda^1 = K \sin K\phi$$
$$a\lambda^3 = \cos K\phi.$$

In exactly one revolution, the inertial axes rotate through an angle $2\pi(1 - K)$ around an axis perpendicular to the orbit. This angle represents a geodesic precession rate

$$\omega = (1 - K)\Omega = [1 - e^{-\frac{1}{2}\lambda}\sqrt{1 - \tfrac{1}{2}av'}]\Omega. \qquad (11\text{-}30)$$

The above derivation is exact for arbitrary functions $v(r)$ and $\lambda(r)$.

For the power-series expansions of e^v and e^λ given above, eq. (11-30) becomes

$$\omega = \frac{\alpha + 2\gamma}{2}\,\frac{\mu}{a}\,\Omega. \qquad (11\text{-}31)$$

To obtain the perihelion advance, eq. (6-10) is evaluated for a circular orbit with the help of eqs. (11-25) and (11-26). Upon retaining only terms of lowest order in μ/r, the result is

$$\sigma = \frac{\mu}{r}\,\frac{2\alpha^2 + \alpha\gamma - \beta}{\alpha}. \qquad (11\text{-}32)$$

The deflection of light is obtained from eq. (11-25) by converting to the variable $u(\phi) = 1/r$:

$$\left(\frac{du}{d\phi}\right)^2 + u^2 e^{-\lambda} = \frac{c^2}{h^2}\,e^{-\lambda}(k^2 e^{-v} - 1).$$

For a light ray, both k and h are infinite, but the ratio k/h is a constant. Hence the orbital equation for a light ray is

$$\left(\frac{du}{d\phi}\right)^2 + u^2 e^{-\lambda} = \frac{1}{R^2}\,e^{-\lambda - v}$$

where $R = h/ck$. With the definitions

$$ue^{\frac{v(u)}{2}} = \frac{\cos\theta}{R}$$

and

$$\zeta = \frac{d\phi}{d\theta}$$

the orbit equation becomes

$$\zeta = \frac{e^{\lambda/2}}{1 + \tfrac{1}{2}u\,\dfrac{dv}{du}}.$$

With the power-series substitutions for v and λ, this becomes

$$\zeta = 1 + (\alpha + \gamma)\mu u + O^2.$$

But now the particle's asymptotic change in ϕ is

$$\Delta\phi = \int_{\theta=-\pi/2}^{\theta=\pi/2} \zeta\, d\theta = \int_{-\pi/2}^{\pi/2}\left[1 + \frac{\mu}{R}(\alpha + \gamma)\cos\theta + O^2\right]d\theta$$

$$= \pi + \frac{2\mu}{R}(\alpha + \gamma) + O^2\left(\frac{\mu}{R}\right).$$

Therefore the angle of deflection of a light ray which passes within a distance R of the point mass is

$$\frac{2\mu}{R}(\alpha + \gamma). \tag{11-33}$$

The gravitational redshift is given by

$$z = e^{\frac{1}{2}\Delta\nu} - 1 \tag{11-34}$$

where z is the redshift defined in Section 9.5c, and $\Delta\nu$ is the difference in the value of the metric exponent ν between the locations of the observer and the source (observer minus source). With the power-series expansion for ν, eq. (11-34) becomes

$$z = \mu\left(\Delta\frac{1}{r}\right)\left[\alpha + O\left(\frac{\mu}{r}\right)\right]. \tag{11-35}$$

Finally, with the power-series expansion for e^ν, equation (11-27) becomes

$$\Omega^2 = \frac{\alpha c^2\mu}{r^3}\left[1 - \frac{2\beta\mu}{\alpha r} + \cdots\right]. \tag{11-36}$$

We can pause at this point to survey the results of these calculations. The line element of eq. (9-16) with the power-series substitutions of eqs. (11-24) gives the geodesic precession of eq. (11-31), the perihelion advance of eq. (11-32), the light deflection of eq. (11-33), the gravitational redshift of eq. (11-35), and the angular velocity (per unit coordinate time) of eq. (11-36).

The identification of μ with the gravitational radius of eq. (6-17) and the requirement that eq. (11-36) reduce to the Newtonian form $\Omega^2 = GM/r^3$ for $r \gg \mu$ imposes the condition $\alpha = 1$. Due to the equivalence principle, the gravitational redshift gives *no further information*. The deflection of light depends on $\alpha + \gamma$; the Einstein value results for $\gamma = 1$. The geodesic precession depends on $\alpha + 2\gamma$; thus an experimental measurement of the geodesic effect would provide an alternative to the measurement of light deflection. Finally, the advance of perihelion depends on the ratio $(2\alpha^2 + \alpha\gamma - \beta)/\alpha$, or, with $\alpha = 1$, on $2 + \gamma - \beta$.

Of the five experiments previously described, two (Newtonian gravity and gravitational redshift) have been carried out to sufficient accuracy to be conclusive. Thus we may with confidence set α equal to unity. The geodesic effect, perihelion advance, and light deflection are then, respectively,

$$\omega = \frac{1 + 2\gamma}{2} \frac{\mu}{a} \Omega$$

$$\sigma = \frac{\mu}{r}(2 + \gamma - \beta)$$

$$\text{defl} = \frac{2\mu}{R}(1 + \gamma).$$

Only the perihelion-advance test supplies any information on β. The Einstein values are $\beta = 0$, $\gamma = 1$.

TABLE II.I *PREDICTIONS OF VARIOUS GRAVITATIONAL THEORIES*

THEORY OF GRAVITY (SR = SPECIAL RELATIVISTIC)	GRAVITATIONAL REDSHIFT $\frac{r^2}{\mu\Delta r} \cdot z$	DEFLECTION OF LIGHT $\frac{R}{\mu} \cdot$ angle	ADVANCE OF PERIHELION $\frac{r\sigma}{\mu}$	GEODESIC PRECESSION $\frac{\omega}{\Omega} \cdot \frac{r}{\mu}$
Scalar SR, (Sec. 6.5)	0	0	-1	$+\frac{1}{2}$
Vector SR, (Sec. 6.6)	0	0	$\frac{1}{2}$	$+\frac{1}{2}$
Tensor SR, (Sec. 6.7)	0	$2(1 + \zeta)^*$	$-1 + 2\zeta$	$+\frac{1}{2}$
Birkhoff, (Sec. 6.7)	0	$+4^*$	$+3$	$+\frac{1}{2}$
Geometrized scalar, (Sec. 7.9)	$+1$	0	$-\frac{1}{2}$	$-\frac{1}{2}$
Einstein	$+1$	$+4$	$+3$	$+\frac{3}{2}$
General line element of present section	α	$2(\alpha + \gamma)$	$\frac{2\alpha^2 + \alpha\gamma - \beta}{\alpha}$	$\frac{\alpha + 2\gamma}{2}$

* These entries refer to *particles* traveling with the speed of light. *Light*, of course, cannot be deflected in any special-relativistic theory because of the basic postulate of rectilinear propagation.

Table 11.1 summarizes the results of the special-relativistic gravitational theories of Chapter 6, the geometrized theory of Section 7.9, Einstein's theory, and the general line element of the present section. The parameter β in the tensor theory has been replaced with ζ to avoid confusion with the β in the present section. The parameters β in the vector theory and α in the tensor theory were chosen to be 0 and -1, respectively, in order that a particle with speed c simulate light at least in terms of its speed. Since the special-relativistic theories have no geodesic effect, the Thomas precession of eq. (3-52) has been entered in the geodesic precession column.

The observed gravitational redshift eliminates all special-relativistic theories. Mercury's perihelion advance then favors a value $\gamma - \beta = 1$.

The deflection of light, if the accuracy can be improved, would then imply $\gamma = 1$ and hence $\beta = 0$. But greater observational accuracy is needed before the values of β and γ can be fixed with precision.

11.9 SATELLITE CLOCK

Consider a satellite revolving in a circular orbit of radius r around a spherical mass M of radius R (e.g., the earth). The line element from the previous section is

$$ds^2 = \left(1 - 2\frac{\mu}{r}\right) dt^2 - \frac{1}{c^2} [dr^2 + r^2(d\theta^2 + \sin^2 \theta \, d\phi^2)]. \quad (11\text{-}37)$$

The β and γ have been neglected, and α has been set equal to unity in accordance with the principle of equivalence. Since eq. (11-37) follows from the equivalence principle alone, independent of Einstein's field equation, any experimental proof of the conclusions to follow is only what is expected on the basis of the principle of equivalence. The square root of eq. (11-37) gives, to first order,

$$\frac{ds}{dt} = 1 - \frac{\mu}{r} - \frac{v^2}{2c^2}, \quad (11\text{-}38)$$

where v is the observer's velocity.

When eq. (11-38) is applied to the satellite, ds is the interval of time on the satellite's clock. Since terms of order $(\mu/r)^2$ have already been neglected, v^2 can be replaced by its Newtonian equivalent $\mu c^2/r$:

$$\frac{ds}{dt} = 1 - \frac{3\mu}{2r}. \quad (11\text{-}39)$$

When eq. (11-38) is applied to a stationary terrestrial observer, we have

$$\frac{ds_0}{dt} = 1 - \frac{\mu}{R} - \frac{\omega^2 R^2}{2c^2}, \quad (11\text{-}40)$$

where ds_0 is the observer's time interval and ω is the earth's angular velocity (more accurately the product of the earth's angular velocity with the cosine of the observer's latitude). Since ωR is small compared with $\mu c^2/R$, eq. (11-40) becomes

$$\frac{ds_0}{dt} = 1 - \frac{\mu}{R}. \quad (11\text{-}41)$$

The quotient of eqs. (11-39) and (11-41) gives the ratio of satellite time to earth time:

$$\frac{ds}{ds_0} = 1 - \frac{3\mu}{2r} + \frac{\mu}{R} .$$

For a satellite which skims the earth's surface, this ratio is given by

$$\frac{ds}{ds_0} - 1 = - \frac{\mu}{2R} = -3.5 \times 10^{-10}.$$

For a 24-hour satellite,

$$\frac{ds}{ds_0} - 1 = +5.4 \times 10^{-10}.$$

And the time ratio is exactly unity for a satellite at a distance $r = \frac{3}{2}R$.

CHAPTER 12

EQUATIONS OF MOTION

12.1 FIELD-TO-PARTICLE TRANSITION

The analysis of Section 5.2 can be applied to a general metric, provided certain revisions are made. First, it is necessary to choose the Gaussian coordinates described in Section 11.3, so that the line element becomes

$$ds^2 = dt^2 - c^{-2}h_{ij}\, dx^i\, dx^j.$$

(This h_{ij} is not to be confused with the quantity used in the weak-field approximation.) Second, it is necessary to use $\epsilon_{\mu\nu\rho\sigma}$ rather than $e_{\mu\nu\rho\sigma}$ in eq. (5-11) because $\epsilon_{\mu\nu\rho\sigma}$ is a tensor. For the above metric, $\epsilon_{\mu\nu\rho\sigma}$ is equal to $c^{-3}\sqrt{h}\,e_{\mu\nu\rho\sigma}$ where h is the determinant of h_{ij}. Therefore, eq. (5-11) becomes

$$d\Pi = c^3 \epsilon_{\mu\nu\rho\sigma}\, dx_0^\mu\, dx_1^\nu\, dx_2^\rho\, dx_3^\sigma.$$

Equations (5-12) and (5-13) remain the same, with

$$dV = \sqrt{h}\,e(ijk)\, dx_1^i\, dx_2^j\, dx_3^k \tag{12-1}$$

for the vectors dx_a^i ($a = 1, 2, 3$) in the space $t = $ const.

The next revision to be made is in eq. (5-14). It is more realistic to assume a field equation

$$\frac{1}{\sqrt{-g}}\frac{\partial}{\partial x^\mu}(\sqrt{-g}A^\mu) = B. \tag{12-2}$$

The reason for this revision will be seen in the applications. In view of the relation $g = c^{-6}h$, eq. (12-2) becomes

$$\frac{1}{\sqrt{h}}\frac{\partial}{\partial x^\mu}(\sqrt{h}A^\mu) = B. \tag{12-3}$$

Equation (12-3) is multiplied by an arbitrary function w to give

$$\frac{1}{\sqrt{h}} \frac{\partial}{\partial x^\mu} (w\sqrt{h}A^\mu) - w_\mu A^\mu - wB = 0 \qquad (12\text{-}4)$$

where $w_\mu = \partial w/\partial x^\mu$. The use of Gauss' theorem, which is independent of the metric, leads to eq. (5-16).

Equations (5-18) remain as they are even for a general metric. The only difference is that eq. (5-14) is replaced by eq. (12-2) and the volume in eq. (5-13) is given by eq. (12-1).

In order to study the motion of a particle we start with the total stress-energy tensor $T^{\mu\nu} = M^{\mu\nu} + S^{\mu\nu}$ which satisfies the conservation equation

$$T^{\mu\nu}{}_{,\nu} = 0 \qquad (12\text{-}5)$$

and is composed of the matter stress-energy tensor $M^{\mu\nu}$ which is to be localized into the particle and the stress-energy tensor $S^{\mu\nu}$ for the external field. Equation (12-5) becomes

$$M^{\mu\nu}{}_{,\nu} = P^\mu \qquad (12\text{-}6)$$

where $P^\mu = -S^{\mu\nu}{}_{,\nu}$. The use of eq. (8-74) puts eq. (12-6) into the form

$$\frac{1}{\sqrt{-g}} \frac{\partial}{\partial x^\nu} (\sqrt{-g}M^{\mu\nu}) = F^\mu \qquad (12\text{-}7)$$

where

$$F^\mu = P^\mu - \begin{Bmatrix} \mu \\ \nu\rho \end{Bmatrix} M^{\nu\rho}. \qquad (12\text{-}8)$$

Equation (12-7) now has the form of eq. (12-2). The corpuscular equations (5-18) then lead to the equations (5-19) to (5-23); the only revision is to replace τ with s. The use of eq. (12-8) gives the additional result

$$f^\mu = p^\mu - \begin{Bmatrix} \mu \\ \nu\rho \end{Bmatrix} m^{\nu\rho}$$

and hence

$$\frac{dm^\mu}{ds} + \begin{Bmatrix} \mu \\ \nu\rho \end{Bmatrix} m^\nu u^\rho = p^\mu. \qquad (12\text{-}9)$$

The substitution of eq. (5-22) into eq. (12-9) gives

$$m\left(\frac{du^\mu}{ds} + \begin{Bmatrix} \mu \\ \nu\rho \end{Bmatrix} u^\nu u^\rho\right) = p^\mu - u^\mu \frac{dm}{ds}. \qquad (12\text{-}10)$$

Multiplication of eq. (12-10) by u_μ gives

$$\frac{dm}{ds} = u_\mu p^\mu. \qquad (12\text{-}11)$$

Equation (12-9) is the generalized equation for the rate of change of momentum of the particle, and eq. (12-11) gives the rate of change of its mass. The substitution of eq. (12-11) into eq. (12-10) gives the equation of motion:

$$m\left(\frac{du^\mu}{ds} + \left\{\begin{matrix}\mu\\\nu\rho\end{matrix}\right\} u^\nu u^\rho\right) = p^\mu - u^\mu u_\nu p^\nu. \tag{12-12}$$

It may be noted that eq. (12-12) also follows from the less rigorous method of Section 5.1. When eq. (9-4) is substituted into eq. (9-3), the result is

$$\left(\rho + \frac{p}{c^2}\right)\left(\frac{du^\mu}{ds} + \left\{\begin{matrix}\mu\\\nu\rho\end{matrix}\right\} u^\nu u^\rho\right) + u^\mu\left[\left(\rho + \frac{p}{c^2}\right)u^\nu\right]_{,\nu} = \frac{1}{c^2} g^{\mu\nu} p_{,\nu}.$$

Multiplication by u_μ allows the evaluation of the second term on the left, and hence its elimination. The result is:

$$\left(\rho + \frac{p}{c^2}\right)\left(\frac{du^\mu}{ds} + \left\{\begin{matrix}\mu\\\nu\rho\end{matrix}\right\} u^\nu u^\rho\right) = \frac{1}{c^2}(g^{\mu\nu} - u^\mu u^\nu)p_{,\nu}.$$

We therefore identify $\dfrac{p_{,\nu}}{(\rho c^2 + p)}$ with the $\dfrac{p_\nu}{m}$ in eq. (12-12).

A free particle follows a geodesic because $S^{\mu\nu} = 0$ and eq. (12-12) reduces to eq. (9-5).

12.2 ELECTROMAGNETISM

The special-relativistic concepts of electromagnetism can be carried over into general relativity with little change. For convenience, all dielectric constants and relative permeabilities will be taken as unity. The charge density J^μ is that vector which, in proper coordinates at a given event, is given by the corresponding special-relativistic definition. The electromagnetic field tensor $F^{\mu\nu}$ determines the motion of a particle of proper mass m and change q by means of the equation of motion

$$\frac{d}{ds}(mu^\mu) + \left\{\begin{matrix}\mu\\\nu\rho\end{matrix}\right\} mu^\nu u^\rho = qu^\sigma F_\sigma{}^\mu. \tag{12-13}$$

The particle's proper mass is constant because eq. (12-13) is orthogonal to the world-velocity u^μ of the particle. The force density f^μ is defined by the vector equation $f^\mu = J^\nu F_\nu{}^\mu$. Other equations may be plucked from Chapter 4 and justified by the two rules: (1) they are tensor relations and (2) they agree in geodesic coordinates with their Chapter 4 counter-parts.

$$\epsilon^{\alpha\beta\gamma\delta} F_{\beta\gamma,\alpha} = 0 \tag{12-14}$$

$$F_{\mu^{\cdot},\alpha}^{\alpha} = \frac{1}{\epsilon_0} J_\mu \tag{12-15}$$

$$f^\mu = -S^{\mu\nu}_{\ ,\nu}$$

$$S^{\mu\nu} = \epsilon_0(F^{\mu\alpha}F_{\alpha\cdot}^{\ \nu} + \tfrac{1}{4}g^{\mu\nu}F^{\alpha\beta}F_{\alpha\beta})$$

$$F_{\mu\nu} = \phi_{\mu,\nu} - \phi_{\nu,\mu} = \frac{\partial\phi_\mu}{\partial x^\nu} - \frac{\partial\phi_\nu}{\partial x^\mu}.$$

However, due to the non-commutation of derivatives in general relativity, the field equations for the vector potential are

$$\phi^\mu_{\ ,\mu} = 0$$

$$g^{\alpha\beta}\phi_{\mu,\alpha\beta} = \epsilon_0^{-1}J_\mu - R_{\mu\nu}\phi^\nu; \tag{12-16}$$

the gravitational field enters through the Ricci tensor.

It may be noted parenthetically that the general-relativistic formulation of electromagnetism in moving media may be obtained directly from Section 4.11. The field equations become

$$\epsilon^{\alpha\beta\gamma\delta} F_{\alpha\beta,\gamma} = 0$$

$$H^{\mu\nu}_{\ ,\nu} = J^\mu. \tag{12-17}$$

If the medium has scalar permittivity ϵ and scalar permeability μ, then eq. (4-104) holds, since it is a tensor equation and is valid in special relativity. Equation (4-104) can be more easily written in the form

$$c^2\mu H^{\mu\nu} = \gamma^{\mu\alpha}\gamma^{\nu\beta}F_{\alpha\beta} \tag{12-18}$$

where $\gamma^{\mu\nu}$ is the tensor defined

$$\gamma^{\mu\nu} = g^{\mu\nu} + \left(\frac{\epsilon\mu}{\epsilon_0\mu_0} - 1\right)u^\mu u^\nu.$$

The determinant γ of the tensor $\gamma^{\mu\nu}$ is obtained by noting the relation $\gamma^{\mu\nu}g_{\nu\sigma} \cdot (u^\sigma u_\tau) = (\epsilon\mu/\epsilon_0\mu_0)(u^\mu u_\tau)$. Therefore $\gamma g = c^2\epsilon\mu$, where g is the determinant of $g_{\mu\nu}$. Multiplication of eq. (12-18) by

$$\frac{\sqrt{-g}}{c^2\mu} = \frac{1}{c}\sqrt{\frac{\epsilon}{\mu}}\frac{1}{\sqrt{-\gamma}}$$

gives

$$\sqrt{-g}H^{\mu\nu} = \frac{1}{c}\sqrt{\frac{\epsilon}{\mu}}\frac{1}{\sqrt{-\gamma}}\gamma^{\mu\alpha}\gamma^{\nu\beta}F_{\alpha\beta}. \tag{12-19}$$

Furthermore, eq. (8-74) and the antisymmetry of $H^{\mu\nu}$ allow eq. (12-17) to be written in the form

$$\frac{\partial}{\partial x^\nu}(\sqrt{-g}H^{\mu\nu}) = \sqrt{-g}J^\mu. \tag{12-20}$$

Inspection of eqs. (12-14), (12-19), and (12-20) shows that the only field variables which enter the field equations and the constitutive relations are $\sqrt{-g}J^\mu$, $\sqrt{-g}H^{\mu\nu}$, $F_{\mu\nu}$, $\gamma^{\mu\nu}$, and, if it is variable, the ratio ϵ/μ.

The field-to-particle transition of Section 12.1 is applied to a charged particle as follows. The electromagnetic field is regarded as composed of two parts. One part, in accordance with eq. (12-15), is due to a current density J^μ which can be localized into a particle. The other part, which will be denoted $F^{\mu\nu}$, is not due to localizable currents. The equation of conservation of charge $J^\mu{}_{,\mu} = 0$ or

$$\frac{1}{\sqrt{-g}}\frac{\partial}{\partial x^\mu}(\sqrt{-g}J^\mu) = 0$$

allows the identification $A^\mu = J^\mu$ and $B = 0$ in eq. (12-2) with the result

$$\frac{dq}{dp} = 0$$

and

$$j^\mu = qu^\mu \tag{12-21}$$

where

$$\frac{j^\mu}{u^0} = \lim_{V\to 0}\int_V J^\mu \, dV$$

and p is a parameter along the world-line of the particle. Thus the particle maintains a constant scalar charge q.

On the other hand, the application of eq. (12-6) with $P^\mu = J^\nu F_\nu{}^\mu$ leads to the equation of motion (12-9) with p^μ given by

$$p^\mu = j^\nu F_\nu{}^\mu. \tag{12-22}$$

The use of eqs. (12-9), (12-21), and (12-22) thus gives eq. (12-13).

12.3 PHOTON DESCRIPTION

The analysis of Section 11.1 may now be applied to a photon, the latter being considered as the localization of the electromagnetic stress-energy tensor $S^{\mu\nu}$. It is assumed that no matter is present, so that $S^{\mu\nu}$ has zero divergence. The three properties of $S^{\mu\nu}$ which will be used in the derivation are then

$$S^{\mu\nu}{}_{,\nu} = 0 \qquad\qquad (12\text{-}23)$$

$$S^{\mu\nu} = S^{\nu\mu} \qquad\qquad (12\text{-}24)$$

$$g_{\mu\nu}S^{\mu\nu} = 0. \qquad\qquad (12\text{-}25)$$

Equation (12-23), by its similarity with eq. (12-6), leads to the equations

$$\frac{d\sigma^{\mu 0}}{dp} = -\begin{Bmatrix}\mu \\ \nu\rho\end{Bmatrix}s^{\nu\rho} \qquad \text{a}$$

and

$$s^{\mu\nu} = u^{\nu}\sigma^{\mu 0} = u^{0}\sigma^{\mu\nu}. \qquad \text{b}$$

$$(12\text{-}26)$$

With the definition $s^{\mu} = \sigma^{\mu 0}$, eqs. (12-26) become

$$\frac{ds^{\mu}}{dp} + \begin{Bmatrix}\mu \\ \nu\rho\end{Bmatrix}s^{\nu}u^{\rho} = 0 \qquad \text{a}$$

and

$$s^{\mu\nu} = u^{\nu}s^{\mu} = u^{0}\sigma^{\mu\nu}. \qquad \text{b}$$

$$(12\text{-}27)$$

Equation (12-24) now requires that s^{μ} be a multiple of u^{μ} (see Section 5.2). Therefore, we may define

$$s^{\mu} = su^{\mu}. \qquad\qquad (12\text{-}28$$

(Note that s here is not proper time.) The substitution of eq. (12-28) into eq. (12-27b) and the use of eq. (12-25) give the result $su_{\mu}u^{\mu} = 0$. Since $s = 0$ is of no physical interest, u^{μ} is a null vector. It must be remembered that u^{μ} was not assumed to be a world-velocity; u^{μ} is $d\xi^{\mu}/dp$ where p is a parameter along the curve. In view of the null nature of u^{μ}, p cannot be taken as proper time, as was done in the case of a particle. The substitution of eq. (12-28) into eq. (12-27a) shows that the acceleration $a^{\mu}(p)$ which was used in Section 8.14 is parallel to u^{μ}; hence the trajectory is a geodesic.

It has been proved that a free photon follows a null geodesic. But the above derivation also provides an avenue for verifying on theoretical grounds the equation $\mathsf{E} = h\nu$ which is basic to quantum mechanics. Therefore, to such a proof we now turn.

It was noted in Section 5.2 (and the same is also true here) that $s^{\mu\nu}$ is a tensor. Therefore, from eq. (12-27b), s^{μ} is a vector. But note that s^{0} or σ^{00} is the localization of the energy density S^{00}:

$$\sigma^{00} = \lim_{V \to 0} \int_{V} S^{00}\, dV.$$

Therefore, s^0c^2 is equal to the energy of the photon. We may, by analogy with eq. (3-74), define

$$s^\mu = s^0 l^\mu \tag{12-29}$$

where l^μ, not a vector, has a temporal component of unity. Now it is necessary to note that, by an appropriate choice of the parameter p, u^μ may be chosen to be equal to s^μ. For suppose that there was one parameter p' for which $s^\mu \neq d\xi^\mu/dp'$. Then we merely define

$$p = \int \frac{d\xi^0}{s^0}$$

to obtain $s^\mu = d\xi^\mu/dp$; and the p so defined is found, from eq. (12-27a), to be a preferred parameter for a free photon.

12.4 THE GENERALIZED DOPPLER EFFECT

A source of light A emits light which is received by an observer B. The light which leaves A at proper time τ_A follows a null geodesic Γ and reaches B at proper time τ_B. Light which leaves A a short time $\delta\tau_A$ later follows a neighboring null geodesic Γ' and reaches B at proper time $\tau_B + \delta\tau_B$. (see Figure 12.1). A parameter p is constructed along both Γ and Γ' which has the following properties: (1) p is a preferred parameter for Γ: $x^\mu(p)$:

$$\frac{d^2x^\mu}{dp^2} + \left\{ \begin{matrix} \mu \\ \nu\rho \end{matrix} \right\} \frac{dx^\nu}{dp} \frac{dx^\rho}{dp} = 0; \tag{12-30}$$

(2) p is a preferred parameter for Γ': $x'^\mu(p)$:

$$\frac{d^2x'^\mu}{dp^2} + \left\{ \begin{matrix} \mu \\ \nu\rho \end{matrix} \right\}' \frac{dx'^\nu}{dp} \frac{dx'^\rho}{dp} = 0; \tag{12-31}$$

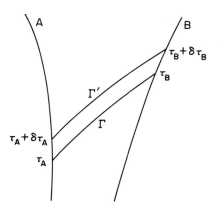

FIGURE 12.1 Generalized Doppler effect.

(3) the intersections of Γ and Γ' with the world-line of A have the same parameter p_A; and (4) the intersections of Γ and Γ' with the world-line of B have the same parameter p_B. This choice is possible because eqs. (12-30) and (12-31) determine p only to within an arbitrary multiplicative constant and an arbitrary additive constant.

The following notation will be used:

$$\delta x^{\mu}(p) = x'^{\mu}(p) - x^{\mu}(p)$$

$$u^{\mu}(p) = \frac{dx^{\mu}}{dp}$$

$$J = g_{\mu\nu}[x^{\sigma}(p)]u^{\mu}(p)\,\delta x^{\nu}(p). \tag{12-32}$$

We will now prove that J is independent of p. Differentiation of eq. (12-32) and the elimination of du^{μ}/dp by the use of eq. (12-30) gives

$$\frac{dJ}{dp} = g_{\mu\nu}u^{\mu}\left(\frac{d\,\delta x^{\nu}}{dp} + \left\{ {\nu \atop \rho\sigma} \right\} u^{\rho}\,\delta x^{\sigma}\right).$$

On the other hand, the difference between the null conditions

$$g_{\mu\nu}[x'^{\sigma}(p)]\frac{dx'^{\mu}}{dp}\frac{dx'^{\nu}}{dp} = 0 \quad \text{and} \quad g_{\mu\nu}[x^{\sigma}(p)]\frac{dx^{\mu}}{dp}\frac{dx^{\nu}}{dp} = 0$$

gives, to first order in δx^{μ},

$$0 = g_{\mu\nu}u^{\mu}\left(\frac{d\,\delta x^{\nu}}{dp} + \left\{ {\nu \atop \rho\sigma} \right\} u^{\rho}\,\delta x^{\sigma}\right).$$

Therefore, J is independent of p; it is a constant along the photon's trajectory.

In particular, we have $J_A = J_B$ where $J_A = u_{\mu A}\,\delta x_A^{\mu}$ and $J_B = u_{\mu B}\,\delta x_B^{\mu}$. But we also have $\delta x_A^{\mu} = w_A^{\mu}\,\delta\tau_A$ and $\delta x_B^{\mu} = w_B^{\mu}\,\delta\tau_B$ where w_A^{μ} and w_B^{μ} are the world-velocities of A and B, respectively. And further, since the number of waves $\nu_A\,\delta\tau_A$ leaving the source is equal to the number of waves $\nu_B\,\delta\tau_B$ reaching the observer, the frequencies ν_A and ν_B of emission and reception have the ratio

$$\frac{\nu_B}{\nu_A} = \frac{\delta\tau_A}{\delta\tau_B}.$$

Therefore, we obtain the result

$$\frac{u_{\mu A}w_A^{\mu}}{\nu_A} = \frac{u_{\mu B}w_B^{\mu}}{\nu_B}. \tag{12-33}$$

With the identification $u^{\mu} = s^{\mu}$ as explained in Section 12.3, eq. (12-33) becomes

$$\frac{s_{\mu A}w_A^{\mu}}{\nu_A} = \frac{s_{\mu B}w_B^{\mu}}{\nu_B}. \tag{12-34}$$

The quantities $s_{\mu A} w_A^\mu$ and $s_{\mu B} w_B^\mu$ are scalars. Therefore, in the respective proper systems of A and B, they assume the values s_A^0 and s_B^0, respectively. But then eq. (12-34) requires that the ratios s_A^0/v_A and s_B^0/v_B be a constant, say h. (This h is not to be confused with the determinant of the spatial metric used in Section 12.1.) Thus we have the relation $s^0 = h\nu$ where h is a constant and s^0 is the energy of the photon.

It has been proved that the equation $\mathsf{E} = h\nu$ holds for photons, with h constant along the trajectory of each photon. It remains for experiment to establish that h is also constant from one photon to another and is, in fact, Planck's constant equal to 6.626×10^{-34} joule-sec.

CHAPTER 13

AUTOMORPHISMS

13.1 INTRODUCTION

If an n-dimensional space possesses a self-mapping such that each point maps into another point, the mapping is called an *automorphism*. A point P with coordinates x^i is mapped into a point P' with coordinates x'^i. The mapping is represented by the function

$$x'^i = f^i(x^j) \tag{13-1}$$

and its inverse

$$x^i = \phi^i(x'^j).$$

It will be assumed that the functions f^i and ϕ^i are continuous and possess as many derivatives as may be needed.

If a space admits automorphisms, then the set of *all* such automorphisms constitutes a *group*. For it is evident that the automorphisms satisfy the three criteria which define a group:

1. The product of two members is another member. The product of two automorphisms

$$A: x'^i = f^i_A(x), \qquad x^i = \phi^i_A(x')$$

$$B: x''^i = f^i_B(x'), \qquad x'^i = \phi^i_B(x'')$$

is the automorphism

$$C: x''^i = f^i_B[f^j_A(x)], \qquad x^i = \phi^i_A[\phi^j_B(x'')]$$

which may be written

$$C: x''^i = f^i_C(x), \qquad x^i = \phi^i_C(x'').$$

310

2. The identity member exists. The identity automorphism is merely

$$I: x'^i = x^i.$$

3. Every member has an inverse. The inverse of the automorphism

$$A: x'^i = f_A^i(x), \qquad x^i = \phi_A^i(x')$$

is the automorphism

$$D: x'^i = f_D^i(x), \qquad x^i = \phi_D^i(x')$$

where $f_D^i \equiv \phi_A^i$ and $\phi_D^i \equiv f_A^i$.

13.2 ONE-PARAMETER GROUPS

If the members of a group of automorphisms are specified by a single parameter a, then the automorphisms form a *one-parameter group*. The parameter can, without loss of generality, be chosen so that the identity automorphism is given by $a = 0$. Equation (13-1) becomes

$$x'^i = f^i(x^j, a). \tag{13-2}$$

The *generator* $\xi^i(x^j)$ is a vector field defined

$$\xi^i(x^j) = \left[\frac{\partial f^i(x^j, a)}{\partial a} \right]_{a=0}. \tag{13-3}$$

The vector nature of ξ^i is proved by merely performing a coordinate transformation $\bar{x}^r = F^r(x^i)$. The inverse transformation will be denoted $x^i = G^i(\bar{x}^r)$. The automorphism in the new coordinates is given by

$$\bar{x}'^r(\bar{x}^s, a) = F^r\{ f^i[G^j(\bar{x}^s), a] \}. \tag{13-4}$$

Application of eq. (13-3) to eq. (13-4) gives

$$\bar{\xi}^r(\bar{x}^s) = \left[\frac{\partial F^r\{ f^k[G^j(\bar{x}^s), a] \}}{\partial x^i} \cdot \frac{\partial f^i[G^l(\bar{x}^t), a]}{\partial a} \right]_{a=0}$$

$$= \frac{\partial F^r(x^k)}{\partial x^i} \xi^i(x^l)$$

which is the transformation law for a contravariant vector.

We will now prove that the differential equation

$$\frac{\partial x'^i}{\partial a} = \xi^i(x') \tag{13-5}$$

is the necessary and sufficient condition for the existence of a one-parameter group of automorphisms $x'^i(x^j, a)$. Any two automorphisms

$$x'^i = f^i(x, a)$$

$$x''^i = f^i(x', b)$$

have as their product the automorphism

$$x''^i = f^i(x, c)$$

where c is given by

$$f^i(x, c) = f^i[f^j(x, a), b].$$ (13-6)

The important thing to notice here is that the new parameter c is a function only of the two initial parameters a and b. This function will be denoted thus: $c = \phi(a, b)$. Equation (13-6) is differentiated with respect to a with x^i and c held constant to give

$$0 = \frac{\partial f^i}{\partial x'^j}(x', b)\frac{\partial x'^j}{\partial a} + \frac{\partial f^i}{\partial b}(x', b)\frac{db}{da}$$

where

$$\frac{db}{da} = -\frac{\dfrac{\partial \phi}{\partial a}}{\dfrac{\partial \phi}{\partial b}}.$$

When b is set equal to zero, the result is

$$\frac{\partial x'^k}{\partial a} = \xi^k(x')A(a)$$ (13-7)

where

$$\xi^k(x') = \left[\frac{\partial f^k(x', b)}{\partial b}\right]_{b=0}$$

and

$$A(a) = -\left[\frac{db}{da}\right]_{b=0}.$$

Equation (13-7) has the important property that the variables x'^i and a are separated on the right-hand side. The function A can be chosen as unity by a redefinition of the parameter:

$$a' = \int A(a)\, da.$$

The result is eq. (13-5).

The proof of the sufficiency of eq. (13-5) makes use of the Taylor series expansion

$$x'^i(x, a) = \sum_{n=0}^{\infty} \frac{1}{n!} C_n^i(x)a^n$$ (13-8)

where the coefficients $C_n^i(x)$ are given by

$$C_n^i = \left[\frac{\partial^n x'^i(x, a)}{\partial a^n}\right]_{a=0}$$

It is easily proved by mathematical induction, with the use of eq. (13-5), that the derivatives of x'^i are given by

$$\frac{\partial^n x'^i}{\partial a^n} = X'^n x^i$$

where the operator X' is defined

$$X' = \xi^k(x') \frac{\partial}{\partial x'^k} .$$

The coefficients C_n^i are therefore, with $a = 0$, given by $C_n^i(x) = X^n x^i$ where X is defined

$$X = \xi^k(x) \frac{\partial}{\partial x^k} .$$

Thus eq. (13-8) becomes

$$x'^i = \sum_{n=0}^{\infty} \frac{1}{n!} a^n X^n x^i. \tag{13-9}$$

Equation (13-9), which is the formal solution of eq. (13-5), represents the one-parameter group which is generated by eq. (13-5).

The relation

$$\xi^i[x'(x, a)] = \xi^j(x) \frac{\partial x'^i(x, a)}{\partial x^j}, \tag{13-10}$$

which follows from eqs. (13-5) and (13-9), has an interesting interpretation. Define the coordinate transformation

$$\bar{x}^i = f^i(x^j, a) \tag{13-11}$$

where the function f^i is the same one which appears in eq. (13-2). Then the right-hand side of eq. (13-10) is the vector $\bar{\xi}^i$ in the new coordinates $\bar{x}^i$. Equation (13-10) becomes

$$\xi^i(\beta) = \bar{\xi}^i(\beta), \tag{13-12}$$

where β is a dummy argument. The point is that the arguments in eq. (13-12) are identical. But the argument of ξ^i is the coordinate x^i, and the argument of $\bar{\xi}^i$ is the coordinate $\bar{x}^i$. Therefore eq. (13-12) states that the vector $\bar{\xi}^i$ in the coordinates $\bar{x}^i$ at a point P is equal to the vector ξ^i in the coordinates x^i at the point P' into which P is mapped by eq. (13-2).

The generator $\xi^i(x^j)$ is the coefficient of the first term in the power series expansion of eq. (13-2):

$$x'^i = x^i + \xi^i(x^j)a + O^2(a). \tag{13-13}$$

Equation (13-13) is known as the *infinitesimal* automorphism.

One of the main points of this section is that the infinitesimal automorphism can be used to generate the finite automorphism of eq. (13-2) by using the generator ξ^i. Equation (13-9) gives one expression for the finite automorphism.

Another expression for the finite automorphism is obtained by means of the following geometrical construction. The vector field $\xi^i(x^j)$, which is assumed to be everywhere single-valued, continuous, and non-zero, is interpreted as the field of the tangents of a congruence of curves. The differential equation for the congruence is

$$\frac{dx^0}{\xi^0} = \frac{dx^1}{\xi^1} = \frac{dx^2}{\xi^2} = \cdots = \frac{dx^{n-1}}{\xi^{n-1}}.$$

We define a new coordinate system

$$\bar{x}^i = F^i(x^j), \qquad x^i = G^i(\bar{x}^j)$$

which has the property that each member of the congruence is given by $\bar{x}^r = \text{const} \ (r = 1, 2, \ldots, n-1)$. The remaining coordinate $\bar{x}^0$ is then a parameter along each curve. Such a coordinate system indeed exists, because it is given by the $n-1$ functionally independent solutions of the equation

$$\frac{\partial F}{\partial x^i} \xi^i = 0.$$

In the special coordinates $\bar{x}^i$, the generator is $\bar{\bar{\xi}}^i = \delta_0^i \bar{\xi}^0$. It is possible to choose $\bar{\xi}^0$ as unity by making an adjustment in $\bar{x}^0$; the new $\bar{x}^0$ is defined to be equal to $\displaystyle\int \frac{d\bar{x}^0}{\bar{\xi}^0(\bar{x}^i)}$ in terms of the old $\bar{x}^0$. Thus, we have a coordinate system in which the generator is $\bar{\bar{\xi}}^i = \delta_0^i$ everywhere. Equation (13-5) which becomes

$$\frac{\partial \bar{x}^0}{\partial a} = 1, \qquad \frac{\partial \bar{x}^r}{\partial a} = 0 \quad (r = 1, 2, \ldots, n-1)$$

has the solution

$$\bar{x}'^i = \bar{x}^i + \delta_0^i a. \tag{13-14}$$

Equation (13-14) gives the finite automorphism in terms of the special coordinates $\bar{x}^i$. Transformation back to the original x^i gives

$$x'^i = G^i[F^j(x^k) + \delta_0^j a]. \tag{13-15}$$

Equation (13-2) has been put into the form of eq. (13-15). The functions $F^i(x^k)$ are the solutions to

$$\frac{\partial F^i}{\partial x^j} \xi^j(x^k) = \delta_0^i,$$

and the functions G^i are the inverse of the F^i. The derivation shows that the mapping of the automorphism is carried along the curves of which $\xi^i(x^k)$ is the tangent.

A point P at $x^i = \alpha^i$ is mapped by the automorphism of eq. (13-2) into a point P' at $x^i = \beta^i$, where $\beta^i = f^i(\alpha^j, a)$. If a new coordinate system $\bar{x}^i$ is defined by eq. (13-11), then P is also at $\bar{x}^i = \beta^i$. Any tensor field $T^i_{.j}$ which exists in the x^i-coordinates can be transformed to the $\bar{x}^i$-coordinates by the usual rule:

$$\bar{T}^i_{.j} = T^k_{.l} \frac{\partial \bar{x}^i}{\partial x^k} \frac{\partial x^l}{\partial \bar{x}^j}. \tag{13-16}$$

The value of $T^i_{.j}$ at the point P' will in general be different from the value of $\bar{T}^i_{.j}$ at the point P. This difference is the *automorphic differential* $\delta T^i_{.j}$ of the tensor $T^i_{.j}$:

$$\delta T^i_{.j} = T^i_{.j}(\beta) - \bar{T}^i_{.j}(\beta). \tag{13-17}$$

When eq. (13-17) is expressed in powers of a with the use of eqs. (13-13) and (13-16), the result is

$$\delta T^i_{.j} = \left(\xi^h \frac{\partial T^i_{.j}}{\partial x^h} - \frac{\partial \xi^i}{\partial x^h} T^h_{.j} + \frac{\partial \xi^h}{\partial x^j} T^i_{.h} \right) a + O^2(a). \tag{13-18}$$

The *automorphic derivative* $\Delta T^i_{.j}$ of a tensor $T^i_{.j}$ is defined

$$\Delta T^i_{.j} = \lim_{a \to 0} \frac{\delta T^i_{.j}}{a}.$$

It follows from eq. (13-18) that $\Delta T^i_{.j}$ is given by

$$\Delta T^i_{.j} = \xi^h \frac{\partial T^i_{.j}}{\partial x^h} - \frac{\partial \xi^i}{\partial x^h} T^h_{.j} + \frac{\partial \xi^h}{\partial x^j} T^i_{.h}. \tag{13-19}$$

Equation (13-19) can be generalized by inspection to tensors with any number of contravariant or covariant indices. For example, if the space possesses a metric tensor g_{ij}, its automorphic derivative is

$$\Delta g_{ij} = \xi^h \frac{\partial g_{ij}}{\partial x^h} + \frac{\partial \xi^h}{\partial x^i} g_{jh} + \frac{\partial \xi^h}{\partial x^j} g_{ih}$$

or

$$\Delta g_{ij} = \xi_{i,j} + \xi_{j,i}. \tag{13-20}$$

Furthermore, in a space which possesses a metric, eq. (13-19) becomes

$$\Delta T^i_{.j} = \xi^h T^i_{.j,h} - \xi^i_{,h} T^h_{.j} + \xi^h_{,j} T^i_{.h}.$$

The automorphic differential of the generator ξ^i was found in eq. (13-12) to vanish identically. The same result is obtained from eq. (13-19); the substitution of ξ^i for $T^i_{.j}$ gives $\Delta \xi^i = 0$.

13.3 LIE'S THREE FUNDAMENTAL THEOREMS*

For an r-parameter group of automorphisms, there exists a generalization of eq. (13-7). The automorphisms

$$x'^i = f^i(x^j; a^\alpha) \qquad (\alpha = 1, 2, \ldots, r) \qquad (13\text{-}21)$$

possess a generator

$$\xi_\alpha^i(x) = \left[\frac{\partial f^i(x; a)}{\partial a^\alpha} \right]_{\text{all } a's = 0}$$

(As before, the automorphism $a^\alpha = 0$ is taken to be the identity automorphism.) The parameter indices will be denoted by Greek letters, and the vector indices by Latin letters. When x^i and a^α appear as arguments of functions, the indices will be omitted for convenience.

The equation which we wish to derive is

$$\frac{\partial x'^k}{\partial a^\alpha} = \xi_\beta^k(x') A_\alpha^\beta(a). \qquad (13\text{-}22)$$

The product of two automorphisms

$$A: \ x'^i = f^i(x; a)$$

$$B: \ x''^i = f^i(x'; b)$$

is another automorphism

$$C: \ x''^i = f^i(x; c)$$

where c^α are given by

$$f^i(x; c) = f^i[f^j(x; a); b]. \qquad (13\text{-}23)$$

The c^α are functions only of the a^α and b^α:

$$c^\alpha = \phi^\alpha(a, b).$$

Equation (13-23) is differentiated with respect to a^α while the x^i and the c^β are held constant. The result is

$$0 = \frac{\partial f^i(x'; b)}{\partial x'^j} \cdot \frac{\partial f^j(x; a)}{\partial a^\alpha} + \frac{\partial f^i(x'; b)}{\partial b^\beta} \cdot \frac{\partial b^\beta}{\partial a^\alpha} \qquad (13\text{-}24)$$

where $\partial b^\beta / \partial a^\alpha$ is given by

$$0 = \frac{\partial \phi^\gamma}{\partial a^\alpha} + \frac{\partial \phi^\gamma}{\partial b^\beta} \frac{\partial b^\beta}{\partial a^\alpha}.$$

With all the b^γ in eq. (13-24) set equal to zero, we obtain eq. (13-22), with

$$A_\alpha^\beta(a) = - \left[\frac{\partial b^\beta}{\partial a^\alpha} \right]_{b^\gamma = 0}.$$

----

* Named after the German mathematician Sophus Lie.

We have derived eq. (13-22) from eq. (13-21) under the assumption that the automorphisms of eq. (13-21) form a group. Lie's *first fundamental theorem* states that if a set of automorphisms $f^i(x; a)$ satisfies eq. (13-22) with $|A_\alpha^\beta(0)| \neq 0$ and $f^i(x; 0) = x^i$, then the automorphisms form a group. The proofs of Lie's theorems will not be given here; they can be found in *Continuous Groups of Transformations* (Princeton University Press, 1933), by Luther Pfahler Eisenhart, pages 22–26 and 54–55.

In the remainder of this section, the primes on the x'^i in eq. (13-22) will be omitted but understood:

$$\frac{\partial x^i}{\partial a^\alpha} = \xi_\beta^i A_\alpha^\beta.$$

(13-25)

The differentiability requirement

$$\frac{\partial^2 x^i}{\partial a^\alpha \, \partial a^\beta} = \frac{\partial^2 x^i}{\partial a^\beta \, \partial a^\alpha}$$

and eq. (13-25) lead to the equation

$$\left[\xi_\tau^k \frac{\partial \xi_\sigma^i}{\partial x^k} - \xi_\sigma^k \frac{\partial \xi_\tau^i}{\partial x^k} \right] A_\alpha^\sigma A_\beta^\tau = \xi_\sigma^i \left(\frac{\partial A_\beta^\sigma}{\partial a^\alpha} - \frac{\partial A_\alpha^\sigma}{\partial a^\beta} \right).$$

(13-26)

Let $\breve{A}_\beta^\alpha$ be the inverse of the matrix A_β^α. Multiplication of eq. (13-26) by $\breve{A}_\gamma^\alpha \breve{A}_\delta^\beta$ gives the result

$$[\xi_\delta, \xi_\gamma]^i = c_{\delta\gamma}^\sigma \xi_\sigma^i$$

(13-27)

where

$$[\xi_\delta, \xi_\gamma]^i = \xi_\delta^k \frac{\partial \xi_\gamma^i}{\partial x^k} - \xi_\gamma^k \frac{\partial \xi_\delta^i}{\partial x^k}$$

and

$$c_{\gamma\delta}^\sigma = \breve{A}_\gamma^\alpha \breve{A}_\delta^\beta \left[\frac{\partial A_\alpha^\sigma}{\partial a^\beta} - \frac{\partial A_\beta^\sigma}{\partial a^\alpha} \right].$$

Since the left-hand side of eq. (13-27) depends only on x^i, the coefficients $c_{\gamma\delta}^\sigma$, which can at the most depend only on the a^α, must be constants.

We have proved that if there exists a set of functions $\xi_\alpha^i(x)$ such that eq. (13-25) is satisfied, then there exists a set of constants $c_{\gamma\delta}^\sigma$ given by eq. (13-27). Lie's *second fundamental theorem* states that if a set of linearly independent functions $\xi_\alpha^i(x)$ and a set of constants $c_{\delta\gamma}^\sigma$ satisfy eq. (13-27), then there exist functions $A_\alpha^\beta(a)$ such that eq. (13-25) is satisfied and has solutions $f^i(x, a)$ which define an r-parameter group of automorphisms with $f^i(x, 0) = x^i$.

The operator notation

$$X_\alpha = \xi_\alpha^i \frac{\partial}{\partial x^i}$$

puts eq. (13-27) into the form

$$[X_\delta, X_\gamma] = c_{\delta\gamma}^\sigma X_\sigma \tag{13-28}$$

where

$$[X_\delta, X_\gamma] = X_\delta X_\gamma - X_\gamma X_\delta.$$

The substitution of eq. (13-28) into the identity

$$[[X_\alpha, X_\beta], X_\gamma] + [[X_\beta, X_\gamma], X_\alpha] + [[X_\gamma, X_\alpha], X_\beta] = 0$$

then gives the result

$$c_{\alpha\beta}^\sigma c_{\sigma\gamma}^\tau + c_{\beta\gamma}^\sigma c_{\sigma\alpha}^\tau + c_{\gamma\alpha}^\sigma c_{\sigma\beta}^\tau = 0. \tag{13-29}$$

We have proved that if there exists a set of functions $\xi_\alpha^i(x)$ and a set of constants $c_{\delta\gamma}^\sigma$ such that eq. (13-27) is satisfied, then the constants satisfy eq. (13-29). Lie's *third fundamental theorem* states that if a set of constants $c_{\delta\gamma}^\sigma$ satisfies eq. (13-29), then there exists a set of functions $\xi_\alpha^i(x)$ such that eq. (13-27) is satisfied.

13.4 METRIC AUTOMORPHISMS

An automorphism is a *metric automorphism* if the space possesses a metric and the metric is preserved by the automorphism. Consider two points $P(\alpha^i)$ and $Q(\alpha^i + d\alpha^i)$ which are mapped by eq. (13-1) into the points $P'(\beta^i)$ and $Q'(\beta^i + d\beta^i)$, where β^i is equal to $f^i(\alpha^j)$. The condition that the line element PQ be equal to the line element $P'Q'$ is

$$g_{ij}(\beta)\, d\beta^i\, d\beta^j = g_{kl}(\alpha)\, d\alpha^k\, d\alpha^l,$$

which may also be written

$$\left[g_{ij}(\beta) - g_{kl}(\alpha) \frac{\partial \alpha^k}{\partial \beta^i} \frac{\partial \alpha^l}{\partial \beta^j} \right] d\beta^i\, d\beta^j = 0.$$

Since $d\beta^i$ is to be arbitrary, we obtain the relation

$$g_{ij}(\beta) = g_{kl}(\alpha) \frac{\partial \alpha^k}{\partial \beta^i} \frac{\partial \alpha^l}{\partial \beta^j}. \tag{13-30}$$

Equation (13-30) is the necessary and sufficient condition for the automorphism of eq. (13-1) to be a metric automorphism.

In the coordinates $\bar{x}^i$ defined by eq. (13-11), the metric tensor at a point P is

$$\bar{g}_{ij}(\beta) = g_{kl}(\alpha) \frac{\partial \alpha^k}{\partial \beta^i} \frac{\partial \alpha^l}{\partial \beta^j} \tag{13-31}$$

where β^i is the $\bar{x}^i$-coordinate of P and α^i is the x^i-coordinate of P. But comparison of eq. (13-31) with eq. (13-30) shows that we have

$$g_{ij}(\beta) = \bar{g}_{ij}(\beta). \tag{13-32}$$

Equation (13-32) can be interpreted in the same way as eq. (13-12). The metric tensor in the $\bar{x}^i$-coordinates at a point P is equal to the metric tensor in the x^i-coordinates at the point P' into which P is mapped by eq. (13-1). Therefore the automorphic derivative of the metric tensor vanishes identically. Equation (13-20) then gives

$$0 = \xi_{i,j} + \xi_{j,i}. \tag{13-33}$$

Equation (13-33), known as Killing's equation, is the necessary and sufficient condition that the automorphism generated by the vector field $\xi^i(x)$ be a metric automorphism. Killing's equation was encountered in two previous contexts. The first occurrence (Section 1.6) was in the study of Euclidean space. The requirement that the space transform into itself was a special case of a metric automorphism in three-dimensional space with the metric $g_{ij} = \delta_{ij}$. The second occurrence (Section 5.6) was in connection with Minkowski space-time in special relativity. In this case the space is four-dimensional, and the metric is the Minkowski metric $g_{ij} = \eta_{ij}$. The metric automorphisms of Minkowski space-time will be considered again in Section 13.5.

It should be noted that eq. (13-33) applies to the generator of *each* automorphism admitted by a space. Although it was assumed that the space admits a one-parameter family of automorphisms characterized by the generator ξ^i, there was *no* assumption made that the space does not admit other automorphisms. Thus eq. (13-33) is by no means limited to spaces which admit only a one-parameter family of automorphisms.

We will now derive the relations

and

$$\xi_{i,jk} = \xi_h R^h_{\ kji} \tag{13-34}$$

$$\Delta R_{ijkl} = 0 \tag{13-35}$$

where R_{ijkl} is the Riemann curvature tensor. Equations (8-39) and (8-40) will be needed:

$$\xi_{i,jk} - \xi_{i,kj} = \xi_h R^h_{\ ijk} \tag{13-36}$$

$$\xi_{i,jkl} - \xi_{i,jlk} = \xi_{h,j} R^h_{\ ikl} + \xi_{i,h} R^h_{\ jkl}. \tag{13-37}$$

The only assumptions which entered eqs. (13-36) and (13-37) were, respectively, the integrability conditions

$$\frac{\partial^2 \xi_i}{\partial x^k \, \partial x^j} = \frac{\partial^2 \xi_i}{\partial x^j \, \partial x^k} \tag{13-38}$$

$$\frac{\partial^3 \xi_i}{\partial x^l \, \partial x^k \, \partial x^j} = \frac{\partial^3 \xi_i}{\partial x^k \, \partial x^l \, \partial x^j}. \tag{13-39}$$

Thus eqs. (13-36) and (13-37) may be regarded, respectively, as the integrability conditions for the existences of $\partial \xi_i / \partial x^j$ and $\partial^2 \xi_i / \partial x^j \partial x^k$. We begin by writing

$$\xi_{i,jk} + \xi_{j,ik} + \xi_{k,ij} + \xi_{i,kj} - \xi_{k,ji} - \xi_{j,\lambda i} = 0. \tag{13-40}$$

Equation (13-40) is obtained directly from eq. (13-33). The substitution of eq. (13-36) for all terms in eq. (13-40) except the first, and the use of the symmetry properties of the Riemann tensor, give eq. (13-34). The substitution of the left-hand side of eq. (13-34) into the left-hand side of eq. (13-37), and the use of the symmetries of R_{ijkl} give

$$\xi^h R_{ijkl,h} + \xi^h{}_{,j} R_{ihkl} + \xi^h{}_{,k} R_{ijhl} + \xi^h{}_{,l} R_{ijkh} = \xi_{i,h} R^h{}_{jkl}.$$

The left-hand side of the above equation is equal to ΔR_{ijkl} except for a term $\xi_{h,i} R^h{}_{jkl}$. Therefore we have

$$\Delta R_{ijkl} = (\xi_{i,h} + \xi_{h,i}) R^h{}_{jkl}.$$

But the quantity in parentheses vanishes by eq. (13-33). Therefore eq. (13-35) is established.

The foregoing derivation is summarized as follows. Equation (13-33), which is the condition for the existence of a metric automorphism, and eq. (13-38), which is the integrability condition for the existence of $\partial \xi^i / \partial x^j$, lead directly to eq. (13-34). Equations (13-33), (13-38), and (13-39)—the latter is the integrability condition for the existence of $\partial^2 \xi^i / \partial x^k \partial x^j$—lead directly to eq. (13-35). Thus eq. (13-34) is the integrability condition for eq. (13-33), and eq. (13-35) is the integrability condition for eq. (13-34).

An interesting property of metric automorphisms is that the product

$$\psi = \xi_i[x(p)] \frac{dx^i(p)}{dp}$$

is constant along any geodesic $x^i(p)$ where p is the preferred parameter. This is proved by differentiating the above product.

$$\frac{d\psi}{dp} = \xi_{i,j} \dot{x}^i \dot{x}^j + \xi_i \left[\frac{d^2 x^i}{dp^2} + \begin{Bmatrix} i \\ jk \end{Bmatrix} \frac{dx^j}{dp} \frac{dx^k}{dp} \right] \tag{13-41}$$

where $\dot{x}^i = dx^i / dp$. The second term on the right-hand side of eq. (13-41) vanishes because p is the preferred parameter. The first term vanishes by virtue of Killing's equation. Therefore if ξ^i is the generator of a metric automorphism, then $\xi_i \dot{x}^i$ is constant along a geodesic. The converse is also true: the condition for $\xi_i \dot{x}^i = \text{const}$ to be an integral of the geodesic equation is that ξ_i be the generator of a metric automorphism; for then $\xi_{i,j} \dot{x}^i \dot{x}^j = 0$ has the solution $\xi_{i,j} + \xi_{j,i} = 0$.

13.5 EXAMPLES OF METRIC AUTOMORPHISMS IN SPACE-TIME

This section is devoted to two examples of automorphisms in four-dimensional space-time. The first example is the Minkowski space-time of special relativity. Rectangular Cartesian coordinates will be used, so that the metric is given by eq. (3-33).

It is clear from our previous study of special relativity that there are ten transformations which leave the line element unchanged. Six of the transformations are the three translations and three rotations of Euclidean geometry. Another three transformations are the Lorentz transformations along each of the three spatial axes. The tenth transformation is the temporal translation $t' = t + \text{const}$, $x'^i = x^i$. Each of the above ten transformations leaves the metric unchanged. Also, the ten transformations are independent of each other.

We found that a metric automorphism could be regarded as a coordinate transformation which leaves the line element unchanged. Therefore, the ten transformations described above are metric automorphisms admitted by Minkowski space-time. Furthermore, the analysis of the preceding sections allows the automorphisms to be obtained with much less difficulty than was encountered in Section 5.6.

Because the Christoffel symbols and the Riemann curvature tensor vanish in Minkowski space-time, eqs. (13-33) and (13-34) immediately become

$$\frac{\partial \xi_\mu}{\partial x^\nu} + \frac{\partial \xi_\nu}{\partial x^\mu} = 0 \qquad (13\text{-}42)$$

$$\frac{\partial^2 \xi_\mu}{\partial x^\nu \partial x^\rho} = 0. \qquad (13\text{-}43)$$

Equation (13-42) is the condition for the existence of metric automorphisms, and eq. (13-43) is the integrability condition for the existence of the vector fields $\xi_\mu(x)$ which generate the automorphisms. The solutions of eq. (13-43) are

$$\xi_\mu = \alpha_\mu + \beta_{\mu\nu} x^\nu \qquad (13\text{-}44)$$

where the α_μ and the $\beta_{\mu\nu}$ are constants. Equation (13-42) imposes antisymmetry on the $\beta_{\mu\nu}$. Thus there are ten independent constants, and it must be concluded that Minkowski space-time admits no more than ten independent metric automorphisms. It may be remembered that eq. (13-44) was obtained in Section 5.6, but by a much lengthier method.

To find the automorphisms generated by the vectors ξ_μ, eq. (13-5) is now utilized. The ten independent generators in eq. (13-44) fall into three categories:

translations	rotations	Lorentz transformations
$(1, 0, 0, 0)$	$(0, -y, x, 0)$	$(x, -t, 0, 0)$
$(0, 1, 0, 0)$	$(0, 0, -z, y)$	$(y, 0, -t, 0)$
$(0, 0, 1, 0)$	$(0, z, 0, -x)$	$(z, 0, 0, -t)$
$(0, 0, 0, 1)$		

One example from each category will suffice to illustrate the method. The generator $(1, 0, 0, 0)$ gives the differential equations

$$\frac{\partial t'}{\partial a} = 1, \qquad \frac{\partial x'}{\partial a} = 0, \qquad \frac{\partial y'}{\partial a} = 0, \qquad \frac{\partial z'}{\partial a} = 0,$$

which have as their solution the translation

$$t' = t + a$$
$$x' = x$$
$$y' = y$$
$$z' = z.$$

The generator $(0, -y, x, 0)$ gives the differential equation

$$\frac{\partial t'}{\partial a} = 0, \qquad \frac{\partial x'}{\partial a} = -y', \qquad \frac{\partial y'}{\partial a} = x', \qquad \frac{\partial z'}{\partial a} = 0$$

which have as their solution the rotation

$$t' = t$$
$$x' = x \cos a - y \sin a$$
$$y' = y \cos a + x \sin a$$
$$z' = z.$$

The generator $\xi^\mu = (x, c^2t, 0, 0)$ gives the differential equations

$$\frac{\partial t'}{\partial a} = x', \qquad \frac{\partial x'}{\partial a} = c^2t', \qquad \frac{\partial y'}{\partial a} = 0, \qquad \frac{\partial z'}{\partial a} = 0,$$

which have as their solution the Lorentz transformation

$$t' = t \cosh ac + c^{-1}x \sinh ac$$
$$x' = x \cosh ac + ct \sinh ac$$
$$y' = y$$
$$z' = z.$$

(The solving of the differential equation is facilitated by the condition that the identity automorphism be given by $a = 0$.) In the Lorentz transformation, the velocity of the transformation is $c \tanh ac$.

The second example of space-time automorphisms which we will examine is the space-time represented by the metric

$$ds^2 = dt^2 - e^{2t}(dx^2 + dy^2 + dz^2). \tag{13-45}$$

Seven metric automorphisms can be written down almost from inspection. Six automorphisms are three spatial translations and three spatial rotations, because the three-dimensional part of the metric is Euclidean. The seventh automorphism is the temporal translation given by

$$\left. \begin{aligned} t' &= t + a \\ x' &= xe^{-a} \\ y' &= ye^{-a} \\ z' &= ze^{-a}. \end{aligned} \right\} \tag{13-46}$$

Each of the seven automorphisms leaves the metric unchanged; hence, they are *metric* automorphisms.

It may be asked whether the metric of eq. (13-45) admits any additional automorphisms. The answer is that there are three others. The most general solution of Killing's equation for the metric of eq. (13-46) contains ten independent arbitrary constants:

$$\xi^0 = A + B_i x^i$$
$$\xi^i = -\tfrac{1}{2}B_i e^{-2t} - \tfrac{1}{2}Ax^i - \tfrac{1}{2}B_k x^k x^i + \tfrac{1}{4}B_i x^k x^k + C_{ik}x^k + D^i$$

where C_{ik} is antisymmetric. The D^i represent spatial translations, the C_{ik} represent spatial rotations, and the A represents the temporal translation. The B_i represent three additional automorphisms which can be regarded as generalizations of the Lorentz transformation. The space-time represented by eq. (13-45) will be studied later in more detail (Sections 14.8 and 16.2).

13.6 CONSERVATION LAWS

Given a four-dimensional space-time which contains a metric $g_{\mu\nu}$ and a zero-divergence stress-energy tensor $T^{\mu\nu}$, the necessary and sufficient condition for the existence of a conserved vector field

$$\Lambda^\mu = T^{\mu\nu}\xi_\nu \tag{13-47}$$

(where ξ_μ is another vector field) is that the space-time admit metric automorphisms. Furthermore, ξ_μ is the group generator so that the number of independent Λ^μ is equal to the number of independent auto-morphisms. The above theorems are proved as follows.

A conservation law in its generalized form is, by definition, the vanishing of the integral of a vector Λ^μ over the three-dimensional bound-ary S of an *arbitrary* region R in space-time. (The reader may wish to refer back to Section 5.6 where the same procedure is used for Minkowski space-time.) The conservation law is therefore written

$$0 = \int_S \Lambda^\mu \sqrt{-g} e(\mu\nu\rho\sigma) \, d^1x^\nu \, d^2x^\rho \, d^3x^\sigma. \tag{13-48}$$

Gauss' theorem may be used to transform eq. (13-48) into a volume integral over the region R. Gauss' theorem, it will be remembered, is independent of the metric. Therefore, the $\sqrt{-g}$ in the integrand must stay with the Λ^μ. Equation (13-48) becomes

$$0 = \int_R \left[\frac{\partial}{\partial x^\mu} (\Lambda^\mu \sqrt{-g}) \right] dx^0 \, dx^1 \, dx^2 \, dx^3. \tag{13-49}$$

Since eq. (13-49) must vanish for an arbitrary region, the integrand must vanish everywhere. But then, by eq. (8-75), the divergence of Λ^μ must vanish everywhere:

$$\Lambda^\mu{}_{,\mu} = 0. \tag{13-50}$$

It follows from eqs. (13-47) and (13-50) and the zero divergence of $T^{\mu\nu}$ that the vector field must satisfy Killing's equation. The ξ_μ is therefore the generator of metric automorphisms, and there are as many Λ^μ as there are independent generators.

As an example of the relation between conservation laws and metric automorphisms, we take the case of Minkowski space-time. The auto-morphisms were found to be given by the generator in eq. (13-44). The conserved vector is therefore

$$\Lambda^\mu = T^{\mu\nu}\alpha_\nu + T^{\mu\nu}\beta_{\nu\rho}x^\rho.$$

The *quantity* which is conserved has density Λ^0 and flux Λ^i. Therefore the conserved quantities are the volume integrals

$$\int \Lambda^0 \, dV = \int T^{0\nu}\alpha_\nu \, dV + \int T^{0\nu}\beta_{\nu\rho}x^\rho \, dV.$$

The translations, represented by the constants α_ν, are found by comparison with eq. (5-31) to be associated with the total 4-momentum. The spatial rotations, represented by the β_{ij}, are seen by comparison with eqs. (5-32) and (5-36) to be associated with angular momentum. The Lorentz trans-formations, represented by the β_{0i}, are seen by comparison with eqs. (5-31) and (5-37) to be associated with the center-of-mass momentum.

13.7 THE MAXIMAL GROUP

There is a maximum number of metric automorphisms which a space can admit. To find this number, we note that the generator ξ_α^μ ($\alpha = 1$, $2, \ldots, r$) for each of the r automorphisms can be expanded in a Taylor series about any point $P(x^i)$:

$$\xi_\alpha^i(x^j + \Delta x^j) = \xi_\alpha^i(x^j) + \left[\frac{\partial \xi_\alpha^i}{\partial x^k}\right]_P \Delta x^k + \frac{1}{2}\left[\frac{\partial^2 \xi_\alpha^i}{\partial x^k \, \partial x^l}\right]_P \Delta x^k \Delta x^l + \cdots.$$

All derivatives higher than the first can, by eq. (13-34), be expressed in terms of $\xi_\alpha^i(P)$ and $[\partial\xi_\alpha^i/\partial x^k]_P$. Furthermore, eq. (13-33) limits the number of independent $[\partial\xi_\alpha^i/\partial x^k]_P$ to $\frac{1}{2}n(n-1)$. The latter condition, with the $n \, \xi_\alpha^i(P)$, provides only $\frac{1}{2}n(n+1)$ arbitrary constants with which to specify the generator field $\xi_\alpha^i(x)$. There is, in addition, another relation between the ξ_α^i and their first derivatives, namely eq. (13-35):

$$0 = \xi^h R_{ijkl,h} + \xi_{h,m}[\delta_i^m R^h{}_{jkl} - \delta_j^m R^h{}_{ikl} + \delta_k^m R^h{}_{lij} - \delta_l^m R^h{}_{kij}]. \quad (13\text{-}51)$$

It is concluded that an n-dimensional space can admit, at the most, $\frac{1}{2}n(n+1)$ metric automorphisms. Furthermore, the maximal group of $\frac{1}{2}n(n+1)$ automorphisms is admitted only if eq. (13-51) holds for *arbitrary* ξ^h and $\xi_{h,m}$.

An n-dimensional space which admits the maximal group of metric automorphisms has a Riemann tensor such that *both* terms in eq. (13-51) vanish identically. The Riemann tensor must therefore have zero gradient

$$R_{ijkl,h} = 0 \qquad (13\text{-}52)$$

and be such that the quantity in brackets in eq. (13-51) is symmetric:

$$\delta_i^m R^h{}_{jkl} - \delta_j^m R^h{}_{ikl} + \delta_k^m R^h{}_{lij} - \delta_l^m R^h{}_{kij} =$$
$$\delta_i^h R^m{}_{jkl} - \delta_j^h R^m{}_{ikl} + \delta_k^h R^m{}_{lij} - \delta_l^h R^m{}_{kij}. \quad (13\text{-}53)$$

Contraction of eq. (13-53) over the indices $m = i$ gives

$$(n-1)R_{ijkl} = g_{il}R_{jk} - g_{ik}R_{jl}. \qquad (13\text{-}54)$$

The antisymmetry of i, j in the Riemann tensor in eq. (13-54) allows eq. (13-54) to be rewritten

$$(n-1)R_{ijkl} = g_{jk}R_{il} - g_{jl}R_{ik}.$$

Multiplication by g^{il} gives

$$nR_{jk} = Rg_{jk}.$$

Equation (13-54) therefore becomes

$$R_{ijkl} = K(g_{ik}g_{jl} - g_{il}g_{jk}) \qquad (13\text{-}55)$$

where

$$K = -\frac{R}{n(n-1)}.$$

It was proved in Section 8.10* that eq. (13-55) implies that the space has constant curvature K. Equation (13-52) is then satisfied by eq. (13-55).

It is also true that a space with constant curvature K admits the maximal group, i.e., that there are no constant-curvature spaces which admit less than $\frac{1}{2}n(n+1)$ metric automorphisms. Coordinates are chosen so that the metric has the canonical form of eq. (8-64). Killing's equation becomes

$$\eta_{ik}\frac{\partial \xi^k}{\partial x^j} + \eta_{jk}\frac{\partial \xi^k}{\partial x^i} = \frac{K\eta_{ij}\eta_{kl}x^k\xi^l}{1+\dfrac{K}{4}r^2} \tag{13-56}$$

where $r^2 = \eta_{kl}x^k x^l$ (and need not be positive). Equation (13-56) has the solutions given by $\xi^i = \xi^i_\alpha$ and $\xi^i = \zeta^i_{\alpha\beta}$ $(\alpha, \beta = 1, 2, \ldots, n)$ where

$$\begin{aligned}
\xi^i_\alpha &= \left(1 - \frac{K}{4}r^2\right)\delta^i_\alpha + \frac{K}{2}x^i\eta_{\alpha k}x^k && \text{a} \\
\zeta^i_{\alpha\beta} &= \delta^i_\alpha\eta_{\beta k}x^k - \delta^i_\beta\eta_{\alpha k}x^k. && \text{b}
\end{aligned} \tag{13-57}$$

Equations (13-57) present $\frac{1}{2}n(n+1)$ independent generator fields (the $\zeta^i_{\alpha\beta}$ are antisymmetric). Thus, by exhibiting the appropriate generators, it has been proved that any space with constant curvature admits the maximum number of metric automorphisms.

To prove that the automorphisms generated by eqs. (13-57) form a *group*, we make use of Lie's second fundamental theorem. Direct calculation with the operators

$$X_\alpha = \xi^i_\alpha \frac{\partial}{\partial x^i} \quad \text{and} \quad Z_{\alpha\beta} = \zeta^i_{\alpha\beta}\frac{\partial}{\partial x^i}$$

shows

$$\begin{aligned}
[X_\alpha, X_\beta] &= KZ_{\alpha\beta} \\
[X_\alpha, Z_{\beta\gamma}] &= (\delta^\epsilon_\beta\eta_{\alpha\gamma} - \delta^\epsilon_\gamma\eta_{\alpha\beta})X_\epsilon \\
[Z_{\alpha\beta}, Z_{\gamma\delta}] &= (\eta_{\alpha\delta}\delta^\mu_\gamma\delta^\nu_\beta - \eta_{\alpha\gamma}\delta^\mu_\delta\delta^\nu_\beta + \eta_{\beta\gamma}\delta^\mu_\delta\delta^\nu_\alpha - \eta_{\beta\delta}\delta^\mu_\gamma\delta^\nu_\alpha)Z_{\mu\nu}.
\end{aligned} \tag{13-58}$$

Therefore eq. (13-28) is satisfied, and Lie's second fundamental theorem guarantees the group nature of the automorphisms.

---

* Schur's theorem applies only to $n \geq 3$. However, the theorem being proved here also applies to the case $n = 2$ because eq. (13-52) is a stronger condition than the Ricci identity.

In three-dimensional space, $\zeta_{\alpha\beta}^i$ assumes the simpler form

$$\zeta_{\alpha\beta}^i = -e(\alpha\beta\gamma)\zeta_\gamma^i \qquad (13\text{-}59)$$

where

$$\zeta_\alpha^i = -e(\alpha\beta\gamma)\,\delta_\beta^i\eta_{\gamma k}x^k.$$

Equations (13-58) become

$$[X_\alpha, X_\beta] = -Ke(\alpha\beta\gamma)Z_\gamma$$

$$[X_\alpha, Z_\beta] = -e(\beta\gamma\delta)\eta_{\alpha\delta}X_\gamma$$

$$[Z_\alpha, Z_\beta] = -e(\alpha\beta\gamma)\eta_{\gamma\epsilon}Z_\epsilon.$$

To sum up the results of this section, an n-dimensional space can admit no more than $\frac{1}{2}n(n+1)$ independent metric automorphisms. An n-dimensional space will admit the maximal group of metric automorphisms if and only if the space has constant curvature. Thus, for example, the admission of ten automorphisms by Minkowski space-time requires Minkowski space-time to have constant curvature (the curvature is indeed constant—i.e., zero). Furthermore, Minkowski space-time cannot admit more than ten automorphisms.

13.8 THE POINCARÉ HALF-PLANE

In the metric of the Poincaré half-plane given by eq. (7-34), Killing's equation becomes

$$\frac{\partial \xi^1}{\partial x} = \frac{\partial \xi^2}{\partial y} = \frac{\xi^2}{y} \qquad (13\text{-}60)$$

$$\frac{\partial \xi^1}{\partial y} + \frac{\partial \xi^2}{\partial x} = 0. \qquad (13\text{-}61)$$

Equation (13-60) has the integral $\xi^2 = F(x) \cdot y$, where $F(x)$ is the constant of integration. Substitution into eqs. (13-60) and (13-61) gives

$$\frac{\partial \xi^1}{\partial x} = F(x) \qquad (13\text{-}62)$$

and

$$\frac{\partial \xi^1}{\partial y} = -F'(x)y. \qquad (13\text{-}63)$$

The integrability condition

$$\frac{\partial^2 \xi^1}{\partial x\,\partial y} = \frac{\partial^2 \xi^1}{\partial y\,\partial x}$$

provides the requirement $F''(x) \cdot y = 0$. Therefore $F(x)$ is a linear function of x, and ξ^1 is, from eq. (13-62), a quadratic:

$$\xi^1 = f(y) + bx + cx^2.$$

Equation (13-63) now gives

$$f'(y) = -2cy.$$

Therefore the solutions are

$$\left.\begin{array}{l} \xi^1 = a + bx + c(x^2 - y^2) \\ \xi^2 = by + 2cxy. \end{array}\right\} \tag{13-64}$$

Since the metric of eq. (7-34) possesses a constant curvature of $K = -1$, we may expect the space to admit the maximal group of three automorphisms. The three generators may, from eq. (13-64), be taken as

$$\xi_1^i = (1, 0)$$
$$\xi_2^i = (x, y)$$
$$\xi_3^i = (x^2 - y^2, 2xy).$$

Application of the equation $\partial x^i / \partial a^\alpha = \xi_\alpha^i$ gives, respectively, the three automorphisms

$$x' = a_1 + x; \qquad y' = y$$
$$x' = e^{a_2}x; \qquad y' = e^{a_2}y$$

$$x' = \frac{1}{a_3} - \frac{x + \dfrac{1}{a_3}}{(a_3)^2\left[\left(x + \dfrac{1}{a_3}\right)^2 + y^2\right]}; \qquad y' = \frac{y}{(a_3)^2\left[\left(x + \dfrac{1}{a_3}\right)^2 + y^2\right]}.$$

The above three transformations leave the form of the metric unchanged. The first is a translation along the x-axis; the second is a dilatation; the third is an inversion about the circle of radius $1/a_3$ with center at $(-1/a_3, 0)$ plus a reflection about the y-axis.

Since the Poincaré half-plane has a constant curvature, there exist coordinates $\bar{x}, \bar{y}$ in which the metric has the canonical form

$$ds^2 = \frac{d\bar{x}^2 + d\bar{y}^2}{[1 - \frac{1}{4}(\bar{x}^2 + \bar{y}^2)]^2}.$$

Accordingly, there exists a transformation $\bar{x}(x, y), \bar{y}(x, y)$ between the coordinates $\bar{x}, \bar{y}$ of the above line element and the coordinates x, y of eq. (7-34). The transformation is hideous to write out, but is easily described; we have

$$\bar{x} = 2(\tanh \tfrac{1}{2}u) \cos \phi$$
$$\bar{y} = 2(\tanh \tfrac{1}{2}u) \sin \phi$$

where u is the geodesic distance along the geodesic through the two points $(0, 1)$ and (x, y), and $\dfrac{\pi}{2} - \phi$ is the angle between the geodesic and the y-axis at the point $(0, 1)$.

13.9 THE HELMHOLTZ-LIE THEOREM

In a three-dimensional space which admits the maximal group of metric automorphisms, all invariants of the group are functions of the line element of eq. (8-64), where K is the curvature of the space. This theorem, known as the Helmholtz-Lie theorem, is proved as follows.

In order that a quantity $F(x^i, dx^j)$ be an invariant under the infinitesimal automorphism

$$x'^i = x^i + \xi^i \, \delta a, \tag{13-65}$$

it must satisfy the equation

$$\xi^i \frac{\partial F(x, z)}{\partial x^i} + z^j \frac{\partial \xi^i(x)}{\partial x^j} \cdot \frac{\partial F(x, z)}{\partial z^i} = 0. \tag{13-66}$$

Equation (13-66) is the result of differentiating eq. (13-65) to get

$$dx'^i = dx^i + \frac{\partial \xi^i}{\partial x^j} \, dx^i \, \delta a \tag{13-67}$$

and then substituting eqs. (13-65) and (13-67) into the condition $F(x', dx') = F(x, dx)$. Equation (13-59) may be substituted for ξ^i in eq. (13-66) to give

$$e(ijk)\left(x_k \frac{\partial F}{\partial x^j} + z_k \frac{\partial F}{\partial z^j}\right) = 0, \tag{13-68}$$

where, for convenience, x_i denotes $\eta_{ij}x^j$ and z_i denotes $\eta_{ij}z^j$. Multiplication of eq. (13-68) by z_i and x_i respectively yields

$$e(ijk)x_k z_i \frac{\partial F}{\partial x^j} = 0 \quad \text{and} \quad e(ijk)x_i z_k \frac{\partial F}{\partial x^j} = 0$$

which imply

$$\left. \begin{aligned} \frac{\partial F}{\partial x^i} &= Ax_i + Bz_i \\ \frac{\partial F}{\partial z^i} &= Cx_i + Dz_i. \end{aligned} \right\} \tag{13-69}$$

Substitution of eqs. (13-69) into eq. (13-68) provides the condition $B - C = 0$. The substitution of eq. (13-57a) for ξ^i and the substitution of eq. (13-69) into eq. (13-66) gives

$$0 = x_i\left[A\left(1 + \frac{K}{4}r^2\right) + \frac{BK}{2}x^kz_k + \frac{KD}{2}z^2\right] + z_iB(1 + \tfrac{1}{4}Kr^2), \quad (13\text{-}70)$$

where $r^2 = x^k x_k$ and $z^2 = z^k z_k$. Equation (13-70) must hold for *arbitrary* x_i and z_i. Therefore $B = 0$ and the quantity in brackets vanishes. Thus far we have

$$\frac{\partial F}{\partial x^i} = Ax_i \quad \text{and} \quad \frac{\partial F}{\partial z^i} = Dz_i$$

where A and D are given by

$$A = -\frac{K\psi}{1 + \dfrac{K}{4}r^2}$$

$$D = \frac{2\psi}{z^2},$$

where ψ is an unknown function. The differential of F is therefore given by

$$dF = \psi\, d\ln\frac{z^2}{\left[1 + \dfrac{K}{4}r^2\right]^2}.$$

Therefore F is a function only of x^i and dx^i in the combination

$$F\left(\frac{\eta_{ij}\,dx^i\,dx^j}{\left[1 + \dfrac{K}{4}\eta_{kl}x^k x^l\right]^2}\right).$$

13.10 GÖDEL'S[B] MODEL

As an example for our study of automorphisms, consider the space-time, known as Gödel's model, described by the line element

$$ds^2 = dt^2 + \frac{2}{c}e^{\frac{x}{a}}\,dt\,dy + \frac{1}{c^2}[\tfrac{1}{2}e^{\frac{2x}{a}}\,dy^2 - dx^2 - dz^2]$$

where a is a constant. Calculation shows that the world-lines $x^i = $ const are geodesics and that the Ricci tensor is

$$R^{\mu\nu} = -a^{-2}\,\delta_0^\mu\,\delta_0^\nu c^2.$$

It then follows from the field equation of general relativity that, if the only physical entity present is a perfect fluid, the fluid has world-lines $x^i = $ const and has constant proper density and constant proper pressure.

Gödel's model admits a four-parameter group of metric automorphisms:

$$t' = t + u_0$$
$$x' = x + u_1$$
$$y' = ye^{-u_1/a} + u_2$$
$$z' = z + u_3$$

where u_α ($\alpha = 0, 1, 2, 3$) are the parameters of the group. The generators are

$$\xi^\mu_\alpha = \delta^\mu_\alpha - \frac{y}{a} \delta^1_\alpha \delta^\mu_2.$$

Direct calculation shows that the ξ^μ_α satisfy eq. (13-27) with

$$c^\gamma_{\alpha\beta} = \frac{1}{a} \delta^\gamma_2 (\delta^1_\alpha \delta^2_\beta - \delta^2_\alpha \delta^1_\beta).$$

Gödel's model is a special case of an n-dimensional space which admits an n-parameter group of transitive metric automorphisms. (*Transitive* means that no point remains unchanged by a finite automorphism.) In the general case, it can be shown that the metric has the form

$$g_{ij} = \gamma_{ab} \breve{\eta}^a_i \breve{\eta}^b_j \qquad (13\text{-}71)$$

where γ_{ab} are constant and η^i_a (and hence the inverse $\breve{\eta}^a_i$) is the matrix defined $[\xi_a, \eta_b]^i = 0$ or

$$\frac{\partial \eta^i_a}{\partial x^j} = \breve{\xi}^b_j \eta^k_a \frac{\partial \xi^i_b}{\partial x^k} \qquad (13\text{-}72)$$

where ξ^i_a is the set of generators. The proof is performed as follows. The integrability condition

$$\frac{\partial^2 \eta^i_a}{\partial x^k \partial x^j} = \frac{\partial^2 \eta^i_a}{\partial x^j \partial x^k}$$

becomes, with the substitution of eq. (13-72),

$$\left\{ [\xi_a, \xi_b]^k \breve{\xi}^c_k \frac{\partial \xi^i_c}{\partial x^l} - \frac{\partial [\xi_a, \xi_b]^i}{\partial x^l} \right\} \eta^l_a = 0$$

which, with the substitution of eq. (13-27), becomes an identity. Therefore eq. (13-72) possesses n independent solutions η^i_a. If we *define* $\gamma_{ab} = g_{ij}\eta^i_a\eta^j_b$, then Killing's equation becomes

$$\xi^k_a \breve{\eta}^b_i \breve{\eta}^c_j \frac{\partial \gamma_{bc}}{\partial x^k} = 0.$$

Thus the γ_{ab} are constants. By this we have proved eq. (13-71). But it is easy to go a step further and prove the relations

$$R_{ijkl} = \rho_{abcd}\breve{\eta}_i^a\breve{\eta}_j^b\breve{\eta}_k^c\breve{\eta}_l^d$$

$$R_{ij} = \rho_{ab}\breve{\eta}_i^a\breve{\eta}_j^b$$

$$\rho_{ab} = \rho_{cabd}\breve{\gamma}^{cd}$$

$$R = \rho_{ab}\breve{\gamma}^{ab},$$

where ρ_{abcd}, ρ_{ab}, and R are constants, and $\breve{\gamma}^{ab}$ is the inverse of γ_{ab}. The constancy of ρ_{abcd} is proved from eq. (13-35) in the same way that the constancy of γ_{ab} is proved from Killing's equation. The use of the relation $g^{ij} = \breve{\gamma}^{ab}\eta_a^i\eta_b^j$ then leads to the equations involving ρ_{ab}.

The quantities η_a^i may be regarded as n independent vector fields (i is the vector index), or they may be regarded as a continuous transformation-matrix field.

If we regard the η_a^i as vector fields, they are the generators of an n-parameter group of non-metric automorphisms. It follows from the definition of η_a^i that the bracket $[[\eta_a, \eta_b], \xi_c]^i$ vanishes. Therefore, the quantities $\bar{c}_{ab}^c$ defined

$$\bar{c}_{ab}^c = \breve{\eta}_k^c[\eta_a, \eta_b]^k$$

are constants. But then, by Lie's second fundamental theorem, the η_a^i form an n-parameter group. The η_a^i are not, however, Killing vectors, since the quantity

$$\eta_a^h\frac{\partial g_{ij}}{\partial x^h} + \frac{\partial \eta_a^h}{\partial x^i}g_{hj} + \frac{\partial \eta_a^h}{\partial x^j}g_{hi}$$

does not vanish.

The above results will now be applied to space-time. If a four-dimensional space-time admits a four-parameter group of metric automorphisms, then the field equation of general relativity becomes

$$-\kappa\tau^{\alpha\beta} = \rho^{\alpha\beta} - \tfrac{1}{2}R\gamma^{\alpha\beta} + \Lambda\gamma^{\alpha\beta} \tag{13-73}$$

where $\tau^{\alpha\beta} = \breve{\eta}_\mu^\alpha\breve{\eta}_\nu^\beta T^{\mu\nu}$. If we assume that the only physical entity present is a perfect fluid with world-velocity $u^\mu = \eta_\alpha^\mu\zeta^\alpha$, proper density ρ, and proper pressure p, then it follows that ζ^α, ρ, and p are constants. This may be shown by differentiating both eq. (13-73) and its contracted form with respect to a coordinate, eliminating the derivatives of p between the two resulting equations while retaining the derivatives of $\rho + pc^{-2}$, and then multiplying the resulting differential equation by ζ_α to obtain the solution

$$\zeta^\alpha = k^\alpha(\rho + pc^{-2})^{-\frac{3}{4}}$$

where k^α is the constant of integration. But the condition $1 = \gamma_{\alpha\beta}\zeta^\alpha\zeta^\beta$ then gives

$$(\rho + pc^{-2})^{\frac{3}{2}} = \gamma_{\alpha\beta}k^\alpha k^\beta.$$

Since the right-hand side of the above equation is constant, so also is the left-hand side. But then ζ^α is constant. And, from the contracted form of eq. (13-73), $\rho - 3pc^{-2}$ is constant. Hence ρ and p are each constant.

The conservation equation $T^{\mu\nu}_{,\nu} = 0$ leads directly to the relations

$$u^\nu u^\mu_{,\nu} = 0 \quad \text{and} \quad u^\nu_{,\nu} = 0. \tag{13-74}$$

It can be shown by means of some calculation which will not be given here that eqs. (13-74) can be transformed into the form

$$\left.\begin{aligned}\zeta^\alpha\zeta^\delta\gamma_{\delta\gamma}\bar{c}^\gamma_{\alpha\beta} &= 0\\ \zeta^\alpha\bar{c}^\beta_{\alpha\beta} &= 0\end{aligned}\right\} \tag{13-75}$$

where $\bar{c}^\gamma_{\alpha\beta}$ are the group parameters for the η^μ_α.

The application to Gödel's model is straightforward. His model admits a four-parameter group of automorphisms. Therefore, if the only physical entity present is a perfect fluid, the fluid must have constant proper density, constant proper pressure, and world-lines such that ζ^α is constant and eqs. (13-75) are satisfied. The differential equation which defines η^μ_α shows that all the η^μ_α in Gödel's model are constant except η^2_2 which must be proportional to $e^{-x/a}$. Thus we may choose

$$\eta^\mu_\alpha = \begin{bmatrix} 1 & 0 & 0 & 0 \\ 0 & 1 & 0 & 0 \\ 0 & 0 & e^{-x/a} & 0 \\ 0 & 0 & 0 & 1 \end{bmatrix}, \qquad \breve{\eta}^\alpha_\mu = \begin{bmatrix} 1 & 0 & 0 & 0 \\ 0 & 1 & 0 & 0 \\ 0 & 0 & e^{x/a} & 0 \\ 0 & 0 & 0 & 1 \end{bmatrix}.$$

We then have

$$\gamma_{\alpha\beta} = \begin{bmatrix} 1 & 0 & 1 & 0 \\ 0 & -1 & 0 & 0 \\ 1 & 0 & \frac{1}{2} & 0 \\ 0 & 0 & 0 & -1 \end{bmatrix}, \qquad \breve{\gamma}^{\alpha\beta} = \begin{bmatrix} -1 & 0 & 2 & 0 \\ 0 & -1 & 0 & 0 \\ 2 & 0 & -2 & 0 \\ 0 & 0 & 0 & -1 \end{bmatrix},$$

$$\rho_{\alpha\beta} = -\frac{1}{a^2}\begin{bmatrix} 1 & 0 & 1 & 0 \\ 0 & 0 & 0 & 0 \\ 1 & 0 & 1 & 0 \\ 0 & 0 & 0 & 0 \end{bmatrix}.$$

Calculation of $\bar{c}^{\gamma}_{\alpha\beta}$ for the above choices of η^{μ}_{α} gives $\bar{c}^{\gamma}_{\alpha\beta} = -c^{\gamma}_{\alpha\beta}$, where the latter is the group parameter of the ξ^{μ}_{α}. Equations (13-75) become

$$0 = \zeta^1(\zeta^0 + \tfrac{1}{2}\zeta^2)$$
$$0 = \zeta^2(\zeta^0 + \tfrac{1}{2}\zeta^2)$$
$$0 = \zeta^1.$$

Hence $\zeta^1 = 0$ and either $\zeta^2 = 0$ or $\zeta^2 = -2\zeta^0$. If the latter, then

$$1 = g_{\mu\nu}u^{\mu}u^{\nu} = \gamma_{\alpha\beta}\zeta^{\alpha}\zeta^{\beta} = -[(\zeta^0)^2 + (\zeta^3)^2]$$

which is impossible. Therefore $\zeta^2 = 0$. These requirements follow from the conservation equation alone. The field equation requires that the only non-vanishing ζ^{μ} be ζ^0.

More will be said about Gödel's model in Section A.5.

CHAPTER 14

FOUNDATIONS OF COSMOLOGY

14.1 ASSUMPTIONS

With the possible exception of quasars, the most distant objects which can be seen are the galaxies. Within the limited region of the universe which is accessible to observation, the galaxies show three characteristics.

Natural Motion. The redshifts of galaxies at a given apparent magnitude deviate from the mean by a small amount. For redshifts as large as 10^{-1}, the scatter in redshift is only about 10^{-3}.* (The redshifts increase with apparent magnitude, but more will be said on this point later.) It is difficult to escape the implication that there exists at each point in the universe a state of *natural motion*. With reference to a local coordinate system in natural motion, the motions of nearby galaxies are small and average out to zero. The possibility that the redshifts may not be due to motion alone does not affect the argument, because differential velocities will still produce differential redshifts. Objects in natural motion sweep out a non-intersecting congruence of *fundamental* world-lines.

ASSUMPTION 1. The congruence of fundamental world-lines fills the universe.

Isotropy. The galaxies give no indication that there are any preferred directions. The spatial density of galaxies shows no obvious gradient in any direction, and the orientations of spiral galaxies show no tendency toward alignment. Thus, for example, a space traveler on a

---

* See Humason[B] et al.

long trip would lose all sense of direction and would be unable to return to his starting point, unless he kept a record of the specific galaxies and clusters of galaxies which he passed. Thus there is *large-scale* isotropy in the *visible part* of the universe. It will be assumed that there is *exact* isotropy *throughout* the universe.

ASSUMPTION 2.   The universe is isotropic.

Homogeneity. The spatial density of galaxies shows no obvious large-scale inhomogeneities. Even the clusters of clusters of galaxies, if they exist, seem to be distributed randomly throughout the visible universe.*
Thus the *visible* universe is, *to a first approximation*, homogeneous. It will be assumed that the *whole* universe is *exactly* spatially homogeneous. This assumption is to be used in the somewhat stronger form:

ASSUMPTION 3.   The view of the universe in its entirety, obtained by any one observer in natural motion, is identical with the view of the universe in its entirety obtained by any other contemporary observer in natural motion.

Assumption 3 is known as the *cosmological principle*. Clearly, this assumption cannot be used until a measurement of time has been defined. Therefore, in order of logic, Assumption 4 will have to be used first:

ASSUMPTION 4.   The following tools are available to all observers in the universe: clocks for measuring time, plane goniometers for measuring angles, and apparatus for the emission and reception of light.

14.2 TWO GALAXIES

Consider two galaxies G and G' in natural motion. Light signals from G to G' generate a two-dimensional surface Σ in space-time. The surface Σ can be extended beyond G and G' by using light signals which originate behind G and travel beyond G'. Similarly, the light signals from G' to G generate another surface Σ'. Now it is necessary that Σ' coincide with Σ, for otherwise the two-way light signals would determine a spatial plane, contrary to the isotropy of Assumption 2. If a third galaxy G'' in natural motion has any part of its world-line in Σ, then all of its world-line is in Σ. Otherwise, the velocity of G'' relative to the line GG' would determine a direction, contrary to Assumption 2.

The surface Σ therefore contains a congruence of non-intersecting fundamental world-lines. The world-lines can therefore be ordered with a continuous parameter u which increases monotonically from G to G'.

---

* See Abell[B].

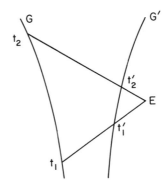

FIGURE 14.1 Two galaxies.

The parameter u is then a label which distinguishes the different funda-mental world-lines in Σ. We will take G as $u = 0$.

The parameter u does not form a complete coordinate system. Some way is needed for labeling the events *along* the world-lines. But such a coordinate system cannot yet be defined, because the observers in the universe are allowed to have only the clocks, goniometers, light bulbs, and photocells of Assumption 4. There is as yet no way to determine simultaneity. We must establish a coordinate system based on light signals.

Any event E in the surface Σ is uniquely specified by the two light signals in Σ which pass through E. Thus the observer G can designate E by the coordinates t_1 and t_2, where t_1 is the time of emission of the light signal which travels from G to E, and t_2 is the time of reception of the light signal which travels from E to G. (See Figure 14.1.) The same light signals will be used by another observer G' to obtain coordinates t_1' and t_2'. In each case, the observer measures time by means of the clock which Assumption 4 allows him to keep.

There is now established a coordinate system t_1, t_2. The next job is to determine the way in which these coordinates transform from one observer to another. We note that either of the coordinates t_1, t_1' specifies the *same* light signal. Therefore t_1' can depend only on t_1, not on t_2:

$$t_1' = p(t_1).$$

Similarly t_2 is a function of t_2':

$$t_2 = q(t_2').$$

Assumption 3 now requires that p and q be the same function; the view of the universe obtained by G must be the same as the view of the universe obtained by G'. Thus the transformation has the form

$$\left. \begin{aligned} t_1' &= p(t_1) \\ t_2 &= p(t_2') \end{aligned} \right\} \tag{14-1}$$

where p is an unknown function. The concept of simultaneity is introduced by eqs. (14-1). If the clock of the observer G' had been advanced by an amount a, then we would have had

$$t_1' = p(t_1) + a$$
$$t_2 = p(t_2' - a).$$

But then eqs. (14-1) can be obtained by replacing $t' - a$ with t'.

The function p in eqs. (14-1) can depend on only one other variable— the parameter u. The transformation is therefore given by

$$t_1' = f(t_1, u)$$
$$t_2 = f(t_2', u). \tag{14-2}$$

Assumption 3 requires that eqs. (14-2) hold for *any* two observers in Σ. Therefore the two transformations of eqs. (14-2) each form a one-parameter group of automorphisms. Direct calculation shows that the two generators

$$S_1(t_1) = \left[\frac{\partial t_1'(t_1, u)}{\partial u}\right]_{u=0} \quad \text{and} \quad S_2(t_2) = \left[\frac{\partial t_2'(t_2, u)}{\partial u}\right]_{u=0}$$

are the same function but with opposite signs. Therefore eq. (13-5) becomes

$$\frac{\partial t_1'}{\partial u} = S(t_1'), \qquad \frac{\partial t_2'}{\partial u} = -S(t_2'). \tag{14-3}$$

The integrals of eqs. (14-3) are

$$\left.\begin{aligned} F(t_1') &= F(t_1) + u \\ F(t_2') &= F(t_2) - u \end{aligned}\right\} \tag{14-4}$$

where the function $F(x)$ is defined

$$F(x) = \int^x \frac{dx}{S(x)}.$$

It is now possible to define a coordinate system t, u in which u determines the world-line and t is the proper time along the world-line. If the world-line G' is chosen to pass through the event E, then both t_1' and t_2' are equal to the proper time t of the event E. Equations (14-4) become

$$\left.\begin{aligned} F(t_1) &= F(t) - u \\ F(t_2) &= F(t) + u. \end{aligned}\right\} \tag{14-5}$$

The coordinate t is known as the *cosmic time*. The cosmic time for an event is independent of the observer, for if G' does not pass through E, then, from eqs. (14-4) we get $F(t_1) + F(t_2) = F(t_1') + F(t_2') = 2F(t)$.

It is interesting to note what happens to the group generator under the transformation of eq. (14-5). In the coordinates t_1, t_2 the generator is $[S(t_1), -S(t_2)]$. In the coordinates t, u the generator becomes $(0, -1)$.

14.3 METRIC

A metric $ds^2(t_i, dt_j)$ for the surface Σ is constructed from the following conditions.

1. ds^2 shall be an invariant.
2. ds^2 shall be a homogeneous quadratic in dt_1 and dt_2.
3. $ds^2 = 0$ shall describe light rays.
4. ds^2 shall equal dt^2 for constant u.

The first condition requires ds^2 to be a function only of the invariants of the two-dimensional space Σ. What, then, are the invariants? Let the coordinates be denoted $x^1 = F(t_1)$ and $x^2 = F(t_2)$. The transformation of eqs. (14-4) is then

$$x'^1 = x^1 + u$$
$$x'^2 = x^2 - u,$$

and the generator becomes $(1, -1)$. Any invariant $\phi(x^i, dx^j)$ must satisfy eq. (13-66) which becomes, in the present context,

$$\frac{\partial \phi}{\partial x^1} - \frac{\partial \phi}{\partial x^2} = 0.$$

Therefore ϕ can depend only on $x^1 + x^2$, dx^1, and dx^2. We immediately recognize $x^1 + x^2$ as $2F(t)$. Thus ds^2 can be a function only of t, $dF(t_1)$, and $dF(t_2)$.

The second condition imposes the form

$$ds^2 = \alpha(t)[dF(t_1)]^2 + \beta(t)[dF(t_1)][dF(t_2)] + \gamma(t)[dF(t_2)]^2.$$

The third condition requires that both α and γ vanish, because a light ray is described by *either* $dt_1 = 0$ *or* $dt_2 = 0$. From eqs. (14-5) we then have left

$$ds^2 = \frac{\beta(t)}{[S(t)]^2} \{dt^2 - [S(t)]^2 du^2\}. \tag{14-6}$$

The fourth condition requires that the coefficient on the right-hand side of eq. (14-6) be unity. Therefore, the metric is

$$ds^2 = dt^2 - S^2(t) du^2 \tag{14-7}$$

where $S(t)$ is an unknown function of the cosmic time, and u is a continuous, monotonic parameter in the surface Σ.

14.4 THREE SPATIAL DIMENSIONS

By the cosmological principle, all that can be said about one pair of galaxies in natural motion can be said about any other pair of galaxies in natural motion. The same group generator $S(t)$ must exist, except possibly for a constant multiplier which, by redefinition of u, can be chosen as unity. Every pair of fundamental world-lines has the same group generator $S(t)$ and therefore the same metric given by eq. (14-7).

The three-dimensional space $t = $ const is defined as follows. An event E is chosen on any fundamental world-line G. Another fundamental world-line G' is selected; we then choose the event E' on G' for which the G' time is equal to the G time of E. It is important to note that the procedure is reciprocal and hence independent of the initial world-line. The locus of all possible events E' so obtained is the three-dimensional space $t = $ const.

Coordinates x^i ($i = 1, 2, 3$) can be set up in each space $t = $ const in such a way that each of the fundamental world-lines keeps the same coordinates x^i. The interval du between two adjacent fundamental world-lines is then a function only of their position, not of their cosmic time: $du^2 = du^2(x^i, dx^j)$.

The two-dimensional surface Σ formed by light rays between two fundamental world-lines intersects any space $t = $ const in a curve $x^i(u)$ where u is the group parameter in Σ. We impose on the coordinates x^i the further condition that $x^i(u)$ be differentiable. This condition is not particularly restrictive, but it does allow us to conclude that du^2 is quadratic in dx^i. Therefore du^2 is given by

$$du^2 = h_{ij}(x^k) \, dx^i \, dx^j, \qquad (14\text{-}8)$$

where the matrix h_{ij} is as yet unknown. But since du^2 is an invariant, it is clear that h_{ij} must be a three-dimensional tensor.

14.5 THE SPATIAL GEOMETRY

The space $t = $ const must, by the cosmological principle and the assumption of isotropy, admit a six-parameter family of metric automorphisms. Three of the automorphisms correspond to the translations from one observer to another. The other three automorphisms represent the degrees of freedom in orienting an observer's coordinate system—two for the polar axis and one for the azimuth origin. The three-dimensional space $t = $ const therefore admits the maximal group of metric automorphisms.

Such a space must, by the conclusions of Section 13.7, have a constant Riemannian curvature κ. (The Greek letter is here used in order to reserve K for the four-dimensional curvature.) The metric, according to Section 8.10, must be given by

$$ds^2 = S'^2(t) \frac{\eta_{ij} \, dx^i \, dx^j}{\left[1 + \dfrac{k}{4} \eta_{kl} x^k x^l\right]^2} \tag{14-9}$$

where the radius of curvature S' and the curvature index k are related to κ by: $\kappa = k/S'^2$. Furthermore, all invariants must, by the Helmholtz-Lie theorem, be functions of eq. (14-9).

The squared interval du^2 has the three properties that it is invariant, it is quadratic in dx^i, and it is non-zero. The first property requires that du^2 be a function of eq. (14-9). The second property requires that du^2 be proportional (to within a factor which can at the most depend on t) to eq. (14-9). The third property requires that η_{ij} be equal to δ_{ij}. We therefore obtain the relation

$$ds^2 = C^2(t)S^2(t) \, du^2 = S'^2(t) \frac{dx^i \, dx^i}{\left[1 + \dfrac{k}{4} x^k x^k\right]^2}, \tag{14-10}$$

where $C(t)$ is the required proportionality factor. We may now identify eq. (14-10) as the product of $-c^2$ with eq. (14-7) for $dt = 0$. Therefore $C = c$. Furthermore, $S(t)$ is arbitrary to within a constant multiplier. Therefore we may choose

$$du^2 = \frac{dx^i \, dx^i}{\left[1 + \dfrac{k}{4} x^k x^k\right]^2}. \tag{14-11}$$

Equation (14-11) is the line element for a space with constant Riemannian curvature $k = 0$ or ± 1. More general coordinates could be used, but the three-dimensional metric tensor h_{ij} in eq. (14-8) still represents a space with constant Riemannian curvature 0 or ± 1. The function $cS(t)$ is then the radius of curvature of the three-dimensional space $t = $ const.

In summary, it has been shown that space-time has the metric of eqs. (14-7) and (14-8). The spatial metric tensor h_{ij} has a constant Riemannian curvature k which is equal to one of the three values -1, 0, or $+1$. If k is not zero, then $cS(t)$ is the radius of curvature of the three-dimensional space. The fundamental world-lines are given by $x^i = $ const. There exist spatial coordinates in which the spatial metric is given by eq. (14-11).

It should be noted for later use that the successive transformations

$$x^1 = \rho \sin \theta \cos \phi, \qquad x^2 = \rho \sin \theta \sin \phi, \qquad x^3 = \rho \cos \theta$$

and

$$\rho = \begin{cases} 2 \tan \dfrac{w}{2}, & k = +1 \\ w, & k = 0 \\ 2 \tanh \dfrac{w}{2}, & k = -1 \end{cases}, \qquad \theta = \theta, \qquad \phi = \phi$$

put eq. (14-11) into the form

$$du^2 = dw^2 + \sigma^2(w)(d\theta^2 + \sin^2 \theta \, d\phi^2) \tag{14-12}$$

where

$$\sigma(w) = \begin{cases} \sin w, & k = +1 \\ w, & k = 0 \\ \sinh w, & k = -1 \end{cases}. \tag{14-13}$$

The metric given by eq. (14-7) and either eq. (14-11) or eq. (14-12) will be called the *cosmological metric*.

One further note on the spatial geometry is pertinent. The three geometries $k = +1, 0,$ and -1 are referred to by the adjectives *spherical*, *Euclidean*, and *hyperbolic*, respectively. The properties of geodesic spheres in each geometry should be familiar to the reader from Section 7.7. Technically, a space with positive curvature is called *spherical* or *elliptical* according as the point $w = \pi$ is identified to be *opposite* to or to be the *same* as the point $w = 0$. Spherical space has total coordinate volume

$$\int_0^\pi 4\pi\sigma^2(w) \, dw = 2\pi^2$$

and hence a total metric volume $2\pi^2 c^3 S^3(t)$. Elliptical space has half as much volume. A straight line which traverses the spherical space once has length $2\pi c S$.

14.6 THE GEOMETRY OF THE COSMOLOGICAL METRIC

The cosmological metric has as the only non-vanishing Christoffel symbols of the second kind

$$\begin{Bmatrix} i \\ 0j \end{Bmatrix} = \frac{\dot{S}}{S} \delta^i_j$$

$$\begin{Bmatrix} 0 \\ ij \end{Bmatrix} = S\dot{S}h_{ij}$$

$$\begin{Bmatrix} i \\ jk \end{Bmatrix} = \begin{Bmatrix} i \\ jk \end{Bmatrix}^{\star}.$$

The star denotes quantities calculated in the three-dimensional sub-space of eq. (14-8), and the dot denotes differentiation with respect to cosmic time. The non-vanishing components of the Riemann curvature tensor are

$$\left.\begin{aligned} R_{0i0j} &= S\ddot{S}h_{ij} \\ R_{ijkl} &= -S^2(\dot{S}^2 + k)(h_{ik}h_{jl} - h_{il}h_{jk}) \end{aligned}\right\} \qquad (14\text{-}14)$$

and those which can be obtained from the above components by the use of the symmetry properties. The Ricci tensor is

$$R_{00} = 3\frac{\ddot{S}}{S}$$

$$R_{0i} = 0$$

$$R_{ij} = -(S\ddot{S} + 2\dot{S}^2 + 2k)h_{ij}$$

and the Einstein tensor is

$$\left.\begin{aligned} G_{00} &= -3S^{-2}(\dot{S}^2 + k) \\ G_{0i} &= 0 \\ G_{ij} &= (2S\ddot{S} + \dot{S}^2 + k)h_{ij}. \end{aligned}\right\} \qquad (14\text{-}15)$$

The geodesic equation (9-5) becomes

$$\frac{d^2t}{ds^2} + S\dot{S}\left(\frac{du}{ds}\right)^2 = 0 \qquad (14\text{-}16)$$

$$\frac{d^2x^i}{ds^2} + \left\{{i \atop jk}\right\}^{\!\star} \frac{dx^j}{ds}\frac{dx^k}{ds} = -2\frac{dx^i}{ds}\frac{dt}{ds}\frac{\dot{S}}{S}. \qquad (14\text{-}17)$$

Note that the fundamental world-lines $x^i = $ const are geodesics. Upon a change of independent variables from s to u, eq. (14-17) becomes

$$\frac{d^2x^i}{du^2} + \left\{{i \atop jk}\right\}^{\!\star} \frac{dx^j}{du}\frac{dx^k}{du} = \frac{dx^i}{du}\frac{d}{du}\ln\left(\frac{1}{S^2}\frac{ds}{du}\right). \qquad (14\text{-}18)$$

In the three-dimensional subspace $t = $ const, the left-hand side of eq. (14-18) is orthogonal to dx^i/du, i.e., to the right-hand side. Since du^2 is never zero, there cannot be any null vectors in the subspace $t = $ const. Therefore, both sides of eq. (14-18) are zero. Two results are thus obtained: the projection of a four-dimensional geodesic onto a space $t = $ const is a three-dimensional geodesic; and the quantity γ defined

$$\gamma = \frac{1}{S^2}\frac{ds}{du} \qquad (14\text{-}19)$$

is a constant along a four-dimensional geodesic. Equations (14-7) and (14-19) then provide the integral of eq. (14-16), which we take in the form

$$\left(\frac{dt}{du}\right)^2 = S^2 + \gamma^2 S^4. \qquad (14\text{-}20)$$

Either of eqs. (14-19) or (14-20) is an equation of motion for particles in cosmological space-time.

Light rays are described either by setting $\gamma = 0$ in eq. (14-20) or by setting $ds^2 = 0$ in eq. (14-7):

$$\frac{dt}{du} = \pm S(t).$$

In the polar coordinates of eq. (14-12), an incoming light ray has the equation of motion

$$\frac{dt}{dw} = -S(t). \qquad (14\text{-}21)$$

For particles, the local momentum (per unit mass), $cSdu/ds$, is found from eq. (14-19) to be equal to $c/\gamma S$. Thus the momentum of a free particle relative to the local state of natural motion varies inversely as $S(t)$. If $S(t)$ is a monotonically increasing function, then the momentum continually decreases. In such a case, the fundamental world-lines are expanding away from each other, and the particle continually advances into places where the natural motion is more like its own.

14.7 AUTOMORPHISMS

Killing's equation for the cosmological metric becomes

$$\frac{\partial \xi^0}{\partial t} = 0 \qquad (14\text{-}22)$$

$$\frac{\partial \xi^0}{\partial x^k} g^{ki} + \frac{\partial \xi^i}{\partial t} = 0 \qquad (14\text{-}23)$$

$$\xi^{i;j} + \xi^{j;i} = -2 \frac{S}{S} h^{ij} \xi^0 \qquad (14\text{-}24)$$

where $\xi^\mu = g^{\mu\nu} \xi_\nu$, the semicolon indicates covariant differentiation in the three-dimensional metric h_{ij}, and the derivative indices are raised by means of h^{ij} (the inverse of h_{ij}). Equation (13-35) becomes

$$\left[\xi^0(S\ddot{S} + \dot{S}\ddot{S}) + 2S\dot{S}\frac{\partial \xi^0}{\partial t} \right] h_{ij} + S\dot{S}(\xi^k_{;i} h_{kj} + \xi^k_{;j} h_{ki}) = 0 \quad (14\text{-}25)$$

$$S\dot{S}(h_{ik}\xi^0_{;j} - h_{ij}\xi^0_{;k}) = \frac{\partial \xi^m}{\partial t} S^2(\dot{S}^2 + k)C_{mijk} \qquad (14\text{-}26)$$

$$\xi^0 C_{ijkl} \frac{d}{dt} [S^2(\dot{S}^2 + k)] + S^2(\dot{S}^2 + k)[\xi^m_{;i}C_{mjkl} + \xi^m_{;j}C_{imkl}$$
$$+ \xi^m_{;k}C_{ijml} + \xi^m_{;l}C_{ijkm}] \qquad (14\text{-}27)$$

where

$$C_{ijkl} = h_{ik}h_{jl} - h_{il}h_{jk}.$$

The substitution of eq. (14-23) into eq. (14-26) gives

$$(\dot{S}^2 + k - S\ddot{S})\left(\frac{\partial \xi^0}{\partial x^j} h_{ik} - \frac{\partial \xi^0}{\partial x^k} h_{ij}\right).$$

Multiplication by h^{ik} gives

$$(\dot{S}^2 + k - S\ddot{S})\frac{\partial \xi^0}{\partial x^j} = 0. \tag{14-28}$$

Multiplication of eq. (14-25) by $h^{im}h^{jn}$ and the use of eqs. (14-22) and (14-24) give

$$\xi^0(S\dot{\ddot{S}} - \dot{S}\ddot{S}) = 0. \tag{14-29}$$

Equation (14-27) is multiplied by $h^{ik}h^{jl}$ to give

$$6\xi^0 \frac{d}{dt} \ln [S^2(\dot{S}^2 + k)] + 4h_{ij}(\xi^{i;j} + \xi^{j;i}) = 0,$$

which, with eq. (14-24), becomes

$$\xi^0\dot{S}(\dot{S}^2 + k - S\ddot{S}) = 0. \tag{14-30}$$

The six spatial automorphisms of Section 14.5 are characterized by the condition

$$\xi^0 = 0. \tag{14-31}$$

The substitution of eq. (14-31) into eqs. (14-22) to (14-24) shows that ξ^i is then a *spatial* generator—it is independent of t and it satisfies the equation $\xi_{i;j} + \xi_{j;i} = 0$.

The question is asked: Does space-time admit more than six metric automorphisms? Clearly, if there is a seventh automorphism, it cannot be purely spatial, because the space $t = $ const already admits the maximal group. The generator for the seventh automorphism must therefore have a non-vanishing temporal component:

$$\xi^0 \neq 0. \tag{14-32}$$

Inequality (14-32), which is the condition that space-time admit more than six metric automorphisms, implies, by eqs. (14-29) and (14-30), the conditions

$$\left.\begin{array}{ll} S^2 \dfrac{d}{dt}\left(\dfrac{\ddot{S}}{S}\right) = 0 & \quad a \\[3mm] \dot{S}(\dot{S}^2 + k - S\ddot{S}) = 0. & \quad b \end{array}\right\} \tag{14-33}$$

The solution of eqs. (14-33) is facilitated by a digression on the subject of constant curvature.

Equation (8-58) is the necessary and sufficient condition that space-time have constant curvature. But then by eqs. (14-14), this is the same as the conditions

$$\ddot{S} = -KS \qquad (14\text{-}34)$$

$$\dot{S}^2 + k + KS^2 = 0. \qquad (14\text{-}35)$$

Equation (14-34) follows from eq. (14-35) if $\dot{S}$ is not identically zero. If $\dot{S}$ is identically zero, then, from eq. (14-34), K is zero, and, from eq. (14-35), k is also zero. The four-dimensional curvature may be classified in three categories: $K > 0$, $K = 0$, and $K < 0$. The spatial curvature k also falls into one of three categories. Therefore, we expect nine different cases for space-times with constant curvature. However, three of the cases are made impossible by the requirement that $\dot{S}^2$ in eq. (14-35) be non-negative. Thus there are six cosmological models with constant curvature. They will be studied in Section 16.3.

Returning to the problem of automorphisms, we now see that the cases of constant curvature are solutions of eqs. (14-33). This is to be expected, because a space-time with constant curvature must admit the maximal group of ten metric automorphisms.

But the cases of constant curvature are not the only solutions to eqs. (14-33). The case $\dot{S} = 0$ is clearly another solution. Thus there are three additional models ($k = +1, 0, -1$). However, the model $\dot{S} = 0$, $k = 0$ also has constant curvature.

The conclusion is that there are eight cosmological models which admit more than six metric automorphisms. Six models are the cases of constant curvature, and the remaining two are the cases $\dot{S} = 0$, $k = +1$, and $\dot{S} = 0$, $k = -1$.

14.8 STATIONARY UNIVERSES

A cosmological model is *stationary* if it presents the same view to observers at *different times*. The cosmological principle of Section 14.1 applies only to observers at different spatial positions. The *perfect cosmological principle* asserts that the universe looks the same to *any* observer in natural motion, regardless of either his position or his time. Thus, only stationary models satisfy the perfect cosmological principle. We proceed now to translate the definition of a stationary universe into the terminology of automorphisms.

To begin with, it is clear that there must exist a metric automorphism whose generator has a non-vanishing temporal component ξ^0. This requirement guarantees that the line element can be carried forward in time without change. But this requirement is not enough. It merely leads to the cases which were derived in the previous section, namely, space-times with constant curvature and space-times with $\dot{S} = 0$. Not all such models are stationary. It is therefore necessary to impose an additional condition on the automorphisms.

It is necessary that the temporal automorphism transform fundamental world-lines into fundamental world-lines. Otherwise, the transformed line element will be expressed in coordinates based on a different congruence of fundamental world-lines. Mathematically, we require that the automorphism $x'^\mu = x'^\mu(x^\nu, a)$ transform the world-lines $x^i = \text{const}$ into the world-lines $x'^i = \text{const}$. This in turn requires that $x'^i(x^\nu, a)$ be independent of x^0. Therefore, ξ^i is independent of t. But then the left-hand side of eq. (14-24) is independent of t. Now ξ^0 cannot depend on t because of eq. (14-22), and h^{ij} by definition contains no t. Therefore, $\dot{S}/S$ must be independent of t:

$$\frac{\dot{S}}{S} = \text{const.} \tag{14-36}$$

We turn now to the integrability conditions (14-28) to (14-30). Equations (14-28) and (14-29) are satisfied by virtue of eqs. (14-36) and (14-23) and the condition $\partial \xi^i / \partial t = 0$. But eq. (14-30) is not trivial. It becomes

$$k\dot{S} = 0. \tag{14-37}$$

Equations (14-36) and (14-37) have four solutions:

(a) $k = +1$, $S = \text{const}$
(b) $k = 0$, $S = \text{const}$
(c) $k = -1$, $S = \text{const}$
(d) $k = 0$, $\dot{S}/S = \text{const} \neq 0$.

A universe which satisfies the perfect cosmological principle must be one of the above four cases. Comparison with eqs. (14-34) and (14-35) shows that cases (b) and (d) are also two of the cases of constant curvature. Case (d) is especially interesting; it is the only non-static stationary model, because the other three stationary models have constant S. The solution to eq. (14-36) is $\ln S(t) = t \cdot \text{const} + \text{const}$, so that the metric is given by eq. (13-45). The temporal automorphism is given by eq. (13-46). This model, known as the *deSitter universe*, will be studied in detail in Section 16.2.

TABLE 14.1 *COSMOLOGICAL MODELS WITH MORE THAN SIX METRIC AUTOMORPHISMS*

Spatial curvature k	Four-dimensional curvature K	Is the model stationary?	Is $S(t)$ constant?	Name of model
0	Zero	Yes	Yes	Minkowski
−1	Zero	No	No	expanding Minkowski
0	Negative constant	Yes	No	deSitter
+1	Negative constant	No	No	Lanczos
−1	Negative constant	No	No	
−1	Positive constant	No	No	
+1	Not constant	Yes	Yes	
−1	Not constant	Yes	Yes	

The cosmological models discussed in this and the previous section are tabulated in Table 14.1. The first six cases have constant curvature. Four of the eight cases are stationary. Three cases have constant S. The deSitter model is the only non-static, stationary model.

CHAPTER 15

OBSERVABLE QUANTITIES

The cosmological metric contains only two unknowns—the function $S(t)$ and the spatial curvature k—but they are not directly observable. It is therefore necessary to relate k and $S(t)$ to observable quantities such as spectral features, brightnesses, and sky distribution of galaxies.

15.1 REDSHIFT

It is assumed that a given spectral line is emitted with the same frequency ν_1 from another galaxy as from laboratory apparatus. However, the frequency ν_0 of reception of the same spectral line will in general be different from ν_1.

The light signals which travel from a galaxy G at coordinate w to an observer O, both in natural motion (see Figure 15.1), follow the family

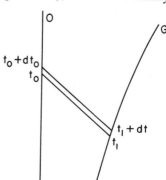

FIGURE 15.1 Light signals from galaxy to observer.

349

of curves defined by eq. (14-21) which has the integral

$$w = \int_{t_1}^{t_0} \frac{dt}{S(t)} . \tag{15-1}$$

In eq. (15-1), t_1 is the time of emission and t_0 is the time of reception. Differentiation of eq. (15-1) for constant w shows that for two light signals emitted at times t_1, $t_1 + dt_1$ and received at times t_0, $t_0 + dt_0$, the differences in time have the relation

$$\frac{dt_0}{S(t_0)} = \frac{dt_1}{S(t_1)} .$$

Since the number of waves must be conserved, i.e., $\nu_0 \, dt_0 = \nu_1 \, dt_1$, the frequencies have the ratio

$$\frac{\nu_0}{\nu_1} = \frac{S(t_1)}{S(t_0)} . \tag{15-2}$$

Therefore the ratio of the received wavelength $\lambda_0 = c/\nu_0$ to the emitted wavelength $\lambda_1 = c/\nu_1$ is

$$\frac{\lambda_0}{\lambda_1} = \frac{S(t_0)}{S(t_1)} .$$

The *redshift* z, a directly observable quantity, is defined $z = (\lambda_0 - \lambda_1)/\lambda_1$ and is therefore given by

$$1 + z = \frac{S_0}{S_1} \tag{15-3}$$

where $S_0 = S(t_0)$ and $S_1 = S(t_1)$. Thus the redshift of a distant galaxy in natural motion gives the ratio of $S(t)$ at the present time to $S(t)$ at the time of emission. It should be noted that the elimination of t_1 between eqs. (15-1) and (15-3) allows w to be expressed as a function of t_0 and z. The power-series expansion for $t_0 - t_1$ in terms of z is

$$t_0 - t_1 = \frac{z}{H}\left[1 - \left(1 - \frac{\alpha}{2}\right)z + \left(1 - \alpha + \frac{\alpha^2}{2} - \frac{\beta}{6}\right)z^2 + O^3(z)\right] \tag{15-4}$$

and the result of substituting eq. (15-4) into the expansion of w in powers of $t_0 - t_1$ is

$$w = \frac{z}{HS_0}[1 + \tfrac{1}{2}(\alpha - 1)z + \tfrac{1}{6}(2 - 4\alpha + 3\alpha^2 - \beta)z^2 + O^3(z)] \tag{15-5}$$

where

$$H = \left(\frac{\dot{S}}{S}\right)_{t=t_0} \tag{15-6}$$

$$\alpha = \frac{1}{H^2}\left(\frac{\ddot{S}}{S}\right)_{t=t_0} \tag{15-7}$$

$$\beta = \frac{1}{H^3}\left(\frac{\dddot{S}}{S}\right)_{t=t_0} .$$

The *Hubble constant H* defined by eq. (15-6) and the *acceleration parameter* α defined by eq. (15-7) will be important in our considerations of observable quantities.

15.2 ASTRONOMICAL DISTANCES

The "distance" to an object depends on the *definition* of distance. In cosmology we will find that different definitions give different results. It is therefore appropriate to review the astronomical methods for determining distance.

For nearby objects, say within our galaxy, there is no ambiguity in the concept of distance. The geometry is Euclidean to extremely good accuracy. The size of the galaxy is too small for cosmological effects to be felt, and the mass of the galaxy is too small for general-relativistic effects to enter. In the linear approximation to general relativity, the deviation from Euclidean space is given by $2GM/Rc^2$ which for a galaxy with $M = 10^{41}$ kg and $R = 10^{21}$ m is only about one part in a million.

The distances to celestial objects are determined by a series of steps.

The first distance that is needed is the earth-sun distance. This distance is determined by obtaining a scale model of the solar system and then measuring any distance in the model. The earlier method was to find the parallax of an asteroid as it passed close to the earth. A more recent method is to time the echo of radar which is reflected by Venus. The aberration of starlight and the annual variations in the radial velocities of stars provide alternate, but less accurate, methods in which the earth's orbital velocity is measured.

The next step is to determine the distances to stars in our galaxy. Trigonometric parallax, in which the earth's orbit is the baseline, is used for distances less than about 100 parsecs.*

The distances to star clusters are obtained by matching their color-magnitude diagrams with the color-magnitude diagram for nearby stars. There also exist spectral criteria for placing individual stars on the color-magnitude diagram. Among the objects within our galaxy whose distances can be determined by the above steps are periodic variable stars.

Variable stars with periods less than a few months include the types known as classical Cepheids (e.g., δ Cephei), type II Cepheids or W Virginis, and RR Lyrae. The distinguishing feature which these stars possess is a correlation between their periods and their absolute magnitudes. The RR Lyrae variables, with periods less than one day, are scattered about a single absolute magnitude† $M_V = +0.3 \pm 0.6$. (The

---

* The *parsec* is a unit of distance equal to 3.086×10^{16} meters.
† See Arp[B] and Sandage[B].

subscript V denotes visual magnitude.) The Cepheids, including the W Virginis stars, have periods between one and 100 days. There is considerable scatter on the period-luminosity diagram, but the average relation is* $\langle M_V \rangle = -1.7 - 2.5 \log (P/\text{days})$ where P is the period. The scatter can be treated in a systematic way—the bluer stars are brighter, and the redder stars are fainter, for a given period.

The distances to nearby galaxies are obtained by means of variable stars and star clusters in the galaxies. The supernovae in the galaxies can then be calibrated for their absolute magnitude at maximum brightness. The HII regions are calibrated for average size. These various distance indicators are then used out as far as possible.

All the methods for obtaining extragalactic distances, with the exception of the use of angular sizes of HII regions, rely upon the inverse-square radiation law. In astronomical notation, this law is stated

$$r_b = 10^{(1/5)(m-M)+1} \text{ parsecs,} \qquad (15\text{-}8)$$

where m and M are respectively the apparent and absolute magnitudes of the source. The *distance modulus* $m-M$ is independent of the kind of magnitude, e.g., photographic, bolometric, etc. The distance r_b defined by eq. (15-8) is known as the *bolometric* distance in order to distinguish it from other definitions of distance.

The most useful unit for intergalactic distances is the megaparsec, abbreviated Mpc and equal to 10^6 psc or 3.086×10^{22} meters. Galaxies are spaced at intervals of the order of a megaparsec.

The faintest objects visible with the 200-inch Hale telescope on Mount Palomar have an apparent magnitude of about $+24$. Thus, Cepheid variables, whose absolute magnitudes range up to about -4, can be seen to distances of about 4 Mpc. The brightest stars, with absolute magnitudes as bright as -9, can be seen to about 40 Mpc.

Variable stars are the most reliable distance indicators to galaxies. Novae and HII regions can be used for approximate estimates. Brightest stars and brightest globular clusters, with absolute magnitudes around -9 and -10, respectively, show promise of being useful in distance determinations.*

But the distance indicators described above can only be used to distances of around 10 or 100 Mpc. Beyond this distance, only the luminosity properties of galaxies and possibly of supernovae can be used.

15.3 LUMINOSITY

The purpose of this section is to derive the relation between the apparent brightness $l(t_0)$ of a galaxy and its absolute luminosity $L(t_1)$.

---

* See Sandage[B].

The subscript 1 denotes quantities at emission and the subscript 0 denotes quantities at reception. The units of L and l are, respectively, watts and watts meter^{-2}. Let $L_\nu(\nu_1, t_1)\, d\nu_1$ be the power emitted by the galaxy between frequencies ν_1 and $\nu_1 + d\nu_1$. Let $l_\nu(\nu_0, t_0)\, d\nu_0$ be the power per unit area received between frequencies ν_0 and $\nu_0 + d\nu_0$. In a time dt_1, the galaxy emits the number

$$\frac{L_\nu(\nu_1, t_1)\, d\nu_1\, dt_1}{h\nu_1}$$

of photons having frequencies between ν_1 and $\nu_1 + d\nu_1$. These photons spread out uniformly on a spherical front of ever-increasing size. By the time the light is received, each photon is redshifted down to an energy $h\nu_0$ or $h\nu_1/(1 + z)$. The spherical front has reached a coordinate radius w from the galaxy, and therefore has an area $4\pi c^2 S^2(t_0)\sigma^2(w)$. Thus the energy per unit area received from the galaxy is

$$\frac{L_\nu(\nu_1, t_1)\, d\nu_1\, dt_1}{4\pi c^2 S^2(t_0)\sigma^2(w)(1 + z)}.$$

This energy is received in a time interval

$$dt_0 = (1 + z)\, dt_1.$$

Therefore l_ν is given by

$$l_\nu(\nu_0, t_0)\, d\nu_0 = \frac{L_\nu(\nu_1, t_1)\, d\nu_1}{4\pi c^2 S^2(t_0)\sigma^2(w)(1 + z)^2}.$$

Integration of both sides of the above equation gives*

$$l(t_0) = \frac{L(t_1)}{4\pi c^2 S^2(t_0)\sigma^2(w)(1 + z)^2}. \tag{15-9}$$

According to the inverse-square law of radiation, the bolometric distance is

$$r_b = \sqrt{\frac{L}{4\pi l}} = cS(t_0)\sigma(w)(1 + z). \tag{15-10}$$

Equations (15-8) and (15-10) provide a relation between the observables m, M, z, and the function $S_0\sigma(w)$.

$$m = M + 5 \log \left[\frac{cS_0\sigma(w)(1 + z)}{10\ \text{psc}}\right]. \tag{15-11}$$

---

* Although the validity of the photon description, on which the derivation of eq. (15-9) is based, was established in Section 12.4, it is satisfying that eq. (15-9) can also be derived with reference to the electromagnetic stress-energy tensor alone. Such a derivation is given in Section A.3.

A more convenient form of eq. (15-11) is the power-series expansion

$$m = M + 5 \log \left(\frac{c}{H \cdot 10 \text{ psc}} \right) + 5 \log z + \tfrac{5}{2} z(\alpha + 1) \log e$$

$$+ \tfrac{5}{24} z^2 \left(9\alpha^2 - 10\alpha - 7 - 4\beta - \frac{4k}{S_0^2 H^2} \right) \log e + O^3(z). \quad (15\text{-}12)$$

Equation (15-12), which is merely a logarithmic expansion of eq. (15-9), is obtained by substituting eqs. (14-13) and (15-5) into eq. (15-11).

Equation (15-12) provides an observational basis for investigating the universe. The redshift z is most accurately obtainable. The apparent bolometric magnitude m must be estimated from the observed magnitude by making the appropriate correction for absorption in our galaxy and absorption in the atmosphere. In addition, there is a correction for red-shift due to the fact that the *observed* frequency is $\dfrac{1}{1+z}$ times the *emitted* frequency. The absolute magnitude M is still more difficult to find; it is obtained only with some uncertainty by using the methods described in Section 15.2.

Note that the spatial curvature k/S_0^2 does not enter the first-order term in eq. (15-12). This makes it an extremely difficult task to determine even the *sign* of k, let alone the value of S_0 for $k \neq 0$. More will be said about eq. (15-12) in Section 18.1.

15.4 RADIATION DENSITY

It is easy to prove that if the universe is Euclidean, is infinite in both extent and age, and contains stationary stars distributed randomly through-out space, then the sky is as bright as the surface of an average star. For one's line of sight must eventually end on the surface of a star. The group-ings of stars into galaxies does not alter this result if the galaxies have a random distribution. Thus *Olber's paradox* requires the sky to be as bright as the sun! Yet the sky is obviously not that bright. Indeed, the night sky is extremely dark by ordinary standards. Therefore, which of the assumptions is wrong?

We shall calculate the average density U of radiant energy under the assumption that the emitters are galaxies which have a spatially uniform number density $\eta(t)$ per unit coordinate volume (i.e., $\eta S^{-3} c^{-3}$ is the density in physical space). The number of galaxies seen in a spherical shell of coordinate radius w and thickness dw is then

$$dN = 4\pi \eta(t_1) \sigma^2(w) \, dw. \quad (15\text{-}13)$$

Note that the density which enters eq. (15-13) is the density at emission, not at reception. The energy density at the observer due to any of the galaxies within the spherical shell is, from eq. (15-9),

$$\frac{l}{c} = \frac{L(t_1)}{4\pi c^3 S^2(t_0)\sigma^2(w)(1+z)^2}.$$

Multiplication by eq. (15-13) and the use of eq. (15-3) gives

$$dU = \frac{\eta(t_1)L(t_1)S^2(t_1)}{c^3 S^4(t_0)} dw \qquad (15\text{-}14)$$

for the contribution to U due to the galaxies within the shell.

Because when one looks to greater coordinate distances, one also looks backward in time in accordance with eq. (14-21), we may replace dw with $dt_1/S(t_1)$ and integrate eq. (15-14) over all past times during which there was emission. The result is

$$U = \frac{1}{c^3 S_0^4} \int^{t_0} \eta(t_1)L(t_1)S(t_1)\, dt_1. \qquad (15\text{-}15)$$

The lower limit in the integral extends as far backward in time as necessary to include all emitters. It will be shown below that eq. (15-15) applies to a spherical universe even if the light from some emitters traverses the universe more than once.

The differential form of eq. (15-15),

$$\frac{1}{S^4(t)}\frac{d}{dt}[U(t)S^4(t)] = \frac{\eta(t)}{c^3 S^3(t)} L(t), \qquad (15\text{-}16)$$

exhibits a remarkable property of U. If there is no emission, so that the right-hand side of eq. (15-16) vanishes, then US^4 is constant. This result is surprising, because one would expect the coordinate density of radiation US^3 to remain constant. There can be no net change in the amount of radiation $US^3\, d^3w$ contained in an element d^3w of coordinate volume due to energy flow because of the assumption of isotropy. Nevertheless, US^3 does vary—as the inverse of S. In an expanding universe, for example, radiant energy is decreasing. But where does it go?

If US^4 is constant, then the equation

$$\frac{d}{dt}(US^3) + \tfrac{1}{3}U\frac{d}{dt}(S^3) = 0$$

is satisfied. But multiplication by the coordinate volume d^3w then gives

$$\frac{d}{dt}(UV) + \tfrac{1}{3}U\frac{dV}{dt} = 0 \qquad (15\text{-}17)$$

where $V = S^3\, d^3w$. Equation (15-17) is recognized as the equation of conservation of energy. The first term is the rate of change of energy contained in the physical volume V. The second term is the product of pressure with the rate of change of volume. Therefore, the radiation energy which is lost in an expanding universe is used up as work in aiding the expansion. Conversely, in a contracting universe, the work done on the radiation increases its energy. It may be recalled from thermodynamics that the energy of radiation in an enclosure of variable volume V varies as $V^{-\frac{1}{3}}$.

We are forced to conclude that two contradictory principles hold: first, there is conservation of energy; and second, the energy in the universe is not constant. This is best illustrated for a spherical universe which has total volume $2\pi^2 c^3 S^3(t)$. Such a universe possesses a total radiant energy $2\pi^2 c^3 S^3(t) U(t)$ which is inversely proportional to $S(t)$. An expanding spherical universe loses radiant energy.

The non-constancy of energy should come as no shock. In Section 14.6 it was found that a free particle which experiences *no forces* loses momentum in an expanding universe.

Finally, we turn to a proof that eq. (15-15) holds for a spherical (or elliptical) universe. By the principle of superposition we may regard the energy per unit volume, $\eta(t) S^{-3}(t) c^{-3} L(t)\, dt$, which was produced in the interval from t to $t + dt$, as continuing without interaction down to the time of observation. (The assumption that there is no intergalactic absorption was implicit in Section 15.3 and in this section.) This energy gives a contribution

$$dU(t_0) = \left(\frac{S(t)}{S(t_0)}\right)^4 \eta(t) S^{-3}(t) c^{-3} L(t)\, dt$$

to the observed density. Integration over all times of emission immediately gives eq. (15-15).

15.5 EFFECT OF INTERGALACTIC ABSORPTION

It was assumed in Section 15.3 that there was no intergalactic absorption. We will obtain the correction to eq. (15-12) due to absorption as follows.

The energy emitted by a source at the origin into a cone of solid angle $d\Omega$ between the times t_1 and $t_1 + dt_1$ occupies a spatial cylinder of length $cS(t)\, dw$ and cross-sectional area $c^2 S^2(t) \sigma^2(w)\, d\Omega$. From eq. (15-1) for constant t_0,

$$dw = -\frac{dt_1}{S(t_1)}$$

so that the cylinder has a volume

$$dV = \frac{c^3 S^3(t) \sigma^2(w)\, dt_1\, d\Omega}{S(t_1)} .$$

By regarding the energy $d\mathcal{E}$ inside the cylinder to consist of photons, it is clear that, without absorption, the change in $d\mathcal{E}$ in a time δt as the cylinder travels a distance $\delta w = \delta t / S(t)$ along the null curve, for $\delta w \gg dw$, is given by eq. (15-2):

$$\frac{\delta \, d\mathcal{E}}{d\mathcal{E}} = \frac{\delta \nu}{\nu} = -\frac{\delta S}{S} = -\frac{\dot{S}}{S} \, \delta t.$$

If the energy $d\mathcal{E}$ does not change according to the above rule, then there is loss due to absorption. If $K\rho \, dx$ is the fractional loss of radiation in traversing a metric distance dx (where ρ is the average density of matter), then the energy equation takes the form

$$\left[\frac{\partial \, d\mathcal{E}}{\partial t} + \frac{1}{S} \frac{\partial \, d\mathcal{E}}{\partial w} \right] \delta t + \frac{\dot{S}}{S} d\mathcal{E} \, \delta t = -K\rho c \, \delta t \, d\mathcal{E}.$$

The substitution of $d\mathcal{E} = U \, dV$ where U is the proper energy density then gives the differential equation

$$0 = \frac{1}{S^3} \frac{\partial}{\partial t} (US^4) + \frac{1}{\sigma^2} \frac{\partial}{\partial w} (U\sigma^2) + K\rho c S U. \qquad (15\text{-}18)$$

The differential equation can be solved by making the substitution

$$U = \frac{S_1^2}{4\pi c^3 S^4 \sigma^2} \cdot f$$

and the change in variable from w to

$$\eta = w - \int_{t_1}^{t} \frac{dt}{S(t)}.$$

Equation (15-18) then becomes

$$\frac{\partial \ln f}{\partial t} = -K\rho c$$

which has the solution

$$f = L_0 e^{-\int_{t_1}^{t} K\rho c \, dt}.$$

The constant of integration L_0 is merely the luminosity of the source.

Upon taking logarithms, the additional term for insertion in eq. (15-12) is

$$\tfrac{5}{2}(\log e) \int_{t_1}^{t_0} K\rho c \, dt.$$

With the substitution $\rho = \rho_0 S_0^3 / S^3$ and the expression of t and $S(t)$ in terms of z by means of eq. (15-3), the additional term becomes

$$\tfrac{5}{2}(\log e) \frac{K\rho_0 c}{H} z[1 + \tfrac{1}{2}(1 + \alpha)z + O^2(z)]. \qquad (15\text{-}19)$$

15.6 APPARENT SIZE

A galaxy's *angular* diameter $\Delta\phi$ can be observed directly. An estimate of the galaxy's *linear* diameter D can then provide information on the cosmological functions $S(t)$ and $\sigma(w)$. From eqs. (14-7) and (14-12), the linear diameter D must be equal to $cS(t_1)\sigma(w)\,\Delta\phi$, where w is the coordinate distance to the galaxy. The time which appears as the argument of the function S is the time at emission. The *angular-size distance* r_s is defined

$$r_s = \frac{D}{\Delta\phi} = cS(t_1)\sigma(w) \tag{15-20}$$

and is the distance which would be attributed to the galaxy by an observer who knew only of Euclidean geometry.

The ratio of bolometric distance to angular-size distance is, from eqs. (15-3), (15-10), and (15-20), equal to $(1 + z)^2$. Thus any comparison of bolometric distances with angular-size distances gives no cosmological information whatever.

In practice eq. (15-20) is difficult to use for two reasons. First, galaxies come in a variety of shapes and sizes. There is no standard diameter. Second, a galaxy's diameter is difficult to define. The brightness density (in units of, say, magnitudes per square degree) decreases from the galaxy's center, and the brightness of the night sky masks the galaxy's outer fringes. It turns out that if a galaxy's diameter is defined by the use of brightness contours, then the angular-size distance is different from that which would result from an object with a well-defined boundary.*

15.7 GALAXY COUNTS

Galaxy counts seem at first sight to promise some information on the spatial geometry. Integration of eq. (15-13) gives the number of galaxies within a coordinate radius w:

$$N(w) = 4\pi \int_0^w \eta(t_1)\sigma^2(w)\,dw \tag{15-21}$$

where $\eta(t_1)$ depends on w through eq. (15-1). If η is assumed to be constant, then eq. (15-21) becomes, with the substitution of eq. (14-13),

$$N(w) = \tfrac{4}{3}\pi\eta w^3 \left[1 - \frac{k}{5}w^2 + O^4(w)\right]. \tag{15-22}$$

---

* See Sandage[B].

Equation (15-22) shows how the counts deviate from the Euclidean value at large distances. But unfortunately the coordinate distance w is not directly observable—and neither is the metric distance. We must choose an observable quantity as the parameter in counting galaxies.

If we choose the redshift z as the independent variable, then the number of galaxies $N(z)$ having redshifts less than z is given by eq. (15-22) after substitution of eq. (15-5):

$$N(z) = \frac{4\pi\eta}{3H^3S_0^3} z^3 \left\{ 1 + \tfrac{3}{2}(\alpha - 1)z + \tfrac{1}{20}\left(35 - 70\alpha + 45\alpha^2 - 10\beta \right.\right.$$

$$\left.\left. - \frac{4k}{H^2S_0^2} \right)z^2 + O^3(z) \right\} \quad (15\text{-}23)$$

If we choose the apparent magnitude m as the independent variable, then the number of galaxies $N(m)$ having apparent magnitudes smaller (brighter) than m is given by eliminating z from eqs. (15-12) and (15-23):

$$N(m) = N_0 10^{\frac{3}{5}(m-M)} \left\{ 1 - 3\rho 10^{\frac{1}{5}(m-M)} + \tfrac{3}{10}\left(25 + 4\alpha + \frac{k}{H^2S_0^2} \right) \right.$$

$$\left. \times \rho^2 10^{\frac{2}{5}(m-M)} + \cdots \right\} \quad (15\text{-}24)$$

where N_0 is the number of galaxies inside a sphere of radius 10 parsecs, and $\rho = 10\, Hc^{-1}$ psc.

Several obstacles stand in the way of utilizing galaxy counts to explore the spatial geometry of the universe.

First, galaxies do not all have the same absolute magnitude. The *luminosity function* $\phi(M)$ is defined so that the density of galaxies having absolute magnitudes between M and $M + dM$ is $\phi\, dM$. The luminosity function is difficult to determine at the faint end due to the existence of extremely faint galaxies. How are equations (15-22) to (15-24) affected? Equations (15-22) and (15-23) remain as they are with

$$\eta = c^3 S^3 \int_{-\infty}^{\infty} \phi\, dM.$$

The successive terms in eq. (15-24) contain the integrals

$$\int \phi 10^{-\frac{3}{5}M}\, dM, \quad \int \phi 10^{-\frac{4}{5}M}\, dM, \quad \int \phi 10^{-\frac{5}{5}M}\, dM, \text{etc.}$$

so that the faint end of the luminosity function is less important. Thus eq. (15-24) is affected by the luminosity function, but eq. (15-23) is not. Nor is eq. (15-23) affected by the dispersion in redshift, since the latter is of order 10^{-3}.

Second, the luminosity function may depend on time: $\phi(M, t)$. Of course, we may expect ϕ to be inversely proportional to S^3, for then the coordinate density of galaxies would be constant But if $S^3\phi$ varies with time, then the assumption of the constancy of η fails. Time derivatives of $S^3\phi$ pop up in the various terms in the expansions in eqs. (15-23) and (15-24), with derivatives up to the nth appearing in the nth order term. Thus we encounter the discouraging situation that a knowledge of the second time derivative of the luminosity function is necessary before galaxy counts can yield information on the spatial curvature. And this leads us to the third point.

Third, the spatial curvature only enters the second-order terms rather than the first-order terms. Yet we are lucky if we can even find the first-order terms! Furthermore, the first-order terms give information only on the first time derivative of the luminosity function and, in $m(z)$, the second derivative of $S(t)$.

Finally, any hope that the functions $k/S^2(t)$ and $\phi(M, t)$ can be constructed from a thorough knowledge of $N(z)$ and $N(m)$ is doomed to failure. This is seen by considering a diagram of z versus m. The points representing galaxies are scattered on the diagram in a distribution which depends both on $\phi(M, t)$ and, through eq. (15-12), on $k/S^2(t)$—since t is a function of z through eq. (15-4). But unless the curves of constant M on the z-m diagram are known, nothing can be learned about the dependence of S and ϕ on t (or z). The choice of a particular type of galaxy—for example the brightest in a cluster—will narrow down the distribution on the z-m diagram to a single curve. But then eq. (15-12) is the obvious means for analyzing the data. More will be said about this in Section 18.1.

It must be concluded that galaxy counts are hopeless as a source of cosmological information unless assumptions are made about the luminosity function.

15.8 COSMOLOGICAL DISTANCES

Two different distances have thus far been defined: angular-size distance and bolometric distance.

$$r_s = cS_0\sigma(w)(1 + z)^{-1}$$

$$r_b = cS_0\sigma(w)(1 + z).$$

The angular-size distance is an underestimate, and the bolometric distance is an overestimate in an expanding universe. A third distance, the *cosmic distance* r_c, may be defined

$$r_c = cS_0w. \tag{15-25}$$

The cosmic distance is the metric distance in a space $t = $ const. Such a measure is of course impossible to perform. Indeed, it is not even certain that any galaxy still exists at the present cosmic time. However, the cosmic distance will be of use in later discussion. The cosmic distance differs from the geometric mean $\sqrt{r_s r_b}$ only by a factor w/σ.

It is common practice in cosmological studies for the cosmic time to be called the *epoch*. The variation in cosmic distance with epoch is given by the relation $r_c(t) = cS(t)w$.

CHAPTER 16

SPECIAL COSMOLOGICAL MODELS

This chapter is devoted to the study of certain special cases of the cosmological metric. Some cases are more important than others because of simplicity or historical usage.

16.1 THE EXPANDING MINKOWSKI UNIVERSE

The expanding Minkowski universe, to be distinguished from the case $\dot{S} = 0$, $k = 0$ of Section 14.7, is useful for its simplicity. The Minkowski metric

$$ds^2 = d\tau^2 - c^{-2}[d\rho^2 + \rho^2(d\theta^2 + \sin^2\theta\, d\phi^2)]$$

may be transformed by the relations

$$\rho = ct \sinh w$$
$$\tau = t \cosh w$$

into the form

$$ds^2 = dt^2 - t^2[dw^2 + \sinh^2 w(d\theta^2 + \sin^2\theta\, d\phi^2)]$$

which is the case of eqs. (14-7) and (14-12) for $S(t) = t$ and $k = -1$. The fundamental world-lines, w, θ, $\phi = $ const, are given by

$$\rho = c\tau \tanh w.$$

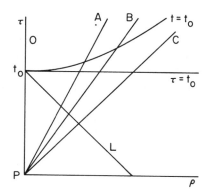

FIGURE 16.1 The expanding Minkowski universe.

Thus a galaxy at coordinate distance w has a recessional velocity

$$v = c \tanh w. \tag{16-1}$$

The expanding Minkowski universe has, according to eqs. (14-14), a zero Riemann curvature tensor and hence a zero Gaussian curvature K. It is a special case of eq. (14-35) with $k = -1$, $K = 0$. Since this space-time has constant curvature, it admits the maximal group of metric automorphisms which are in fact the same as for Minkowski space-time.

Figure 16.1 represents the expanding Minkowski universe for a given θ and ϕ. Note that the coordinates are τ and ρ rather than t and w so that the constructions of special relativity may be applied directly. The τ-axis is the world-line of the observer O. The world-lines A and B for any two galaxies in natural motion are those of objects moving with constant velocities. The line C given by $\rho = c\tau$ represents an object traveling with the speed of light from the singular event P at which all fundamental world-lines originate.

Nothing exists in the region of the diagram to the right of C. By Assumption 1, Section 14.1, there exists a state of natural motion in every part of the universe. But no fundamental world-line exists to the right of C. Actually, Figure 16.1 represents a mapping from the coordinates t, w to the coordinates τ, ρ, and the cone $\rho = c\tau$ represents the infinite boundary of the space $0 \leq w < \infty$. Geometrically, the expanding Minkowski universe is the same as the static Minkowski universe $\dot{S} = 0$, $k = 0$; the difference lies in the choice of fundamental world-lines and hence of the cosmological coordinates t, w.

The space $\tau = t_0$ which is contemporary with the observer in *his* time has radius t_0/c. The space $t = t_0$, which is contemporary with the observer in *cosmic* time and is represented by the hyperbolic curve in Figure 16.1, has the spatial metric

$$c^2 S^2(t_0)[dw^2 + \sinh^2 w(d\theta^2 + \sin^2 \theta \, d\phi^2)].$$

In this hyperbolic geometry, a circle of radius cSw has a circumference $2\pi cS \sinh w$, which is larger than the Euclidean value. Thus the space $t = t_0$ is larger than a Euclidean infinity! The feat of compressing an infinite universe into a finite mapping at $\tau = t_0$ is accomplished by means of the Fitzgerald contraction. If the galaxies near the limit C are moving with nearly the speed of light, then their spatial density is severely contracted so that, in fact, an infinite number can be packed into the space at the boundary—without crowding!

The observer sees neither the space $\tau = t_0$ nor the space $t = t_0$, but only events along his backward light cone L, given by $\rho = c(t_0 - \tau)$. Thus a galaxy at coordinate distance w is seen by the observer at cosmic time t_1, observer's time τ_1, and observer's distance ρ_1 (see Figure 16.2) given by

$$
\begin{aligned}
t_1 &= t_0 e^{-w} && \text{a} \\
\rho_1 &= \tfrac{1}{2}ct_0(1 - e^{-2w}) && \text{b} \\
\tau_1 &= \tfrac{1}{2}t_0(1 + e^{-2w}). && \text{c}
\end{aligned}
\quad \text{(16-2)}
$$

Equation (16-2a) comes from eq. (15-1). A galaxy at the horizon C is thus seen at $t_1 = 0$, $\tau_1 = \tfrac{1}{2}t_0$, $\rho_1 = \tfrac{1}{2}ct_0$. The universe has a radius $\tfrac{1}{2}ct_0$. But this radius is not measurable by the observer. He can only observe angular sizes, redshifts, and apparent magnitudes. The angular-size distance is equal to ρ_1, but the bolometric distance is different from ρ_1.

To find the bolometric distance to a galaxy in natural motion at coordinate distance w, we first note that the redshift z is given by eq. (15-3):

$$
1 + z = \frac{t_0}{t_1} = e^w. \tag{16-3}
$$

This redshift is due to special-relativistic motion, as may be verified with eqs. (3-75), (16-1), and (16-3). Objects near the horizon C have redshifts with approach ∞. It may also be noted that eqs. (16-2a) and (16-2c) give the time dilation of special relativity:

$$
\frac{t_1}{\tau_1} = \sqrt{1 - \frac{v^2}{c^2}}.
$$

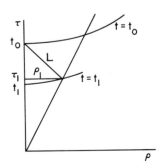

FIGURE 16.2 Coordinates at epoch of observation.

The bolometric distance given by eq. (15-10) is

$$r_b = \tfrac{1}{2} c t_0 (e^{2w} - 1),$$

which is equal to $(1 + z)^2 \rho_1$. A galaxy at the horizon has infinite bolometric distance.

Finally, it is noted that the observer's time t_0 is equal to the inverse of the Hubble constant. As the epoch increases, H decreases.

16.2   DESITTER UNIVERSE

The deSitter universe is given by $k = 0$ and $\ln S(t) = t/b + \text{const}$, where b is a constant. By a suitable translation of the time coordinate, the additive constant may be chosen to be $-\ln c$. The metric

$$ds^2 = dt^2 - \frac{1}{c^2} e^{\frac{2t}{b}} [dw^2 + w^2(d\theta^2 + \sin^2 \theta \, d\phi^2)] \qquad (16\text{-}4)$$

is seen, from eqs. (14-34) and (14-35), to have a constant space-time curvature $K = -1/b^2$.

Although the contracting deSitter universe where $b < 0$ is a mathematical possibility, we will disregard it for two reasons: it can be easily obtained from the expanding deSitter universe by simple modifications, and the actual universe appears to be expanding. Thus we will take $b > 0$.

The deSitter universe has two curious properties in that it is the only non-static stationary model, and it exhibits a horizon.

It was noted in Section 14.8 that the deSitter universe is the only non-static stationary model. The fundamental world-lines expand away from each other, but they also present the same appearance at any cosmic time. Thus the deSitter universe is noteworthy in that it is the only cosmological model which satisfies the two requirements: the perfect cosmological principle and a non-zero Hubble constant.

In order to understand why an observer in the deSitter model would have a horizon, we must first determine his *observable* universe. His backward light cone is given by eq. (15-1):

$$e^{-\frac{t_1}{b}} = \frac{w}{a} + e^{-\frac{t_0}{b}}, \qquad (16\text{-}5)$$

where $a = bc$. Equation (16-5) requires that t_1 be less than t_0; this is to be expected. But it further states that for a given w, the *maximum* t_1 is equal to

$$b \ln \frac{a}{w} . \qquad (16\text{-}6)$$

Thus we have the surprising result that an observer cannot see a galaxy at coordinate distance w when the galaxy's epoch exceeds expression (16-6).

What then does the observer see as he watches the galaxy? In the first place, the galaxy's redshift becomes larger and larger. The redshift is given by

$$z = e^{\frac{t_0 - t_1}{b}} - 1$$

which approaches ∞ as t_0 approaches ∞. Furthermore, the ratio of bolometric distance to angular-size distance, which equals $(1 + z)^2$, approaches ∞, thus giving the appearance that the galaxy becomes intrinsically fainter and fainter. The angular-size distance approaches a, while the bolometric distance roars off to infinity. The cosmic distance approaches a.

Such a horizon as the one just described does not exist in the expanding Minkowski model of Section 16.1. If the observer there is willing to wait long enough, he can see *any* event on *any* fundamental world-line; for any w and any t_1 in eq. (16-2a), there is a solution for t_0.

Another difference between the deSitter model and the expanding Minkowski model is in the behavior of light rays which travel into the future. In the deSitter model, a light ray which leaves the event $t = 0$, $w = 0$ is described by

$$w = a\left(1 - e^{-\frac{t}{b}}\right).$$

Thus the ray asymptotically approaches the coordinate $w = a$, but never reaches it. In the expanding Minkowski model, a light ray which leaves the event $t = t_1$, $w = 0$ is described by

$$w = \ln \frac{t}{t_1}.$$

Thus the ray eventually reaches *any* coordinate w.

The two models are similar in the respect that an observer at a given event in either model can see fundamental world-lines at any coordinate distance w. For a given t_0 (positive in the Minkowski case), both eq. (16-2a) and eq. (16-5) have solutions $t_1 < t_0$ for *any* $w > 0$.

The deSitter universe has the property that the cosmic distance of any fundamental world-line at the present epoch is exactly proportional to its redshift: $cS(t_0)w = az$.

An alternate form for the deSitter metric

$$ds^2 = \left(1 - \frac{r^2}{a^2}\right) dt'^2 - \frac{1}{c^2}\left[\frac{dr^2}{\left(1 - \frac{r^2}{a^2}\right)} + r^2(d\theta^2 + \sin^2\theta \, d\phi^2)\right]$$

is obtained by use of the transformation

$$e^{-\frac{2t'}{b}} = e^{-\frac{2t}{b}} - \frac{w^2}{a^2}$$

$$e^{\frac{t}{b}} = \frac{r}{w}$$

to new coordinates t', r, θ, ϕ. The deSitter universe in these coordinates is compressed into a cylinder of radius a. These coordinates have the disadvantage that t' is no longer cosmic time.

The deSitter universe can be regarded as a four-dimensional surface in five-dimensional Minkowski space. The new coordinates z_0, z_1, z_2, z_3, and z_4 are given by

$$\left.\begin{aligned}
z_0 &= b \sinh \frac{t}{b} + \frac{w^2}{2bc^2} e^{\frac{t}{b}} \\[2mm]
z_4 &= b \cosh \frac{t}{b} - \frac{w^2}{2bc^2} e^{\frac{t}{b}} \\[2mm]
z_1 &= \frac{w}{c} e^{\frac{t}{b}} \sin \theta \cos \phi \\[2mm]
z_2 &= \frac{w}{c} e^{\frac{t}{b}} \sin \theta \sin \phi \\[2mm]
z_3 &= \frac{w}{c} e^{\frac{t}{b}} \cos \theta.
\end{aligned}\right\} \qquad (16\text{-}7)$$

Equation (16-4) becomes

$$ds^2 = dz_0^2 - dz_1^2 - dz_2^2 - dz_3^2 - dz_4^2,$$

and the constraint which results from going to an additional dimension is

$$b^2 + z_0^2 = z_1^2 + z_2^2 + z_3^2 + z_4^2. \qquad (16\text{-}8)$$

The construction is most easily visualized in three dimensions by plotting z_0, z_4, and $z = \sqrt{z_1^2 + z_2^2 + z_3^2}$. (See Figures 16.3a and 16.3b.) Equation (16-8) produces a single-sheet hyperboloid of revolution.

The straight-line generators of the hyperboloid, given by

$$z_0 = \pm(z \cos \theta - z_4 \sin \theta)$$
$$b = z_4 \cos \theta + z \sin \theta$$

for arbitrary θ, represent light paths. For an observer at the event E: ($z = 0$, $z_4 = b$, $z_0 = 0$), one light path L_1 has the equation

$$z_0 = -z, \qquad z_4 = b.$$

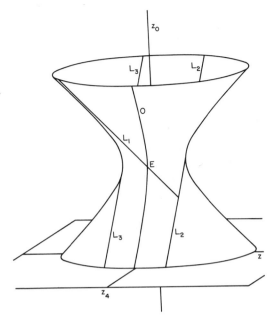

FIGURE 16.3a DeSitter universe in five dimensions.

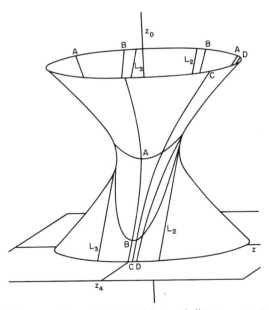

FIGURE 16.3b Same as Figure 16.3a but with sample lines $t = $ const and world-lines included. AAA and BBB are two spaces $t = $ const, and CC and DD are two fundamental world-lines.

The original coordinate w along the backward light path L_1, as a function of z, is given by

$$w = \frac{az}{b - z}. \quad (z > 0)$$

The light path ends at the generator $z = b$ indicated by L_2 in Figure 16.3a. The expanding deSitter universe is mapped onto half of the hyperboloid, i.e., the part between the generators

$$z_4 = -z_0, \quad z = b \quad \text{and} \quad z_4 = -z_0, \quad z = -b$$

indicated by L_2 and L_3, respectively, in Figure 16.3a. The forward progress of L_1 is given by

$$w = -\frac{az}{b - z}.$$

In the limit as z approaches ∞, w approaches a (as was noted earlier). The fundamental world-lines are the intersections of the hyperboloid with the planes

$$z_0 + z_4 \text{ proportional to } z.$$

(Negative values of z cause no difficulty because we may consider $z_1 = 0$, $z_2 = 0$, $z_3 = z$; the hyperboloid then represents events on the spatial line $z_1 = z_2 = 0$.) In fact all geodesics are intersections with the planes

$$\alpha z + \beta z_4 + \gamma z_0 = 0$$

with $\gamma^2 < \alpha^2 + \beta^2$. The spaces $t = $ const are the intersections of the hyperboloid with the planes

$$z_0 + z_4 = \text{const.}$$

The back side of the hyperboloid represents the contracting deSitter universe.

16.3 CONSTANT CURVATURE

Equation (14-35) is the differential equation for $S(t)$ in space-times which have constant curvature K. Six different cases arise, depending on the values of the spatial curvature k and the space-time curvature K. The latter will, when non-zero, be denoted $|K| = b^{-2}$.

Case 1. $k = 0$, $K = 0$. The solution $S(t) = $ const represents the static Minkowski space-time of special relativity.

Case 2. $k = -1$, $K = 0$. The solution $S(t) \propto t$ represents the expanding Minkowski universe which was studied in Section 16.1.

Case 3. $k = 0$, $K = -b^{-2}$. The solution $S(t) \propto e^{t/b}$ represents the deSitter universe which was studied in the previous section.

Case 4. $k = +1$, $K = -b^{-2}$. The solution $S(t) = b \cosh (t/b)$ represents the Lanczos universe which first contracts to a volume $2\pi^2 b^3 c^3$ and then expands. Since, by the uniqueness theorem of Section 8.10, all space-times with the same constant curvature may be transformed into each other, the Lanczos universe is the same as the deSitter universe, except that a different congruence is used for the fundamental world-lines. More will be said about this under Case 5.

Case 5. $k = -1$, $K = -b^{-2}$. The solution $S(t) = b \sinh (t/b)$ repre-sents a universe which contracts to a singular event $t = 0$ and then expands. Again, as in Case 4, the space-time is the same as that of the deSitter universe, but a different congruence is used for the fundamental world-lines.

For simplicity in comparing Cases 4 and 5 with Case 3, we choose $b = c = 1$. Further, the temporal coordinate in the deSitter universe is chosen to be

$$\tau = e^{-t}$$

so that the metric for Case 3 is

$$ds^2 = \frac{d\tau^2 - dw^2 - w^2(d\theta^2 + \sin^2 \theta \, d\phi^2)}{\tau^2}. \tag{16-9}$$

Space-time is mapped onto the quarter-plane $w > 0$, $\tau > 0$ with $\tau \to 0$ for $t \to \infty$ (see Figure 16.4). Geodesics, from eqs. (14-19) and (16-9), are hyperbolas which are symmetric about the w-axis and have 45-degree asymptotes:

$$(w + \beta)^2 = \tau^2 + \gamma^2 \tag{16-10}$$

where β and γ are constants. Light paths are 45-degree lines.

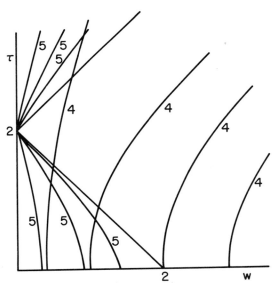

FIGURE 16.4 Fundamental world-lines of constant-curvature cases 4 and 5. The surfaces of constant cosmic time for the respective cases are obtained by interchanging τ and w.

The transformations from Cases 4 and 5 to Case 3 are:

$$2 \tan^{-1} \ln t_4 + w_4 = 2 \tan^{-1} \tfrac{1}{2}(\tau + w)$$
$$2 \tan^{-1} \ln t_4 - w_4 = 2 \tan^{-1} \tfrac{1}{2}(\tau - w)$$

Case 4

$$\tanh^{-1} \operatorname{sech} t_5 + w_5 = 2 \tanh^{-1} \tfrac{1}{2}(\tau + w)$$
$$\tanh^{-1} \operatorname{sech} t_5 - w_5 = 2 \tanh^{-1} \tfrac{1}{2}(\tau - w).$$

Case 5

The subscripts 4 and 5 refer to the coordinates in Cases 4 and 5, respectively, when the standard forms—eqs. (14-7) and (14-12)—are used. Note that the point $w_5 = \infty$ maps into the point $\tau = 0$, $w = 2$. Case 5 encompasses only a part of space-time. The relation between Cases 5 and 3 is similar to the relation between Cases 2 and 1.

The fundamental world-lines of Case 4 are given by

$$(w + A)^2 = A^2 + 4 + \tau^2. \quad (A = \text{const})$$

(See Figure 16.4.) The fundamental world-lines of Case 5 are given by

$$(w + B)^2 + 4 = B^2 + \tau^2. \quad (B = \text{const})$$

Every fundamental world-line in Case 5 passes through the event $\tau = 2$, $w = 0$. The fundamental world-lines of Case 3 are of course given by $w = \text{const}$, the limit of eq. (16-10) as both β and γ approach ∞ in such a way that $\gamma \pm \beta$ is constant. The surfaces of constant cosmic time are obtained for Cases 4 and 5 by interchanging w and τ in the equations for the fundamental world-lines.

On the hyperboloid of Section 16.2, the fundamental world-lines of Case 4 are the intersections of the hyperboloid with planes which pass through the line $z = 0$, $3z_0 + 5z_4 = 0$ which does not intersect the hyperboloid. The fundamental world-lines of Case 5 are the intersections of the hyperboloid with planes which pass through the line $z = 0$, $5z_0 + 3z_4 = 0$ which intersects the hyperboloid at the two events $z = 0$, $z_4 = \pm\tfrac{5}{4}$, $z_0 = \mp\tfrac{3}{4}$. One of the two events is the singular vertex for the fundamental world-lines of expanding Case 5. The other event is the vertex for contracting Case 5.

Case 6. $k = -1$, $K = +b^{-2}$. The solution $S(t) = b \sin t/b$ represents a universe which begins at a singular event $t = 0$, expands, slows down, stops expanding at $t = \pi b/2$, contracts, and ends at a singular event $t = \pi b$. The whole universe has lifetime πb. An observer in this universe could determine the parameter b by measuring the Hubble constant and the acceleration parameter:

$$H = b^{-1} \cot t/b; \qquad \alpha = -\tan^2 t/b.$$

Hence we have

$$b = (H\sqrt{-\alpha})^{-1}.$$

CHAPTER 17

GENERAL-RELATIVISTIC COSMOLOGY

17.1 THE USE OF THE FIELD EQUATION

It will be assumed throughout this chapter that the field equation of general relativity given by eq. (9-12) is valid. The cosmological constant Λ will be retained in order to study its effect on cosmological models. From eqs. (14-15) it immediately follows that the stress-energy tensor $T^{\mu\nu}$ must have the form

$$\kappa T^{00} = \frac{3}{S^2}(\dot{S}^2 + k) - \Lambda$$

$$\kappa T^{0i} = 0$$

$$\kappa T^{ij} = g^{ij}\left[\frac{1}{S^2}(2S\ddot{S} + \dot{S}^2 + k) - \Lambda\right]$$

or simply

$$T^{\mu\nu} = (\rho + pc^{-2})\delta_0^\mu\delta_0^\nu - pc^{-2}g^{\mu\nu} \qquad (17\text{-}1)$$

where $\rho(t)$ and $p(t)$ are given by

$$\kappa\rho = \frac{3}{S^2}(\dot{S}^2 + k) - \Lambda \qquad (17\text{-}2)$$

$$\kappa p = -\frac{c^2}{S^2}(2S\ddot{S} + \dot{S}^2 + k) + c^2\Lambda. \qquad (17\text{-}3)$$

Equation (17-1) indicates that the cosmological metric is produced by a perfect fluid which follows the fundamental world-lines and has uniform

372

proper density $\rho(t)$ and uniform proper pressure $p(t)$. Equations (17-2) and (17-3) are the equations of motion of the cosmological fluid due to its own gravity.

The effect of the density, pressure, and cosmological constant on the function $S(t)$ is more clearly seen by eliminating $\dot{S}^2 + k$ from eqs. (17-2) and (17-3):

$$\frac{\ddot{S}}{S} = \frac{\Lambda}{3} - \frac{\kappa}{6}\left(\rho + \frac{3p}{c^2}\right).$$ (17-4)

Equation (17-4) shows features which have been noted before. A positive cosmological constant has the effect of a disruptive force, while the density and pressure produce an attractive force. It is the combination $\rho + 3pc^{-2}$, as was noted in eq. (9-64), which appears as the source of gravitational effects. Thus, for a given energy density, radiation is twice as effective as matter. Note also that pressure enters eq. (17-4) with a negative sign. Thus regardless of how much the cosmological fluid may be compressed due to a decrease in $S(t)$, any pressure which is built up by the compression only tends to aid the compression.

The substitution of eq. (17-1) into the Bianchi identity in the form $T^{\mu\nu}{}_{,\nu} = 0$ yields the relation

$$0 = \frac{d}{dt}(\rho c^2 S^3) + p\frac{d}{dt}(S^3)$$ (17-5)

which may alternately be obtained from eqs. (17-2) and (17-3). Thus the equations of motion may be chosen as eqs. (17-2) and (17-5).

Equation (17-5) has an interesting physical interpretation. Multiplication by c^3 and by a constant coordinate volume d^3w gives the equation

$$0 = \frac{dE}{dt} + p\frac{dV}{dt}$$ (17-6)

where V is the physical volume $c^3 S^3 d^3w$ and E is the energy $\rho c^2 V$ contained therein. Equation (17-6) is immediately recognized as the hydrodynamic equation for conservation of energy. The fluid loses energy to expansion and gains energy from contraction, a phenomenon which was encountered in Section 15.4.

The normal procedure for solving problems in hydrodynamics is to introduce an equation of state $\rho(p, t)$. Unfortunately, even if the cosmological fluid had an equation of state, there is no way to examine it by laboratory tests. Indeed, the very concept of a cosmological pressure is in itself unusual. Therefore let us examine the interpretation to be placed on both the cosmological density and the cosmological pressure.

The cosmological density $c^2\rho(t)$ is the average proper density of all forms of energy. This energy includes electromagnetic radiation and neutrinos as well as the rest-mass energy within galaxies and of the intergalactic medium, if it exists. The density $c^2\rho(t)$ is thus interpreted as the sum of the average densities of energy in the following forms: rest-mass, electromagnetic, kinetic, neutrino, and any other forms which may exist, such as magnetic and gravitational.

The cosmological pressure $p(t)$ represents, in the hydrodynamic analogue, the interactions between molecules, in this case galaxies! In addition, there will be a contribution due to radiation and neutrinos. Section A.8 will give justification for interpreting $p(t)$ as the sum of $\frac{2}{3}$ the average density of kinetic energies of the galaxies (since $v \ll c$) and $\frac{1}{3}$ the sum of the average density of energy in the following forms: electromagnetic radiation, neutrinos, electrostatic, magnetic, and gravitational.

We may regard $p(t) \ll c^2\rho(t)$ at the present epoch for the following reasons. The kinetic energies and internal gravitational energies of galaxies are of the order of 10^{-6} of their rest-mass energies. There is evidence (see Section 18.4) that the density of electromagnetic radiation is much smaller than the average density of rest-mass energy. The density of neutrinos, if due only to stars, is also just as small. The magnetic field of 10^{-5} gauss or 10^{-9} wbr m^{-2} which is thought to exist within galaxies, even if it existed in intergalactic space, would have an energy density of the order of 10^{-4} times the average density of rest-mass energy.

The special case of a space-time with constant Gaussian curvature K requires, from eqs. (14-34), (14-35), (17-2), and (17-3),

$$\rho c^2 = -p = -\frac{c^2}{\kappa}(3K + \Lambda). \tag{17-7}$$

Thus all cosmological models which admit the maximal group of automorphisms, i.e., all the cases studied in Chapter 16, require a negative pressure equal to the energy density! Under the interpretation of cosmological pressure given above, there exists no physical solution to eq. (17-7), because the only possible negative contribution to the pressure comes from the gravitational energies of the galaxies; and this can hardly be as large as the rest energies of the galaxies. Equation (17-7) therefore requires that both ρ and p vanish. But then we may ask exactly what it is, if not matter, that follows the fundamental world-lines.

The constant-curvature models can be rescued by relaxing either the assumption of the field equation of general relativity or the hydrodynamic interpretation of cosmological pressure. We will not pursue either approach except to note some properties of the steady-state model in Section 18.8.

17.2 ZERO-PRESSURE MODELS

Since the cosmological pressure is small, a suitable approximation is made by neglecting it altogether. With $p = 0$, eq. (17-5) becomes

$$\rho S^3 = \text{const} \tag{17-8}$$

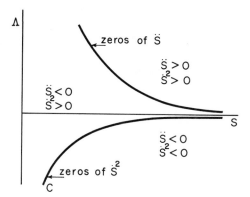

FIGURE 17.1 The Λ-S plane for $k = 0, -1$.

and eq. (17-2) then becomes

$$\dot{S}^2 = \frac{\kappa \rho_0 S_0^3}{3S} + \frac{\Lambda S^2}{3} - k. \qquad (17\text{-}9)$$

The subscript 0 denotes values at the present epoch. Division of eq. (17-9) by S^2 and evaluation at the present epoch gives

$$H^2 = \frac{\kappa \rho_0}{3} + \frac{\Lambda}{3} - \frac{k}{S_0^2} \qquad (17\text{-}10)$$

where H is the Hubble constant defined by eq. (15-6). The acceleration parameter is obtained from eqs. (15-7) and (17-4):

$$\alpha = - \frac{\kappa \rho_0}{6H^2} + \frac{\Lambda}{3H^2}. \qquad (17\text{-}11)$$

The qualitative behavior of $S(t)$ can be studied by treating Λ temporarily as a variable. Equation (17-9) then determines a curve $\dot{S}^2 = 0$ in the S-Λ plane. This curve, which is labeled C in Figures 17.1 and 17.2, is

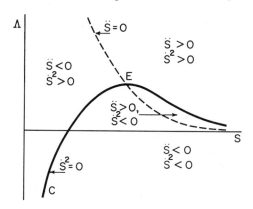

FIGURE 17.2 The Λ-S plane for $k = +1$.

asymptotic to both the negative Λ-axis and the positive S-axis. For $k = 0$ or -1, the curve C increases monotonically with increasing S but never crosses the S-axis. For $k = +1$, the curve C increases to a maximum E above the S-axis and then decreases monotonically with increasing S. The maximum E is given by $S = S_E$, $\Lambda = \Lambda_E$, where

$$\left.\begin{aligned} S_E &= \frac{\kappa \rho_0 S_0^3}{2} \\[2ex] \Lambda_E &= \frac{4}{(\kappa \rho_0 S_0^3)^2} \end{aligned}\right\} \tag{17-12}$$

Only those points in the S-Λ plane which lie above or on C can represent real possibilities because eq. (17-9) cannot be negative. Since Λ is a constant of the motion, the point representing the model must move horizontally left or right, according as $\dot{S}$ is negative or positive. If the point is on C, then the model is momentarily static.

It is interesting to ask for models which are permanently static. Equation (17-4) becomes

$$\frac{\ddot{S}}{S} = \frac{\Lambda}{3} - \frac{\kappa \rho_0 S_0^3}{6 S^3},$$

so that all derivatives of $S(t)$ higher than the second may be expressed as a linear combination of powers of $\dot{S}$ and $\ddot{S}$. Therefore the necessary and sufficient condition that a model be static is that both $\dot{S}$ and $\ddot{S}$ vanish. The curve $\ddot{S} = 0$ in the S-Λ plane is given by

$$\Lambda = \frac{\kappa \rho_0 S_0^3}{2 S^3}$$

which intersects C only for $k = +1$ and only at E. Thus the only static zero-pressure universe is the *Einstein universe* $S = S_E$, $\Lambda = \Lambda_E$. The fact that the curve $\ddot{S} = 0$ intersects C at E is not unique to zero-pressure models. In general, the slope of the curve $\dot{S} = $ const in the S-Λ plane is related to $\ddot{S}$ by the equation

$$S^2 \frac{d\Lambda}{dS} = -6\ddot{S}$$

which is proved by regarding ρ as a function of S and S as a function of both Λ and $\dot{S}$ through eq. (17-2) and then taking partial derivatives.

Each of the possible cosmological models may be deduced from Figures 17.1 and 17.2. The *oscillating* universe is caught between the Λ-axis and the curve C. Such a model begins at the singular state $S = 0$, expands until S reaches a maximum, and then contracts back to $S = 0$. The oscillating model results for the values

$$k = -1, \quad \Lambda < 0$$
$$k = 0, \quad \Lambda < 0$$
$$k = +1, \quad \Lambda < 0$$
$$k = +1, \quad 0 < \Lambda < \Lambda_E, \quad S < S_E'.$$

The *monotonic world of the first kind* either begins at $S = 0$ and expands monotonically forever, or contracts monotonically to $S = 0$. It can never reverse its motion for finite S because $\dot{S}$ is never zero. This model results for the values

$$k = -1, \quad \Lambda \geq 0$$
$$k = 0, \quad \Lambda \geq 0$$
$$k = +1, \quad \Lambda > \Lambda_E.$$

The *monotonic world of the second kind* contracts monotonically to a minimum S and then expands monotonically. It results for the case

$$k = +1, \quad 0 < \Lambda < \Lambda_E, \quad S > S_E.$$

The case $\Lambda = \Lambda_E$ requires special consideration. For $S < S_E$ and $\dot{S} > 0$ the model expands from $S = 0$ and approaches E asymptotically. For $S < S_E$ and $\dot{S} < 0$, the model leaves E asymptotically and contracts to $S = 0$. For $S > S_E$ and $\dot{S} < 0$, the model contracts monotonically and approaches E asymptotically. For $S > S_E$, $\dot{S} > 0$, the model leaves E asymptotically and expands monotonically forever. Each model takes an infinite time to reach or leave E.

The Einstein universe is the only static model in zero-pressure, general-relativistic cosmology. The parameters S and Λ can be determined from a single observation, e.g., the density ρ:

$$S = \sqrt{\frac{2}{\kappa\rho}}$$

$$\Lambda = \frac{\kappa\rho}{2}.$$

The Einstein universe has a volume

$$2\pi^2 \left(\frac{2c^2}{\kappa\rho}\right)^{\frac{3}{2}}.$$

Unfortunately, the Einstein universe is unstable. Any horizontal perturbation from E in Figure 17.2 produces a value of $\ddot{S}$ which has the same sign as $S - S_E$.

In what follows, our attention will be restricted to models in which the Hubble constant is positive, i.e., models which are expanding at the present epoch. The observational basis will be discussed in Section 18.2.

Note that three parameters completely specify a model. The five parameters α, H, Λ, ρ_0, and k/S_0^2 are related by the two equations (17-10) and (17-11) so that there remain only three independent parameters. Determination of the type of model is made with the use of eqs. (17-12).

17.3 THE DENSITY-AGE DIAGRAM

The *age* t_0 of a model which expands from the singular state $S = 0$ is the interval of cosmic time from the singular epoch to the present epoch. (The same symbol is used for age as for cosmic time at the present epoch, because it is assumed that the cosmic time in models which expand from a singular event is measured from the singular event.) The age is given by the integral

$$t_0 = \int_0^S \frac{dS}{\dot{S}}$$

or, more explicitly, with the substitution of eq. (17-9), by

$$H t_0 = \int_0^1 \frac{\sqrt{x}\, dx}{\sqrt{\dfrac{\kappa \rho_0}{3H^2} + \dfrac{\Lambda}{3H^2} x^3 - \dfrac{k}{S_0^2 H^2} x}} . \qquad (17\text{-}13)$$

We may thus choose the three independent parameters*

$$q = \frac{\kappa \rho_0}{3H^2} \qquad (17\text{-}14)$$

$$\tau = H t_0$$

$$H = \left(\frac{\dot{S}}{S} \right)_{t_0} .$$

The first two parameters specify the model, and the third parameter provides the scale of the physical dimensions of the model. Thus the various members of the family can be represented as points on the τ-q diagram. (See Figure 17.3.)

---

* The deceleration parameter q which appears in the current literature is what we here call $-\alpha$. It is not to be confused with the ratio which we here call q, although for the cases $\Lambda = 0$ our q is twice the q in the literature.

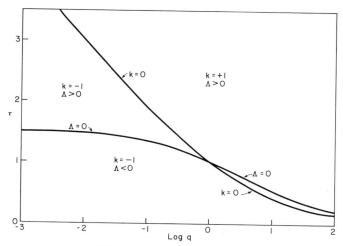

FIGURE 17.3 Density-age diagram.

Models which have $k = 0$ fall on the curve

$$\tau = \tfrac{2}{3}f(q)$$

where $f(q)$ is given by

$$f(q) = \begin{cases} = \dfrac{1}{\sqrt{1-q}}\sinh^{-1}\sqrt{\dfrac{1}{q}-1} & 0 < q < 1 \\[2ex] = 1 & q = 1 \\[2ex] = \dfrac{1}{\sqrt{q-1}}\sin^{-1}\sqrt{1-\dfrac{1}{q}}. & q > 1 \end{cases}$$

Models with $k = +1$ lie above the curve, and models with $k = -1$ lie below the curve.

Models which have $\Lambda = 0$ fall on the curve

$$\tau = \frac{qf(q) - 1}{q - 1}.$$

Models with $\Lambda > 0$ lie above the curve, and models with $\Lambda < 0$ lie below the curve.

The diagram of Figure 17.3 is known as the *density-age diagram* because the coordinates are, except for the scale factor H, the logarithm of the density ρ_0 and the age t_0. The factor H has been retained in constructing the diagram because it is q, not ρ_0, which is directly observed (see Section 18.3), and because H has, in the past, been subject to observational uncertainty. But given a set of values for H, t_0, and q, one may determine which kind of zero-pressure model is thereby implied by use of the density-age diagram.

For later reference we here rewrite eqs. (17-10) and (17-11) with q rather than ρ_0:

$$H^2(1 - q) = \frac{\Lambda}{3} - \frac{k}{S_0^2} \qquad \text{a}$$

$$\alpha = -\frac{q}{2} + \frac{\Lambda}{3H^2}. \qquad \text{b}$$

(17-15)

17.4 ZERO COSMOLOGICAL CONSTANT

This section treats those models in which both the pressure and the cosmological constant are zero. Equations (17-9) and (17-15) become, respectively,

$$\dot{S}^2 = \frac{\kappa \rho_0 S_0^3}{3S} - k \qquad (17\text{-}16)$$

$$H^2(q - 1) = \frac{k}{S_0^2} \qquad (17\text{-}17)$$

$$\alpha = -\frac{q}{2}. \qquad (17\text{-}18)$$

The case $k = 0$ has received considerable attention because of its simplicity. It should be noted that in *any* $k = 0$ model the parameter cS is not a unique length; it can be chosen as the cosmic distance between *any* pair of fundamental world-lines and is then called the *expansion parameter*. For $k = 0$, eq. (17-16) has the solution

$$S(t) \propto t^{\frac{2}{3}}.$$

Differentiation of the above proportion shows that $\tau = \frac{2}{3}$. Equations (17-17) and (17-18) give respectively $q = 1$ and $\alpha = -\frac{1}{2}$. This model, known as the *Einstein-deSitter* universe, expands forever at an ever-decreasing rate. For later reference we will express the motion in the parametric form

$$S = \tfrac{1}{2}A\psi^2$$
$$t = \tfrac{1}{6}A\psi^3$$

where A is a constant and ψ is the parametric variable.

The case $k = +1$ is curious in two respects. First, for any given cosmic time, the model has a finite volume. Second, the discussion of Section 17.2 shows that the model is of the oscillating type, i.e., it has a beginning and an end. The solution of eq. (17-16) is, in parametric form,

$$S = A(1 - \cos \psi)$$
$$t = A(\psi - \sin \psi)$$

where

$$A = \frac{\kappa}{6} \rho_0 S_0^3 = \frac{1}{2H} \frac{q}{(q-1)^{\frac{3}{2}}}.$$

The curve $S(t)$ is a cycloid. The universe expands from $S = 0$ to $S = 2A$ (with maximum volume $16\pi^2 c^3 A^3$) in a time πA and then contracts again to $S = 0$. The total life-time for the universe is $2\pi A$. The ratio of the maximum S to the present S is

$$\frac{2A}{S_0} = \frac{1}{1 - \frac{1}{q}}.$$

From eq. (17-17), $q > 1$.

The case $k = -1$ has the parametric solution

$$S = A(\cosh \psi - 1)$$
$$t = A(\sinh \psi - \psi)$$

where

$$A = \frac{\kappa}{6} \rho_0 S_0^3 = \frac{1}{2H} \frac{q}{(1-q)^{\frac{3}{2}}}.$$

From eq. (17-17), $0 < q < 1$. The model begins at $S = 0$ and expands forever. It asymptotically approaches the expanding Minkowski universe of Section 16.1.

The three zero-Λ models have the following two properties in common. First, the differential dt is given by $dt = S\, d\psi$ in terms of the parameter ψ. Therefore a light ray travels in such a way that in a parameter interval $\Delta\psi$ it traverses a coordinate distance $\Delta w = \Delta\psi$.

Second, the bolometric distance r_b to a galaxy in natural motion, defined by eq. (15-10), has a closed form when expressed in terms of the galaxy's redshift:

$$r_b = \frac{2c}{q^2 H} [qz - (2-q)(\sqrt{1+qz} - 1)].$$

Fock has discovered a convenient parametric form:

$$\frac{r_b H}{c} = y + \frac{y^2}{2}, \qquad z = y + \frac{q y^2}{4}, \qquad y > 0.$$

17.5 RADIATION

In Sections 17.2 through 17.4 the cosmological pressure was assumed to be zero. In this section the assumption is made that the cosmological pressure is due only to electromagnetic radiation, and that there is no interaction between the radiation and the matter in the universe. The pressure is then given by $p = \frac{1}{3}U$, where U is the energy density of radiation. The density ρ now contains the contribution Uc^{-2}, so that eq. (17-5) becomes

$$\frac{d}{dt}\left[(\rho c^2 + U)S^3\right] + \frac{1}{3}U\frac{d}{dt}(S^3) = 0$$

or

$$\frac{d}{dt}(\rho c^2 S^3) + \frac{1}{S}\frac{d}{dt}(US^4) = 0 \qquad (17\text{-}19)$$

where ρ will here denote the density of matter *alone*. The assumption that there is no interaction between matter and radiation requires that each of the two terms in eq. (17-19) vanish separately. The solutions are therefore $\rho S^3 = $ const and

$$US^4 = \text{const.} \qquad (17\text{-}20)$$

The ratio U/ρ varies as $1/S$. Thus in an expanding universe, the ratio of radiation density to matter density decreases. Equation (17-20) is familiar to us from Section 15.4.

Models which contain radiation as described above are qualitatively no different from those in Section 17.2. Equation (17-2) becomes

$$\dot{S}^2 = \frac{\kappa\rho_0 S_0^3}{3S} + \frac{\kappa U_0 S_0^4}{3c^2 S^2} + \frac{\Lambda S^2}{3} - k$$

so that the curve $\dot{S}^2 = 0$ in the S-Λ plane remains qualitatively the same.

Assuming that the ratio $\gamma = U_0/\rho_0 c^2$ is small at the present epoch, there was an epoch t_1 in the past, given by $S(t_1) = \gamma S(t_0)$, at which the densities of radiation and matter were equal. This condition, in itself, does not lead to an unusual relation between matter and radiation. The energy density of the solar constant is considerably in excess of the average density in the universe, yet nothing strange happens to us. However, at the time t_1, the densities of radiation and matter were greater than their present values:

$$\rho_1 c^2 = U_1 = \frac{\rho_0 c^2}{\gamma^3} = \frac{U_0}{\gamma^4},$$

where the subscript 1 refers to the epoch t_1. Thus if $\rho_0 = 5 \times 10^{-28}$ kg m^{-3} and $\gamma = 10^{-4}$, then $\rho_1 = 5 \times 10^{-16}$ kg m^{-3}. Furthermore, not only would the density ρ_1 be greater than ρ_0, but the matter which is now assembled in galaxies would most likely have been dispersed in the form of a primordial gas. At the higher density, this gas would provide a smaller mean-free path for photons—a few tens of persecs for the figures quoted above—so that there would be interaction between radiation and matter. We could expect the earlier stages of the universe to have thermal equilibrium.

We will nevertheless pursue the model with non-interacting radiation and matter in order to see how the pressure affects the age. In the case $k = 0$, $\Lambda = 0$, the age integral becomes

$$H\sqrt{q}\, t_0 = \int_0^1 \frac{x\, dx}{\sqrt{\gamma + x}}$$

with

$$\frac{1}{q} = 1 + \gamma.$$

The integral possesses a closed form

$$Ht_0 = \tfrac{2}{3}(1 + \gamma)^{\frac{1}{2}}[2\gamma^{\frac{3}{2}} + (1 + \gamma)^{\frac{1}{2}}(1 - 2\gamma)].$$

The Einstein-deSitter model results when γ is set equal to zero; $Ht_0 = \tfrac{2}{3}$. For a pure radiation universe, $\gamma \to \infty$ and Ht_0 becomes $\tfrac{1}{2}$. Thus the effect of the inclusion of radiation is to decrease the age. For small γ we find

$$Ht_0 = \tfrac{2}{3}[1 - \gamma + 2\gamma^{\frac{3}{2}} + O^2(\gamma)]$$

so that for $\gamma = 10^{-2}$ the decrease in age is only 1 per cent.

CHAPTER 18

COSMOLOGICAL OBSERVATIONS

18.1 THE MAGNITUDE-REDSHIFT RELATION

The most promising means for detecting the structure of the universe is the magnitude-redshift relation. If all galaxies had the same absolute magnitude M, then their positions on the diagram of apparent magnitude versus redshift would fall on the curve $m(z)$ given by eq. (15-12). A certain amount of scatter would result due to the random motions of galaxies, but this scatter will diminish at large z if the plot is m versus $\log z$.

Unfortunately, galaxies do not have identical absolute magnitudes. This fact is evident merely from noting the dispersion in apparent magnitude of the galaxies in a cluster, all the members of which are presumably at the same distance and have the same age. Thus a large scatter about the ideal $m(z)$ curve results from the dispersion in absolute magnitudes. However, the scatter can be diminished by choosing a particular class of galaxy. The most useful such choice has been found to be the brightest galaxy in each cluster of galaxies.

But even when one determines a curve $m(z)$ on which galaxies of a certain class fall, there are still a number of formidable obstacles which stand in the way of comparing observation with theory.

First, the redshift correction must be applied to the apparent magnitudes. This is necessary because we observe magnitudes in a particular spectral range. Due to redshift the spectral distribution of the galaxy is shifted relative to the "window" of the pass-band wavelengths.

Second, intergalactic absorption, although small, may not be completely negligible. Intergalactic matter which could dim galaxies at 100 Mpc by $0^m\!.02$ could dim galaxies at 500 Mpc by $0^m\!.1$.

Third, we cannot exclude the possibility that galaxies of a given type may have various absolute magnitudes due to evolution. When we observe a galaxy at a distance of 500 Mpc or 1.5×10^9 light years, we see it as it was at an epoch 1.5×10^9 years prior to our epoch. If the galaxy's evolution will cause it to brighten (or dim) appreciably in that interval of time, then the M in eq. (15-12) must be the absolute magnitude which the galaxy would have at the present epoch.

Although very little is known about galaxy formation and evolution, we can deduce the formal correction which must be applied to eq. (15-12) in the event that galaxy evolution is appreciable. It is assumed that the galaxy's absolute magnitude can be expanded in a power series about the present epoch:

$$M(t) = M_0 - \dot{M}_0(t_0 - t) + \tfrac{1}{2}\ddot{M}_0(t_0 - t)^2 + \cdots .$$

The substitution of eq. (15-4) then gives

$$M(t) = M_0 - \frac{\dot{M}_0}{H} z + \left[\frac{\ddot{M}_0}{2H^2} + \frac{\dot{M}_0}{H}\left(1 - \frac{\alpha}{2}\right) \right] z^2 + \cdots . \qquad (18\text{-}1)$$

The substitution of eqs. (15-19) and (18-1) into eq. (15-12) gives

$$m = M_0 + 5 \log \frac{c}{H \cdot 10 \text{ psc}} + 5 \log z + Az + Bz^2 + O^3(z)$$

where

$$A = \tfrac{5}{2}(\log e)\left(1 + \alpha + \frac{K\rho_0 c}{H}\right) - \frac{\dot{M}_0}{H}$$

$$B = \tfrac{5}{24}(\log e)\left[9\alpha^2 - 10\alpha - 7 - 4\beta - \frac{4k}{S_0^2 H^2} + \frac{6K\rho_0 c}{H}(1 + \alpha) \right]$$

$$+ \frac{\ddot{M}_0}{2H^2} + \frac{\dot{M}_0}{H}\left(1 - \frac{\alpha}{2}\right).$$

$$(18\text{-}2)$$

18.2 THE HUBBLE CONSTANT

To the lowest order in z, eqs. (15-8) and (15-12) provide the relation

$$cz = Hr_b. \qquad (18\text{-}3)$$

Thus the Hubble constant H is the ratio of cz to bolometric distance for nearby galaxies. Since the most common astronomical units for velocity and distance are km/sec and Mpc, respectively, it is usual for H to be given in terms of the unit km/sec-Mpc.

The very existence of the Hubble constant is a cosmological prediction which must be checked against observation. Furthermore, the redshift-magnitude diagram for galaxies reveals a slope of 5 in accordance with eq. (18-2). Therefore the Hubble constant exists and is non-zero; further-more, it is positive. The problem is to measure its value.

The first estimate of H was given by Edwin Hubble, who pioneered in the study of galaxies. Unfortunately, he mistook HII regions to be bright stars, and he underestimated the absolute magnitudes of Cepheid variables. With the r_b in eq. (18-3) too small for each galaxy, Hubble's[B] value for H, 530 km/sec-Mpc, was too large.

Subsequent modification and correction of Hubble's techniques gave larger distances to the galaxies, and hence lowered the value of H. Current estimates* of H place its value at 110 ± 30 km/sec-Mpc. In the discussion which follows, the adopted value for H will be:

$$\left. \begin{aligned} H &= 100 \text{ km/sec-Mpc} \\ H^{-1} &= 3.1 \times 10^{17} \text{ sec} = 9.8 \times 10^9 \text{ yr} \\ H^2 &= 1.02 \times 10^{-35} \text{ sec}^{-2}. \end{aligned} \right\} \qquad (18\text{-}4)$$

It has become a common practice in astronomy to determine the distances to more remote galaxies by the use of eq. (18-3) rather than eq. (15-8). The redshift of the galaxy (or the average redshift for a cluster of galaxies) is multiplied by c and divided by H. Such a distance estimate, of course, depends on the value for H which is adopted by the investigator.

18.3 AVERAGE DENSITY

There exist two methods for determining the masses of galaxies.

One method is used for individual galaxies which are near enough for the rotational velocity to be measured at various points within each galaxy. Let $v(r)$ be the rotational velocity at a distance r from the center of the galaxy. Then from Newtonian gravity, the mass of the galaxy is given by

$$M = \frac{1}{G} \lim_{r \to \infty} v^2 r.$$

The velocities are obtained directly from Doppler shifts in the spectra. Distances within the galaxy are the products of the corresponding angular distances with the distance between the galaxy and us. And the distance

---

* Van den Bergh[B] in 1960 had 120(+25, −20), the Santa Barbara conference in 1961 (see Sandage[B] and Sérsic[B]) had 98 ± 20, and Sérsic[B] in 1962 had 116 ± 9.

to the galaxy in turn depends on the value of H that is used, as was noted in the previous section. Thus the masses of galaxies by the velocity-curve method are inversely proportional to the adopted value of H.

The other method for obtaining masses of galaxies is a statistical method with two variations.

For a double galaxy, the difference in redshift between the two members gives their relative velocity along the line of sight. The component of the linear separation of the two galaxies perpendicular to the line of sight is obtained from their angular separation and from their distance, which in turn depends on the Hubble constant. Although the space velocities and actual separation for a double galaxy cannot be known, a statistical analysis for a large number of double galaxies yields information on the masses of various types of galaxies which comprise double galaxies. The validity of the results depends, of course, on the assumption that each pair of galaxies is in Keplerian motion around each other. The important feature for us to note is that again, as in the previous method, the masses of galaxies are inversely proportional to H.

For a cluster of galaxies, the assumption that the cluster has a fairly permanent existence yields an estimate of its total mass. The virial theorem requires that the sum of twice the total kinetic energy and the total gravitational energy of the cluster equal zero. The deviations of the redshifts of the members from the mean redshift of the cluster give a rough estimate of the kinetic energy per unit mass in the cluster. The gravitational potential energy depends on the spatial distribution of the galaxies; the latter is obtained from angular separations and the distance to the cluster. The total mass comes out equal to G^{-1} times the product of a characteristic distance and the square of a characteristic velocity. Thus again we have galaxy masses which are inversely proportional to H.

When we say that galaxy masses are inversely proportional to H, we do not mean that at a later epoch the masses of galaxies must change according to the new value of H. Rather, the estimate of galaxy masses makes use of H in such a way that two investigators using different values H_1 and H_2 obtain masses which are in the ratio $H_2 : H_1$.

The average density of the material in galaxies is simply the quotient of the total of all galaxies in a simple region divided by the volume of the region. The mass is proportional to H^{-1} and the volume is proportional to H^{-3}. Thus the estimate of the average density ρ_0 is proportional to H^2, and the parameter q defined by eq. (17-14) is independent of H.

For the Hubble constant of eq. (18-4), the average density of material in individual galaxies based on their average mass-luminosity ratio* is

$$\rho_0 = 5 \times 10^{-31} \text{ gm cm}^{-3} = 5 \times 10^{-28} \text{ kg m}^{-3}. \qquad (18\text{-}5a)$$

---

* Van den Bergh[B], with H adjusted to 100 km/sec-Mpc.

The average density of galaxy material based on the masses and distribution of clusters of galaxies is estimated* to be

$$\log \frac{\rho_0}{\text{kg m}^{-3}} = -26.7 \pm 0.5.$$

The discrepancy between the two values for the average density is due principally to the well-known discrepancy between velocity-curve masses and cluster masses. The mass-luminosity ratio for cluster galaxies comes out about 50 times as large as the mass-luminosity ratio for individual galaxies by the velocity-curve method. Thus, if the unseen matter which is thought to contribute to cluster masses is also present throughout space, then the average density of matter may be as high as

$$\rho_0 = 2 \times 10^{-29} \text{ gm cm}^{-3} = 2 \times 10^{-26} \text{ kg m}^{-3}. \tag{18-5b}$$

It may be noted for future reference that the q defined by eq. (18-4) with eqs. (18-5a) and (18-5b) is, respectively, 0.027 and 1.0.

18.4 RADIATION DENSITY

For a source of radiation with bolometric luminosity L, the energy in the space between radii r_1 and r_2 is $(L/4\pi c)(r_2 - r_1)$, i.e., proportional to $r_2 - r_1$. Thus the most significant contribution of a star's radiation to the cosmological average comes at interstellar distances. And, in turn, the most significant contribution of a galaxy's radiation to the cosmological average comes at intergalactic distances. Thus we are forced to take *intergalactic* radiation to be representative of the cosmological average.

The observational task is to measure the intensity of extragalactic radiation averaged over the whole sky. This task proves to be extremely difficult due to absorption, scattering, and emission of light by galactic material, zodiacal material, and, in the case of terrestrial observations, the earth's atmosphere.

No accurate measurements of the extragalactic radiation at all wavelengths have yet been made. The main problem is the background from the earth's atmosphere. In the radio, the problem is the galactic background emission. We cannot even be certain that the average density of intergalactic radiation is less than the average density of matter! The arguments for a cool interstellar medium with a temperature as low as $30°K$ are of no help, since the blackbody radiation density for such a temperature is about 14 times larger than eq. (18-5a).

Two sets of measurements are worth mentioning. One team† reports that the *optical* extragalactic sky brightness cannot exceed 1.6×10^4 tenth-visual-magnitude stars per steradian. By arbitrarily assuming a bolometric

---

* Abell[B], with H adjusted to 100 km/sec-Mpc.
† Roach[B].

correction identical with that of the sun, we arrive at a radiation density of about $2 \times 10^{-32} c^2$ kg m^{-3}. The sky brightness at the *radio* frequencies 4.08×10^9 Hz and 9.4×10^9 Hz (the hertz, abbreviated Hz, is a unit equal to one cycle per second) is found to be 2×10^{-20} and 8×10^{-20} watt m^{-2} ster^{-1} Hz^{-1}, respectively.[*] The radio observations are noteworthy in three respects: The brightness is isotropic and hence extragalactic; the brightness is in excess of the estimated galactic component; and the brightness at the two frequencies coincide with 3°K blackbody radiation.

We may reasonably expect the extragalactic radiation to consist of two components: (1) The integrated light of galaxies, and (2) the primordial radiation remaining from earlier stages in the universe before galaxy formation. The latter, if it is of the blackbody type, must correspond to a temperature no greater than 3°K in order to agree with the radio observations. The corresponding energy density is $7 \times 10^{-31} c^2$ kg m^{-3}. An estimate of the integrated starlight by Felton[B] places the energy density at $1.7 \times 10^{-32} c^2$ kg m^{-3}. The theory of the origin of cosmic rays indicates a starlight density of the same order of magnitude.[†] Thus, subject to the above assumptions, we may conclude that the radiation density is less than the matter density by a factor of about 10^{-3}.

18.5 AGES

When Sandage[B] in 1961 announced the ages of five star clusters based on Hoyle's theory of stellar evolution, there appeared to be a glaring discrepancy between the cluster ages and the ages of relativistic cosmological models. The clusters were M3, M5, M13, M67, and NGC 188. Sandage's ages were, respectively, 26, 24, 22, 10, and 15 billion years. These ages are larger than the 9.8 billion years of eq. (18-4) which is the maximum age for non-accelerated relativistic models. We expect the clusters, as members of the universe, to have ages *less* than the age of the universe.

However, in the same year Arp[B] and Woolf[B] showed that Sandage's ages had been overestimated. Arp concluded that the cluster ages should be halved according to an improved reddening law. Woolf proved that if Sandage's age of M3 were correct, then some stars in M3 should have burned up more than their mass! Woolf's revision placed the age of M3 at 7 billion years. Thus Sandage's ages need to be quartered, and there is no discrepancy between the cluster ages and the cosmological age.

The age of the oldest cluster mentioned above is 7 ± 1 billion years. For comparison, the age of the solar system, dated by radioactivity, is 4.5 billion years.[‡] We will adopt the relation

$$t_0 \geq 8 \times 10^9 \text{ yr.} \tag{18-6}$$

---

[*] Penzias[B] and Roll[B].
[†] Ginzburg[B].
[‡] Allen[B].

18.6 THE ACCELERATION PARAMETER

The first three cosmological quantities given in this chapter—H, ρ_0, and t_0—are obtained from relatively nearby observations. More distant observations are used for other cosmological quantities. We have our choice of either using counts of galaxies—eq. (15-24)—or the magnitude-redshift relation—eq. (18-2). However, the former provides no cosmological information in its first-order term. Therefore we must rely upon the magnitude-redshift relation.

Baum[B] has found that, neglecting absorption and evolution, the coefficient A in eq. (18-2) corresponds to

$$\alpha = -1 \pm \tfrac{1}{2}, \tag{18-7}$$

which means that the magnitude-redshift relation is linear to first-order in z. The above value for the acceleration parameter is not so precise as to exclude values, for example, near zero.

We expect the absorption term in A to be positive and the evolutionary term to be negative—the latter because the galaxies should be brightening up. Thus the actual value of α is probably smaller but not larger than eq. (18-7). Therefore, the universe is most likely in a state of deceleration.

18.7 ZERO-PRESSURE, GENERAL-RELATIVISTIC MODELS

Equations (18-4) through (18-7), as they stand, are not consistent with any zero-pressure, general-relativistic model.* However, the observed values are not so certain as to preclude the possibility of future revision. We can consider, for the example, the Einstein-deSitter universe defined by $q = 1$ and $\alpha = -\tfrac{1}{2}$. Then $\Lambda = 0$ and $k = 0$. For an assumed Hubble constant of 80 km/sec-Mpc, the age is 8.15×10^9 yrs. These values are consistent with eqs. (18-5b), (18-6), and (18-7), when it is remembered that ρ_0 is proportional to H^2.

The low value of H demanded by this example, although possible, is thought by many astronomers to be improbable. It would be more satisfying to find a model for which the four observable parameters H, ρ_0, t_0 and α are closer to eqs. (18-4) through (18-7). Unfortunately, the quest for such a model encounters considerable difficulty. A larger cosmological constant will give a larger age, but it will also give a larger acceleration parameter.

---

* See Section A.7.

There are three types of zero-pressure models which have no age problem. A monotonic universe of the second kind has no singular event $S = 0$. An asymptotic universe with $S > S_E$ takes an infinite time to expand from the Einstein universe. The third type of model without an age problem is the *Lemaître universe*. The cosmological constant is assumed to be only slightly larger than Λ_E. The model is then a monotonic universe of the first kind, but it takes a long time to get past the point $S = S_E$. For any $S_0 > S_E$, the age can be made larger than any given value merely by choosing $\Lambda - \Lambda_E$ sufficiently small. Unfortunately, all three of the above models have acceleration parameters which are larger than unity.

Although we cannot decide precisely which model applies, we can place bounds on the cosmological constant and the spatial curvature. Counts of galaxies produce a log N vs. m relation (see Section 15.7) which is linear to within one magnitude out to at least $m = 20$. For absolute magnitudes of order -20, the distance $cS_0 w$ is about 10^3 Mpc. The linearity of the relation requires either that $k = 0$ or that w be less than, say, 3. Hence cS_0 is larger than 3×10^2 Mpc, and we have

$$\left| \frac{k}{S_0^2} \right| < 10^{-33} \text{ sec}^{-2}.$$

Since H^2 and $\kappa\rho_0$ from eqs. (18-4) and (18-5) are hardly as large as 10^{-33} sec^{-2}, eq. (17-10) provides a bound on Λ:

$$|\Lambda| < 3 \times 10^{-33} \text{ sec}^{-2}.$$

Thus the length $c/\sqrt{|\Lambda|}$ is larger than 2×10^2 Mpc. This gives little information on S_0 and Λ, but it does give the satisfying assurance that the geometry and the gravitation within a cluster of galaxies are, respectively, Euclidean and Newtonian to a high degree of accuracy—provided of course that general relativity applies.

18.8 THE STEADY-STATE UNIVERSE

The expanding model which satisfies the perfect cosmological principle is known as the *steady-state model*. As was noted in Section 14.8, the *geometry* is that of the deSitter universe. We come now to examine the *physical* implications of the perfect cosmological principle.

The assumption that the universe must present the same view to different observers at different times requires that the average density ρ be a constant. But in the deSitter universe, the matter follows the fundamental world-lines. Therefore, the matter appears to recede from any observer. In order that the density remain constant, there must be a continual formation of matter out of nothing. A simple calculation gives the rate of creation of matter.

It was noted in Section 16.2 that the model possesses a horizon at cosmic distance $r_c = a = bc$. From eq. (15-25), the rate of change of the distance to any fundamental world-line per unit cosmic time is cr_c/a. Hence at the horizon this "velocity" is equal to c. In a cosmic time dt, the material within a spherical shell of radius a and thickness $c\, dt$ flows past the horizon. Thus the rate at which mass passes the horizon is $4\pi \rho a^2 c$. New mass must therefore appear at a rate $3\rho/b$ (in units of kg m^{-3} sec^{-1}) or $3/b$ (in units of kg kg^{-1} sec^{-1}). For the Hubble constant of eq. (18-4), the rate of appearance of matter is

$$3H = 3/b = 9.6 \times 10^{-18} \text{ kg kg}^{-1} \text{ sec}^{-1}.$$

For the density of eq. (18-5a), the volume rate is

$$3H\rho = 5 \times 10^{-45} \text{ kg m}^{-3} \text{ sec} = 1.4 \times 10^5 \text{ kg psc}^{-3} \text{ sec}^{-1}.$$

Such a rate is too small to detect by present methods.

The average age of matter in the steady-state universe is $1/3H$, which, for eq. (18-4), is 3.3×10^9 yr. To prove this, consider the matter within a constant element of coordinate volume d^3w. In the time interval between t and $t + dt$, a mass $3H\rho S^3(t)d^3w$ is formed. This mass then has, at the epoch t_0, an age $t_0 - t$. The average age is therefore

$$\frac{\int_{t=-\infty}^{t_0} 3H\rho S^3(t)(t_0 - t)d^3w\, dt}{\int_{t=-\infty}^{t_0} 3H\rho S^3(t)d^3w\, dt} = \frac{1}{3H}.$$

The calculation for average age is altered if the matter is transmuted, for example, by radioactivity, into another form. Suppose that a fraction $\chi\, dt$ of mass disappears in time dt, where χ is a constant. Then the mass which was created at time t has only a fraction $e^{-\chi(t_0-t)}$ remaining to the present epoch. Therefore the average age is given by

$$\frac{\int_{t=-\infty}^{t_0} 3H\rho S^3(t)e^{-\chi(t_0-t)}(t_0 - t)d^3w\, dt}{\int_{t=-\infty}^{t_0} 3H\rho S^3(t)e^{-\chi(t_0-t)}d^3w\, dt} = \frac{1}{3H + \chi}.$$

As was noted in connection with eq. (17-7), it is possible to have a general-relativistic model for each of the space-times of constant curvature and hence for the steady-state model. The sacrifice which must be made is to have a cosmological pressure equal to the negative energy density. However, the proponents of the steady-state theory usually advocate a gravitational theory which is an alteration of Einstein's theory.

Observationally, the steady-state universe fares no better than the Lemaître universe. The lengthy age—infinite in the steady-state theory—is offset by the large acceleration parameter which is $+1$ in the steady-state model. Further, because of its simplicity and susceptibility to observational contradiction, the steady-state model has been attacked by some radio astronomers as being inconsistent with the log N vs. m relation for radio sources.

18.9 EXAMPLES OF COSMOLOGICAL DISTANCES

In this section we give examples of distances in various cosmological models. The models which have been selected are listed in Table 18.1.

TABLE 18.1 *MODELS SELECTED FOR DISTANCE CALCULATIONS*

MODEL	α	t_0 IN 10^9 YR FOR $H = 100$ km/sec-Mpc
Spherical, $\Lambda = 0$, $p = 0$, $q = 2$	-1	5.6
Einstein-deSitter	-0.5	6.5
Hyperbolic, $\Lambda = 0$, $p = 0$, $q = 0.03$	-0.015	9.3
Expanding Minkowski	0	9.8
Steady state	$+1$	∞

The reason for choosing the particular q-values of 0.03 and 2 is to agree, respectively, with eq. (18-5a) and eq. (18-7).

Three kinds of distance were discussed in Section 15.8—apparent-size, bolometric, and cosmological. To these we now add two more distances which will be denoted r_1 and r_l.

A light ray is emitted at cosmic time t_1 by a source G in natural motion and is received at cosmic time t_0 by an observer O also in natural motion (see Figure 15.1). Define

$$r_1 = cS(t_1)w$$

where w is the coordinate distance between O and G. We define the distance r_l covered by the light ray as the integral

$$r_l = c \int_{t=t_1}^{t_0} S(t) \, dw = c(t_0 - t_1).$$

Thus r_1 is the cosmic distance at emission and r_l is the metric distance covered by the light signal.

We imagine that we have found four objects in natural motion with redshifts respectively of 0.2, 0.5, 2, and 4. The reasons for these choices are as follows. To the date of publication, a number of clusters of galaxies

TABLE 18.2 *COSMOLOGICAL DISTANCES*

MODEL	REDSHIFT z	r_s	DISTANCES IN UNITS OF c/H r_1	r_c	r_b	r_l	t_1/t_0
Spherical	0.2	0.139	0.140	0.168	0.200	0.154	0.731
	0.5	0.222	0.226	0.340	0.500	0.283	0.505
	2	0.222	0.243	0.730	2.000	0.476	0.167
	4	0.160	0.186	0.928	4.000	0.528	0.076
	∞	0.000	0.000	1.571	∞	0.571	0.000
Einstein-deSitter	0.2	0.145	0.145	0.174	0.209	0.160	0.761
	0.5	0.245	0.245	0.367	0.551	0.304	0.544
	2	0.282	0.282	0.845	2.536	0.538	0.192
	4	0.221	0.221	1.106	5.528	0.607	0.089
	∞	0.000	0.000	2.000	∞	0.667	0.000
Hyperbolic	0.2	0.153	0.152	0.182	0.220	0.166	0.826
	0.5	0.277	0.269	0.404	0.623	0.332	0.652
	2	0.435	0.362	1.085	3.913	0.660	0.308
	4	0.457	0.315	1.575	11.43	0.788	0.174
	∞	0.000	0.000	4.953	∞	0.954	0.000
Expanding Minkowski	0.2	0.153	0.152	0.182	0.220	0.167	0.833
	0.5	0.278	0.270	0.405	0.625	0.333	0.667
	2	0.444	0.366	1.099	4.000	0.667	0.333
	4	0.480	0.322	1.609	12.00	0.800	0.200
	∞	0.500	0.000	∞	∞	1.000	0.000
deSitter	0.2	0.167	0.167	0.200	0.240	0.182	
	0.5	0.333	0.333	0.500	0.750	0.405	
	2	0.667	0.667	2.000	6.000	1.099	
	4	0.800	0.800	4.000	20.00	1.609	
	∞	1.000	1.000	∞	∞	∞	

are known to have redshifts ranging up to 0.2. One cluster* has a redshift of nearly 0.5. The new class of object, the quasar which has been discovered in the last decade, includes members with redshifts† as large as 2. (At the time of writing, there is uncertainty in the interpretation of the redshifts of quasars, whether they are cosmological, gravitational, or local Doppler. We will assume them to be cosmological.) The redshift of 4 is merely thrown in for good measure, and $z = \infty$ is included for interest.

For each model, we may calculate six quantities: $r_s, r_1, r_c, r_b, r_l,$ and t_1/t_0. (The latter quantity does not exist for the deSitter universe.) Table 18.2 gives the result of the calculations. The unit for the distances in Table 18.2 is c/H, which for $H = 100$ km/sec-Mpc is 2998 Mpc.

Several features in the table may be noted by inspection. First, there is a general trend for a given type of distance at a given redshift to get larger as one passes each model in succession. Second, some entrees are

---

* See Humason[B] et al. and Baum[B].
† See McCrea[B].

identical with others: z with the deSitter r_c (as has been noted) and the spherical r_b; the deSitter r_l and the Minkowski r_c; and the Minkowski r_l and the deSitter r_s and r_1. Third, the angular-size distance does not increase monotonically with z in the three zero-pressure models; there is a maximum at a finite z, and the distance goes to zero for infinite z. The reason for this behavior is that the object is seen at the beginning of the expansion when it was near to the observer. It may be remarked that in the zero-pressure models of Section 17.4, the observer can see no further than the coordinate distance $w = \psi_0$, where ψ_0 is the parameter at the present epoch.

The most obvious lesson to learn from Table 18.2 is that the "distance" to a source depends on the type of distance and on the cosmological model. It is meaningless to give a distance to an object with a large redshift without specifying both the type of distance and the cosmological model.

18.10 THE INITIAL STATE $S = 0$

In those models which expand from the singular state $S = 0$, two questions naturally arise. What was the nature of the singular state? What was the nature of the universe before the singular state?

The singular state cannot be described by known laws of physics because the densities are too high. As we turn the clock backward and observe the expanding universe in contraction, the density ρ must rise at least as fast as S^{-3}. The appreciable presence of radiation (which varies as S^{-4}) or kinetic energy (which for small velocities varies as S^{-5}) would make the density increase more rapidly than S^{-3}. Thus, for a present density as given by eq. (18-5a), the density at $S = 1.5 \times 10^{-15}S_0$ is at least the density of an atomic nucleus! Now physics knows nothing about the state of matter at densities higher than that of a nucleus, but if the universe could somehow come through the singular state, then all of its previous history, whatever that may have been, would most likely be destroyed at the singularity.

As an example, suppose our universe to be of the spherical, zero-pressure, zero-cosmological-constant type. Then the universe will eventually stop expanding and begin contracting. The contraction is a gravitational effect due to the contents of the universe. As the state $S = 0$ is approached, those contents are increasingly mashed against themselves. Thus higher pressures are produced which, in contexts other than gravity, would tend to stop the implosion. But in Einstein's gravitation, as was noted in Section 17.1, the buildup in pressure only accelerates the implosion.

Some cosmologists have sought to avoid the singularity by relaxing the assumption of isotropy and endowing the universe with angular momentum. The angular momentum could be very small at the present epoch but would build up under contraction so as to prevent collapse to the state $S = 0$.

Other cosmologists have relaxed the assumption of homogeneity and propose that different parts of the universe undergo singular collapse at different times. Some have suggested that the quasars should be identified with these events.

Returning to the homogeneous, isotropic oscillating model, we may ask what happens after the universe passes the singularity. Does it pursue another cycle of expansion and contraction, or might its k change from $+1$ to 0 or -1? And if the universe pursues another cycle, is it identical with the present cycle? Some authors have envisaged a universe which alternately expands and contracts in identical cycles, so that $S(t)$ is really a multi-cycle cycloid.

Many questions remain to be answered. The purpose of these chapters has not been to prescribe any particular cosmological models, but rather to provide a theoretical framework into which to fit, as far as possible, the cosmological observations. At the time of writing, the quasars, or quasi-stellar radio sources are a subject of controversy; some scientists suggest that they are nearby objects, while others feel that they are distant objects in natural motion.

Perhaps someday we will have enough observational data to fit satisfactorily a particular cosmological model. We might then be able to predict the past and future of our universe. Thus man's insatiable appetite for knowledge of the world in which he lives will have taken him to the very limits of space and time.

We have here presented theories of the universe based on natural law. It is an inherent trait of mankind to ponder the past and future of the world in which we live. But lest the reader be carried away by soaring speculations about the structure of the universe which are related to natural laws alone, it is well to be reminded of matters of more immediate importance—particularly man's own existence. There are the theoretical Biblical views of the younger writer and the more practical humanitarian views of the elder. But whatever view the reader chooses, the study of the concepts and effects of special relativity, general relativity, and cosmology provides a source of stimulating and provocative thought. It is hoped that the reader has enjoyed the contents of this book as much as the writer has enjoyed preparing it.

Selected Optional Topics

A.I RIGID-BODY MOTIONS IN SPECIAL RELATIVITY

The various points within a body, designated by a set of three parameters ξ^i ($i = 1, 2, 3$), follow a congruence of world-lines given by

$$x^0 = t$$
$$x^i = x^i(t, \xi^j).$$

If the body is a *solid* body, we require that $x^i(t, \xi^j)$ have the form

$$x^i = a^i_j(t)\xi^j + b^i(t) \tag{A-1}$$

where the a^i_j satisfy the condition

$$a^j_i a^k_i = \delta^{jk}. \tag{A-2}$$

The above condition allows the body to undergo translation and rotation, but no dilatation or shear. By a suitable translation and rotation of the spatial coordinates x^i, we may choose $a^i_j(0) = \delta^i_j$ and $b^i(0) = 0$. Differentiation of eq. (A-2) shows that $\dot{a}^j_i a^k_i$ is antisymmetric; therefore we may define $\omega^i(t)$ thus:

$$\dot{a}^j_i(t)a^k_i(t) = e(jkl)\omega^l(t). \tag{A-3}$$

Then

$$\dot{a}^j_i(0) = e(jil)\omega^l(0).$$

Under an infinitesimal Lorentz transformation given by $y^\mu = x^\mu + l^\mu_{.\nu}x^\nu$ with $l^{\mu\nu} + l^{\nu\mu} = 0$, the congruence is given by

$$
\left.
\begin{aligned}
y^0 &= x^0 + l_k a^k_i \xi^l + l_m b^m &\quad \text{a} \\
y^i &= a^i_j \xi^j + b^i + l^i_{.k} a^k_i \xi^l + l^i_{.k} b^k + c^2 l_i x^0 &\quad \text{b}
\end{aligned}
\right\} \tag{A-4}
$$

where $l_i = l_{0i}$. But the a's and b's appearing in eq. (A-4) are functions of x^0, not y^0. We wish to have coefficients which are functions of $u = y^0$, and we wish to have a new set of parameters η^i, in place of ξ^i, which become equal to y^i in the space $u = 0$:

$$y^0 = u$$
$$y^i = A^i_j(u)\eta^j + B^i(u).$$

The calculation is considerably simplified by the fact that $l^\mu_{.\nu}$ represents an *infinitesimal* transformation. Thus only terms of first order in the l's are retained. Equation (A-4a) becomes

$$t = u - l_k a^k_i(u)\xi^l - l_m b^m(u)$$

which is then substituted as the argument of the a^i_j and the b^i in the first two terms on the right-hand side of eq. (A-4b). Further, the expansion for ξ^i in terms of η^i which is obtained by setting $u = 0$ in eq. (A-4b) is also substituted into eq. (A-4b). The result is

$$y^i = A^i_j(u)\eta^j + B^i(u) + [a^i_l(u)e(ljm)\omega^m(0)l_k - \dot a^i_j(u)l_l a^l_k(u)]\eta^j\eta^k \quad \text{(A-5)}$$

where

$$A^i_j(u) = a^i_j(u) + a^i_k(u)\dot b^k(0)l_j - a^i_k(u)l^k_j$$
$$\quad - \dot a^i_j(u)l_k b^k(u) - \dot b^i(u)l_k a^k_j(u) + l^i_k a^k_j(u) \quad \text{(A-6)}$$
$$B^i(u) = b^i(u) - \dot b^i(u)l_k b^k(u) + l^i_k b^k(u) + c^2 l_i u.$$

In order that the congruence represent rigid-body motion in the y^μ coordinates, the last term in eq. (A-5) must vanish identically:

$$a^i_l(u)e(ljm)\omega^m(0)l_k + a^i_l(u)e(lkm)\omega^m(0)l_j$$
$$= \dot a^i_j(u)l_l a^l_k(u) + \dot a^i_k(u)l_l a^l_j(u). \quad \text{(A-7)}$$

Define

$$A_i(u) = l_k a^k_i(u).$$

Note that $l^\mu_{.\nu}$ and hence l_k is independent of u. But then, by eq. (A-2),

$$A_i A_i = l_k l_k. \quad \text{(A-8)}$$

Thus A_i is a vector with constant magnitude. Equation (A-7) is multiplied by l_i to give

$$A_i(u)\omega^m(0)[e(ljm)l_k + e(lkm)l_j] = \dot A_j(u)A_k(u) + \dot A_k(u)A_j(u). \quad \text{(A-9)}$$

But from eq. (A-8),

$$\dot A_i(u)A_i(u) = 0,$$

and from eq. (A-9),

$$\dot A_i(u)A_i(u) = e(klm)A_k(u)l_l\omega^m(0).$$

Therefore we have

$$e(klm)A_k(u)l_l\omega^m(0) = 0. \tag{A-10}$$

When eq. (A-9) is multiplied by $l_j l_k$, the result is

$$(A_k l_k)\frac{d}{du}(A_j l_j) = e(lmn)A_l(u)l_m\omega^n(0)(l_p l_p).$$

By eq. (A-10), the right-hand side of the above equation vanishes. Therefore, $A_k l_k$ is a constant. And at $u = 0$, $A_k l_k = l_l l_l$; hence, the latter relation holds for all u. But A_i has the same magnitude as l_i. Therefore,

$$A_i = l_i = a_i^k(u)l_k. \tag{A-11}$$

Multiplication of eq. (A-11) by $a_i^l(u)$ gives

$$l_i = a_j^i(u)l_j. \tag{A-12}$$

Equation (A-9) becomes

$$l_l\omega^m(0)[e(ljm)l_k + e(lkm)l_j] = 0.$$

Multiplication of the above equation by l_k gives

$$(l_k l_k)e(ljm)l_l\omega^m(0) = 0.$$

Hence, unless $l_k l_k = 0$, we have

$$\omega^i(0) = kl_i,$$

where k is a constant.

Equation (A-7) becomes

$$ka_l^i l_m[e(ljm)l_k + e(lkm)l_j] = \dot{a}_j^i l_k + \dot{a}_k^i l_j.$$

Multiply the above equation by l_k, noting from eq. (A-11) that $\dot{a}_i^k(u)l_k$ is zero. For $l_k l_k \neq 0$ we then have

$$\dot{a}_j^i(u) = ke(kjl)a_k^i(u)l_l. \tag{A-13}$$

Multiply eq. (A-13) by $a_j^m(u)$. By eq. (A-3), the left-hand side becomes $e(iml)\omega^l(u)$, and we have

$$e(iml)\omega^l(u) = ke(kjl)a_k^i(u)a_j^m(u)l_l. \tag{A-14}$$

But

$$e(ijk) = e(pqr)a_i^p a_j^q a_k^r. \tag{A-15}$$

On multiplication by $a_j^s a_k^t$, eq. (A-15) becomes

$$e(ijk)a_j^s a_k^t = e(pst)a_i^p.$$

Hence eq. (A-14) becomes

$$e(iml)\omega^l(u) = ke(nim)a_p^n l_p$$

which, by eq. (A-12), is

$$e(iml)\omega^l(u) = ke(iml)l_l.$$

Thus we have the result

$$\omega^i(u) = kl_i. \tag{A-16}$$

The angular velocity ω^i is a constant! The only solid-body motions are rotations with constant angular velocity about the fixed axis l_i.

The condition

$$A_i^j(u)A_i^k(u) = \delta^{jk}$$

is multiplied by $A_l^j(u)\breve{A}_k^m(u)$, where $\breve{A}_k^m$ is the inverse of A_m^k, to give

$$A_j^i(u)A_k^i(u) = \delta_{jk}. \tag{A-17}$$

Equation (A-17) with the substitution of eq. (A-6) leads to:

$$\dot{b}^i(0) = \dot{b}^k(u)a_i^k(u) + \frac{\dot{b}^k(u) - \dot{b}^k(0)}{l_m l_m} l_k l_i.$$

Multiplication by l_i shows that $\dot{b}^k(u)l_k$ is equal to $\dot{b}^k(0)l_k$. Hence

$$\dot{b}^i(0) = \dot{b}^k(u)a_i^k(u). \tag{A-18}$$

Upon translation to new coordinates $\bar{x}^i$ given by

$$\bar{x}^i = x^i + e(ijk)\omega^j\dot{b}^k(0)\omega^{-2}$$
$$\bar{\xi}^i = \xi^i + e(ijk)\omega^j\dot{b}^k(0)\omega^{-2},$$

the motion of eq. (A-1) is given by

$$\bar{x}^i = a_j^i(t)\bar{\xi}^j + \bar{b}^i(t)$$

where

$$\bar{b}^i(t) = b^i(t) + \frac{1}{\omega^2}e(ijk)\omega^j\dot{b}^k(0) - \frac{1}{\omega^2}a_j^i(t)e(jkl)\omega^k\dot{b}^l(0). \tag{A-19}$$

Equation (A-19) may be differentiated to give

$$\dot{\bar{b}}^i(t) = \dot{b}^i(t) - \frac{1}{\omega^2}\dot{a}_j^i(t)e(jkl)\omega^k\dot{b}^l(0).$$

Substitution of eq. (A-18) gives

$$\dot{\bar{b}}^i(t) = \dot{b}^i(t) - \frac{1}{\omega^2}\dot{a}_j^i(t)e(jkl)\omega^k a_l^m(t)\dot{b}^m(t). \tag{A-20}$$

Multiplication of eq. (A-15) by a_k^t gives

$$e(ijk)a_k^t = e(pqt)a_i^p a_j^q.$$

Thus eq. (A-20) becomes

$$\dot{\bar{b}}^i(t) = \dot{b}^i(t) - \frac{1}{\omega^2} \dot{a}^i_j(t)e(pqm)a^p_j(t)a^q_k(t)\omega^k \dot{b}^m(t). \qquad \text{(A-21)}$$

The second term on the right-hand side of eq. (A-21) becomes, with the help of eqs. (A-3), (A-11), and (A-16),

$$\frac{\omega^i\omega^k\dot{b}^k(t) - \omega^2\dot{b}^i(t)}{\omega^2}.$$

Thus $\dot{\bar{b}}^i(t)$ becomes

$$\dot{\bar{b}}^i(t) = \frac{\omega^i\omega^k\dot{b}^k(t)}{\omega^2}. \qquad \text{(A-22)}$$

Multiplication of eq. (A-18) by $a^j_i(u)$ gives

$$\dot{b}^j(t) = a^j_k(t)\dot{b}^k(0).$$

Substitution of this result into eq. (A-22) and the use of eqs. (A-16) and (A-11) gives

$$\dot{\bar{b}}^i(t) = \frac{\omega^i\omega^k\dot{b}^k(0)}{\omega^2}.$$

Integration gives immediately

$$\bar{b}^i(t) = \frac{\omega^i\omega^k\dot{b}^k(0)}{\omega^2}t. \qquad \text{(A-23)}$$

Equations (A-16) and (A-23) show that the only motion which is judged to be solid-body motion by *both* of two observers in uniform relative motion is that motion which consists of a uniform translation in the direction of relative velocity plus a constant angular velocity about the direction of relative velocity—that is, a screw motion along the direction of relative motion.

A.2 CLASSICAL ESTIMATES OF THE VELOCITY OF GRAVITY

Before the advent of either special or general relativity, it was natural to regard gravitation as a force field which is propagated with some velocity γ relative to the ether. Two different theories immediately present themselves. Either it is gravitational *force* or it is gravitational *potential* which is propagated with velocity γ.

Consider the first of the two possibilities. Suppose that the gravitational force on the earth due to the sun is falling upon the earth with a velocity γ. Then by the same calculation which, in the case of light, leads to aberration of starlight, there should be a component

$$\frac{GM_\odot}{r^2}\frac{v}{\gamma}$$

of the solar acceleration in the direction of the earth's motion, where r is the radius of the earth's orbit and v is the earth's orbital velocity. Since the earth's energy must then be increasing at the rate

$$\frac{d\mathcal{E}}{dt} = \frac{GM_\odot}{r^2}\frac{v^2}{\gamma},$$

we expect the radius of the earth's orbit to be increasing at the rate

$$\frac{dr}{dt} = 2\frac{v^2}{\gamma}. \tag{A-24}$$

(The method of perturbation of orbital elements is used in Section A.4.) The celestial longitude $l(t)$ of the earth may be expanded in a power series:

$$l(t) = n_0 t + A(n_0 t)^2 + \cdots \tag{A-25}$$

where n_0 is the present mean motion given by

$$n_0 = \left(\frac{v}{r}\right)_{\text{present}},$$

and t is the time measured from the present. The second-power term gives rise to an acceleration

$$\frac{d^2 l}{dt^2} = 2An_0^2 = \frac{dn}{dt}$$

where we have substituted $n = dl/dt$. However, the relation $n^2 r^3 = \text{const}$ and eq. (A-24) provide the result

$$\frac{dn}{dt} = -3n^2 \frac{v}{\gamma}.$$

Therefore the coefficient of the second-power term is

$$A = -\frac{3}{2}\frac{v}{\gamma}.$$

The observed motions of the moon and the planets require that A be extremely small. For example, in the case of the earth, the velocity is $10^{-4}c$. If γ were equal to c, then A would be -1.5×10^{-4}. In one century, the second-power term in eq. (A-25) would become -60 radians or $-1''2 \times 10^7$. But the largest admissible variation is $2''$. Therefore $\gamma > 6 \times 10^6 c$. The observations of the other planets and of the moon give results which are also of the same order of magnitude.

The above method was first used by Laplace. Other methods have been used since his time, but the assumption that gravitational *force* travels with a speed γ seems always to lead to a relation $\gamma > 10^6 c$.

Suppose now that it is the sun's gravitational potential which is propagated with a velocity γ. The situation is completely different because the gravitational field intensity is the *gradient* of the gravitational potential. Suppose the sun to be moving with a uniform velocity v relative to the gravitational ether. The equipotential of strength $-GM/r$ is centered a distance rv/γ behind the sun. The perturbed potential Φ' differs from the "instantaneous" potential Φ by an amount of order v/γ. Hence the perturbed force differs from the "instantaneous" force by an amount of order v/γ. Consequently, a planetary orbit will fail to close upon itself by a distance of order v/γ. But since the perturbing force is also of order v/γ, the work done on the planet is of order $(v/\gamma)^2$. For the solar motion of 20 km/sec, this ratio, for γ equal to c, is less than 10^{-8}. Such a small perturbation would completely escape detection.

The two methods thus give entirely different results. If gravitational *force* is propagated with a finite velocity, then that velocity must be at least as large as $10^6 c$. But if gravitational *potential* is propagated with a finite velocity, then the velocity can even be less than c. From the standpoint of general relativity, we see that it is the *potential* $g_{\mu\nu}$ which is propagated with a velocity which, in the weak-field approximation, is equal to the speed of light.

A.3 ZERO DIVERGENCE OF THE ELECTRO-MAGNETIC STRESS-ENERGY TENSOR

There frequently arise situations in which space-time contains electromagnetic radiation which has no interaction with any matter which may be present. In such a situation the divergence of the electromagnetic stress-energy tensor is zero throughout the region of consideration.

$$S^{\mu\nu}{}_{,\nu} = 0. \tag{A-26}$$

Two cases will be studied in this section.

The first case is that of isotropic radiation in a static metric

$$ds^2 = g_{00}(x^k)\, dt^2 + g_{ij}(x^l)\, dx^i\, dx^j. \tag{A-27}$$

The stress-energy tensor in locally Minkowski coordinates $\bar{x}^\alpha$ is given by eq. (4-35):

$$\bar{S}^{\alpha\beta} = \frac{\bar{U}}{3c^2} (4\delta_0^\alpha\delta_0^\beta - \eta^{\alpha\beta}).$$

Multiplication by the transformation matrices

$$\frac{\partial x^\mu}{\partial \bar{x}^\alpha} \frac{\partial x^\nu}{\partial \bar{x}^\beta}$$

then gives, in the coordinates of eq. (A-27),

$$S^{\mu\nu} = \frac{\bar{U}}{3c^2} (4\delta_0^\mu \delta_0^\nu g^{00} - g^{\mu\nu}). \tag{A-28}$$

The expansion of eq. (A-26) by the use of the metric of eq. (A-27) and the substitution of eq. (A-28) gives for $\mu = 0$ an identity and for $\mu \neq 0$ the equation

$$\frac{\partial \bar{U}}{\partial x^i} = -2\bar{U} \frac{\partial \ln g_{00}}{\partial x^i}.$$

Thus the proper energy density $\bar{U}$ is proportional to g_{00}^{-2}. The blackbody-radiation temperature T, given by $T^4 \propto \bar{U}$, is then proportional to $1/\sqrt{g_{00}}$. In the Newtonian approximation,

$$\frac{dT}{T} = -\frac{d\Phi}{c^2}$$

where Φ is the Newtonian gravitational potential. A vertical rod of length L in thermal equilibrium on the earth's surface has a relativistic temperature difference ΔT between its ends given by $\Delta T \simeq LgT/c^2$. Needless to say, ΔT is extremely small.

The other case for consideration in this section is that of galaxy emission in the cosmological metric. The electromagnetic stress-energy tensor for radiation traveling radially outward away from the origin is, in locally Minkowski coordinates, $\bar{S}^{\alpha\beta} = c^{-2}\bar{U}\bar{l}^\alpha\bar{l}^\beta$ where $\bar{l}^\alpha = (1, c, 0, 0)$. Transformation to the cosmological coordinates of eqs. (14-7) and (14-12) gives

$$\left.\begin{aligned} S^{\mu\nu} &= c^{-2}Ul^\mu l^\nu \\ l^\mu &= \left(1, \frac{1}{S}, 0, 0\right) \end{aligned}\right\} \tag{A-29}$$

where $U(t, w)$ is the local energy density—the bar has been dropped for convenience. The use of the cosmological metric and the substitution of eq. (A-29) into eq. (A-26) gives the following results. The components $\mu = 2$ and $\mu = 3$ of eq. (A-26) are identities. The components $\mu = 0$ and $\mu = 1$ are identical with each other:

$$S(t) \frac{\partial f(t, w)}{\partial t} + \frac{\partial f(t, w)}{\partial w} = 0 \tag{A-30}$$

where

$$f(t, w) = S^4(t)\sigma^2(w)U(t, w).$$

With the introduction of a new variable

$$F(t) = \int^t \frac{dt}{S(t)}$$

to replace t, eq. (A-30) becomes

$$\frac{\partial f}{\partial F} + \frac{\partial f}{\partial w} = 0$$

which has the general solution $f(F - w)$. Note that along a null line we have $d(F - w) = 0$. Hence f is constant along a null line.

Let the subscript 1 refer to the source, which is at the origin, and the subscript 0 to the observation at an event (t_0, w_0, θ, ϕ). In the neighborhood of the source, the energy density is

$$U_1 = \frac{f(F_0 - w_0)}{S_1^4 w_1^2}.$$

But the luminosity is

$$L_1 = 4\pi c^3 S_1^2 w_1^2 U_1.$$

Hence we find

$$f(F_0 - w_0) = \frac{L_1 S_1^2}{4\pi c^3}.$$

At the event of observation, the energy density is

$$U_0 = \frac{f(F_0 - w_0)}{S_0^4 \sigma^2(w_0)} = \frac{L_1 S_1^2}{4\pi c^3 S_0^4 \sigma^2(w_0)}. \tag{A-31}$$

Multiplication of eq. (A-31) by c and the use of eq. (15-3) gives eq. (15-9).

A.4 ORBIT PERTURBATIONS

The elliptical orbit of a satellite revolving around a center O (see Figure A.1) is specified by five quantities:

Ω = the angle from the reference direction in the reference plane to the ascending node.

i = the angle of inclination between the orbit plane and the reference plane.

ω = the angle from the ascending node in the orbit plane to the perihelion P.

e = eccentricity of orbit.

a = semi-major axis of orbit.

Suppose that an impulse (per unit mass) is imparted to the satellite at some point Q in its orbit. The impulse can be resolved into three orthogonal components R, S, and W. (See Figure A.2.) R is directed radially away

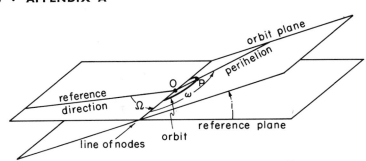

FIGURE A.I   Elements of Keplerian orbit.

from O, S is directed in the orbit plane perpendicular to the line OQ, and W is directed perpendicular to the orbit plane. The impulse will cause an instantaneous change in the orbital elements Ω, i, ω, e, and a. For example, for a *small* impulse, the change in Ω is

$$\Delta\Omega = \frac{Wr}{h}\frac{\sin u}{\sin i}$$

where $u = \omega + \theta$, θ is the angle POQ, r is the distance OP, and

$$h = r^2 \frac{d\theta}{dt}.$$

If we replace the impulse by a continual force (per unit mass) having components R, S, W, then the *rates of change* of the orbital elements are

$$\left.\begin{aligned}
\frac{d\Omega}{dt} &= \frac{Wr}{h}\frac{\sin u}{\sin i} \\[2mm]
\frac{di}{dt} &= \frac{Wr}{h}\cos u \\[2mm]
\frac{d\omega}{dt} &= -\frac{pR}{he}\cos\theta + \frac{S(p+r)}{he}\sin\theta - \frac{Wr}{h}\cot i \sin u \\[2mm]
\frac{de}{dt} &= \frac{1-e^2}{h}\left[aR\sin\theta + \frac{S}{e}\left(\frac{ap}{r} - r\right)\right] \\[2mm]
\frac{da}{dt} &= \frac{2a^2}{h}\left[S\frac{p}{r} + Re\sin\theta\right],
\end{aligned}\right\} \quad \text{(A-32)}$$

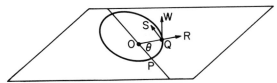

FIGURE A.2   Resolution of perturbing impulse into orthogonal components.

where $p = a(1 - e^2)$. The above equations give the rate of change of the orbital elements of a satellite moving under an inverse-square force due to the application of a small perturbing force R, S, W. These results will be applied to three cases.

In the vector and tensor theories of gravity in Sections 6.6 and 6.7, there was a term which involved the permutation symbol. We propose to examine the effect of such a term by regarding it as a perturbation on a Keplerian orbit.

For the vector theory, the perturbing acceleration $\zeta e(\mu\nu\rho\sigma)u_\sigma F_{\nu\rho}$ in eq. (6-41) is, for the potential of eq. (6-38), equal to

$$\frac{EGM}{r^3} \cdot \delta_i^\mu e(ijk)x^j u^k.$$

This represents a spatial vector of magnitude $EGMh/r^3$ perpendicular to the orbit plane. Thus $R = S = 0$ and $W = EGMh/r^3c^2$, and eqs. (A-32) show that e and a are unaffected. The other three orbital elements change at the rates

$$\frac{d\Omega}{dt} = \frac{EGM}{c^2 h} \frac{\sin u}{\sin i} \frac{d\theta}{dt}$$

$$\frac{di}{dt} = \frac{EGM}{c^2 h} \cos u \frac{d\theta}{dt}$$

$$\frac{d\omega}{dt} = -\frac{EGM}{c^2 h} \cot i \sin u \frac{d\theta}{dt}.$$

All three of the above equations are immediately seen to have integrals which are periodic in u. Hence there are no *secular* variations, i.e., perturbations which accumulate over more than one period.

There is, however, another perturbation not included among the five orbital elements. It is the displacement l of the orbit plane from the center of force. For a circular orbit, the perturbing force $EGMh/r^3c^2$ is balanced by the component GMl/r^3 of the central force. Hence $l = hE/c^2$; l is proportional to the angular momentum (per unit mass) h of the satellite. But such a displacement is not observed in the solar system to the accuracy of the measurements.

In the tensor theory, the perturbing force is

$$-\frac{2EGM}{c^2 r^3} e(ijk)x^j u^k$$

and hence the same results apply as in the vector theory.

The second application of eqs. (A-32) is to an artificial satellite around the rotating earth. The contribution to the acceleration of the satellite due to the earth's rotation was found in Section 11.7 to be

$$f^i = \frac{2IG}{c^2 r^5} e(ijk)v^k(3\Omega^l x^l x^j - \Omega^j r^2)$$

where $r^2 = x^i x^i$, v^i is the velocity of the satellite, I is the earth's moment of inertia, and Ω^i is the angular velocity of the earth. The resolution of f^i into the components R, S, W gives

$$R = \frac{\alpha h \cos i}{r^4}$$

$$S = -\frac{\alpha h e \cos i \sin \theta}{pr^3}$$

$$W = \frac{\alpha h}{r^3} \sin i \left(2 \frac{\sin u}{r} + \frac{e}{p} \sin \theta \cos u \right)$$

where $\alpha = 2IG\Omega c^{-2}$, and use has been made of the relations

$$\frac{d\theta}{dt} = \frac{h}{r^2}, \qquad \frac{dr}{dt} = \frac{he}{p} \sin \theta.$$

When the above expressions for R, S, and W are substituted into eqs. (A-32) and those terms which have periodic integrals are discarded, the results are

$$\frac{d\Omega}{d\theta} = \frac{2\alpha}{ph} \sin^2 u$$

$$\frac{d\omega}{d\theta} = -\frac{2\alpha}{ph} \cos i(1 + \sin^2 u)$$

$$\frac{di}{d\theta} = \frac{de}{d\theta} = \frac{da}{d\theta} = 0.$$

Thus the only secular changes in the orbit are

$$\frac{d\Omega}{d\theta} = \frac{\alpha}{ph}$$

$$\frac{d\omega}{d\theta} = -\frac{3\alpha \cos i}{ph}.$$

The orbit retains its shape and size and maintains a constant angle of inclination. However, the line of nodes advances with angular velocity

$$\frac{\alpha}{a^3(1 - e^2)^{\frac{3}{2}}}$$

and the line of apsides regresses relative to the nodes with angular velocity

$$\frac{3\alpha}{a^3(1 - e^2)^{\frac{3}{2}}} \cos i.$$

For a small inclination i, i.e., for an equatorial orbit, the advance of perigee is

$$\sigma = \frac{d\Omega}{d\theta} + \frac{d\omega}{d\theta} = -\frac{2\alpha}{ph}$$

as was previously found in Section 11.7.

A third case is the classical estimate of the velocity of gravity. In Section A.2, it was suggested that, in the classical view of gravity, the gravitational force of the sun on the earth is directed along a line which makes an angle v/γ with the direction to the sun, where γ is the velocity of gravity. If the planetary orbit is not circular, then the planetary velocity v must be replaced by h/r. The tangential perturbing force is therefore

$$S = \frac{h}{r\gamma} \cdot \frac{GM}{r^2} = \frac{\beta h^2}{r^3}$$

where $\beta = GM/\gamma h$. The normal component W is zero. It remains to determine the radial component R. If we follow Laplace's original method of regarding the sun as moving relative to the earth, the "retarded" force due to the sun is $GM/(r - \dot{r}\,\Delta t)^2$, where Δt is the time r/γ required for gravity to transverse the distance between sun and earth. Then

$$R = -2\frac{GM}{r^2} \cdot \frac{\dot{r}}{\gamma} = -2\frac{\beta h \dot{r}}{r^2}.$$

(We of the twentieth century might prefer the opposite sign for R, from the analogy with the Doppler effect of photons.)

The effect on the orbit due to the perturbation can be calculated either from the equation of motion or from eqs. (A-32). By the latter method, neither Ω nor i is affected. The *secular* perturbations in ω, e, and a are given by

$$\frac{d\omega}{d\theta} = 0$$

$$\frac{de}{d\theta} = \frac{\beta e}{2}$$

$$\frac{da}{d\theta} = \frac{2a\beta}{1 - e^2}(1 - \tfrac{1}{2}e^2).$$

Direct calculation of $dp/d\theta$ gives

$$\frac{dp}{d\theta} = 2p\beta.$$

The substitution $\beta = \gamma^{-1}\sqrt{GM/p}$ and integration gives

$$\frac{p}{p_0} = (1 + \phi)^2$$

$$\frac{e}{e_0} = \sqrt{1 + \phi}$$

where

$$\phi = \sqrt{\frac{GM}{p_0}} \cdot \frac{\theta}{\gamma}$$

where p_0 and e_0 are the values of p and e, respectively, at $\theta = 0$.

The most easily observed effect of the perturbation is the change in period due to the change in a. Neither the eccentricity nor the actual radius a can be measured as accurately as the period.

A.5 GÖDEL'S MODEL

In Section 13.10 the line element for the Gödel model was presented and discussed from the standpoint of its automorphisms. In this section we will discuss the suitability of Gödel's model for describing the universe. When Gödel suggested his model as a possible description of the universe, he noted the homogeneity of the model. (Another property, perhaps the most interesting of all, is that the world-lines of the matter in the model are in absolute rotation with angular velocity $\sqrt{4\pi G\rho}$ relative to a local inertial frame.) However, Gödel's definition of homogeneity is the existence of a mapping of any event into any other event. *We* will define *spatial homogeneity* by requiring that space-time possess a family of space-like, non-intersecting hypersurfaces, each of which admits at least a three-parameter group of transitive automorphisms. Note that we are *not* assuming spatial isotropy. It will now be proved that our definition of homogeneity implies the existence of a congruence of world-lines which do *not* possess absolute rotation.

By our assumption of homogeneity, space-time possesses a family of non-intersecting space-like hypersurfaces. Construct the congruence of world-lines which intersects each hypersurface normally. Choose coordinates x^μ such that $x^0 = $ const gives each hypersurface and $x^i = $ const gives each world-line. Since any spatial vector δx^μ ($\delta x^0 = 0$) is orthogonal to the adjacent world-line tangent $du^\mu = du^0 \delta^\mu_0$, we have the condition

$$0 = g_{0k} \, du^0 \, \delta x^k$$

for *arbitrary* δx^k. Thus, in the chosen coordinates, the time-space term in the line element vanishes:

$$g_{0i} = 0.$$

The condition that the four-dimensional space-time admit a spatial Killing vector ξ^μ is stated by the equations

$$0 = g_{\mu\lambda} \frac{\partial \xi^\lambda}{\partial x^\nu} + g_{\nu\lambda} \frac{\partial \xi^\lambda}{\partial x^\mu} + \xi^\lambda \frac{\partial g_{\mu\nu}}{\partial x^\lambda}$$

$$0 = \xi^0,$$

which become

$$0 = \xi^k \frac{\partial g_{00}}{\partial x^k}$$

$$0 = g_{ik} \frac{\partial \xi^k}{\partial x^0}$$

$$0 = g_{ik} \frac{\partial \xi^k}{\partial x^j} + g_{jk} \frac{\partial \xi^k}{\partial x^i} + \xi^k \frac{\partial g_{ij}}{\partial x^k}.$$

The last equation merely states that ξ^i is a three-dimensional Killing vector. But note that the other two equations require that g_{00} be independent of x^i and that ξ^k is independent of x^0. Since g_{00} now depends only on x^0, we can, by a suitable redefinition of x^0, choose $g_{00} = 1$. But then, with both g_{00} and g_{0i} constant, we have $[00, \mu] = 0$ and hence $\begin{Bmatrix} \mu \\ 00 \end{Bmatrix} = 0$. But then the geodesic condition for the world-lines $x^i = \text{const}$ is satisfied. Hence the world-lines are geodesics. Further, the coordinates are the kind used in Section 11.1; hence we can apply eq. (11-15) to find the rotation of the geodesics. But since g_{0i} vanishes, the rotation is zero. Therefore, *if space-time is homogeneous by our definition, then there exists an irrotational congruence of time-like geodesics.*

We have proved that our definition of homogeneity (as contrasted with Gödel's) requires that space-time admit an irrotational congruence of time-like geodesics. On the other hand, it was proved in Section 13.10 that the only geodesics in Gödel's model which the general-relativity field equation allows matter to follow are those given by $x^i = \text{const}$. Therefore Gödel's model, with matter following the geodesics prescribed by general relativity, is not spatially homogeneous by our definition.

The validity of Section 11.3 is now called into question. It was stated there that it is always possible to find an irrotational congruence of geodesics. Gödel's model at first sight seems to be a counter example.

However, it was not required that *matter* follow the irrotational congruence in Section 11.3.

Gödel's model possesses irrotational congruences of geodesics in limited regions of space-time. They are obtained as follows. The time-like geodesics in Gödel's model are given by

$$
\left.
\begin{aligned}
t &= \frac{\sqrt{2}}{d} \left[\frac{bd}{\sqrt{2}} (s_0 - s) - 2\phi d \right] + t_0 \\[2mm]
x &= -\frac{2b}{c} \ln \left(1 - \frac{2fw}{1 + w^2} \right) \\[2mm]
y &= \frac{2\sqrt{2}\, bf}{c} \frac{1 - w^2}{1 + w^2} + y_0 \\[2mm]
z &= as + z_0
\end{aligned}
\right\}
\qquad \text{(A-33)}
$$

where

$$
w = f + d \cdot \tan \left[\frac{bd}{\sqrt{2}} (s_0 - s) \right] = \tan \phi
$$

$$
d^2 + f^2 = 1
$$

$$
2b^2 f^2 + a^2 + b^2 = 1
$$

and a, b, c, t_0, y_0, z_0, and s_0 (and hence d and f) are the constants of integration. (Do not confuse the a and c here with those used in Section 13.10; the latter have been taken as unity here.) We may choose the hypersurface

$$
t = \tau - e^{\xi}(y - \eta)
$$

which, in the neighborhood of the event $x^\mu = (\tau, \xi, \eta, \zeta)$, is space-like with unit normal

$$
u^\mu = \left[\frac{2\sigma - 1}{\nu}, 0, \frac{2e^{-x}}{\nu} (1 - \sigma), 0 \right]
$$

where

$$
\sigma = e^{\xi - x}
$$

$$
\nu^2 = 1 - 2(1 - \sigma)^2.
$$

If we identify u^μ with the world-velocity of the geodesics of eqs. (A-33), then it is a straightforward, though tedious, procedure to obtain a, b, c, d, f, t_0, y_0, z_0, and s_0 (with s_0 chosen so that s is zero on the hypersurface) as functions of the spatial intersection (x', y', z') of each geodesic with the hypersurface. Thus the new coordinates defined

$$
\begin{aligned}
\bar{t} &= s \\
\bar{x} &= x' \\
\bar{y} &= y' \\
\bar{z} &= z'
\end{aligned}
$$

and given by equations (A-33) with a, b, c, d, f, t_0, y_0, z_0, and s_0 expressed as functions of x', y', and z' are Gaussian coordinates as described in Section 11.3.

One might object that the Gaussian coordinates constructed above exist only in a limited region of space-time in the Gödel model, because $|1 - \sigma|$ must be less than $1/\sqrt{2}$. But it was *not* claimed in Section 11.3 that *one* set of Gaussian coordinates could be found for *all* of space-time. Indeed, the writer suspects that it is impossible to find any family of hypersurfaces which are everywhere space-like in the Gödel model.

A.6 FIVE-DIMENSIONAL COSMOLOGY

It is possible to embed the cosmological space-time of eq. (14-7) in a Minkowski space of five dimensions. For the two cases of non-zero spatial curvature $k = \pm 1$, we define new variables z_0, z_1, z_2, z_3, and z_4 thus:

$$z_0 = \int^t \sqrt{1 + k\dot{S}^2(t)}\, dt \tag{A-34}$$

$$z_i = \frac{S(t)x^i}{1 + \dfrac{kr^2}{4}} \qquad i = 1, 2, 3$$

$$z_4 = S(t)\, \frac{1 - \dfrac{kr^2}{4}}{1 + \dfrac{kr^2}{4}}$$

where $r^2 = x^i x^i$, and x^i is the spatial coordinate which appears in the canonical form of eq. (14-11). The z's are related by the identity

$$z_4^2 + k z_i z_i = S^2(t) \tag{A-35}$$

and the metric becomes

$$ds^2 = dz_0^2 - (dz_1^2 + dz_2^2 + dz_3^2) - k\, dz_4^2. \tag{A-36}$$

The case $k = +1$ can be easily studied by suppressing two of the dimensions. With $z_2 = z_3 = 0$ and $z_1 = z$, eq. (A-35) represents a surface of revolution about the z_0-axis since, by eq. (A-34), t is a function of z_0. Furthermore, the angle ψ about the z_0-axis is seen by the substitutions $z_4 = S \cos \psi$, $z = S \sin \psi$ and comparison of eq. (A-36) with eq. (14-7), to be the coordinate u of eq. (14-7). Thus the fundamental world-lines are the intersections of the surface with planes through the z_0-axis.

The case $k = 0$ is much more difficult to put into five-dimensional form. It can be easily verified that the definitions

$$
\left.\begin{aligned}
z_0 &= \frac{S}{2a}(a^2 + r^2) + f(t) \\[2mm]
z_4 &= \frac{S}{2a}(a^2 - r^2) - f(t) \\[2mm]
z_i &= Sx^i \qquad i = 1, 2, 3
\end{aligned}\right\}
\tag{A-37}
$$

where the x^i are the canonical spatial coordinates, a is an arbitrary constant, and $f(t)$ is defined

$$
f(t) = \frac{1}{2a}\int^t \frac{dt}{\dot{S}(t)}
$$

produce the line element

$$
ds^2 = dz_0^2 - dz_i\, dz_i - dz_4^2
$$

and the identities

$$
z_0 + z_4 = aS(t)
\tag{A-38}
$$

$$
z_0^2 - z_i z_i - z_4^2 = 2aS(t)f(t).
\tag{A-39}
$$

The right-hand side of eq. (A-39) is a function of $z_0 + z_4$ by virtue of eq. (A-38). Thus eq. (A-39) represents a hypersurface in the five-dimensional space. However, only a part of the hypersurface represents the cosmological model, since, by eq. (A-38), $z_0 + z_4$ cannot change sign.

It is impossible to obtain the static Minkowski model from the above representation, because $f(t)$ diverges. However, the static Minkowski model can be obtained from the expanding Minkowski model in which $k = -1$. The z_0, $z_i z_i$, and z_4 here then become, respectively, the zero, ρ^2/c^2, and τ in Section 16.1.

The deSitter universe is given by $S = c^{-1}e^{t/b}$. The identification $r = w$ and the definition $a = bc$ then transforms eqs. (A-37) into eqs. (16-7).

A.7 THE λ-μ DIAGRAM

A convenient diagram for use in studying the zero-pressure cosmological models is constructed with the use of the definitions

$$
\lambda = \frac{\Lambda}{\kappa\rho_0}
$$

$$
\mu = \frac{3k}{\kappa\rho_0 S_0^2}.
$$

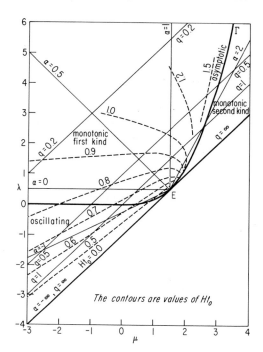

FIGURE A.3 The λ-μ diagram for cosmological models. The dashed contours are values of Ht_0.

From eqs. (17-10), (17-11), and (17-14) we immediately obtain the relations

$$\frac{1}{q} = 1 + \lambda - \mu \tag{A-40}$$

$$\frac{\alpha}{q} = -\tfrac{1}{2} + \lambda. \tag{A-41}$$

From eq. (A-40), the curves of constant q on the λ-μ diagram (see Figure A.3) are straight lines with slope $d\lambda/d\mu = +1$ and λ-intercept $(1/q) - 1$. Since q is non-negative, only the part of the diagram above the line $q = \infty$ is real. From eq. (A-41), the curves of constant α are straight lines which pass through the point $E(\lambda = \tfrac{1}{2},\ \mu = \tfrac{3}{2})$ and have slope $(1 - \alpha^{-1})^{-1}$. The ratios S_0/S_E and Λ/Λ_E from eqs. (17-12) are, respectively, given by

$$\frac{S_0}{S_E} = \tfrac{2}{3}|\mu|$$

$$\frac{\Lambda}{\Lambda_E} = \frac{27}{4}\frac{\lambda}{|\mu|^3}.$$

Thus the Einstein universe is represented by the point E. The asymptotic models $\Lambda = \Lambda_E$ fall on the curve Γ given by

$$\lambda = \tfrac{4}{27}\mu^3.$$

The curve Γ also arises from the requirement that the age integral of eq. (17-13) exist. The models which expand from the singular state $S = 0$ lie to the left of Γ. The regions for the various types can be identified from the descriptions given in Section 17.2. The oscillating models fall between the line $q = \infty$ and the curve which is formed from the line $\lambda = 0$, $\mu < 0$ and the cubic curve Γ from $\mu = 0$ to $\mu = \frac{3}{2}$. The monotonic models of the first kind fall above the oscillating models and to the left of Γ for $\lambda > \frac{1}{2}$. The monotonic models of the second kind fall between Γ and $q = \infty$ to the upper right of E. The asymptotic models which expand from $S = 0$ lie on Γ between $\mu = 0$ and $\mu = \frac{3}{2}$. The asymptotic models which expand from E lie on Γ above E.

The point λ, μ representing a model depends on the epoch t_0 of observation. It is easy to verify from the definitions of λ and μ and from eq. (17-8) that λ and μ are given by

$$\lambda = \frac{\Lambda S^3}{\kappa \rho S^3}$$

$$\mu = \frac{3kS}{\kappa \rho S^3}$$

where the denominator is constant. Therefore the point λ, μ moves along the cubic curve $\lambda/\mu^3 = \text{const}$ in such a way that μ is proportional to S.

The curves of constant τ can be filled in by numerical integration* of eq. (17-13) which, with the present notation, becomes

$$\sqrt{q}\,\tau = \int_0^1 \frac{\sqrt{x}\,dx}{\sqrt{1 + \lambda x^3 - \mu x}}\,.$$

The λ-μ diagram has three observable quantities depicted on it: q, α, and τ. The curves of constant τ are asymptotic to straight lines; for large μ and λ, the 1 in the denominator of the above integral can be neglected leaving, for $\lambda < 0$, $\mu < 0$, a simple integral:

$$\tau = \sqrt{\frac{\mu - \lambda}{\lambda}}\,\sin^{-1}\sqrt{\frac{\lambda}{\mu}}\,.$$

For $\lambda/\mu = \frac{1}{2}$, this expression gives $\tau = 0.785$. Thus for the acceleration parameter $\alpha = -1$, τ asymptotically approaches 0.785 at large negative λ and μ.

It was stated in Section 18.7 that eqs. (18-4) through (18-7) are not consistent with any zero-pressure, general-relativistic model. This is proved as follows. From eqs. (18-4) and (18-6), the condition on τ is $\tau \geq 0.82$.

---

* See Stabell[B] and Refsdal. Their σ_0 and q_0 are, respectively, our $\frac{1}{2}q$ and $-\alpha$.

From eqs. (18-5), q lies between 0.027 and 1. It is apparent from Figure A.3 that τ increases along the line $\alpha = -1$ as one goes toward smaller values of q; τ is 0.627 at $q = 1$ and approaches 0.785 at $q = 0$. Therefore, strictly speaking, the values $\tau \geq 0.82$ and $\alpha = -1$ are inconsistent with each other. However, as was pointed out in Section 18.7, the observations thus far lack precision for determining exact values of the cosmological parameters.

A.8 COSMOLOGICAL DENSITY AND PRESSURE

The cosmological density ρ and pressure p may be written

$$\rho = \rho'' + \frac{1}{c^2} [U_k + U_g + U_e + U_m + U_r] \tag{A-42}$$

$$p = p'' + \tfrac{2}{3}U_k + \tfrac{1}{3}[U_g^- + U_e + U_m + U_r] \tag{A-43}$$

where ρ'' and p'' are the mass density and pressure which are *intrinsic* to the molecules of the cosmological fluid, and the U's are the average densities of energy in the following forms:

$U_k =$ kinetic energy of the molecules.
$U_g =$ gravitational interactions of molecules.
$U_e =$ electrostatic interactions of molecules.
$U_m =$ magnetic interactions of molecules.
$U_r =$ electromagnetic radiation.

It is assumed that the intragalactic and intergalactic gravitational fields are weak enough for the Newtonian concept of gravitational field energy to hold. Further explanation of eqs. (A-42) and (A-43) will follow their proof.

Equations (14-7) and (17-1) represent, respectively, the cosmological metric tensor $g_{\mu\nu}$ and the stress-energy tensor of the cosmological fluid; in what follows, the latter will be written $\mathfrak{C}_{\mu\nu} - \tfrac{1}{2}g_{\mu\nu}g'^{\alpha\beta}\mathfrak{C}_{\alpha\beta}$. The Ricci tensor $R_{\mu\nu}$ calculated from $g_{\mu\nu}$ is related to $\mathfrak{C}_{\mu\nu}$ by the field equation

$$R_{\mu\nu} = -\kappa\mathfrak{C}_{\mu\nu} + \Lambda g_{\mu\nu}. \tag{A-44}$$

But the cosmological fluid is only a first approximation. The actual metric tensor $g'_{\mu\nu}$ is related to the actual stress-energy tensor field $\mathfrak{C}'_{\mu\nu} - \tfrac{1}{2}g'_{\mu\nu}g'^{\alpha\beta}\mathfrak{C}'_{\alpha\beta}$ through its Ricci tensor $R'_{\mu\nu}$ and the field equation

$$R'_{\mu\nu} = -\kappa\mathfrak{C}'_{\mu\nu} + \Lambda g'_{\mu\nu}. \tag{A-45}$$

It will be assumed that the matter that is present is in the form of a perfect fluid with proper density ρ', proper pressure p', and world-velocity u'^{μ}. The tensors $\mathfrak{C}'_{\mu\nu}$ and $\mathfrak{C}_{\mu\nu}$ are then

$$\mathfrak{C}'_{\mu\nu} = \left(\rho' + \frac{p'}{c^2}\right)u'_{\mu}u'_{\nu} - \frac{1}{2}\left(\rho' - \frac{p'}{c^2}\right)g'_{\mu\nu} \tag{A-46}$$

$$\mathfrak{C}_{\mu\nu} = \left(\rho + \frac{p}{c^2}\right)\delta^0_{\mu}\delta^0_{\nu} - \frac{1}{2}\left(\rho - \frac{p}{c^2}\right)g_{\mu\nu}. \tag{A-47}$$

We will be concerned with the differences between primed and unprimed quantities:

$$h_{\mu\nu} = g'_{\mu\nu} - g_{\mu\nu}$$
$$\delta R_{\mu\nu} = R'_{\mu\nu} - R_{\mu\nu}$$
$$\delta\mathfrak{C}_{\mu\nu} = \mathfrak{C}'_{\mu\nu} - \mathfrak{C}_{\mu\nu}$$
$$\delta\rho = \rho' - \rho$$
$$\delta p = p' - p$$
$$\delta u_{\mu} = u'_{\mu} - \delta^0_{\mu}.$$

Equations (A-44) and (A-45) then give

$$\delta R_{\mu\nu} = -\kappa\,\delta\mathfrak{C}_{\mu\nu} + \Lambda h_{\mu\nu} \tag{A-48}$$

and eqs. (A-46) and (A-47) provide an expression for $\delta\mathfrak{C}_{\mu\nu}$ in terms of $\rho, p, \delta\rho, \delta p$, and δu_{μ}. The necessary calculations are straightforward, and only the major steps will be explained.

The first task is to obtain a first-order theory and to deduce the orders of magnitude of various quantities. We shall apply the foregoing theory to the cosmological medium which is composed of galaxies having average separations the order of a length $\lambda \simeq 1$ Mpc. In the calculation of $\delta R_{\mu\nu}$, Irvine[B] has shown that the Riemann-curvature terms are of order $\dfrac{\lambda^2 H^2}{c^2}$ and $\dfrac{\lambda^2 k}{S^2 c^2}$ relative to the leading term $h_{\mu\nu,\alpha}{}^{\alpha}$. Hence, neglecting them, eq. (A-48) becomes

$$h_{\mu\nu,\alpha}{}^{\alpha} = -2\kappa\,\delta\mathfrak{C}_{\mu\nu}.$$

(The covariant differentiations and the raising of the index α are done by means of $g_{\mu\nu}$.) The first-order solution is therefore

$$\Box^2 h_{00} = -\kappa\,\delta\rho \tag{A-49}$$
$$\Box^2 h_{0i} = -2\kappa\rho'\,\delta u_i$$
$$\Box^2 h_{ij} = \kappa g_{ij}\,\delta\rho.$$

Thus, in the first-order approximation, the following relations hold:

$$h_{ij} = -g_{ij}h_{00}$$

$$h_{00} = O\left(\frac{\lambda^2 \kappa \rho}{c^2}\right) \simeq 10^{-7}$$

$$h_{0i} = O\left(\frac{\lambda^2 \kappa \rho v}{c^3}\right) \simeq 10^{-10}.$$

The velocities which are used in the order-of-magnitude estimates are the random velocities of galaxies—of order 200 km/sec.

The orders of magnitude are therefore as follows:

$$h_{00} = O^1$$
$$h_{0i} = O^{\frac{3}{2}}$$
$$h_{ij} = O^1$$
$$\frac{\partial}{\partial x^i} \simeq \frac{1}{\lambda}$$
$$\frac{\partial}{\partial t} \simeq O^{\frac{1}{2}} \cdot \frac{1}{\lambda}.$$

The expansion of $\delta R_{\mu\nu}$ in terms of $h_{\mu\nu}$ and $g_{\mu\nu}$ contains terms of first order, second order, etc., in the $h_{\mu\nu}$. The second-order terms are found, with the use of the above orders of magnitude, to be given by

$$\left. \begin{aligned} c^{-2}\,\delta R_{00} &= \tfrac{1}{4}\nabla^2 h^2 - h\nabla^2 h + O^3 \\ c^{-2}\,\delta R_{ij} &= \tfrac{1}{4}g_{ij}\nabla^2 h^2 - \tfrac{1}{4}(h^2)_{,ij} - \tfrac{1}{2}hh_{,ij} + O^3 \end{aligned} \right\} \tag{A-50}$$

where h denotes h_{00}. The derivatives may, in view of the approximations, be regarded as ordinary derivatives; and δR_{0i} will not be needed.

The next step is to perform an averaging. The averaging is spatial and is taken over regions which are large compared with λ but small compared with cosmological lengths, e.g., $c\,|\Lambda|^{-\frac{1}{2}}$, cS, cH^{-1}, $c(\kappa\rho)^{-\frac{1}{2}}$. No further properties of the averaging will be needed until later.

The assumption of cosmological isotropy requires that the average $\bar{T}_{ij}$ of any spatial tensor T_{ij} be a multiple of g_{ij}. Otherwise the tensor $T_{ij}g^{jk}$ would have non-degenerate eigenvectors. (The g_{ij} commutes with the averaging to sufficient accuracy for our purposes.) Isotropy also requires that the average of any spatial vector be zero.

The average $\bar{h}_{\mu\nu}$ of the $h_{\mu\nu}$ can be *chosen* as zero for the following reasons. First, both the $\bar{g}'_{0i}$ and the g_{0i} are clearly zero. Second, the average $\bar{g}'_{ij}$ of the g'_{ij} is a multiple of g_{ij}. The factor of proportionality can at most depend on t. Thus the proportionality factor can be absorbed into the expansion parameter $S(t)$ by *defining* g_{ij} to be equal to $\bar{g}'_{ij}$. Finally

$\bar{g}'_{00}$ may in general be different from unity; however, it can at most depend only on t. Therefore we can *choose* $\bar{g}'_{00} = 1$ by a suitable redefinition of the time coordinate.

The averages of eqs. (A-50) are

$$c^{-2}\overline{\delta R_{00}} = \tfrac{1}{4}\overline{\nabla^2 h^2} - \overline{h\nabla^2 h} \\ c^{-2}\overline{\delta R_{ij}} = g_{ij}[\tfrac{1}{3}\overline{\nabla^2 h^2} + \tfrac{1}{6}\overline{h\nabla^2 h}]$$

(A-51)

and the averages $\overline{\delta\mathscr{C}_{00}}$ and $\overline{\delta\mathscr{C}_{ij}}$ are

$$\overline{\delta\mathscr{C}_{00}} = \tfrac{1}{2}\overline{\delta\rho} + \frac{3}{2}\frac{\overline{\delta p}}{c^2} + \frac{\overline{\rho' v^2}}{c^2} + \tfrac{1}{2}\overline{\rho' h} \\ \overline{\delta\mathscr{C}_{ij}} = -g_{ij}\left[\tfrac{1}{2}\overline{\delta\rho} - \frac{1}{2}\frac{\overline{\delta p}}{c^2} + \frac{1}{3}\frac{\overline{\rho' v^2}}{c^2} - \tfrac{1}{2}\overline{\rho' h}\right]$$

(A-52)

where $v^2 = -c^2 g^{kl}\,\delta u_k\,\delta u_l$. Equation (A-48) becomes

$$\overline{\delta R_{\mu\nu}} = -\kappa\,\overline{\delta\mathscr{C}_{\mu\nu}}.$$

(A-53)

It is now necessary to specify the kind of averaging. We define the average $\bar{\rho}'$ of ρ' to be

$$\bar{\rho}' = \frac{\int \rho'\,dV}{\int dV}$$

(A-54)

where dV is equal to $\sqrt{-|g_{lm}|}\,e(ijk)\,d^1x^i\,d^2x^j\,d^3x^k$. Thus for the cosmological metric $g_{\mu\nu}$ and the cosmological world-velocity $u^\mu = \delta_0^\mu$, dV is proper volume. But ρ' is the proper density as referred to the metric $g'_{\mu\nu}$ and the world-velocity u'^μ. Therefore $\rho'\,dV$ is not proper mass. But this same problem was encountered in Section 10.1 where the solution was found to be the use of the factor $\sqrt{-g}\,u^0$. We thus have the relation

$$dV = dV_p\,\frac{\sqrt{-|g_{ij}|}}{\sqrt{-|g'_{\mu\nu}|}\,u'^0}$$

which, to the order to which we are working, is

$$dV = dV_p\left[1 - \frac{1}{2}\frac{v^2}{c^2} + \tfrac{3}{2}h + O^2\right].$$

Equation (A-54) becomes

$$\bar{\rho}' = \bar{\rho} - \frac{1}{2}\frac{\overline{\rho' v^2}}{c^2} + \tfrac{3}{2}\overline{\rho' h},$$

(A-55)

where $\bar{\rho}$ is the average proper density (in terms of the cosmological metric and world-velocity) of the proper mass which, in the metric $g'_{\mu\nu}$ and world velocity u'^μ, has proper density ρ'. It is not necessary to distinguish between $\hat{\rho}$ and ρ' in the higher order terms since the difference is of second order in eqs. (A-52) and (A-55).

One further property of the averaging is needed. Since g_{ij} does not, to our accuracy, vary over the individual regions of averaging, the volume element dV can be taken merely as the product of the coordinate differentials $d^k x^i$. But then the partial derivative $\partial/\partial x^j$ commutes with the averaging. And since the averaging is spatial, the derivative $\partial/\partial t$ also commutes with the averaging. Thus the derivative $\partial/\partial x^\mu$ and the averaging commute with each other. This commutation property has two consequences which are of immediate importance. First, we know that the terms in $\delta R_{\mu\nu}$ which are of first order in the $h_{\mu\nu}$ are second-derivatives of the $h_{\mu\nu}$; but, since $\bar{h}_{\mu\nu} = 0$, these terms vanish, and we were justified in ignoring them in arriving at eqs. (A-51). Second, the term $\overline{\nabla^2 h^2}$ which appears in eqs. (A-51) may be considered to be the gradient of the average of a vector; and the latter vanishes due to isotropy.

One further detail is needed. The terms $\overline{\rho' h}$ and $\overline{h\nabla^2 h}$ which appear in eqs. (A-51), (A-52), and (A-55) are equivalent. For we have, from eq. (A-49),

$$\overline{\rho' h} = \rho \bar{h} + \overline{h\,\delta\rho} = \overline{h\,\delta\rho} = \frac{1}{\kappa}\,\overline{h\nabla^2 h}.$$

Equations (A-51), (A-52), (A-53), and (A-55) provide two relations among the quantities $\bar{\rho}$, ρ, $\bar{p}'$, p, $U_k = \frac{1}{2}\overline{\rho' v^2}$, and $U_g = \dfrac{1}{4\kappa}\,\overline{h\nabla^2 h}$. The two relations may be written

$$\rho c^2 = \hat{\rho} c^2 + U_k + U_g$$

$$p = \bar{p}' + \tfrac{2}{3}U_k + \tfrac{1}{3}U_g.$$

The electromagnetic field is included by the insertion of the electromagnetic stress-energy tensor into the field equation. For the accuracy to which we are working, it is sufficient to use the special-relativistic approximation. In special relativity, with $\bar{S}_{0i} = 0$ and $\bar{S}_{ij} = \frac{1}{3}\bar{S}_{kk}\delta_{ij}$, we find

$$\bar{S}_{\mu\nu} = c^{-2}U[\tfrac{4}{3}\delta_\mu^0\delta_\nu^0 - \tfrac{1}{3}\eta_{\mu\nu}]$$

where U is the average density of electromagnetic energy. Comparison with eq. (5-3) shows that the effective average pressure is $\frac{1}{3}U$. The division of U into the separate terms $U_e + U_m + U_r$ is made for convenience in cosmological applications.

Equations (A-42) and (A-43) have been derived, and we may consider the significance of the various terms. ρ'' is $\bar{\rho}$, the average density of mass in the form of galaxies. U_k is the average density of kinetic energy, including both the translations and the rotations of galaxies. U_g is the average Newtonian gravitational energy. The gravitational energy of an isolated Newtonian system in Euclidean space was found in Section 6.5 to be

$$\epsilon_g = \frac{1}{2} \int \rho \Phi \, dV = -\frac{1}{8\pi G} \int g^2 \, dV$$

where Φ is the Newtonian potential, $g_i = \partial\Phi/\partial x^i$, and ρ is the mass density. Since h is approximately $2\Phi c^{-2}$, we expect $U_g = \overline{\frac{1}{4}\rho' h} = \frac{1}{4\kappa} \overline{h \nabla^2 h} = -\frac{1}{4\kappa} \overline{(\nabla h)^2}$. The electromagnetic energy density is regarded to have three contributions: U_e from electrostatic interactions between galaxies; U_m from intergalactic and intragalactic magnetic fields; and U_r from electromagnetic radiation. p'' or $\bar{p}'$ is the average of the internal pressures of stars, interstellar gas, and intergalactic gas. If there is a "cosmological" pressure, such as $-\rho c^2$ in the constant-curvature models, it should be included in p''. Neutrinos may be included in U_r since they travel with the speed of light. Equations (A-42) and (A-43), except for the electromagnetic terms, were derived by Irvine[B] from kinematic considerations.

A.9 RECENT VALUES OF OBSERVED QUANTITIES

The purpose of this section is to provide a depository for the results of measurements of observational parameters which are publicized between the writing of this book and its publication. Section numbers indicate where the parameters are discussed in this book.

Cosmic Radiation, Section 18.4. Welch at the American Astronomical Society meeting in December 1966 and Penzias at the Texas relativistic astrophysics symposium in New York (hereafter abbreviated TRASNY) in January 1967 presented the following table.

TABLE A.I COSMIC RADIATION

WAVELENGTH (CM)	SKY TEMPERATURE (°K)		INVESTIGATORS
	WELCH	PENZIAS	
21.1	3.5 ± 1	3.2 ± 1	Penzias, Wilson
20.7	2.8 ± 1.2	2.8 ± 0.6	Howell, Shakeshaft
7.35	3.5 ± 1.0	3.3 ± 1	Penzias, Wilson
3.2	3.0 ± 1.0	3 ± 0.5	Roll, Wilkinson
1.5	$1.7 \begin{cases} +1.0 \\ -0.8 \end{cases}$	$2.0 \begin{cases} +0.8 \\ -0.7 \end{cases}$	Welch

Peebles at TRASNY displayed a graph having the following limits for the sky background.

TABLE A.2 SKY BACKGROUND

WAVELENGTH (MICRONS)	FLUX (WATT M^{-2} Hz^{-1} STER^{-1})	INVESTIGATORS
0.5	4×10^{-23}	Roach and Smith
2	1.1×10^{-20}	Harwit

Acceleration Parameter, Section 18.6. Sandage has constructed the magnitude-redshift relation for the brightest galaxy in each of a number of clusters of galaxies. A preliminary value of -1.65 ± 0.3 for the acceleration parameter α was reported by Horace W. Babcock in *Bulletin of the California Institute of Technology*, vol. 75, no. 4 (1966): *The President's Report*, pp. 69, 70. Sandage reported on his work at TRASNY. He had 29 points and got a value $\alpha = -1.8 \pm 0.7$. In Babcock's report, a preliminary correction for evolution raised α to -0.5 ± 0.3, but at TRASNY Sandage pointed out that current evidence indicates that galaxies are brightening up rather than fading from a youthful brilliance. Therefore, as explained in Section 18.6, the actual value of α may be smaller but not larger than the value -1.8 ± 0.7.

Perihelion Advance, Section 9.5a. Dicke has long doubted the accuracy of the perihelion test of general relativity. At TRASNY he reported the results of an experiment-observation of the sun performed by him and Goldenberg in which the sun's oblateness (ratio of the difference between equatorial and polar radii to the average radius) was found to be $5 \pm 0.7 \times 10^{-5}$. Dicke then argued that the consequent solar gravitational quadrupole moment was on the one hand responsible for about $3''$ of the $43''$ per century discrepancy in Mercury's perihelion advance, and was on the other hand due to the sun having a rapidly rotating interior. Dicke's result, which depends strongly on the theory of the sun's structure, has not been accepted by everyone in the scientific community.

Average Density, Section 18.3. As this book goes to press, there is an announcement (*Time*, May 3, 1968, p. 50) of an observation by Richard Henry of low-energy x-rays which may be due to ionized hydrogen in intergalactic space with a density given approximately by eq. (18-5b) and a temperature of several 10^5 °K. Such a possibility had been envisioned for several years (D. W. Sciama, *Quarterly Journal of the Royal Astronomical Society*, vol. 5, pp. 196–211, 1964). The *Time* article also hints that Sandage's value for the acceleration parameter may now be smaller than, possibly half, the value given earlier in this section.

APPENDIX B

Bibliography

This bibliography is in three sections. Section B.1 gives the references noted in the text by the superscript^B. Section B.2 gives parallel reading and the sources of the more specialized theoretical treatments. Section B.3 describes the publications by H. P. Robertson which are relevant to relativity and cosmology.

B.1 References Denoted by the Superscript ^{B} in the Text

Abell. *Annual Review of Astronomy and Astrophysics*, edited by Leo Goldberg, Armin J. Deutsch, and David Layzer, published by Annual Reviews, Inc., Palo Alto, California, Volume 3, 1965. In the article "Clustering of Galaxies" by G. O. Abell, pp. 1–22, see pp. 19 and 20 for the density based on clusters. Abell's H of 75 km/sec-Mpc is revised to 100 km/sec-Mpc to give the figures quoted in the text.

Adams. Walter S. Adams, *Proceedings of the National Academy of Sciences*, vol. 11, 1925, pp. 382–387: "The Relativity Displacement of the Spectral Lines in the Companion of Sirius."

Airy. George Biddell Airy published his results in two places: *Proceedings of the Royal Society of London*, vol. 20, 1871, pp. 35–39; *Philosophical Magazine*, vol. 43, 1872, pp. 310–313.

Allen. *Astrophysical Quantities*, second edition, by C. W. Allen, published by Athlone Press, 1963. The age of the earth is given in section 48, p. 110.

Arp. Halton Arp, *Astrophysical Journal*, vol. 135, 1962. There are two articles: pp. 311–332 and pp. 971–975. Arp obtains revised cluster ages and RR Lyrae M_V's due to a revised reddening law.

Baum. William A. Baum. Baum's measurements of galaxy redshifts are published in *Problems in Extra-Galactic Research*, edited by G. C. McVittie, Macmillan, 1962. The book presents the I.A.U. Symposium no. 15 of August 10–12, 1961.

Baum's article "Photoelectric Magnitudes and Redshifts" is found on pp. 390–400. In this article, Baum hints that the magnitude-redshift relation is linear. The abstract in *Astronomical Journal*, vol. 65, 1960, p. 483 by Baum and R. Minkowski refers to 3C295 with a redshift of 0.46.

Baum was curiously reluctant to publish his own value of the acceleration parameter, but others have quoted it freely for him. The value may be found in Sandage's^B announcement of the age discrepancy and in the minutes of the meeting of the Royal Astronomical Society of Friday, May 12, 1961 published in *The Observatory* vol. 81, 1961, pp. 113–118. Baum's remarks are on pp. 114–116.

Bell. W. E. Bell and E. P. Hincks, *Physical Review*, vol. 84, 1951, "The Lifetime of the μ^+-Meson," p. 1243. They quote previous work on the μ-meson lifetime.

Birkhoff. George D. Birkhoff published his theory in at least two places: *Boletin de la Sociedad Matematica Mexicana*, vol. 1, no. 3, 1944, pp. 1–23 (the pages are numbered in each number rather than in each volume); *Proceedings of the National Academy of Sciences*, vol. 30, 1944, pp. 324–334.

Cedarholm. J. P. Cedarholm and C. H. Townes. There are two articles, the first jointly with G. F. Bland and B. L. Havens in *Physical Review Letters*, vol. 1, 1958, pp. 342–343, and the second alone in *Nature*, vol. 184, 1959, pp. 1350–1351. In spite of the difference in the array of authors, the two articles are essentially the same. It is concluded from the behavior of maser beams of NH_3 molecules that, on the basis of the ether theory, the earth's velocity is less than $\frac{1}{30}$ km/sec, in spite of its revolution velocity of 30 km/sec!

Clemence. G. M. Clemence published two tables, the first in *Reviews of Modern Physics*, vol. 19, 1947, pp. 361–364, and the second, with revisions for the uncertainties of Venus and general precession, in *Proceedings of the American Philosophical Society*, vol. 93, 1949, pp. 532–534.

Cranshaw. H. J. Hay, J. P. Schiffer, T. E. Cranshaw, and P. A. Egelstaff, *Physical Review Letters*, vol. 4, 1960, pp. 165–166. They observed the expected frequency shift of $\Delta\nu/\nu = 2.44 \times 10^{-20} \omega^2$ for rotational speeds up to 500 cycles per second.

Dicke. R. H. Dicke, *Science*, vol. 129, 1959, pp. 621–624, "New Research on Old Gravitation." The article is not technical, and he gives his result in a diagram rather than in the text! Aluminum and gold show equivalence to an accuracy of approximately 3×10^{-10}.

Eötvös. Roland V. Eötvös, Desiderius Pekár, and Eugen Fakete, *Annalen der Physik*, vol. 68, 1922, pp. 11–66.

Felton. James E. Felton, *Astrophysical Journal*, vol. 144, 1966, pp. 241–243, "Energy Density of Starlight in the Metagalaxy."

Fizeau. M. H. Fizeau, *Comptes Rendus de l'Académie des Sciences*, vol. 33, 1851, pp. 349–355.

Ginzburg. *The Origin of Cosmic Rays* by V. L. Ginzburg and S. I. Syrovatskii, translated by H. S. H. Massey, edited by D. ter Haar, published by Macmillan, 1964.

Gödel. Kurt Gödel, *Reviews of Modern Physics*, vol. 21, 1949, pp. 447–450.

Hammar. G. W. Hammar, *Physical Review*, vol. 48, 1935, pp. 462–463.

Hoek. M. Hoek, *Archives Néerlandaises des Sciences Exactes et Naturelles*, vol. 3, 1868, pp. 180–185.

Hubble. Edwin Hubble, *The Realm of the Nebulae*, Yale University Press, 1936. On p. 170 is $H = 530$ km sec^{-1} Mpc^{-1}.

Humason. M. L. Humason, N. V. Mayall, and A. R. Sandage, *Astronomical Journal*, vol. 61, 1956, pp. 97–162, "Redshifts and Magnitudes of Extragalactic Nebulae."

Irvine. William M. Irvine, *Annals of Physics*, vol. 32, 1965, pp. 322–347.

Ives and Stilwell. Herbert E. Ives and G. R. Stilwell, *Journal of the Optical Society of America*. They published a description of the experiment and preliminary observations in vol. 28, 1938, pp. 215–226, and they published the final results in vol. 31, 1941, pp. 369–374.

Jánossy. *Cosmic Rays* by L. Jánossy, second edition, published by Oxford at the Clarendon Press, 1950. In particular, see pp. 169–172 and 198–201.

Kennedy and Thorndike. Roy J. Kennedy and Edward M. Thorndike, *Physical Review*, vol. 42, 1932, pp. 400–418.

Klüber. *Vistas in Astronomy*, edited by Arthur Beer, published by Pergamon Press. Volume 3, 1960, "The Determination of Einstein's Light-Deflection in the Gravitational Field of the Sun" by H. von Klüber, pp. 47–77. He concludes that (a) some kind of deflection exists, (b) the angle is a little larger than the Einstein value if the hyperbolic rule is used, and (c) extrapolation from large distances causes some uncertainty.

Lange. Ludwig Lange, *Berichte über die Verhandlungen der Königlich Sächsischen Gesellschaft der Wissenschaften zu Leipzig. Mathematische-Physische Klasse*, published by Hirzel in Leipzig. The spine of the volumes in the library which I used said "Berichte Kgl. Sächs. Akad. d. Wissensch. Math-Phys. Kl." Volume 37, 1885, pp. 333–351. Lange's laws are on pp. 337–338.

McCrea. W. H. McCrea, *Astrophysical Journal*, vol. 144, 1966, pp. 516–533.

McVittie. *General Relativity and Cosmology*, by G. C. McVittie, published by Chapman and Hall Ltd., London, 1956. He gives an excellent summary of work on astronomical verification of the gravitational redshift (p. 98) and work on light deflection (p. 94).

Michelson. Albert A. Michelson did experiments with light, sometimes jointly with Edward W. Morley, Henry G. Gale, and Fred Pearson. In 1881, Michelson published initial results of the MM experiment in *American Journal of Science*, vol. 122, 1881, pp. 120–129. Improved results were published by Michelson and Morley in the same journal, vol. 134, 1887, pp. 333–345. In 1925, Michelson took up the problem of detecting the earth's rotation by the method of Sagnac's experiment. A double paper appeared in *Astrophysical Journal*, vol. 61, 1925, pp. 137–145 by Michelson, Gale, and Pearson.

Penzias. A. A. Penzias and R. W. Wilson, *Astrophysical Journal*, vol. 142, 1965, pp. 419–421.

Pogány. B. Pogány, *Annalen der Physik*, vol. 80, 1926, pp. 217–231, "Über die Wiederholung des Harres-Sagnacschen Versuches."

Popper. Daniel M. Popper, *Astrophysical Journal*, vol. 120, 1954, pp. 316–321, "Red Shift in the Spectrum of 40 Eridani B."

Pound. R. V. Pound and J. L. Snider, *Physical Review Letters*, vol. 13, 1964, pp. 539–540.

Roach. F. E. Roach and L. L. Smith, *Astronomical Journal*, vol. 70, 1965, p. 689. This is only an abstract.

Roll. P. G. Roll and David T. Wilkinson, *Physical Review Letters*, vol. 16, 1966, pp. 405–407.

Rossi. Bruno Rossi, Norman Hilberry, and J. Barton Hoag, *Physical Review*, vol. 57, 1940, pp. 461–469.

Sagnac. G. Sagnac, *Comptes Rendus de l'Académie des Sciences*, vol. 157, 1915, pp. 708–710 and 1410–1413.

Sandage. Allan R. Sandage announced the discrepancy between stellar ages and cosmological ages in the abstract *Astronomical Journal*, vol. 66, 1961, p. 53.
    Sandage then published his work on cluster ages and RR Lyrae M_V's in the *Astrophysical Journal*, vol. 135, 1962, pp. 333–365. (Note that this is divided into two articles.)
    Sandage wrote a chapter in the book cited in the article under Baum[B]. In this chapter ("The Distance Scale," pp. 359–378), Sandage summarizes the data on RR Lyrae, Cepheid variables, and other distance indicators. He gives a Hubble constant of 98 $\pm$ 15 km/sec-Mpc.
    Sandage's article on cosmology in *Astrophysical Journal*, vol. 133, 1961, pp. 355–392 is an excellent summary of observational problems. The difference between angular-size distance by finite-sized objects and angular-size distance by isophotal diameters is explained in section IV, "Angular Diameters," pp. 376–384.
    An article on the correlation of quasar redshifts and colors is in *Astrophysical Journal*, vol. 146, 1966, pp. 13–24. The largest redshift in his table is 2.12.

Sérsic. J. L. Sérsic found a Hubble constant of 125 $\pm$ 5 km/sec-Mpc in *Zeitschrift für Astrophysik*, vol. 50, 1960, pp. 168–177 and 116 $\pm$ 9 km/sec-Mpc in *Annales d'Astrophysique*, vol. 25, 1962, pp. 206–213. Both articles are in English. The latter mentions the value 98 $\pm$ 20 from the Santa Barbara Conference.

Stabell. R. Stabell and S. Refsdal, *Monthly Notices of the Royal Astronomical Society*, vol. 132, 1966, pp. 379–388. Their q_0 is our $-\alpha$, and their σ_0 is our $q/2$.

Van den Bergh. Sidney Van den Bergh gave a Hubble constant of 120 ($+25$, -20) km/sec-Mpc in *Journal of the Royal Astronomical Society of Canada*, vol. 54, 1960, pp. 49–57, and 100 ($+20$, -17) km/sec-Mpc in *Zeitschrift für Astrophysik* vol. 49, 1960, pp. 198–200. Both articles are in English.
    Van den Bergh gave an average density of 6.8 $\times$ 10^{-31} gm cm^{-3} for H = 120 km/sec-Mpc in *Zeitschrift für Astrophysik*, vol. 53, 1961, pp. 219–222, also in English.

Whitrow. *Vistas in Astronomy*, edited by Arthur Beer. Vol. 6, 1965, "Relativistic Theories of Gravitation," pp. 1–67 by G. J. Whitrow and G. E. Morduch.

Whittaker. *A History of the Theories of Aether and Electricity*, by Edmund T. Whittaker. The first edition was published by Longmans, Green, and Co., London, 1910. A revised edition was published in two volumes: the first volume "The Classical Theories" was published in 1951 by Thomas Nelson and Sons; the second volume "The Modern Theories 1900–1926" was published in 1954 by the Philosophical Library, New York. The revised edition carries the reader past 1910 and includes Einstein's proposals that c is constant (1905), $\epsilon = mc^2$ (1905), and $\epsilon = h\nu$ (1906), and Einstein's theory of gravity (principle of equivalence in 1907, general relativity in 1915, and the cosmological constant in 1917). Whittaker's book is an excellent history of electromagnetism and relativity. See Table B.1 for page references in Whittaker of topics referred to in text.

TABLE B.I *LOCATION IN WHITTAKER (BOTH EDITIONS) OF TOPICS IN TEXT*

	PAGE IN WHITTAKER	
TOPIC	FIRST EDITION	FIRST VOLUME, REVISED EDITION
Bradley discovers aberration	99	94
Arago is quoted	116	109
Theory that ether density is proportional to n^2	116	110
Hoek's experiment	118	111
Airy's experiment	120	113
Hertz extends electromagnetism to moving bodies	365	329
MM experiment	417	391
Fitzgerald contraction	432	404
Wilson's experiment	432	404

Wilson. Harold A. Wilson published two accounts of his experiment, first with a relative permeability of unity in *Philosophical Transactions of the Royal Society of London*, Series A, vol. 204, 1905, pp. 121–137 dated 1904, and later for a high relative permeability jointly with Marjorie Wilson in *Proceedings of the Royal Society of London*, series A, vol. 89 1914, pp. 99–106, dated 1913. The difference in dates is due to the fact that some journals do not end each volume on December 31.

Woolf. N. J. Woolf, *Astrophysical Journal*, vol. 135, 1962, pp. 644–646. An abstract is in *Astronomical Journal*, vol. 67, 1962, p. 286.

B.2 Parallel and Extended References. This section contains a list of some books and articles which are sources for some material in the text, provide parallel presentation, or provide extension of various theories beyond what is given in the text. The items are listed in the order in which the subjects appear in the text, and the authors are included in the name index.

Section 3.2. J. Liouville, *Journal de Mathématiques pures et appliqués*, vol. 12, 1847, pp. 265–290, "Note au sujet de l'article précédent."

Section 4.2. E. G. Cullwick, *Electromagnetism and Relativity*, Longmans, Green, and Co., 1957. Excellent text for electromagnetism in moving media in special relativity.

Section 4.3. J. L. Synge, *Relativity: the Special Theory*, Interscience, New York, 1956. Recommended as a text on special relativity.

Section 5.5. C. Møller, *The Theory of Relativity*, Oxford, London, 1952 and 1962. The centroid disk is in section 64 of chapter VI.

M. H. L. Pryce, *Proceedings of the Royal Society of London*, vol. 195, 1948, pp. 62–81, "The Mass-Centre in the Restricted Theory of Relativity and its Connection with the Quantum Theory of Elementary Particles."

Section 6.9. A. Einstein, *Jahrbuch der Radioaktivität und Elecktronik*, vol. 4, 1907, pp. 411–462, "Über das Relativitätsprinzip und die aus demselben gezogenen Folgerungen." *Annalen der Physik*, 4th series, vol. 35, 1911, pp. 898–908, "Über den Einfluss der Schwerkraft auf die Ausbreitung des Lichtes."

Section 7.3. E. W. Barankin, *American Mathematical Monthly*, vol. 49, 1942, pp. 4–14, "Heat Flow and Non-Euclidean Geometry."

Chapter 8. Luther Pfahler Eisenhart, *Riemannian Geometry*, Princeton University Press, 1926 and 1960. Robertson's approach to Riemannian geometry is the same as Eisenhart's, because Robertson was taught by Eisenhart.

Section 8.12. Tullio Levi-Civita, *Der Absolute Differentialkalkül*, Julius Springer, Berlin, 1928. Levi-Civita makes reference to Pérès' formula on p. 105, section 8, chapter 4.

Sections 10.1 to 10.3. W. deSitter, *Monthly Notices of the Royal Astronomical Society*, vol. 77, 1916–1917, pp. 155–184, "On Einstein's Theory of Gravitation and its Astronomical Consequences" (1916).

Tullio Levi-Civita, *American Journal of Mathematics*, vol. 59, 1937, pp. 225–234, "Astronomical Consequences of the Relativistic Two-Body Problem."

Arthur Eddington and G. L. Clark, *Proceedings of the Royal Society of London*, series A, vol. 166, 1938, pp. 465–475, "The Problem of n Bodies in General Relativity Theory."

A. Einstein, L. Infield, and B. Hoffmann, *Annals of Mathematics*, 2nd series, vol. 39, 1938, pp. 65–100, "The Gravitational Equations and the Problem of Motion." The same thing is later presented by Einstein and Infeld in *Canadian Journal of Mathematics*, vol. 1, 1949, pp. 209–241, "On the Motion of Particles in General Relativity Theory." See also Robertson's article on Section 10.3, cited in Table B.2.

Section 10.4. Hermann Weyl, *Annalen der Physik*, 4th series, vol. 54, 1917, pp. 117–145, "Zur Gravitationstheorie," and vol. 59, 1919, pp. 185–188, "Bemerkung über die axialsymmetrischen Lösüngen der Einsteinschen Gravitationsgleichungen."

Rudolf Bach and H. Weyl, *Mathematische Zeitschrift*, vol. 13, 1922, pp. 134–145, "Neue Lösüngen der Einsteinschen Gravitationsgleichungen."

P. Y. Chou, *American Journal of Mathematics*, vol. 53, 1931, pp. 289–308, "The Gravitational Field of a Body with Rotational Symmetry in Einstein's Theory of Gravitation."

Sections 11.5, 11.7. Hans Thirring and J. Lense wrote articles in *Physikalische Zeitschrift* as follows: volume 19 (1918), pp. 33–39 by Thirring and pp. 156–163 by Thirring and Lense; volume 22 (1921), pp. 29–30 by Thirring. The first article carries the rotating shell to second order in the angular velocity, the second article gives the rates of change of elements of satellite orbits due to general-relativistic effects of rotation of the central body, and the third article is an extension of the first article.

Section 12.2. W. Gordon, *Annalen der Physik*, 4 folge, vol. 72, 1923, pp. 421–456, "Zur Lichtfortpflanzung nach der Relativitätstheorie."

Section 13.3. Wilhelm Killing, *Journal für die reine und angewandte Mathematik*, vol. 109, 1892, pp. 121–186, "Über die Grundlagen der Geometrie."

Section 13.6. Kornel Lanczos, *Zeitschrift für Physik*, vol. 59, 1929–30, pp. 514–539 (1929), "Über eine invariante Formulierung der Erhaltungssätze in der allgemeinen Relativitätstheorie."

Sections 15.3, 15.7, and 18.1. W. Mattig, *Astronomische Nachrichten*. The magnitude-redshift relation is the subject of vol. 284, 1957–1959, pp. 109–111 (1957), and the counts of galaxies is the subject of vol. 285, 1959–1960, pp. 1–2 (1958).

Section 16.3. Kornel Lanczos, *Physikalische Zeitschrift*, vol. 23, 1922; pp. 537–539, "Ein vereinfachendes Koordinatensystem für die Einsteinschen Gravitationsgleichungen," and pp. 539–543, "Bemerkung zur de Sitterschen Welt."

Section 17.2. A. Friedman, *Zeitschrift für Physik*, vol. 10, pp. 377–386, "Über die Krümmung des Raumes," (1922) and vol. 21, pp. 326–332, "Über die Möglichkeit einer Welt mit constanter negativer Krümmung des Raumes" (1924).

Section A.3. Richard C. Tolman, *Proceedings of the National Academy of Sciences*, vol. 21, 1935, pp. 321–326, "Thermal Equilibrium in a General Gravitational Field."

B.3 Robertson's Articles. The publications of H. P. Robertson consist of one book, two abstracts, and 35 articles. We may immediately eliminate the book and the abstracts from further consideration, because the book is Robertson's translation of a work by Weyl, and the abstracts are of one of the articles. The 35 articles may be grouped according to subject matter as follows: 24 on relativity and cosmology, 5 on quantum mechanics and atomic structure, 4 on mathematics, and 2 on other physics. We will restrict our attention to the 24 articles which are relevant to this book.

Of these articles, 14 contain material which, in whole or in part, is included in this book. These 14 articles are given in Table B.2 in the order in which the relevant material appears in this book. Only twelve items appear in the table because the three papers in item 8 actually form one paper.

The remaining 10 articles, here numbered from 13 to 22, are on the following subjects.

Review of cosmology and geometry.
13. *Science*, vol. 76, 1932, pp. 221–226, "The Expanding Universe."
14. *Proceedings of the American Philosophical Society*, vol. 93, 1949, pp. 527–531, "On the Present State of Relativistic Cosmology."
15. Published in two places. *Helv. Phys. Acta Supplementum IV*, pp. 128–146 (1956) and *Jubilee of Relativity Theory, Bern 1955*, published by Birkhäuser Verlag, Basel, 1956. "Cosmological Theory."
16. *Library of Living Philosophers*, Albert Einstein: Philosopher-Scientist, 1949, vol. VII, pp. 315–332. (A popular article on geometry.)

TABLE B.2 ROBERTSON'S ARTICLES RELATED TO THIS BOOK

	In this book Chap.	Sec.	Originally published Year	Name of Journal	Vol.	Pages	Title of Article
1	3	12–14	1949	Reviews of Modern Physics	21	378–382	Postulate vs. Observation in the Special Theory of Relativity
2*	4	9	1937	Monthly Notices of the Royal Astronomical Society	97	423–438	Dynamical Effects of Radiation in the Solar System
3*	5 12	2 1–3	1937	Proceedings of the Edinburgh Mathematical Society	5	63–81	Test Corpuscles in General Relativity
4	7	3, 8, 9	1950	American Mathematical Monthly	57	232–245	The Geometries of the Thermal and Gravitational Fields
5	10	3	1938	Annals of Mathematics	39	101–104	The Two Body Problem in General Relativity
6	11	8	1962	A book: Space Age Astronomy, edited by Armin J. Deutsch and Wolfgang B. Klemperer			Chapter 11: Relativity and Cosmology, pp. 228–235
7*	14		1929	Proceedings of the National Academy of Sciences	15	822–829	On the Foundations of Relativistic Cosmology
8*	14		1935 1936 1936	Astrophysical Journal	82 83 83	284–301 187–201 257–271	Kinematics and World Structure
9*	15	3	1938	Zeitschrift für Astrophysik	15	69–81	The Apparent Luminosity of a Receding Nebula
10*	16	2	1928	Philosophical Magazine	5	835–848	On Relativistic Cosmology
11	16, 17		1933	Reviews of Modern Physics	5	62–90	Relativistic Cosmology
12	17 18	3 1	1955	Publications of the Astronomical Society of the Pacific	67	82–98	The Theoretical Aspects of the Nebular Redshift

* Most significant papers.

The line element $ds^2 = \rho^{-2}(dx^2 + dy^2 + dz^2 + \sigma^2 dt^2)$.

17. *Proceedings of the National Academy of Sciences*, vol. 11, 1925, pp. 590–592, "Transformations of Einstein Spaces."

18. *Transactions of the American Mathematical Society*, vol. 29, 1927, pp. 481–496, "Dynamical Space-Times Which Contain a Conformal Euclidean 3-Space."

Absolute parallelism.

19. *Annals of Mathematics*, vol. 33, 1932, pp. 496–520, "Groups of Motions in Spaces Admitting Absolute Parallelism."

Heat in general relativity.

20. With R. C. Tolman, *Physical Review*, vol. 43, 1933, pp. 564–568, "On the Interpretation of Heat in Relativistic Thermodynamics."

Special Cosmologies.

21. Milne's. *Zeitschrift für Astrophysik*, vol. 7, 1933, pp. 153–166.

22. Page's. *Physical Review*, vol. 49, 1936, pp. 755–760.

The best way to describe Professor Robertson's contributions to relativity and cosmology is in the context of a biological sketch. Robertson was born on January 27, 1903, in Hoquiam, Washington. From 1918 to 1923 he attended the University of Washington where he received his B.S. in 1922 and his M.S. in 1923 in the mathematics department. In 1923 he married Angela.

Papers 17 and 18 are the result of his work at the California Institute of Technology for which he received his Ph.D. in 1925.

His discovery of the linear cosmological redshift is contained in paper 10 which is the result of two years at Göttingen, Germany. His interest had turned from mathematics to cosmology.

Robertson began thinking in terms of cosmological symmetries. In paper 7 he deduced the cosmological line element from group theory and used Killing's equation to deduce the stationary cases. Six years later he published in paper 8 the derivation which is presented in this text.

He was rapidly becoming an authority on cosmology. After two years at Caltech (1927–1929) he spent 18 years at Princeton, and became popular for both technical and public talks on cosmological theory. Paper 11 is an excellent review of the cosmological theories which had been proposed up to 1933. A more popular review of cosmology is found in paper 13.

Robertson's most productive years, 1933–38, saw a number of important papers published. Paper 8 has already been mentioned. Paper 3 provided a rigorous proof that the equations of motion for particles and photons in general relativity follow from the differential conservation laws for the stress-energy tensors of matter and radiation. Paper 2 put to rest the problem of radiation pressure on particles in special relativity. Paper 9 settled the question of whether the denominator of the formula for the apparent brightness of a distant galaxy should contain $(1 + z)$ or $(1 + z)^2$.

As far as relativity and cosmology was concerned, Robertson's most productive period was over. The principal reason for this decline was his desire to devote time to the needs of the United States armed forces. He was, at various times from 1943 to 1960: liaison officer in the London Mission of the Office of Scientific Research and Development; consultant to the Office of the Secretary of War; chief of the Scientific Intelligence Advisory Section of Supreme Headquarters, Allied Expeditionary Force in France; director in the Weapons Systems Evaluation Group of the Department of Defense; scientific advisor to the Supreme Allied Commander in Europe; and member of the Defense Science Board.

In spite of his heavy contributions to the government, however, Robertson found time for further work in cosmology. Paper 12 in 1955 is principally review, but Robertson takes great pains to express all cosmological parameters in terms of observational quantities; he also introduces the density-age diagram.

Meanwhile, Robertson in 1947 moved from Princeton to Caltech, where he taught the relativity course until his death in 1961.

We may turn now to Robertson's unpublished material. The material in Robertson's notes naturally falls into the four categories constructed from the two conditions: published or unpublished; and relevant or not relevant to relativity and cosmology. It is the work which falls into the category of unpublished and relevant to relativity and cosmology which is of special interest. Some of this work is merely Robertson's scratchwork in studying the work of others. But there are several pieces of work which appear to be original with Robertson. Most of these works are included in this book as follows (dates indicate Robertson's notation): rigid-body motion in special relativity (1952) in Section A.1; the analysis of Gödel's model in Sections 13.10 and A.5 (1949); extending the parabolic pendlebahn past the Schwarzschild singularity (1936 and 1937) in Section 9.6; inclusion of absorption in the magnitude-redshift relation in Section 15.5; and a minor problem: orbits around a variable mass in Section 10.5.

Second order plane gravitational waves is the subject of a piece of work dated 1936. Robertson finds the line-element to be

$$ds^2 = (1 - 2\epsilon^2 fg)(dt^2 - dx^2) - [1 + 2\epsilon\psi + 4\epsilon^2\psi^2 - 2\epsilon^2(F + G)] \, dy^2$$
$$- [1 - 2\epsilon\psi + 4\epsilon^2\psi^2 - 2\epsilon^2(F + G)] \, dz^2 + O^3(\epsilon)$$

where $\psi = f + g$,

$$F = \int_0^{t-x} d\xi \int_0^{\xi} \left[\frac{df}{d\xi}\right]^2 d\xi$$

$$G = \int_0^{t+x} d\eta \int_0^{\eta} \left[\frac{dg}{d\eta}\right]^2 d\eta,$$

and f and g are functions, respectively of $\xi = t - x$ and $\eta = t + x$.

About 1960, Robertson's interest turned to two subjects: the observational verification of the coefficients of the general spherically symmetric line-element of Section 11.8; and the general-relativistic effects in the dynamics of the earth-moon-sun system. His results of a calculation of the latter showed that general relativity introduces three effects: perihelion advance of the moon's perigee; the geodesic effect due to revolution around the sun; and a new effect which he called the *solar effect*. The advances in the moon's node and perigee per century are given in Table B.3.

TABLE B.3 *ADVANCE PER CENTURY OF MOON'S NODE AND PERIGEE*

	NODE	PERIGEE
Perihelion advance	0.″000	+0.″061
Geodesic effect	+1.912	+1.912
Solar effect	+0.213	−0.213
Observed advance	−6,967,944.±2″	+14,643,536.±2″

Robertson died on August 26, 1961 as a result of injuries received in an automobile accident.

For the sake of completeness, we here list the articles by Robertson not pertaining to relativity and cosmology.

Bulletin of the American Mathematical Society, vol. 30, 1924, p. 14.

Mathematische Annalen, vol. 98, 1928, pp, 749–752.

Proceedings of the National Academy of Sciences, vol. 14, 1928, pp. 153–154.

Physical Review, vol. 31, 1928, pp. 973–989 (with Jane Dewey).

Journal of the Franklin Institute, vol. 207, 1929, pp. 535–537.

Bulletin of the American Mathematical Society, vol. 35, 1929, pp. 686–690 (with H. Weyl).

Physical Review, vol. 34, 1929, pp. 163–164.

Annals of Mathematics, vol. 31, 1930, pp. 281–291.

Physical Review, vol. 40, 1933, pp. 583–591 (with J. B. Miles).

Physical Review, vol. 46, 1934, pp. 794–801.

Proceedings of the Cambridge Philosophical Society, vol. 36, 1940, pp. 209–223.

Abstract of the Material in this Book

This appendix is an abstract of the material in the book. Each chapter is discussed separately, and the superscript numbers correspond to the sections within each chapter.

Chapter I Euclidean Space. [5]All possible transformations from one set of rectangular Cartesian coordinates to another set in three-dimensional Euclidean space are found to consist of rotations and translations. [6]An infinitesimal transformation is characterized by a vector ξ^i which satisfies Killing's equation. [7]Any solid body has an axis of rotation on which the motion is parallel to the axis.

[9]Free particles serve to define *inertial frames* and the measurement of *time*. Free particles move in straight lines in inertial frames, and they cover equal distances in equal times. [11]It can then be proved that the apparent force on a particle in an arbitrary rectangular Cartesian coordinate system is the sum of the real force, the d'Alembert terms for the linear and angular acceleration of the coordinates, the centrifugal effect due to the particle's position and the rotation of the coordinate system, and the Coriolis effect due to the particle's velocity and the rotation of the coordinate system.

[12,13]A brief review of Newtonian gravity and planetary orbits is given at the end of Chapter 1.

Chapter 2 Classical Electromagnetism. [3]After a review of the derivation of field energy, field momentum, and field stress in classical electromagnetism, [4]it is proved that electromagnetic radiation with energy $\mathcal{E}$ has mass $\mathcal{E}c^{-2}$ and momentum $\mathcal{E}c^{-1}$, where c is the speed of light. [5]A self-consistent electromagnetic theory for moving media is constructed but is found to contain a fatal flaw—disagreement with experiment. [6]Another nineteenth century theory is also examined from an experimental point of view. [7]The ether theory sailed through one experiment after another until it was wrecked on the [10]Michelson-Morley experiment. The latter experiment required a radically new theory, and [11]the Fitzgerald contraction seemed to be the answer.

Chapter 3 The Lorentz Transformation.

[1]The assumption of two postulates—the Fitzgerald contraction and the principle of relativity which states that there is no preferred inertial frame—lead to the Lorentz transformation between inertial frames. The Lorentz transformation can also be obtained from the two postulates that the principle of relativity holds and that light has the same velocity in any inertial frame. [2]A rigorous analysis shows that the only transformations which leave the velocity of light constant in complex four-dimensional space-time are translations, rotations, dilatations, inversions, and Kelvin's transformation. Among these five types, the only transformation which leaves the velocity $\partial \bar{x}^i / \partial \bar{x}^0$ non-zero and independent of x^i for constant x^i is the rotation. [3]It is then seen that the Lorentz transformation is a rotation in four dimensions.

[5]Several consequences of the Lorentz transformation are examined: time dilation, the Fitzgerald contraction, the limitation on the speed of signals, and the light cone. Explanations are given for [6]the twin paradox and [7]the rotating ring. [8]Studies of cosmic rays provide observational verification of the time dilation. [9]The concept of four-dimensional vectors and tensors is introduced, and [10]the concept of velocity is examined.

[11]One curious consequence of the Lorentz transformation is the Thomas precession. A body in torque-free, accelerated motion undergoes a real, non-physical rotation—real in the sense that it is measurable, non-physical in the sense that the centrifugal and Coriolis effects vanish.

[12]An effort is made to construct the Lorentz transformation with as few assumptions as possible by utilizing various experiments. The use of definitions, constructions, and four reasonable postulates reduces the number of independent components of the transformation matrix to four. Three experiments—Michelson-Morley, [13]Kennedy-Thorndike, and [14]Ives-Stilwell—are used to reduce the number of unknowns in the transformation to only one—the velocity itself.

[15]A description of light rays is given at the end of the chapter. It is shown how to transform both frequency and direction from one inertial frame to another.

Chapter 4 Electromagnetism in Special Relativity.

[1]It is proved that the four-dimensional current density J^μ is a vector by the use of the property that if the equations $J^\mu = 0$ and $\partial J^\mu / \partial x^\mu = 0$ hold in one system, then they hold in all systems. [2]By the use of the field equation for the four-dimensional electromagnetic potential ϕ^μ, it is proved that ϕ^μ is a vector. The electromagnetic field tensor $F^{\mu\nu}$ is examined—its form, its

field equations, and its properties. [3]The electromagnetic stress-energy tensor is defined and its properties are examined in considerable detail, after which [4]the transformation rules for electromagnetic radiation are derived. [5]The equation of motion for a charged particle is examined first in vector form and then in [6]Lagrangian form. [7]The case of the motion of a charged particle in uniform, perpendicular electric and magnetic fields gives results which differ from the classical theory. [8]The case of constant proper acceleration is noted.

[9]The radiation pressure on a particle is put into relativistic form. Applications are made to two cases: a particle in a uniform radiation field and a particle in the sun's radiation field.

Given at the end of the chapter are: [10]the electromagnetic potential of a moving charge; and [11]the special-relativistic relations for the electromagnetic field in moving bodies.

Chapter 5   Matter. [1]The equation of motion for a perfect fluid is obtained from its stress-energy tensor and is found to resemble the equation of motion of a particle. [2]It is rigorously proved that if a particle is regarded as the limit of a finite distribution of matter, then the corpuscular equation of motion results from the conservation law of the stress-energy tensor of the matter. The rate of change of the particle's 4-vector momentum with respect to proper time is equal to the total force acting on the particle. If the stress-energy tensor has zero self-contraction, as for the electromagnetic field, then the particle, now a photon, must follow a null curve.

[3]Gauss' theorem is proved for four-dimensional space.

[4]An isolated distribution of matter is found to possess ten conserved quantities: total spatial momentum, total energy, total spatial angular momentum, and velocity of the center of mass. [5]Attempts to define the center of mass lead to a relation between the total angular momentum of the distribution and the minimum size which the distribution can possess. [6]The ten conservation laws are found to have a one-to-one correspondence with the ten independent coordinate transformations among Cartesian inertial frames in special relativity.

Chapter 6   Special-Relativistic Gravitation Theories. [1]After noting the inconsistency between Newtonian gravity and special relativity, [2]a formalism is obtained for convenience in dealing with planetary orbits in any theory.

[3,4]The first candidate for a special-relativistic gravitation theory is a vector theory similar to electromagnetism. The similarity of Newton's law with Coulomb's law would lead us to identify the Newtonian gravitational potential with the temporal component of a 4-vector. However,

the theory gives a perihelion advance of $\mu/2p$ in contrast with the Einstein value of $3\mu/p$.

[5]The second candidate is a theory in which the gravitational potential is a scalar. However, the perihelion advance is $-\mu/p$.

[6]The third candidate is a generalized vector theory which, unlike electromagnetism, also contains a *symmetric* field tensor. The arbitrary parameter in the theory can be so chosen that the perihelion advance is $3\mu/p$, but then a particle with the speed of light does not simulate a photon.

[7]The fourth candidate is a symmetric-tensor-potential theory which contains two arbitrary parameters. The parameters may be chosen so that the perihelion advance is $3\mu/p$ and a particle with the speed of light has the Einstein deflection of $4\mu/R$, but still a particle with the speed of light does not simulate a photon. Birkhoff's tensor theory is noted.

[8]All gravitational theories based on special relativity fail for two reasons. One reason is that, by postulate, light has rectilinear propagation and hence cannot exhibit the Einstein deflection. The other reason is the gravitational redshift. [9]The principle of equivalence requires that space-time in the neighborhood of masses not be that of special relativity. We are forced to turn to non-Euclidean geometry for a correct formulation of gravitation.

Chapter 7 Differential Geometry. [1]The geometry of a two-dimensional surface in three-dimensional space is studied. The Gaussian curvature K of the surface at a point P is the product of the maximum curvature and the minimum curvature for all possible directions through P. Geodesics are introduced, and the role of Gaussian curvature is examined in a brief study of geodesic circles and geodesic triangles.

[2]The n-dimensional metric

$$ds^2 = e^{2F(x)} dx^i dx^i$$

is studied in detail. Examples are provided by the heat metric in [3–5]two and [8]three dimensions. [6]The concept of Gaussian curvature is extended to the n-dimensional metric, and an important theorem is proved: Gaussian curvature can be defined only for a two-dimensional surface embedded in the n-dimensional space; but if the curvature is, at each point, independent of the choice of the surface through the point, then the curvature is also constant throughout the space. [7]The three cases of constant curvature (K positive, zero, or negative) are examined.

[9]An attempt is made to geometrize both the heat-metric theory and the scalar gravitational theory of Section 6.5.

Chapter 8 Riemannian Geometry. [1]Chapter 8 is a study of the more general geometry represented by the arbitrary Riemannian metric

$$ds^2 = g_{ij}(x) dx^i dx^j.$$

[2]The study of geodesics introduces the Christoffel symbols and [3]leads to the definition of geodesic coordinates. [4]The parallel displacement of a vector around a closed curve gives rise to the Riemann-Christoffel tensor R_{ijkl}. [5]The symmetry properties of R_{ijkl} are discovered, and the number of independent components of R_{ijkl} is found to be $\frac{1}{12}n^2(n^2 - 1)$. [6]Tensor derivatives are defined, and formulas are given for the commutators of second tensor derivatives. [7]The Bianchi identity is derived.

[8]With the introduction of unit orthogonal vectors [9]it is found possible to identify R_{ijkl} with Gaussian curvature. In particular, the product $R_{ijkl}a^i b^j a^k b^l$ formed from two orthogonal unit vectors a^i, b^i is equal to the Gaussian curvature in the surface defined by a^i, b^i. [10]If K is independent of direction at each point in the space, then K is constant throughout the space. [11]If R_{ijkl} vanishes everywhere, then there exists a coordinate system in which the Christoffel symbols vanish everywhere. [12]Gauss' integral theorem on curvature is proved for an arbitrary 2-space embedded in an n-dimensional space. The chapter concludes with: [13]the definition of tensor forms of the permutation symbol; [14]an expanded definition of geodesics to include null geodesics; and [15]the definition of volume.

Chapter 9 General Relativity.

[1]Space-time is regarded as a four-dimensional Riemannian space having a metric

$$ds^2 = g_{\mu\nu}\, dx^\mu\, dx^\nu.$$

[2]The equivalence principle implies that particles which are free from non-gravitational forces follow geodesics. Thus gravity is the manifestation of the components $g_{\mu\nu}$ of the metric tensor. [3]The search for a field equation for gravity leads to Einstein's field equation.

[4]The field equation is applied to the case of spherical symmetry in empty space to give an exact solution for $g_{\mu\nu}$, the so-called Schwarzschild solution. The application of the equation of motion shows that orbits in the Schwarzschild field have a perihelion advance $3\mu/p$ and a light deflection $4\mu/R$. [5]Observational evidence for perihelion advance, light deflection, and gravitational redshift is presented.

[6]Further investigation of the orbit equations yields curious results for the case that the particle which produces the field is smaller than the Schwarzschild singularity $r = 2\mu = 2GM/c^2$. [7]The solution for the interior of a spherically symmetric particle with constant proper density is obtained. It is found that the particle's radius must exceed $(9/4)\mu$.

[8]The weak-field approximation, in which only terms of first order in the deviations $h_{\mu\nu} = g_{\mu\nu} - \eta_{\mu\nu}$ of the metric from that of special relativity are retained, is presented. The orbital problem for the linear theory leads to a perihelion advance of $5\mu/p$ and a light deflection of $4\mu/R$. [9]There is a brief study of plane gravitational waves in the weak-field approximation.

Chapter 10   Selected Topics in General Relativity. [1]In the lowest approximation to gravity, i.e., Newtonian gravity, the squares of the velocities of the planets are of the same order as the relevant gravitational potentials $\Phi(x)$. The weak-field approximation shows that for the planetary case, the metric tensor is given by

$$g_{00} = 1 + 2\Phi/c^2 + O^2$$
$$g_{0i} = O^{\frac{3}{2}}/c$$
$$g_{ij} = -c^{-2}(1 - \Phi/c^2)\delta_{ij} + c^{-2}O^2$$

where O denotes terms of order Φ/c^2. In order to obtain an approximation which is higher than Newtonian, it is necessary to obtain g_{00} to the second order. An expression is obtained for

$$\theta = g_{00} - 1 - 2\Phi/c^2$$

correct to O^2, and the equation of motion is written in terms of Φ, h_{0i}, and θ. [2]The results are applied to the case of N isolated, interacting particles. [3]The case $N = 2$, the two-body problem, can be applied to a double star. To second order, the orbits are planar and coplanar, the perihelion advance is the same as in the planetary case ($3\mu/p$ with μ given by the total mass), and the center of mass experiences no secular acceleration.

[4]The case of rotational symmetry, subject to one simplifying assumption, is explored.

[5]The last section treats the effect on planetary orbits due to the *variation* in the sun's gravitational field due to radiation.

Chapter 11   Inertial Frames. [1]A coordinate system is defined such that any chosen geodesic is the origin $x^i = 0$ and that the metric tensor has $g_{00} = 1$ and g_{0i} independent of x^0. [2]Locally Cartesian coordinates are constructed, and the coordinate acceleration is found to consist of contributions which are the generalizations of: absolute acceleration, Coriolis effect, centrifugal force and d'Alembert forces, and Newtonian gravity.

[3]A congruence of geodesics is found to have, in the Coriolis sense, an absolute rotation if, in the coordinates based on the congruence, the angular velocity

$$\omega^i = -\frac{c^2}{2} e(ijk) \frac{\partial g_{0k}}{\partial x^j}$$

is non-zero. Conversely, if there exists a coordinate system in which ω^i vanishes everywhere, then there exists a non-rotational congruence of geodesics given by $x^i = $ const. It is always possible in any small-enough region of space-time to construct a non-rotational congruence of geodesics.

[4]An *inertial frame* for an observer in geodesic motion is defined as a frame in which the Coriolis effect vanishes. This condition is the same as requiring that the unit vectors of his coordinate axes be carried by parallel displacement. Two cases are examined in which the local inertial axes have an absolute rotation relative to axes which are inertial at infinity! [5]One case is that of an observer inside a spinning shell. [6]The other case is an observer on a revolving planet. The latter effect, known as geodesic precession, is found for the earth to be 0″02 per year. [7]The effect of the earth's rotation on an earth-satellite is examined.

[8]The equations of motion in an arbitrary spherically symmetric metric

$$ds^2 = \left[1 - 2\frac{\mu}{r} + 2\beta\left(\frac{\mu}{r}\right)^2 + \cdots\right] dt^2$$
$$ - c^{-2}\left[\left(1 + 2\gamma\frac{\mu}{r} + \cdots\right) dr^2 + r^2(d\theta^2 + \sin^2\theta\, d\phi^2)\right]$$

provide expressions for perihelion advance, light deflection, gravitational redshift, and geodesic effect. The Einstein values are obtained for $\beta = 0$, $\gamma = 1$. The choice of the first-order term in g_{00} to agree with Newtonian gravity automatically gives the gravitational redshift. [9]The rate of satellite-clock time relative to earth-clock time is given.

Chapter 12 Equations of Motion. [1]The field-to-particle transition of Section 5.2 is revised so as to apply to a general metric. The results are essentially unaltered. [2]The generalized formulation of electromagnetism is presented with a derivation of both the invariance of charge and the force on a charge. [3]Particular attention is paid to the photon, and [4]it is proved that, for a given photon, the ratio of energy to frequency is independent of the observer.

Chapter 13 Automorphisms. [1]The concept of automorphisms is defined, and [2]the one-parameter automorphism

$$x'^i = f^i(x^j, a)$$

is examined in some detail. The equation

$$\frac{\partial x'^i}{\partial a} = \xi^i(x')$$

where

$$\xi^i(x) = \left[\frac{\partial f^i(x, a)}{\partial a}\right]_{a=0}$$

is found to be the necessary and sufficient condition for the existence of a *group* of automorphisms. It is possible to choose coordinates in which $\xi^i = \delta_0^i$. The automorphic derivative is derived for later use. [3]Lie's three fundamental theorems are presented.

[4]A *metric* automorphism is an automorphism in which the automorphic derivative of the metric tensor vanishes. Killing's equation $0 = \xi_{i,j} + \xi_{j,i}$, which came up earlier in connection with transformations of a space into itself, is found to be the necessary and sufficient condition for the automorphism generated by ξ^i to be a metric automorphism. Several interesting properties are derived: (a) the automorphic derivative of R_{ijkl} vanishes; (b) $\xi_i \, dx^i/dp$ is constant along a geodesic; [5](a simple, short derivation of the ten metric automorphisms of Minkowski space-time is given) and [6](c) the product of ξ_μ with the stress-energy tensor is a conserved quantity. [7]An *n*-dimensional space can admit, at the most, $\frac{1}{2}n(n+1)$ metric automorphisms, and, if it does, it has constant curvature. [9]The Helmholtz-Lie theorem is stated and proved: in a three-dimensional space which admits the maximal group of automorphisms, all invariants of the space are functions of the line element. [10]Gödel's model is discussed from the point of view of automorphisms.

Chapter 14 Foundations of Cosmology. [1]The observational evidence allows us to assume the existence of a congruence of fundamental world-lines which fills the universe. The universe is also assumed to be isotropic and spatially homogeneous. [2]The light signals between any two observers in natural motion produce a one-parameter group of automorphisms having a generator $S(t)$. A cosmic time t is then defined, and [3]a metric ds^2 is introduced by means of the four conditions: (a) ds^2 is invariant, (b) ds^2 is homogeneous quadratic in the coordinate differentials, (c) $ds^2 = 0$ describes light rays, and (d) on fundamental world-lines $ds^2 = dt^2$. The metric is then found to be

$$ds^2 = dt^2 - S^2(t) \, du^2.$$

[4]The extension from one to three spatial dimensions makes du^2 a three-dimensional metric. [5]The admission by the space $t = $ const of the six automorphisms required by isotropy and homogeneity then specifies that the space have constant curvature; the latter may, without loss of generality, be chosen as $k = -1$, 0, or $+1$. [6]A study of geodesics supplies two conclusions: the projection of any four-dimensional geodesic along the fundamental world-lines onto a space $t = $ const is a three-dimensional geodesic; and the quantity $S^{-2} \, ds/du$ is constant along a geodesic.

[7]There are only eight specific models which admit more than six automorphisms. Six of the cases are those which, as is to be expected, have constant four-dimensional curvature. The other two have constant S and non-zero k. [8]One of the constant-curvature universes—the deSitter universe—is the *only* model which is both stationary and non-static.

Chapter 15 Observable Quantities. [1]The redshift z of a galaxy in natural motion is given by

$$1 + z = \frac{S(t_0)}{S(t_1)}$$

where t_0 and t_1 are the cosmic times, respectively, of observation and emission of the light. [2]The methods of measuring astronomical distances are reviewed. [3]The apparent magnitude of a galaxy is expanded in powers of its redshift. [4]Olber's paradox is resolved by utilizing the observed expansion of the universe. The density of electromagnetic radiation is derived and is [5]corrected for intergalactic absorption.

Further subjects considered in this chapter are: [6]the relation of angular size to linear size for distant objects; [7]information to be gained from counts of galaxies to successive magnitudes; and [8]a review of the different distances obtained from various criteria.

Chapter 16 Special Cosmological Models. The six cases of constant-curvature cosmologies are studied in some detail. The static Minkowski universe is omitted, because it is the space-time of special relativity. [1]The expanding Minkowski model provides considerable insight into the concepts encountered in cosmology because of the property that events which are contemporary with an observer by his Lorentz time as well his cosmic time can be identified. [2]The deSitter universe is studied in detail. [3]The other two constant-curvature models with negative curvature are found to be the same as deSitter space-time, but with different congruences for the fundamental world-lines. Finally, the remaining case of constant-curvature models is briefly noted.

Chapter 17 General-Relativistic Cosmology. [1]The introduction of the field equations of general relativity requires that the material in the universe be interpreted as a uniform fluid which has natural motion and isotropic pressure p. The conservation equation shows that in an expanding universe, energy is lost as work done by the expansion because of the pressure p. The interpretation of p is discussed, and it is concluded that $|p/c^2|$ is probably small compared with the density ρ—a devastating blow to the constant-curvature models which require $p = -\rho c^2$! [2]The various types of zero-pressure models are noted and discussed. [4]Models with both zero pressure and zero cosmological constant are studied in greater detail. [3]The density-age diagram is presented, and [5]the influence of radiation is examined.

Chapter 18 Cosmological Observations. The observational data are collected—[2]the Hubble constant, [3]the average density, [5]stellar ages, and [6]the acceleration parameter. [7]Although the nominal values are inconsistent with any zero-pressure general-relativistic model, the observational uncertainties do not preclude such models. [8]The steady-state theory is presented; [9]numerical examples of distances in various models are given; and [10]the initial state $S = 0$ is briefly considered.

Appendix A Selected Optional Topics. [1]In special relativity, the only motion which is judged by *both* of two observers in uniform relative motion to be rigid-body motion is a screw along the axis of relative motion. [2]Classical concepts of gravity propagation are discussed. [3]Two cases of non-interacting electromagnetic radiation are studied: the equilibrium blackbody radiation density in an arbitrary static metric; and the derivation of the formula for the apparent luminosity of a distant galaxy by using the differential conservation law applied to the electromagnetic stress-energy tensor. [4]Orbit perturbation theory is applied to three cases: (a) the skew terms in the vector and tensor gravity theories of Chapter 6; (b) a satellite revolving around the rotating earth; and (c) the classical gravity propagation of Section A.2. [5]Gödel's model is examined further with two conclusions: Gödel's concept of homogeneity is different from ours; and although the field-producing matter in Gödel's model is in rotation, there exist non-rotational geodesics. [6]The transformations for expressing cosmological space-time in five-dimensional Euclidean-like space are presented. [7]The λ-μ diagram is presented by Noonan to simplify discussion of the zero-pressure general-relativistic cosmological models. [8]The cosmological pressure is given quantitatively in terms of the average densities of the various forms of energy—kinetic, gravitational, and electromagnetic.

Appendix B Bibliography. Appendix B contains [1]the references referred to in the text, [2]additional reading, and [3]Robertson's articles. Included with the latter is a biographical outline and a note about Robertson's unpublished work.

Appendix C Abstract of the Material in this Book. [1]The concept of motion in Euclidean space provides the starting point. [2]Classical electromagnetism was then found to clash with experiments involving moving media or motion through the ether. [3]The Lorentz transformation provided a solution to those difficulties but introduced a four-dimensional context in which to fit the physical world—[4]first electromagnetism and then [5]ponderable matter. [6]But gravity remains as a misfit, irreconcilable to special relativity. [7]Non-Euclidean geometry is needed, and a study is made, first of simple cases in order to grasp the concept of curvature, [8]and then of Riemannian geometry with its curvature tensor. [9]Space-time is now regarded as a four-dimensional Riemannian space, and Einstein's gravitational field equation is found to have the delightful property that the physical conservation laws follow as the result of a mathematical identity. We then examine some consequences both [9,10]of Einstein's equation and [11,12]of the Riemannian formulation of space-time.

[13]The preparation for cosmology is made by studying the concept of the transformation of a Riemannian space into itself. [14]Viewed as such transformations, the symmetry properties which are assumed to hold, on a large scale, throughout the universe require the cosmological metric to

have a specific form: $dt^2 - S^2(t) \, du^2$. [15]The relation of observable quantities to cosmological quantities is examined and [16]specific cosmological models are studied. [17]Invocation of Einstein's equation provides an equation of motion for $S(t)$. [18]Cosmological observations are discussed without any firm conclusions. Appendices provide [A]studies of selected topics, [B]bibliography, and [C]a summary of the material in the book.

Name Index

The following index contains the names of people in Chapters 1–18 and Appendices A and B. The superscript[B] indicates text references covered in Section B.1 of Appendix B (pp. 424–428).

447

Subject Index

This index covers Chapters 1–18 and Appendix A. Italics indicate definitions; boldface page numbers indicate principal references.